AF644635

About Pearson

Pearson is the world's learning company, with presence across 70 countries worldwide. Our unique insights and world-class expertise comes from a long history of working closely with renowned teachers, authors and thought leaders, as a result of which, we have emerged as the preferred choice for millions of teachers and learners across the world.

We believe learning opens up opportunities, creates fulfilling careers and hence better lives. We hence collaborate with the best of minds to deliver you class-leading products, spread across the Higher Education and Test Preparation spectrum.

Superior learning experience and improved outcomes are at the heart of everything we do. This product is the result of one such effort.

Your feedback plays a critical role in the evolution of our products and you can contact us - reachus@pearson.com. *We look forward to it.*

CLASS

6

Trishna's

PEARSON IIT FOUNDATION

Science

Seventh Edition

2025

Pearson

Photo Credits

Chapter 1 Opener: Tatiana Popova / 123RF
Chapter 2 Opener: Cheuk-king Lo / Pearson Education Asia Ltd
Chapter 3 Opener: Vaclav Volrab / 123RF
Chapter 4 Opener: KPG_Payless / Shutterstock
Chapter 5 Opener: Andrew Goodsell / Shutterstock
Chapter 6 Opener: Studio 8 / Pearson Education Ltd
Chapter 7 Opener: merzavka / 123RF
Chapter 8 Opener: BlueRingMedia / Shutterstock
Chapter 9 Opener: Shawn Hempel / Shutterstock
Chapter 10 Opener: pedrosala / Shutterstock
Chapter 11 Opener: Roblan / Shutterstock
Chapter 12 Opener: 82841 / Shutterstock
Chapter 13 Opener: Chad Zuber / Shutterstock
Chapter 14 Opener: bestdesign36 / 123RF
Chapter 15 Opener: Hannamariah / Shutterstock

ISBN 978-93-6159-868-5

First Impression

Published by Pearson India Education Services Pvt. Ltd, CIN: U72200TN2005PTC057128.
Head Office: 1st Floor, Berger Tower, Plot No. C-001A/2, Sector 16B, Noida - 201 301, Uttar Pradesh, India.
Registered Office: Featherlite, 'The Address' 5th Floor, Survey No 203/10B, 200 Ft MMRD Road, Zamin Pallavaram, Chennai – 600 044.
Website: in.pearson.com, Email: companysecretary.india@pearson.com

Compositor: Saksham Printographics, Delhi
Printed in India by Saurabh Printers Pvt. Ltd.

Brief Contents

Contents

CHEMISTRY

Preface

"If you have a great ambition, take as big a step as possible in the direction of fulfilling it. The step may only be a tiny one, but trust that it may be the largest one possible for now."

Mildred McAfee

The *Pearson IIT Foundation* Series has been created keeping in mind the learner's ambition to excel in a competitive examination like IIT-JEE. The series can be used in addition to the books being studied in school to attain that extra edge required to strengthen the concepts and prepare well for future endeavours.

Why Start Early with Pearson IIT Foundation

Classes VI to X are the base years of a learner's academic life. In these years learner explore their interests and determine the goals they wish to attain. *Pearson IIT Foundation* series is filled with interactive learning that not only nurtures a learner's interest in science and mathematics but also strengthens their concepts.

The series uses real-life examples and application-based problems to teach theoretical concepts. The objective of this series is to help learners cultivate an analytical mind.

Most of the lessons to be learnt are introduced to the learners in the books for class VI. As they get promoted to higher classes, new topics are added to these lessons. This additive method helps the learners' span their learning over four standards, from VI-X. Thus, learners are not overwhelmed by the introduction of completely new lessons every time they are promoted to a new class.

While their learning is being spanned across five years, so is their ability to resolve doubts for further conceptual clarity. For instance, they can use concepts learnt in class VI to solve questions in class VII. If, in case, they get stuck while answering a question, the learners can infer for themselves that they might be lacking in conceptual clarity. They can then approach their teachers, requesting them to explain the concept once again. This helps the learner to clarify their concepts while revising the lessons previously learnt.

Since classes VI-X are deemed to be a student's formative years, we, at Pearson, aim to provide a foundation level course which serves more than just a standard curriculum.

Here is how it makes a difference to a learner's overall learning...

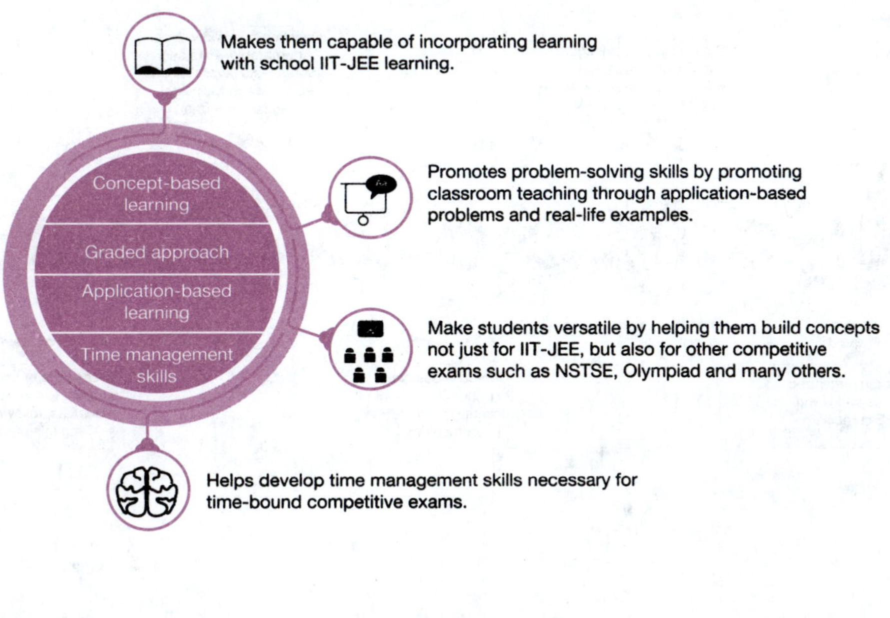

Other Uses of the Series

Instead of limiting themselves to IIT-JEE, a learner can also use this series to prepare for several other competitive examinations such as NSTSE, National and International Olympiads, NEET, BITSAT, etc. This series offers a level of concept learning that empowers learners to handle the challenging nature of questions posed in these examinations. Moreover, this will also allow the learners to have an early insight into their key strengths as well as improvement areas and help them work on themselves.

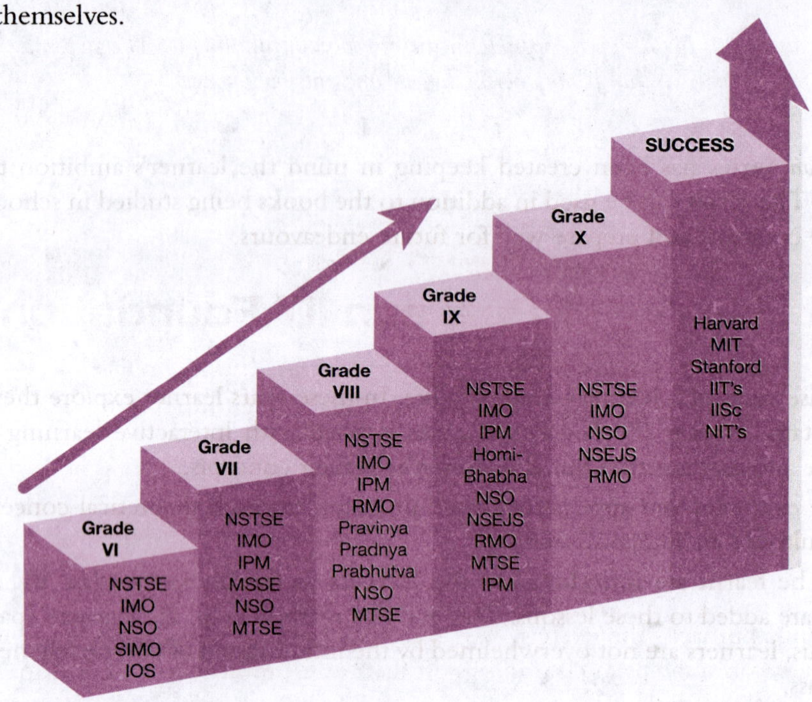

[IMO: International Mathematics Olympiad; NSO: National Science Olympiad, IOS: International Olympiad of Science, NSTSE: National Level Science Talent Search Examination, MTSE: Maharashtra Talent Search Examination, RMO: Regional Mathematical Olympiad, PPP: Pravinya Pradnya Prabhutva, NSEJS: National Standard Examination in Junior Science, IIT: Indian Institute of Technology, IISc: Indian Institute of Science, NIT: National Institute of Technology.]

Highlights of the Series

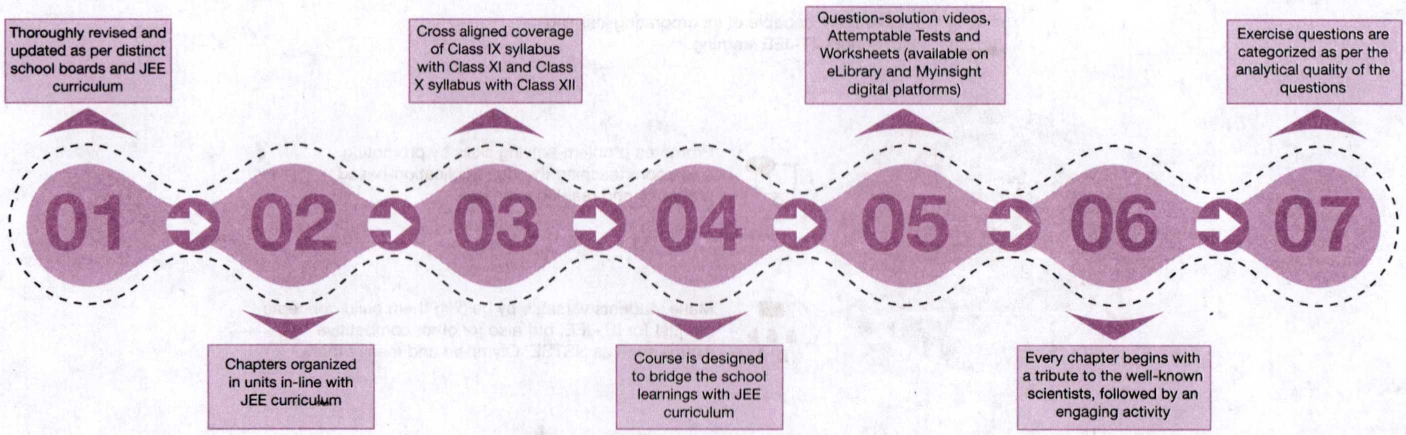

Pearson IIT Foundation series provides a perfect blend of learning through theory and practice questions with a fusion of school and JEE curriculum. It is imperative to note that this series would be as profound as you want it to be. Therefore, to get maximum benefit from this book, we recommend following the given study plan.

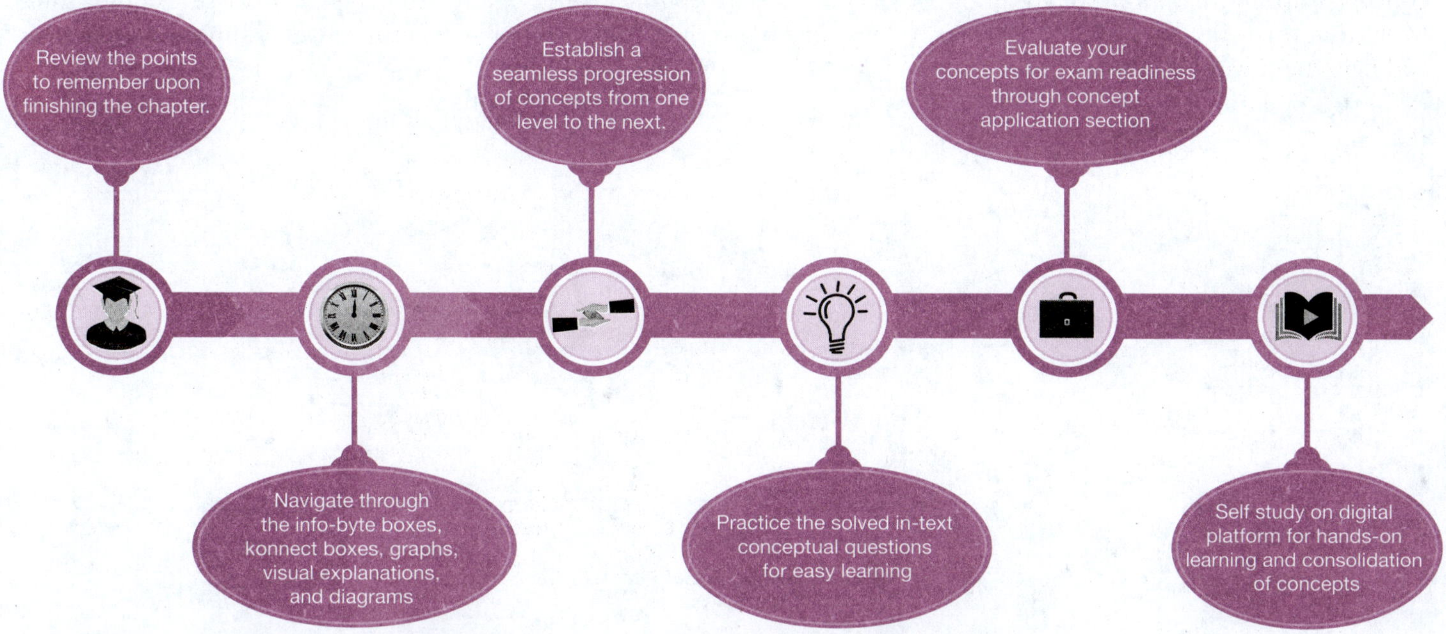

To provide a graded learning approach, the exercise part of each chapter is categorized by using four icons for question tagging. The question categorization helps the learners assess their own problem-solving and analytical skills and motivates them to improve to reach their objectives.

The following icons are used to categorize the questions with specific meanings:

Real-life Situations Questions: 

Analytical Questions: 

Conceptual Questions: 

Value-based Questions: 

With this refined and well-tuned course from Pearson, students will become more confident when they enter the competitive world for actual IIT-JEE preparation. The effort put in today will transform into a valuable asset, contributing to success in future competitive examinations.

Chapter Insights

Remember

Before beginning this chapter, you should be able to:

- Recall various physical quantities such as length, area, volume, mass, time, speed, etc.
- Know the usage of few measuring devices

Remember section will help them to memorize and review the previous learning on a particular topic

Key points will help the students to identify the essential points in a chapter

Key Ideas

After completing this chapter, you should be able to:

- Understand various physical quantities, units and their conversions

Scientific Crypt

A Tribute to Blaise Pascal (1623–1662)

Pascal was a French mathematician, physicist, inventor, and philosopher. His earliest mathematical work was on conic sections; he wrote a significant treatise about projective geometry at the age of 16. His work in the fields of hydrodynamics and hydrostatics centered on the principles of hydraulic fluids. His inventions include the hydraulic press and the syringe. He proved that hydrostatic pressure depends not on the weight of the fluid but on the elevation difference.

Pascal performed experiments on Torricellian vacuum and found that the air pressure decreases with altitude i.e., the air pressure on a high mountain must be less than at a lower altitude. In honor of Blaise Pascal, the SI unit of pressure is named as pascal (Pa).

FUN TIME

CROSSWORD

Scientific Crypt provides information about well-known scientists related to the chapter. The engaging activity is also given in the form of a crossword to keep the learners interested.

INTRODUCTION

The act or process of determining the size or value of a certain quantity is measurement. A number is assigned to an attribute or characteristic of an object in this act of measuring.

Introduction section helps to lay the foundation of the following chapter and leads the way for further learning

Importance of Measurement

Measurement is essential for maintaining accuracy in our everyday life. It plays an essential role in our lives.

Examples: For buying milk.
For buying rice, sugar, etc., from a grocery shop.
For getting a dress stitched at a tailoring shop.
For checking a patient's body temperature.
For finding out the speed of a vehicle.
For checking the speed of an object falling on the ground.

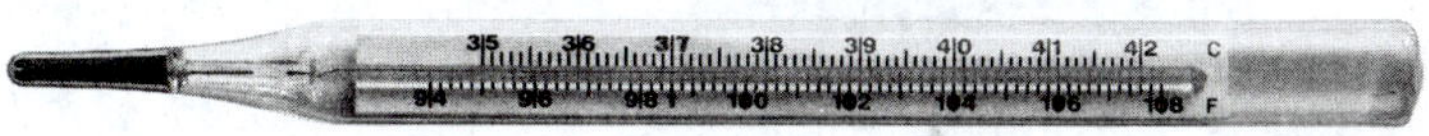

Concepts are explained in a well-structured and lucid manner

Konnect boxes are some add-on information of related topic

Konnect

- Everything in the universe interacts via fundamental forces.
- The gravitational force has the widest influence as it acts between all masses, but it's the weakest.

Info Bytes!

Large distances such as distance between planets are measured in light years.
1 light year = 9.46053×10^{12} km

Info bytes are interesting trivia and facts that engage young minds and keep the grey cells ticking!

EXAMPLE 1.4 Express 5 centimetres in metres.

SOLUTION

1 m = 100 cm

$\Rightarrow$ 1 cm = 10^{-2} m

$\Rightarrow$ 5 cm = 5×10^{-2} m

Here 10^{-2} is 'centi' which is a submultiple.

Examples are given in the form of in-text exercises to reinforce the concepts learnt in a particular chapter

Illustrative examples solved in a logical and step-wise manner

POINTS TO REMEMBER

- ✔ Measurement is essential for maintaining accuracy in our everyday life. It plays an essential role in our lives.
- ✔ Quantities which can be measured physically are called physical quantities.
- ✔ Units which are used to measure large quantities are called multiple units.
- ✔ Whenever we measure width, thickn depth, distance and height, we are measur length. The SI unit of length is 'metre'.
- ✔ Everybody in the universe is in motion. our daily life we see many things mov around us.

Points to remember summarises the concepts and topics presented in each chapter

PRACTICE QUESTIONS CLASSROOM WING

Very Short Answer Type Questions

Directions for questions from 1 to 5.
Select the correct alternative from the given options.

1. Which of the following is a fundamental quantity?
   (a) Length (b) Area
   (c) Volume (d) Force
2. Which of the following unit is a derived unit?

Directions for questions from 16 to 20.
Select the correct alternative from the given options.

16. The SI unit of mass is
   (a) kg (b) gram
   (c) second (d) g cm^{-3}
17. Area is measured in
   m^2 (b) cm^2
   mm^2 (d) All of these

Short Answer Type Questions

41. Define physical quantity and give any two examp
42. Define derived physical quantity and give any examples.
43. Define multiple units.
44. Define unit and write any three examples.

Essay Type Questions

95. (a) Given that the time taken by an oil dropper to drop 100 oil drops is 800 min, find the time taken to drop 10 oil drops in hours.
   (b) On dropping 3 identical bullets into a measur-

96. (a)

Different typologies of questions have been included in the *Classroom Wing* which help students to develop the problem-solving skill

Competition Wing at the end of the chapter incorporated for competitive examination inline with JEE syllabus

PRACTICE QUESTIONS COMPETITION WING

Level 1: Apply Your Concepts

Directions for questions from 1 to 5.
Fill in the blanks.

1. In SI system mass is measured in ______.
2. Unit of ______ is the same in all the systems of
3.

Directions for questions from 13 to 16.
Fill in the blanks.

13. In case of Vernier calipers, the smallest measurement possible is ____ cm.
   ^{2} = ______ m^2
   Fahrenheit scale of temperature, the LFP is ______

Graded as per complexity: Level 1; Level 2; and Level 3

Level 2: Review Your Concepts

33. Abhi who is interested in physics measured the vol ume of an irregular shaped body with concepts give by his physics teacher. When he immersed the body water contained in a measuring jar, the level of wat is increased from 500 ml to 1500 ml. Find the volun of the body and also find the length of the edge of tl cube whose volume is equal to the volume of the give irregular shaped body.

Level 3: Assess Your Concepts

36. Abhi, Vasu, Maahi and Lucky are good friends. Durir summer vacation they met at Vasu's home to play. Vasu father is good at mathematics and physics, so he used play with Vasu and his friends by asking subject-relate questions in the middle of their play. He asked a que tion; "how will you write the weight of your 1 lit water bottle in physics?" Select the correct form writing the weight from the options given below.
   (a) Abhi wrote 10 n
   (b) Vasu wrote 10 newtons
   (c) Maahi wrote 10.N
   (d) Lucky wrote 10, N.

41. Define physical quantity and give any two examples.
42. Define derived physical quantity and give any two examples.
43. Define multiple units.
44. Define unit and write any three examples.
45. Define fundamental unit and write any two examples
46. What is the SI unit of density?
47. Write the correct notation for the following.
   (a) 2 Kg (b) 4 Newtons
   (c) 6 metres (d) 35 Gram
   (e) 7 S

48. Match the entries in Column A Column B.

	Column A
(A)	SI unit of electric current
(B)	CGS unit of time

33. Abhi who is interested in physics measured the volume of an irregular shaped body with concepts given by his physics teacher. When he immersed the body in water contained in a measuring jar, the level of water is increased from 500 ml to 1500 ml. Find the volume of the body and also find the length of the edge of the cube whose volume is equal to the volume of the given irregular shaped body.

34. Keshav observed that the increase in the temperature of a body is given by $T_1 = 2t^2$ for the first 5 minutes and $T_2 = 3t$ for the next 5 minutes, where T_1, T_2 and 't' are

The icons are used for categorisation of the questions in Classroom Wing and Competition Wing

Hints and Explanations

CLASSROOM WING

Very Short Answer Type Questions

11. $\frac{kg}{g} = \frac{10^3 \text{ g}}{g} = 10^3 : 1$

12. $4 \times \text{side} = 20$

Side $= \frac{20}{4} = 5$ cm

13. $\frac{m^3}{m^2}$ = metre

14. $\frac{4}{3}\pi r^3 = \frac{704}{21}$

$r^3 = \frac{704}{21} \times \frac{3}{4} \times \frac{7}{...}$

25. The shape of six's maximum and minimum thermometer is in the shape of the English alphabet *U*.

26. The angle between the minutes hand and hours hand in a clock, at 12:30 p.m. is greater than 90°.

27. Temperature is a fundamental physical quantity.

28. Time is a fundamental quantity since it is independent of other quantities.

29. The device used to measure temperature is Thermometer.

30. Kelvin is the unit of temperature which is not followed by the word 'degree'.

Hints and Explanations for key questions of classroom wing and competition wing along with highlights on the common mistakes that students usually make in the examinations

COMPETITION WING

Level 1: Apply Your Concepts

6. Parabolic

7. The number of divisions on a Fahrenheit scale of temperature, having LFP and UFP as 32 °F and 212 °F respectively, is,

212 – 32 = 180

8. Given, mass of the wooden block of volume = 500 kg.

Volume of the wooden block = 1 m × 1 m × 1 m = 1 m^3

Therefore, density of wooden block, $d = \frac{\text{mass}}{\text{volume}}$

$= \frac{500}{1}$ kg/m^3 = 500 kg/m^3

We have, density of water, d_w = 1000 kg/m^3

Then, Relative density $= \frac{\text{Density of wooden block}}{\text{Density of water}}$

$= \frac{500}{1000} = 0.5$

9. A body or particle is said to be moving with uniform speed, if it travels equal distances in equal intervals of time.

10. Given, Height, h = 50 m

Acceleration due to gravity = 10 m/s^2

Initial velocity of the body, u = 0

14. 1 km^2 = 1 km × 1 km = 1000 m × 1000 m = 10^6 m^2

15. For a Fahrenheit scale of temperature, the LFP is 32°F and UFP is 212°F.

16. For a body which is moving with a uniform velocity of 25 m/s.

Instantaneous velocity = uniform velocity

Therefore, instantaneous velocity = 25 m/s

17. We know, 1000 cm^3 = 1 L

Therefore, 1 m^3 = (100 cm)^3 = 10^6 cm^3 = 1000 × 1000 cm^3 = 1000 L

18. If 'R' be the radius of the given sphere, then its volume $= \frac{4}{3}\pi R^3$.

19. SI unit of temperature is K (kelvin).

20. Distance is always positive.

21. $1000 \frac{a^2b^2c^3}{d} = 1000 \text{ cm}^3$

22. Mercury is used in thermometer to measure a wide range of temperatures as it has low freezing point (–39°C) and a high boiling point (357°C).

23. Given,

WORKSHEET
CHAPTER 2: DYNAMICS

DW

Directions for questions from 1 to 5:
Select the correct alternative from the following options.

1. A bullet of mass 100 g moving with a velocity of 100 m s^{-1} is stopped by a plank. If the bullet travels a distance of 10 cm in the plank before it comes to rest, find the average force exerted by the plank.
(a) 100 N (b) 1000 N
(c) 2500 N (d) 5000 N

2. Find the power developed by an engine in filling water

a rough surface, the total work done by the frictional force is zero.

8. The orbital velocity of a satellite is inversely proportional to the radius of the orbit.

9. When a stone is tied to a string and rotated in a circular path, the work done by the tension of the string is zero.

10. A satellite revolving in an orbit closer to the surface of the earth has more speed than one which is moving in an orbit of higher radius.

DW: Downloadable worksheets supplementing textual exercises for hand-on learning

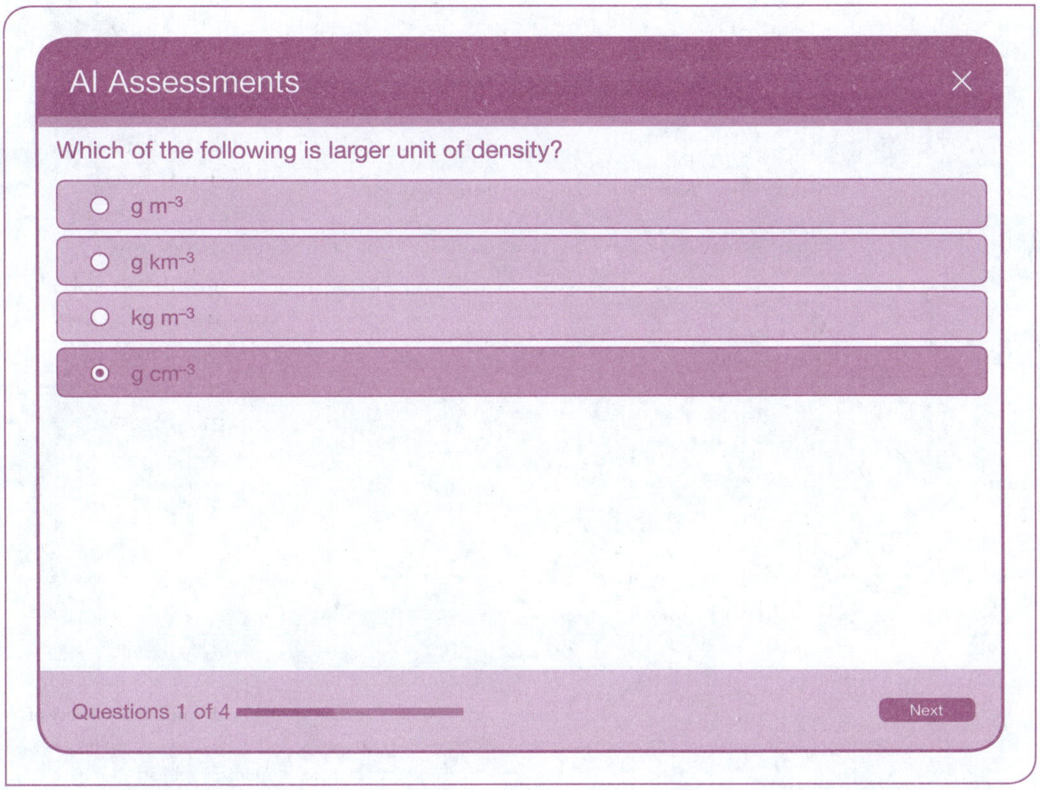

AT

AT: Attemptable Tests for assessing understanding of concepts and getting a clear picture of your exam readiness

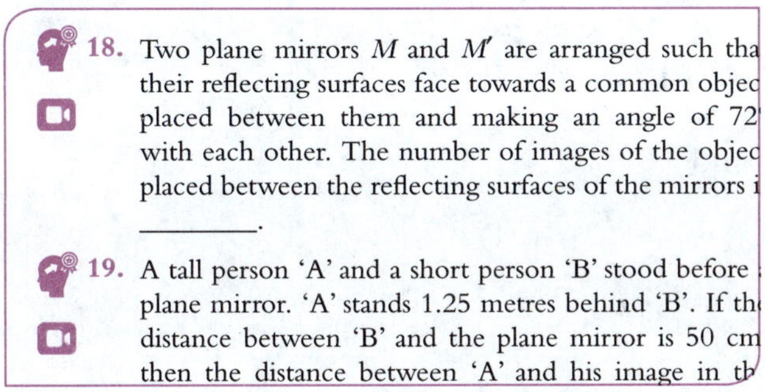

18. Two plane mirrors *M* and *M′* are arranged such tha
their reflecting surfaces face towards a common objec
placed between them and making an angle of 72
with each other. The number of images of the objec
placed between the reflecting surfaces of the mirrors i
________.

19. A tall person 'A' and a short person 'B' stood before
plane mirror. 'A' stands 1.25 metres behind 'B'. If th
distance between 'B' and the plane mirror is 50 cm
then the distance between 'A' and his image in th

Video icon: Audio and visual learning to difficult questions for effective learning and retention

Unit I

Physics

In this Unit

CHAPTER 1

Measurements and Motion

Remember

Before beginning this chapter, you should be able to:

- Recall various physical quantities such as length, area, volume, mass, time, speed, etc.
- Know the usage of few measuring devices used in our daily life

Key Ideas

After completing this chapter, you should be able to:

- Understand various physical quantities, units and their conversions
- Describe various ways of measuring physical quantities, which are used commonly in our daily life
- Differentiate rest and motion; distance and displacement; speed and velocity
- Define types of motion

Scientific Crypt

A Tribute to Lord Kelvin (William Thomson) (1824–1907)

The Lord Kelvin was a British mathematician, mathematical physicist and engineer. He has contributed significantly to unifying physics. He was the Professor of Natural Philosophy at the University of Glasgow, where he undertook significant research and mathematical analysis of electricity, the formulation of the first and second laws of thermodynamics. He proposed an absolute temperature scale in which "a unit of heat descending from a body A at the temperature T° of this scale, to a body B at the temperature (T−1)°, would give out the same mechanical effect [work], whatever be the number T." Such a scale would be quite independent of the physical properties of any specific substance. He worked with James Prescott Joule to develop an absolute thermodynamic temperature scale, which came to be called the Kelvin scale. The SI unit of absolute temperature is named after kelvin (K) in his honor.

FUN TIME

CROSSWORD

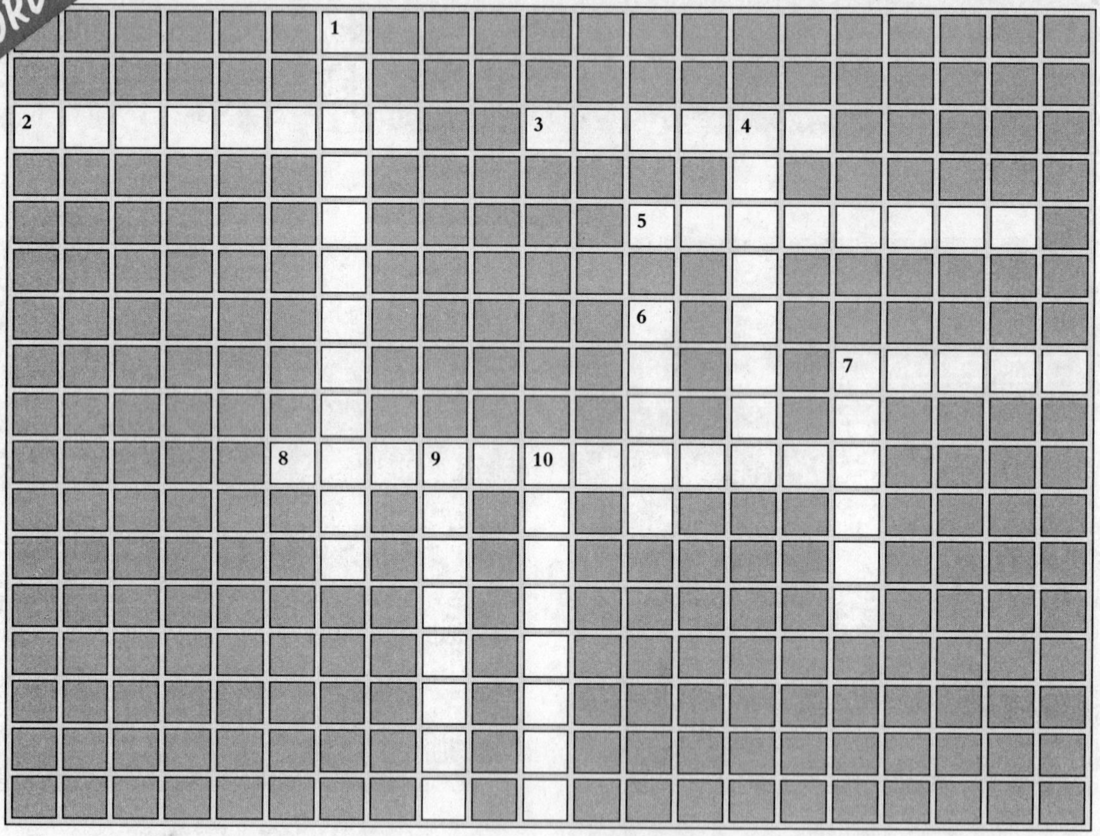

Across

2. Total path travelled, in this case, 200 m.
3. Three-dimensional space occupied by an object.
5. A measure similar to speed but it takes direction into account.
7. The SI unit used to measure dimensions like width, depth, and height.
8. Straight line measurement from start to finish, irrespective of the path taken.

Down

1. Rate at which velocity changes over time.
4. Type of units used for measuring large quantities.
6. Measurement of how fast something moves without considering direction.
7. The state of being in movement, observable in the universe and everyday surroundings.
9. The type of quantities that can be measured tangibly.
10. Ensured through proper measurement in our daily tasks and routines.

INTRODUCTION

The act or process of determining the size or value of a certain quantity is measurement. A number is assigned to an attribute or characteristic of an object in this act of measuring.

Importance of Measurement

Measurement is essential for maintaining accuracy in our everyday life. It plays an essential role in our lives.

Examples: For buying milk.
For buying rice, sugar, etc., from a grocery shop.
For getting a dress stitched at a tailoring shop.
For checking a patient's body temperature.
For finding out the speed of a vehicle.
For checking the speed of an object falling on the ground.

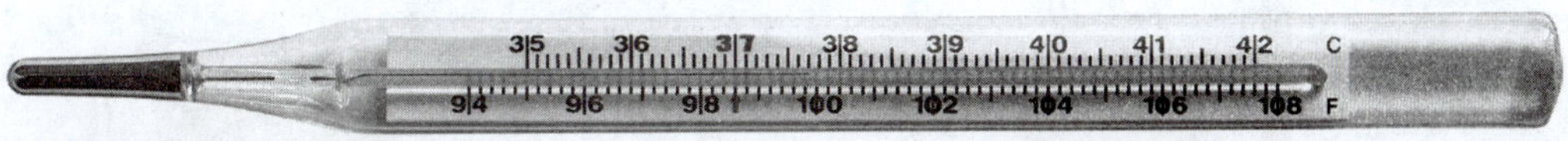

Figure 1.1 A clinical thermometer; used to measure human body temperature

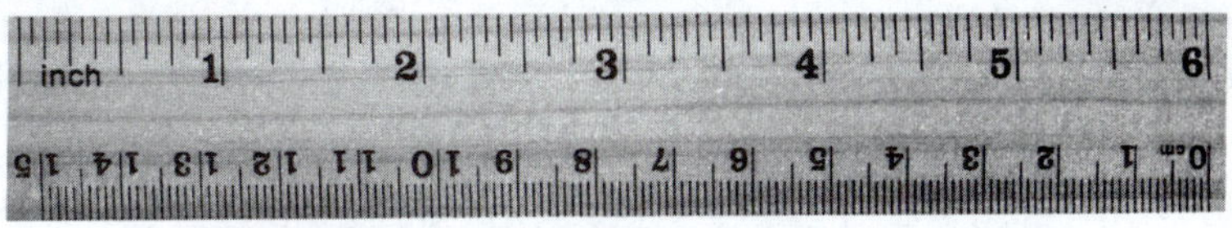

Figure 1.2 A ruler; used to measure distances

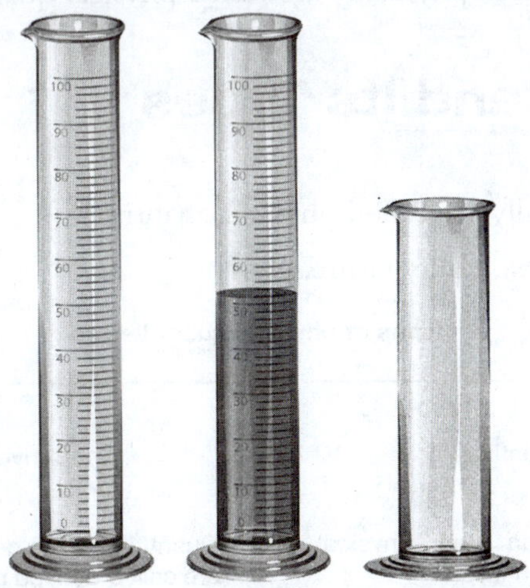

Figure 1.3 Graduated cylinder; used to measure volume of liquids

Measurement involves assigning a number (magnitude) and a unit to the physical quantity. Without the units, the measurement is not complete.

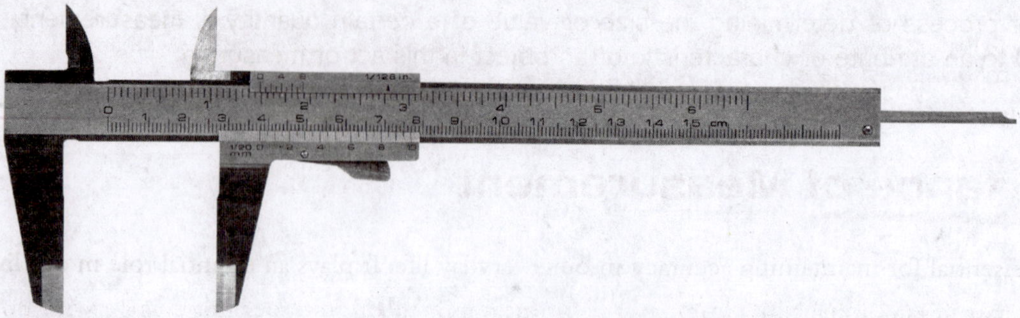

Figure 1.4 A Vernier scale; used to measure external and internal diameters of an object

Figure 1.5 A beam balance; used to measure mass

Figure 1.6 A measuring jar; used to measure oils/kerosene

Generally, we come across many terms in our daily lives, such as length, height, time, mass, faith, hope, affection, etc. Among these, only a few can be measured. For example, mass as 2 kg, length as 5 m, and time as 3 seconds and so on. But quantities, such as faith, hope, or affection cannot be expressed in numbers but can be expressed only as more or less. Only those quantities which can be measured physically are called physical quantities.

Physical Quantity and Its Types

Quantities which can be measured physically are called physical quantities.

Examples: Length, mass, time, volume, area, temperature, etc.

Types of physical quantities

Fundamental physical quantities

↓

Quantities which do not depend on other physical quantities are called fundamental quantities.

↓

Explanation: To measure time we do not involve mass or any other fundamental quantity, so time is a fundamental physical quantity.

↓

Examples: Mass, length, time, temperature, etc.

Derived physical quantities

↓

Quantities which depend on other physical quantities are called derived quantities.

↓

Explanation: To measure the area of a rectangle we use its length and breadth. Area of a rectangle = Length × Breadth. Therefore, area is a derived quantity.

↓

Examples: Area, volume, speed, etc.

EXAMPLE 1.1 Categorize the following into fundamental and derived physical quantities.

(a) Weight **(b)** Mass **(c)** Density **(d)** Volume **(e)** Speed

SOLUTION

Fundamental physical quantities: Mass

Derived physical quantities: Weight, density, volume, speed.

Units and Its Types

Unit is a standard that is used for making comparisons in measurements. Unit does not change with time, temperature, and place, and is accepted by people all over the world.

Types of units

Fundamental units

Units used to measure fundamental physical quantities.

***Explanation*:** To measure time, we use seconds but units, such as kilograms or metres are not involved. So, second is a fundamental unit.

***Examples*:** metre, kilogram, second, kelvin.

Derived units

Units used to measure derived physical quantities.

***Explanation*:** To measure the speed of a vehicle, we involve unit of distance, i.e., metres and unit of time, i.e., seconds. Therefore, metre per second is a derived unit.

***Examples*:** density – kilogram per cubic metre; speed – metre per second

Systems of Measurement

The collection of units of measurement and rules relating them to each other is called system of measurement.

We have three systems of measurement. They are: CGS, FPS, and MKS which acronyms for centimetre, gram and second; foot, pound and second; and metre, kilogram and second, respectively.

Systems of Measurement

CGS/French System

- Length is measured in centimetres
- Mass is measured in grams
- Time is measured in seconds

FPS/British System

- Length is measured in feet
- Mass is measured in pounds
- Time is measured in seconds

MKS System

- Length is measured in metres
- Mass is measured in kilograms
- Time measured in seconds

Apart from the above-mentioned systems of measurement, we have the fourth system of measurement known as the SI system. SI stands for System International.

Advantages of SI system over other systems

(i) SI is a system based on certain set of fundamental units.

(ii) SI assigns only one unit to a particular physical quantity.

(iii) SI system has multiples and sub-multiples of the system can be expressed as a power of 10.

EXAMPLE 1.2 Which system of measurement is accepted worldwide?

SOLUTION

System International (SI) system of measurement is accepted worldwide.

Fundamental Units of SI System

All the physical quantities in Physics can be expressed in terms of seven fundamental quantities.

Quantity	Unit	Symbol
Length	Metre	m
Mass	Kilogram	kg
Time	Second	s
Electric current	Ampere	A
Temperature	Kelvin	K
Luminous intensity	Candela	Cd
Amount of substance	Mole	Mole

Konnect

In ancient days **cubit** and **hand-span** were used to measure length.

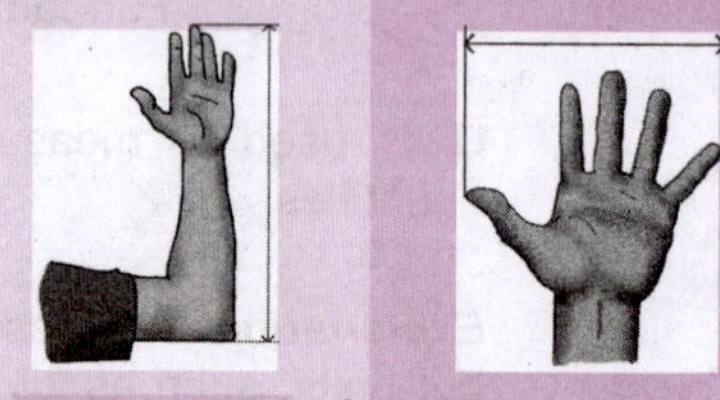

Figure 1.7 A cubit and a hand-span

Rules for Writing SI Units

1. The symbols used for units are always written in lowercase.

S. No.	Quantity	Unit ✓	Unit ✗
1	Mass	kg	Kg
2	Length	m	M
3	Time	s	S

2. Name of the unit should start with lowercase letter even if it is named after scientists.

S. No.	Quantity	Unit ✓	Unit ✗
1	Temperature	kelvin	Kelvin
2	Force	newton	Newton
3	Temperature	celsius	Celsius
4	Length	metre	Metre

3. Symbol of unit named after a scientist, should start with an uppercase letter.

S. No.	Quantity	Unit ✓	Unit ✗
1	Temperature	°C	°f
2	Electric current	A	a
3	Force	N	n

4. Symbols of units should not be followed by full stop.

S. No.	Quantity	Unit ✓	Unit ✗
1	Length	m	m.
2	Time	s	s.
3	Density	kg/m^3	kg/m^3.

Full stop can be used after a unit only when it is written at the end of sentence.

5. The symbols for units are never written in plural, but when written in unit name, then plurals can be used.

S. No.	Quantity	Unit ✓	Unit ✗
1	Length	3 m, 3 metres	3 ms
2	Time	2 s, 2 seconds	2 ss
3	Mass	20 kg, 20 kilograms	20 kgs
4	Force	3 newtons, 3 N	3 NS

6. Negative powers are used for the units in the denominator of a compound unit.

S. No.	Quantity	Unit ✓	Unit ✗
1	Density	$kg\ m^{-3}$	$(kg\ m)^{-3}$
2	Speed	$m\ s^{-1}$	$(m\ s)^{-1}$

7. Space should be left between the value and unit, and also between two units of a compound unit.

S. No.	Quantity	Unit ✓	Unit ✗
1	Temperature	273 K	273K
2	Current	5 A	5A
3	Density	$5\ kg\ m^{-3}$	$5\ kgm^{-3}$

8. Space should be maintained between the value or number and the multiple or submultiple used and no spaces should be given between multiple or submultiple and unit.

S. No.	Quantity	Unit ✓	Unit ✗
1	Length	15 mm	15mm
2.	Density	$10\ kg\ m^{-3}$	$10\ k\ gcm^{-3}$
3.	Pressure	$3\ N/m^2$	$3\ N/m^2$

EXAMPLE 1.3 Write the correct representation for the below-mentioned units according to SI system.

(a) Density = 25 kgm^{-3} (b) Length = 100 mm (c) Mass = 2 kg

SOLUTION

(a) Density = 25 kg m^{-3} (b) Length = 100 mm (c) Mass = 2 kg

Multiple Units and Submultiple Units

Multiple Units

Units which are used to measure large quantities are called multiple units.

Example: Distance between two cities, i.e., from Hyderabad to Warangal is 1,80,000 metres.

Distance = 1,80,000 m = 180 × 10^3 m = 180 km

Submultiple Units

Units which are used to measure smaller quantities are called submultiple units.

Info Bytes!

Large distances such as distance between planets are measured in light years.
1 light year = 9.46053 × 10^{12} km

Konnect

Kilo is a multiple unit of gram.

EXAMPLE 1.4 Express 5 centimetres in metres.

SOLUTION

1 m = 100 cm

⇒ 1 cm = 10^{-2} m

⇒ 5 cm = 5 × 10^{-2} m

Here 10^{-2} is 'centi' which is a submultiple.

List of Important Few Prefixes Used in SI System

Prefix	Abbreviation	Multiples
Deca	da	10^1
Kilo	k	1000 = 10^3
Mega	M	1000000 = 10^6
Giga	G	1000000000 = 10^9
Tera	T	1000000000000 = 10^{12}

Prefix	Abbreviation	Submultiples
Deci	d	$\frac{1}{10} = 10^{-1}$
Centi	c	$\frac{1}{10} = 10^{-2}$
Milli	m	$\frac{1}{1000} = 10^{-3}$

Info Bytes!

Very small length such as the size of atoms and molecules is expressed using micro and ångstrom units.
1 ångstrom (Å) = 10^{-10} m
1 micron (μ) = 10^{-6} m

(Continued)

Micro	μ	$\frac{1}{1000000} = 10^{-6}$
Nano	n	$\frac{1}{1000000000} = 10^{-9}$
Pico	μ μ or p	$\frac{1}{1000000000000} = 10^{-12}$

EXAMPLE 1.5 Express the following quantities in terms of multiples and submultiples for length, mass, and time.

(a) Length = 0.000005 meters **(b)** Mass = 70000 grams

(c) Time = 0.00000003 seconds

SOLUTION

(a) Length = 5×10^{-6} meters = 5 μm (micrometers)

(b) Mass = 7×10^{4} grams = 70 kg (kilograms)

(c) Time = 3×10^{-8} seconds = 30 ns (nanoseconds)

EXAMPLE 1.6 What are the units of the following quantities in SI system?

(a) Force **(b)** Velocity **(c)** Density **(d)** Relative density

SOLUTION

SI unit of

(a) Force = kg m s^{-2} = newton

(b) Velocity = $\frac{\text{Displacement}}{\text{Time}} = \frac{\text{m}}{\text{s}} = \text{m s}^{-1}$

(c) Density = $\frac{\text{Mass}}{\text{Volume}} = \frac{\text{kg}}{\text{m}^3} = \text{kg m}^{-3}$

(d) Relative density = $\frac{\text{Density of substance}}{\text{Density of water}} = \frac{\text{kgm}^{-3}}{\text{kgm}^{-3}}$

Since relative density is a ratio of two similar units, it has no units of its own.

EXAMPLE 1.7 The unit of force in SI system is newton (N) and in CGS system is dyne. One newton is equal to 1 kg m s^{-2} and 1 dyne is equal to 1 g cm s^{-2}. How many dynes make one newton?

SOLUTION

Given that: 1 N = 1 kg m s^{-2}

1 dyne = 1 g cm s^{-2}

But 1 kg = 1000 g and 1 m = 100 cm

$\therefore$ 1 N = 1 kg m s^{-2} = (1 kg) (1 m s^{-2})

$$= \frac{(1\,\text{kg})(1\,\text{m})}{(1\,\text{s})^2} = \frac{(1000\text{ g})(100\text{ cm})}{(1\,\text{s})^2} = 10^5 \text{ g cm s}^{-2} = 10^5 \text{ dyne}$$

Measurement of Length, Area, Volume and Mass

Measurement of Length

Whenever we measure width, thickness, depth, distance, and height, we are measuring length. The SI unit of length is 'metre'.

Metre: It is the distance between two marks on a platinum–iridium (9 : 1) bar kept at the International Bureau of Weights and Measures at Paris in France, maintained at a fixed temperature of 0°C.

Multiple and Submultiple Units of Length

1. 1 centimetre = 10 millimetres
2. 1 metre = 100 centimetres = 10^2 cm
3. 1 kilometre = 1000 metres = 10^3 m
4. 1 hectometre = 100 metres = 10^2 m
5. 1 decametre = 10 metres = 10 m
6. 1 decimetre = $\frac{1}{10\text{th}}$ metre = 10^{-1} m
7. 1 centimetre = $\frac{1}{100\text{th}}$ metre = 10^{-2} m
8. 1 millimetre = $\frac{1}{1000\text{th}}$ metre = 10^{-3} m

Info Bytes!

The world's longest measured distance without any gaps or overlaps is the Earth's equator, approximately 40,075 kilometers.

Konnect

Mercury is used in thermometers because it remains liquid over a wide temperature range and expands and contracts uniformly in response to temperature changes.

Devices for Measuring Length

Table 1.1 Description of Important Measurement Devices

Device	Procedure to measure
1. Ruler 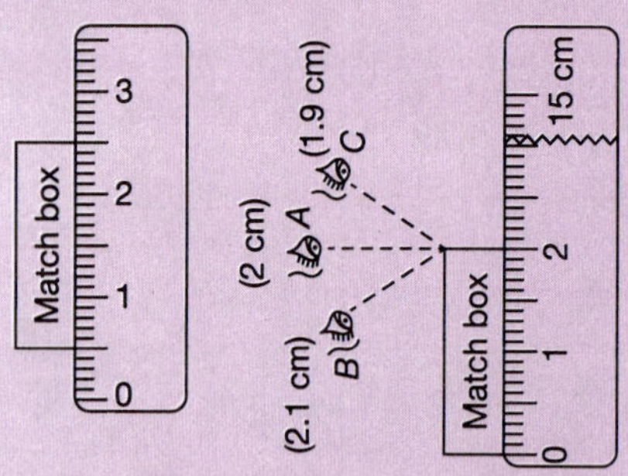 	• The smallest measurement that can be measured using a ruler is 1 mm. • To measure the length of a match box, place the match box near the ruler. • See that one end of the box is at the zero reading of the ruler as shown in the figure, then the scale at the other end is the length of the box (i.e., 2 cm). **Precautions:** (i) Readings should always be noted correctly by observing from position 'A', i.e., exactly above. (ii) The readings are observed in a slanted position 'B' (i.e., 2.1 cm) and 'C' (i.e., 1.9 cm). This error in measurement is called parallax error. (iii) If the edges of the ruler are worn out, then place the box at any other position near the ruler and subtract reading at the starting end (i.e., 1 cm) of box from the final end (i.e., 2.5 cm) of the box to measure the length of the box (i.e., 2.5 – 1.5 = 1 cm).
2. Measuring tape 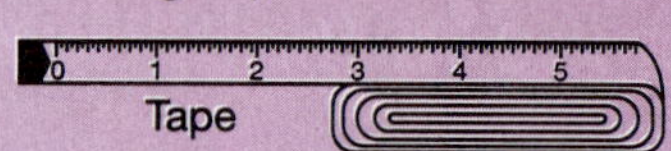 	• This is used to measure large lengths, such as land required to construct a house, fields, etc. • The smallest measurement possible is 1 mm.

(Continued)

Table 1.1 *(Continued)*

Device	Procedure to measure
3. Calipers and scale 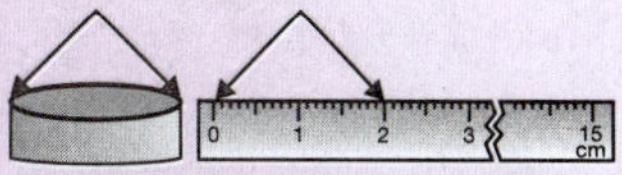 (a) Measuring the external diameter of a pipe 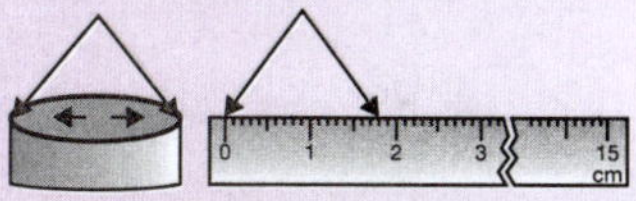 (b) Measuring the inner diameter of a pipe	• They are used to measure the inner diameter and outer diameter as shown in the figure, and check the length of the diameter on metre scale.
4. Thread and scale 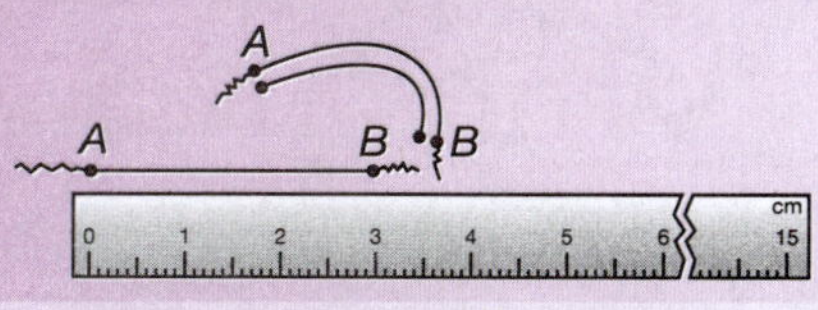 	• To measure curved lengths, spread the thread on a curved surface and mark the initial and final points. Now spread the same thread on the scale such that the initial point is at zero scale as shown in the figure and note the measurement.
5. Rectangular boxes and scale 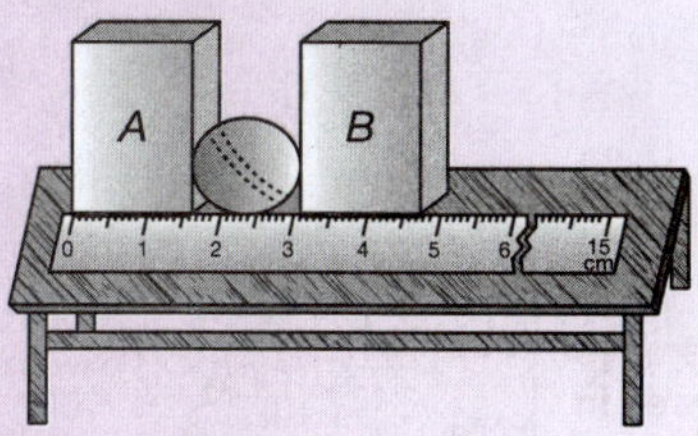 	• To find the diameter of a cricket ball, arrange the rectangular boxes, ball and a scale as shown in the figure. • The difference in readings taken for each face touching the ball is the length of the diameter of the ball. ***Example:*** Diameter = 3.1 – 1.6 = 1.5 cm
6. Scale 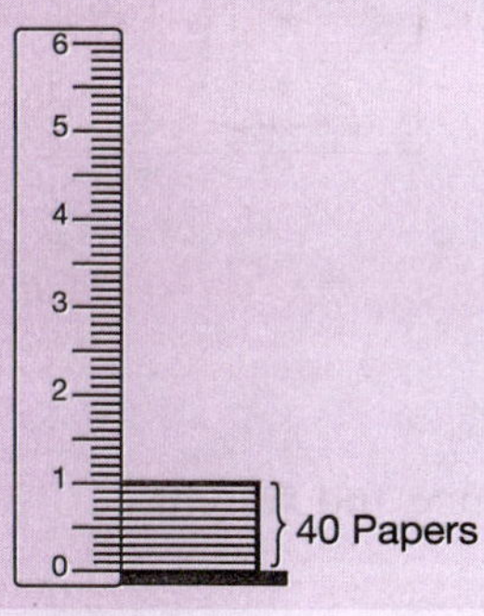 	• Thickness of paper: Measurement of thickness of paper with a scale is not possible since the thickness of paper is less than 1 mm. In such cases, place a bundle of papers, say about 40 pages as shown in the figure. Find the thickness of 40 papers with the help of a scale and divide it by 40 to get the thickness of each paper as shown in the figure. ***Example:*** Thickness of 40 papers = 1 cm Thickness of each paper = $\frac{1\text{ cm}}{40}$ = 0.025 cm
7. Vernier calipers 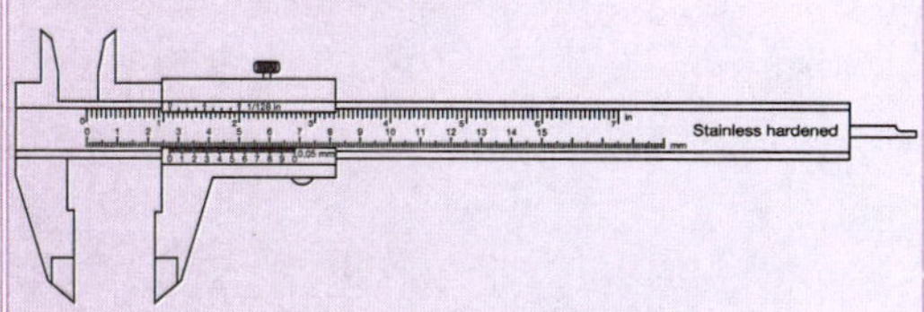 	• Used to measure very small lengths, depths, etc. • The smallest measurement possible is 0.01 cm.
8. Screw gauge 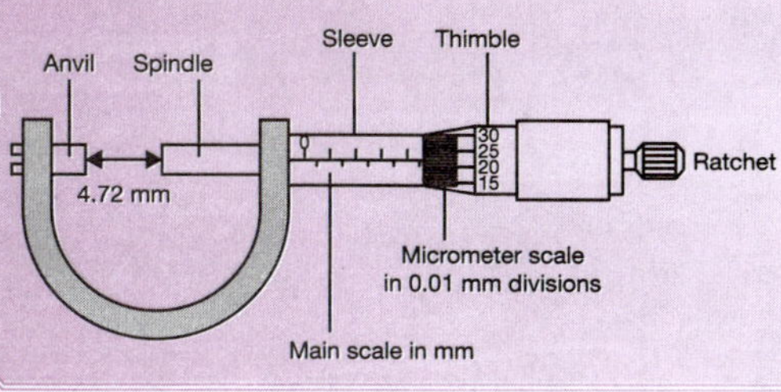 	• Used to measure smaller lengths, thickness of paper, etc. • Smallest measurement possible is 0.01 mm.

Measurement of Area

Different objects occupy different surfaces.

Example: In a study room, the study table occupies some surface depending on its size.

Area: Measurement of surface is called area.

Unit: The SI unit of area is square metre.

1. **Multiple units** used to measure area are hectare and square kilometre.

   1 hectare = 100 m × 100 m = 10^4 m^2

   1 km^2 = 1 km × 1 km = 1000 m × 1000 m = 10^6 m^2

2. **Submultiple unit** used to measure area is square centimetre.

Methods of measuring area

- Regular surfaces → Applying formulae → Example: Area of a room = 4 m × 3 m (In square shape) = 12 m^2

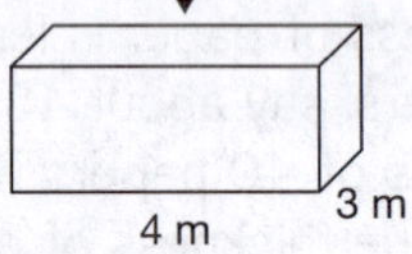

- Irregular surfaces → Graph method → Example: Spread an irregularly shaped object on a graph paper and draw the outline. Remove the object and count the number of squares in the outline.
  Number of complete squares = 4
  Number of incomplete squares more than half = 4
  Therefore, approximate area of object = 4 + 4 = 8 cm^2

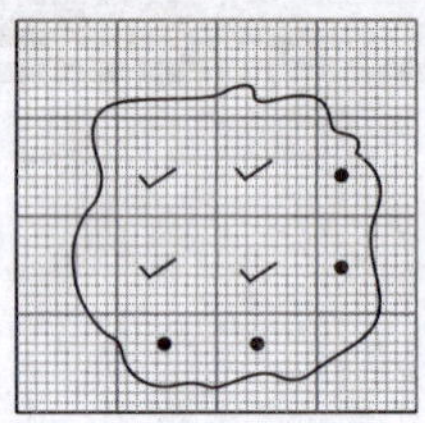

Measurement of Mass

When we buy groceries at a shop we measure the mass of objects with the help of balance and weights.

Mass: The amount of matter contained in an object is called mass.

Unit: The SI unit of mass is kilogram.

Multiple and Submultiple Units of Mass

1. 1 gram = 1000 milligrams
2. 1 kilogram = 1000 grams
3. 1 quintal = 100 kilograms
4. 1 metric tonne = 10 quintals

Table 1.2 Different Ways to Measure Mass

(a) Beam balance: This balance possesses a beam having support at its centre and two identical pans suspended at equal distances from the centre of the beam.	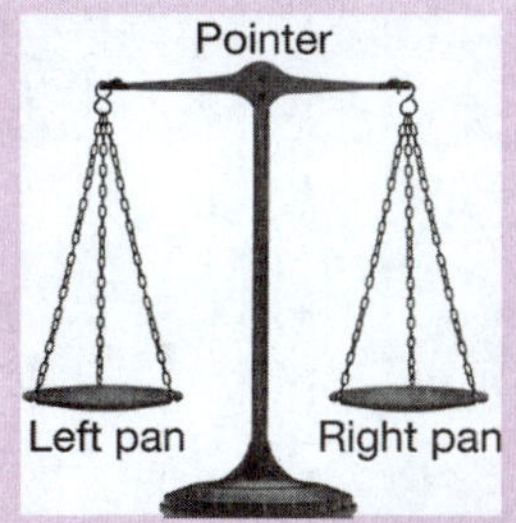
(b) Grocer's balance: The object to be weighed is placed on one pan and its equivalent standard weights on other pan or vice versa.	
(c) Physical balance: • Used for more accurate measurements. • Mostly used by goldsmiths and also in chemical labs.	

EXAMPLE 1.8 The mass of a lorry is three metric tonnes. Find its mass in terms of quintals and kilograms.

SOLUTION

Mass = 3 metric tonnes

Mass = 3 × 10 quintal = 30 quintal

⇒ Mass = 30 × 100 kilogram = 3000 kg

Measurement of Volume or Capacity

Volume of a box or container is measured in cubic metres (i.e., m^3) or cubic centimetre. (i.e., cm^3). Practically, we see that the volume of petrol or diesel to be filled in a vehicle at petrol banks is expressed in terms of litres.

Volume: The three-dimensional space occupied by an object is known as its volume or capacity.

Units: Though volume of a container is expressed in cubic metres (or m^3), for the sake of convenience, the same volume can also be expressed in litres.

1. $1\ m^3 = 1000\ L$

   'L' represents litre

For transparent liquids (water), reading is measured differently (lower meniscus) whereas, for colored liquids, upper meniscus should be highlighted.

Figure 1.8 A graduated cylinder

Multiple and Submultiple Units of Volume or Capacity

1. 1 L = 1000 mL
2. 1 mL = 1 cm^3
3. 1 L = 1000 cm^3
4. 1 m^3 = 10^6 cm^3
5. 1000 L = 1 m^3

Konnect

While measuring the volume of a liquid using a measuring jar, the lower meniscus reading should always be noted as shown in Figure 1.8.

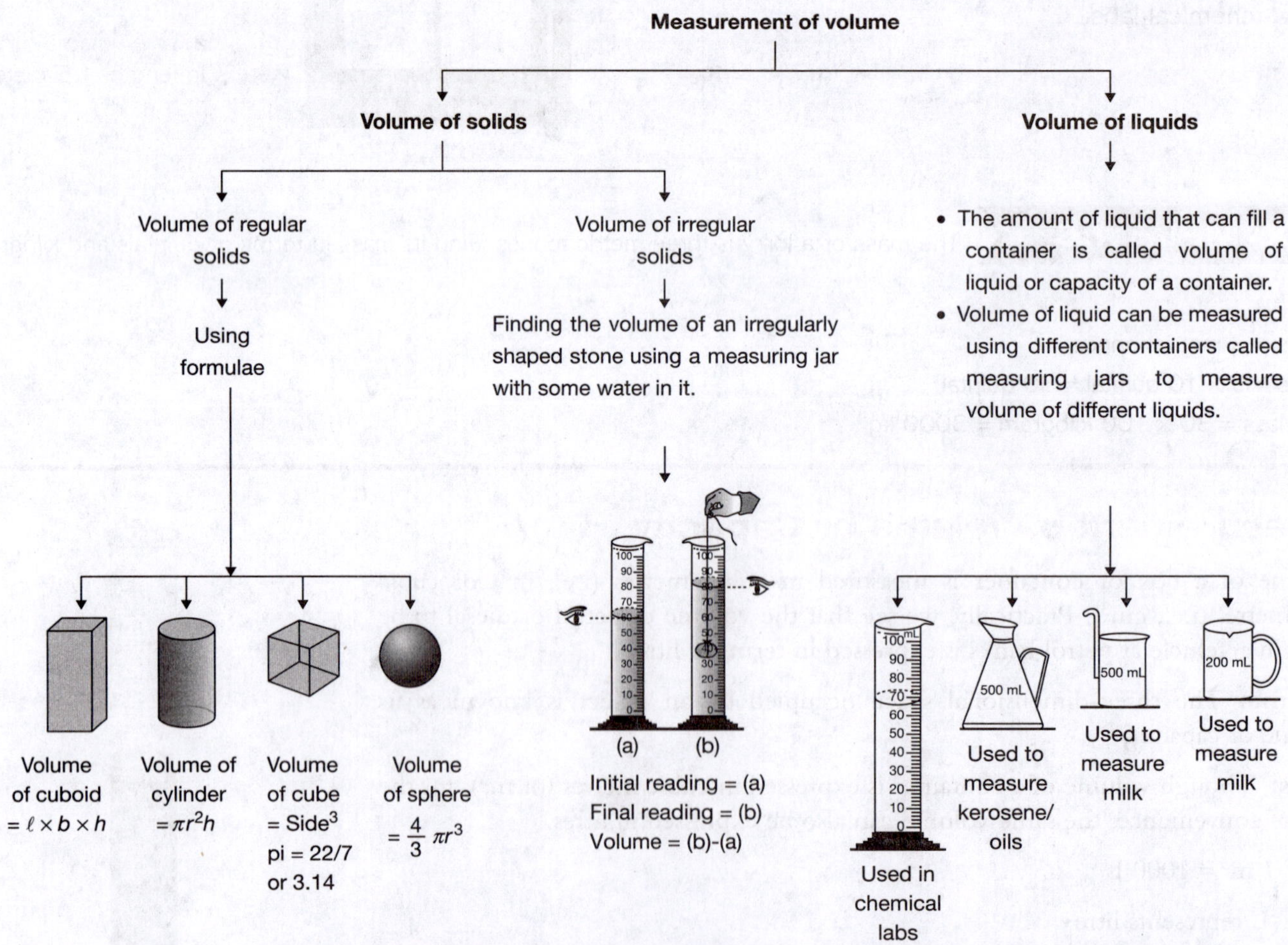

Figure 1.9 Measurement of volume

Activity

Aim: To measure the volume of an irregularly shaped stone.

Apparatus: Measuring cylinder, sufficient thread, stone, and water.

Principle: Volume of the liquid displaced is equal to the volume of the submerged object.

Procedure: **Step 1:** Pour some water into a measuring cylinder and note the reading of lower meniscus as shown in the figure.

Step 2: Tie a thread to the stone and suspend it in the water contained in the measuring cylinder. Now note down the reading of lower meniscus as shown in figure.

Step 3: Volume of water displaced = ______

∴ Volume of the stone = ______

Precautions: Position of the eye must be at the same level of the bottom of meniscus.

Conclusion: Volume of an irregularly shaped stone = ______

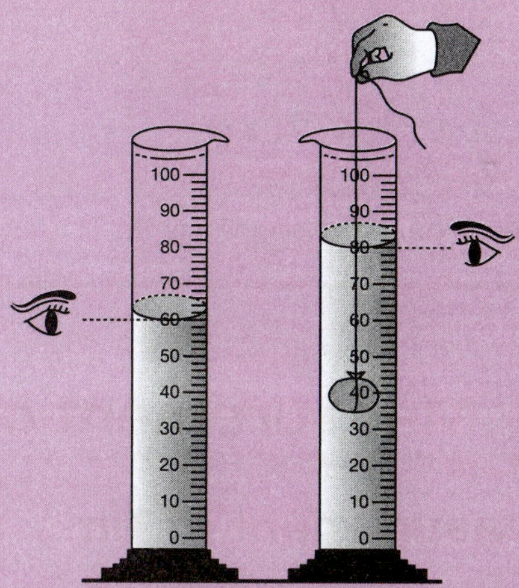

Figure 1.10 Measuring volume of a stone (an irregular object)

EXAMPLE 1.9 Sarah has a rectangular water tank in her backyard. She wants to know the volume of water it can hold in litres. The dimensions of the water tank are 2 meters in length, 1.5 meters in width, and 0.8 meters in height.

SOLUTION

$V = 2\text{ m} \times 1.5\text{ m} \times 0.8\text{ m} = 2.4$ cubic meters = 2400 liters

EXAMPLE 1.10 If the relative density of substance '*A*' and '*B*' is 4 and 5, respectively. Then the density of '*A*' with respect to that of '*B*' is ______.

(a) 20 (b) 1.25 (c) 0.8 (d) 9

SOLUTION

RD = Density of substance/Density of water (dw)

$4 = d_A/d_w$

$d_A = 4d_w$

$5 = d_B/d_w$

$dB = 5d_w$

$d_A/d_B = (4d_w)/(5d_w) = 4/5 = 0.8$

Hence, the correct option is (c), which is 0.8.

EXAMPLE 1.11 If the relative density of '*x*' and '*y*' is 3 and 2, respectively. Then the density of '*x*' with respect to that of '*y*' is ______.

(a) 6 (b) 5 (c) 1.5 (d) 1

SOLUTION

$$\text{RD} = \frac{\text{Density of substance}}{\text{Density of water } (d_w)}$$

$$3 = \frac{d_x}{d_w},\ d_x = 3\ d_w$$

$$2 = \frac{d_y}{d_w},\ d_y = 2\,d_w$$

$$\frac{d_x}{d_y} = \frac{3d_w}{2d_w} = \frac{3}{2} = 1.5$$

Hence, the correct option is (c).

Measurement of Time, Temperature and Approximation

Measurement of Time

If somebody asks you, how long do you take to reach home from school? Then, you might answer 30 minutes.

- **Time:** The interval between two events is called time.
  We measure time with the help of a mean solar day.
- **Mean solar day:** Time taken by the earth to complete one rotation about its own axis is called mean solar day (i.e., 24 hours).
- **SI unit of time:** Second is the standard unit of time.
- **Special units of time:** Apart from SI unit of time, i.e., second, other special units are also allowed worldwide for convenience in daily life activities.

Examples: How much time do you spend in your school every day? The answer to this question will be quite lengthy and inconvenient to express in seconds (i.e., $8 \times 60 \times 60 = 28{,}800$ seconds), whereas it is convenient to express in hours (i.e., 8 hours).

1 minute = 60 seconds

1 hour = 60 minutes

1 day = 24 hours

1 year = 365 days (approximately)

1 decade = 10 years

1 century = 10 decades

1 millennium = 10 centuries

Info Bytes!

Before clocks, ancient civilizations, including the Egyptians and Chinese, used sundials and water clocks to measure time.

Devices for Measuring Time

In ancient days water clock, sand clock, sundial, etc., were used.

Pendulum clocks are still in use (one oscillation = two seconds).

The time interval of an event can be measured using a stopwatch and a stop clock. An electronic stopwatch is more accurate when compared to a stop clock and stopwatch up to 0.01 s. This watch does not have a minute or a second hand.

Electronic watches are used to measure the timings of athletic activities. These watches can measure with an accuracy of hundredth part of a second.

Atomic watches are used for scientific purposes. These are accurate up to 10 millionth part of a second.

Pendulum clock

Alarm clock

Sand clock

Pocket-watch

Wall clock

Digital watch

Figure 1.11 Devices for measuring time

Learning About a 24-hour Clock

A day consists of 24 hours, therefore, train and aeroplane schedules are expressed in 24-hour clock.

In a 24-hour Clock

1. A day starts from midnight of a day and ends at next midnight.
2. Time from 12 o' clock at midnight to 12 o' clock at noon is expressed as a.m. (antimeridian).
3. Time from 12 o' clock at noon to 12 o' clock at midnight is expressed as p.m. (postmeridian).
4. 00 hours = 12 o' clock at midnight
5. 12 hours = 12 o' clock at noon

Table 1.3 Table of Flight Schedule in a 24-Hour Clock and a 12-Hour Clock

Route	Days of Operation	Flight No.	Departure	
			24-hour clock	12-hour clock
Delhi to Mumbai	Daily	UK929	06:10	06:10 a.m.
	Daily	UK943	07:25	07:25 a.m.
	Daily	UK987	14:55	02:55 p.m.
	Daily	UK979	18:15	06:15 p.m.

Table 1.3 *(Continued)*

Ahmedabad to Delhi	Daily	UK953	15:20	03:20 p.m.
	Daily	UK956	12:35	00:35 p.m.
Mumbai to Ahmedabad	Daily	UK980	17:35	05:35 p.m.
	Daily	UK939	10:20	10:20 a.m.
Delhi to Goa	Daily	UK953	17:25	05:25 p.m.
Delhi to Hyderabad	Daily	UK862	14:30	02:30 p.m.
	Daily	UK829	06:40	06:40 p.m.
Hyderabad to Delhi	Daily	UK879	17:15	05:15 p.m.
	Daily	UK830	09:30	09:30 p.m.

Activity

Joshua's flight is scheduled at 16:00 hours from Hyderabad to Delhi. Mention the schedule of the flight in 12-hour clock time.

The schedule of flight in 12-hour clock time is _____ 04:00 p.m.

EXAMPLE 1.12 Complete the following table.

Train	Place	Arrival Time (24-hour clock)	Time (12-hour clock)
Charminar Express	Secunderabad	18:50	
Krishna Express	Tirupathi	6:30	

SOLUTION

The time 18:50 is expressed as 18:50 in 24-hour clock system and it is expressed as 6:50 p.m. in 12-hour clock system. Time 6:30 is expressed as 6:30 in 24-hour clock system and it is expressed as 6:30 a.m. in 12-hour clock system.

Measurement of Temperature

The feeling of hotness or coldness is due to the difference in temperatures.

Temperature: The degree of hotness or coldness is the measure of temperature.

Units: The SI unit of temperature is kelvin.

The other units of temperature are degree Celsius (°C) and degree Fahrenheit (°F).

Devices to Measure Temperature

A thermometer is used to measure temperature.

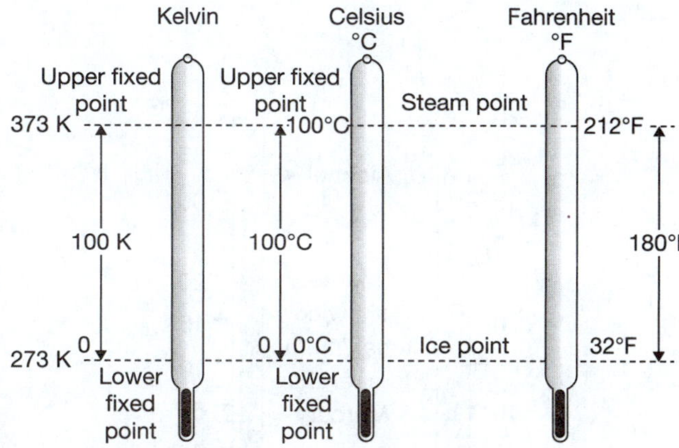

Figure 1.12 Thermometers showing different scales of measuring temperature

- **Construction of thermometer:** A thermometer is made of a glass tube, with a capillary tube inside it. To the end of this, there is a cylindrical bulb filled with mercury or alcohol.
- **Calibration of thermometer:** The lower marking on thermometer is the melting point of pure water while the upper marking is the boiling point of pure water.
- **Celsius scale:** The gap between the lower fixed point (LFP) and upper fixed point (UFP) on a thermometer is divided into hundred units and each unit is 1°C. The LFP is 0°C while the UFP is 100°C.
- **Kelvin scale of temperature:** 0°C is equal to 273 K. To convert Celsius scale into Kelvin scale, just add 273 to the value in degree Celsius.

  Example: 17°C = 273 + 17 = 290 K
- **Fahrenheit scale of temperature:** The LFP is 32°F and UFP is 212°F.

  This scale is used mostly on clinical thermometers since the same gap between LFP and UFP is divided into 180 divisions whereas the same gap is divided into 100 divisions in Celsius and Kelvin scales. In converting the temperature from Celsius to Fahrenheit, the formula is $F = (9/5)C + 32$.

Types of Thermometers

1. **Laboratory thermometer:** It is calibrated from – 10°C to 100°C. Each part is 1°C.

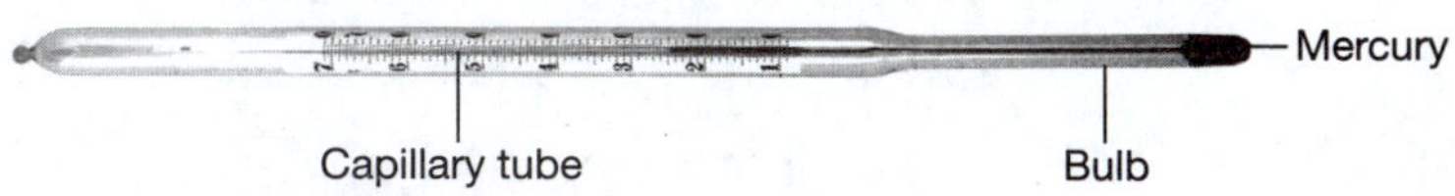

Figure 1.13 A laboratory thermometer

2. **Clinical thermometer:** It is used by doctors to measure human body temperature calibrated from 35°C to 43°C. The normal body temperature is 36.8°C (i.e., 98.4°F).

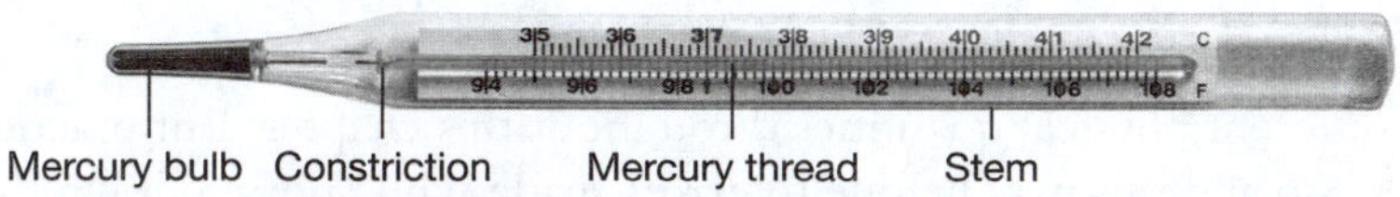

Figure 1.14 A clinical thermometer

Figure 1.15 A digital thermometer

3. **Digital Thermometer:** Digital thermometers measure the temperature by means of an electronic circuit.

   Constriction in capillary tube (kink) avoids backflow of mercury and keeps the level of mercury constant till the temperature is noted.

3. **Six's Maximum and Minimum thermometer:** It is used to measure minimum and maximum temperatures recorded in a day. This equipment is used in meteorology and horticulture.

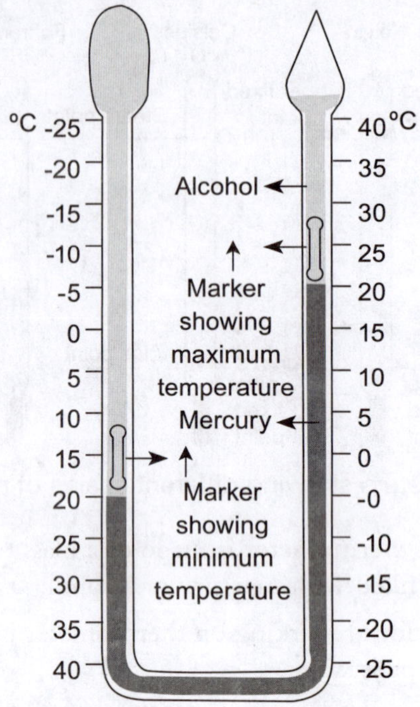

Figure 1.16 Six's maximum and minimum thermometer

Konnect

Mercury is used in thermometers because it remains liquid over a wide temperature range and expands and contracts uniformly in response to temperature changes.

Reasons Why Mercury is Used in Thermometer

(a) It is opaque and shiny. It can be easily seen through the glass to note the reading.

(b) It does not stick to the glass.

(c) It is a good conductor of heat.

(d) Used over a wide range of temperatures since it has low freezing point (–39°C) and a high boiling point (357°C).

EXAMPLE 1.13 Aishwarya is suffering from fever and her temperature was 39°C. What is her temperature in Fahrenheit and Kelvin scale of temperature?

SOLUTION

(i) K = °C + 273 = 39 + 273 = 312 K

(ii) $\frac{°C}{5} = \frac{F-32}{9} \Rightarrow F = \left(\frac{°C \times 9}{5}\right) + 32 = \left(\frac{39 \times 9}{5}\right) + 32 = 102.2°F$

Approximation

Now, you have learned the methods to measure different physical quantities throughout this chapter. But practical values will always differ by some value with theoretical value and this may be due to errors made while noting down the values. Such kind of errors can be rectified by taking the average value.

Example: The length of a thread is measured by three persons A, B, and C, their observation of length is 5 cm, 5.1 cm, 4.9 cm, respectively.

$$\text{Average length} = \frac{(5+5.1+4.9)}{3} = 5 \text{ cm}$$

EXAMPLE 1.14 The apples harvested from an orchard for three weeks are as follows:

Week 1 - 300 kilograms
Week 2 - 250 kilograms
Week 3 - 200 kilograms
Calculate the average mass of apples yielded per week.

SOLUTION

Average mass of apples yielded per week = (300 + 250 + 200)/3 = 250 kilograms.

Activity

Aim: To measure the diagonal length of your TV screen in inches.

Apparatus: Scale

Procedure: Take a metre scale. Measure the length of the diagonal of screen in centimeters. Convert the reading in terms of inches. If 1 inch = ____ centimeters. The diagonal of the screen = ____ cm = ____ inches.

EXAMPLE 1.15 Convert a temperature of 35°C to the Kelvin scale using the relation $K = °C + 273$.

SOLUTION

$K = °C + 273$

$K = 35 + 273$

$K = 308$ K

EXAMPLE 1.16 Write any five units of time.

SOLUTION

Second, minute, hour, day, week, month, year (any five).

EXAMPLE 1.17 How may seconds make one day?

SOLUTION

1 day = 24 × 60 × 60 = 86,400 seconds

EXAMPLE 1.18 Find the time taken by the minutes hand to make a 45° angle at the centre of the clock.

SOLUTION

For 360° → 1 hour

For 45° → $\frac{45}{360}$ hours $= \frac{1}{8}$ hours $= \frac{60 \text{ minutes}}{8} = 7.5$ minutes

EXAMPLE 1.19 If the angle between the hour hand and the minute hand of a clock is approximately 90 degrees, and the hour hand is pointing at 3 while the minute hand is at 9, what time does the clock show?

SOLUTION

To have an angle of approximately 90 degrees between the hour and minute hands, the hour hand must be halfway between two numbers on the clock face. In this case, the hour hand is pointing at 3, which means it is at the 15-minute mark. So, the time shown by the clock is 3 hours and 45 minutes.

Motion

Everybody in the universe is in motion. In our daily life we see many things moving around us.

Examples: Birds flying, vehicles moving, people walking, etc. We say that a book is in a state of rest on a table but in fact, the book is also moving along with the earth around the sun.

Rest and Motion

Rest and motion are two states of body which express the position of a body with respect to an observer (or) frame of reference with passage of time. Rest and motion are not absolute terms.

Example: Consider yourself waiting for a local train on a railway platform. You find that the trees nearby are at rest but if you observe the same trees from a moving train, you feel that they are moving away or towards you.

Figure 1.17 Difference in state of an object with respect to the frame of reference

From the above example, it is clear that the same object is said to be in motion or rest with respect to its relative position with the observer.

States of body

Rest

A body is said to be at rest if it does not change its position with respect to the observer or its immediate surroundings.

Examples: Stone lying on the ground, position of trees and houses.

Motion

A body is said to be in motion if it changes its position with respect to the observer or its immediate surroundings.

Examples: Moving buses, crawling insects.

Distance and Displacement

Consider a rat travelling from one point to another along a path as shown in the figure. The length of the path he travelled is 200 m, it is called **distance**. The length of the straight line joining initial point and the cheese is called **displacement**, i.e., 120 m.

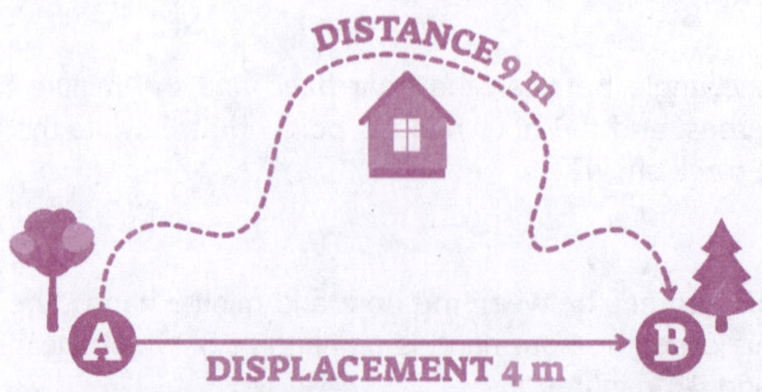

Figure 1.18 Illustration showing difference between distance and displacement

Table 1.4 Comparison between Distance and Displacement

Distance	Displacement
The length of the path travelled by a body in a certain interval of time is called distance travelled by the body.	The shortest distance from the initial to the final position of the body is called displacement.
Units: • SI unit: Metre (m) • CGS unit: Centimetre (cm)	Units: • SI unit: Metre (m) • CGS unit: Centimetre (cm)
Denoted by 'S'	Denoted by '$\vec{s}$'
It has only magnitude.	It has both magnitude and direction.
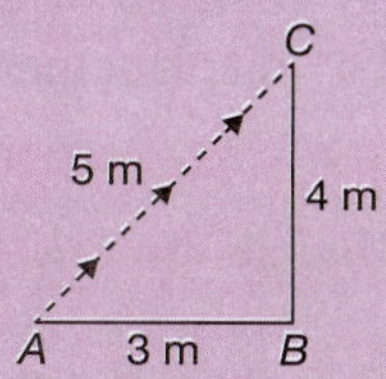 ***Example:*** A person travelled from 'A' to 'B' and then from 'B' to 'C'. Distance travelled = 3 + 4 = 7 m • It can be more than or equal to the magnitude of displacement. • It is always positive and can never be zero.	***Example:*** In the same example, the person is displaced from 'A' to 'C'. Then this length of line joining 'A' to 'C' which is 5 m is the displacement of the person from point 'A' to point 'C'. Displacement in position of the person = 5 m • Its magnitude can be less than or equal to the distance. • It can be positive, negative, or zero.

EXAMPLE 1.20 A boy travelled in a circular path and reached to the initial position 'O'. If the radius of the circle is 7 m. Find the distance covered and the displacement of the body.

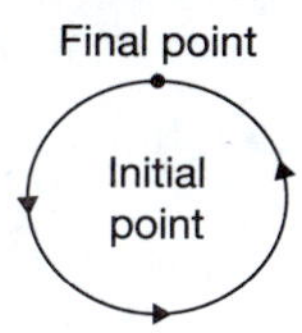

SOLUTION

Since the initial and final position of the boy is coinciding, the length of the straight line drawn from the initial position to the final position is zero. Therefore, displacement is zero.

Radius = 7 m

Distance travelled = Circumference of circle = $2\pi r$

$= 2\times\frac{22}{7}\times 7 = 44$ m $\quad\therefore\ \vec{s} = 0$ and $S = 44$ m

Speed and Velocity

Although speed and velocity are used interchangeably in daily life, they represent different physical quantities in physics.

1. Both speed and velocity measure how fast something moves.
2. Velocity involves the direction of motion but speed does not.
3. Velocity and displacement both include direction.

Info Bytes!

Velocity is speed with a direction.

The value of velocity can be negative only by reversing the direction of motion.

Speed = 25 m s^{-1} Velocity = −25 m s^{-1} | Speed = 25 m s^{-1} Velocity = + 25 m s^{-1}

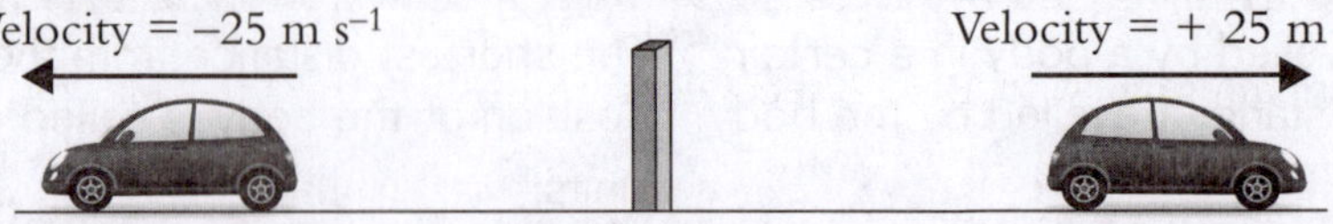

Table 1.5 Differences between Speed and Velocity

Speed	Velocity
Definition: The distance travelled by a body in unit time is called speed.	***Definition***: The distance travelled by a body in a particular direction, i.e., displacement in unit time is called velocity.
Unit: SI unit: $\frac{\text{metre}}{\text{second}}$ (or) m s^{-1} CGS unit: cm s^{-1}	***Unit***: SI unit: m s^{-1}; CGS unit: cm s^{-1}
Formula: Speed = $\frac{\text{Distance (S)}}{\text{time}}$	***Formula***: Velocity (V): = $\frac{\text{Displacement}(\vec{s})}{\text{Time}}$
Types of speed (a) ***Uniform speed***: A body is said to be moving with uniform speed if it covers equal distances in equal intervals of time. 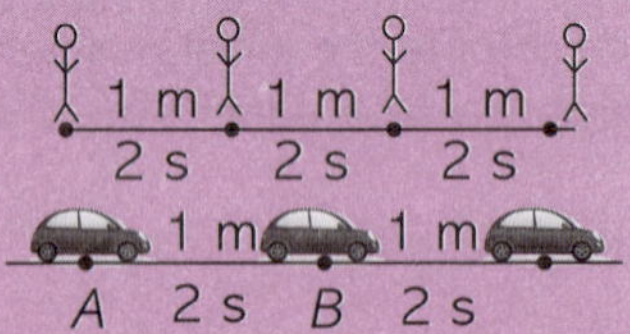	**Types of velocity** (a) ***Uniform velocity***: If a body covers equal distances in equal intervals of time along a particular direction, then the body is said to be moving with uniform velocity. 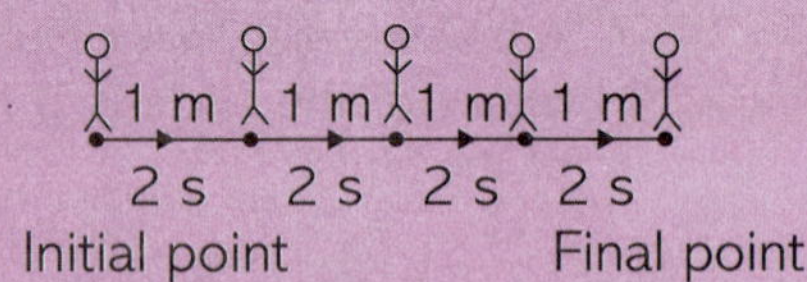 Odometer measures distance covered by the vehicle.
(b) ***Variable (or) non-uniform***: A body is said to be moving with non-uniform speed if it covers unequal distances in equal intervals of time.	(b) ***Variable (or) non-uniform:*** A body is said to be moving with non-uniform speed if it covers unequal distance in equal intervals of time in a specified direction (or) equal distance in equal intervals time in different directions 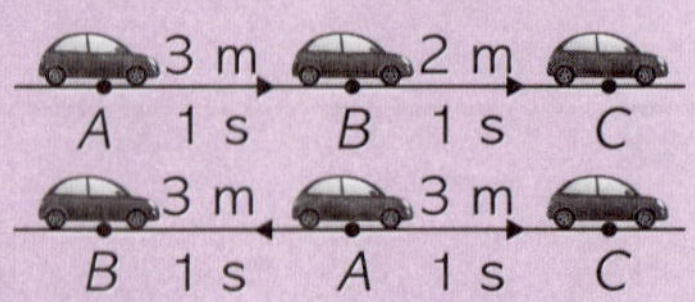
(c) ***Instantaneous speed***: Speed of a body at a particular instant of time is called instantaneous speed (during variable speed). * Speedometer of a vehicle measures the instantaneous speed.	(c) ***Instantaneous velocity***: The velocity of a body moving with variable velocity at a particular instant of time is called instantaneous velocity.
(d) Average speed = $\frac{\text{Total distance}}{\text{Total time taken}}$	(d) Average velocity = $\frac{\text{Total displacement}}{\text{Total time taken}}$

EXAMPLE 1.21

Find the speed and velocities for the case given below.

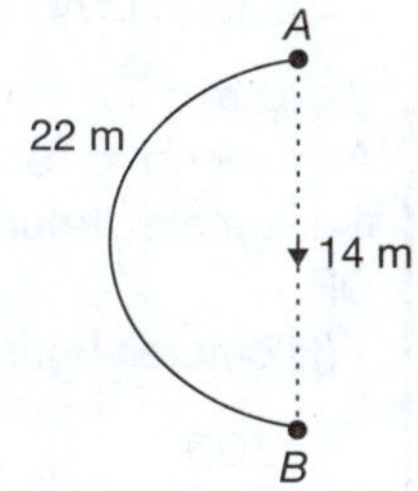

SOLUTION

Particle moving in semicircular path from 'A' to 'B' in 2 seconds.

Distance = 22 m

Displacement = 14 m

$$\text{Speed} = \frac{\text{Distance}}{\text{Time}} = \frac{22}{2} = 11 \text{ m s}^{-1}$$

$$\text{Velocity} = \frac{\text{Displacement}}{\text{Time}} = \frac{14\text{m}}{2} = 7 \text{ m s}^{-1}$$

1 (kilometer/hour) = 1000 (meters)/3600 (seconds)

OR

1 (kilometer/hour) = 5/18 (meters/second)

1 kilometre per hour = 1 kmph = $\frac{5}{18}$ m s^{-1}

1 mile per hour = 1 mph = 0.447 m s^{-1}

Acceleration

Generally, bodies do not move with constant velocity. Consider the motion of an ant, it moves from place to place in different directions and with different velocities. If the velocity of the ant increases with time, then the ant is said to be accelerated and if the velocity of the body decreases with time, then the motion is said to be decelerated or retarded.

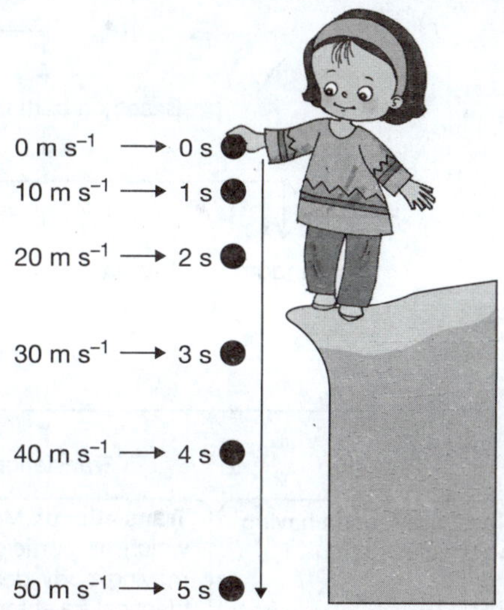

Figure 1.19 Ball released at a height is under acceleration due to gravity

Rate of change of velocity with time is called **acceleration**.

$$\text{Acceleration} = \frac{\text{Change in velocity}}{\text{Time taken for change}}$$

Example: Consider a cyclist started at point 'A' with an initial velocity 'u' at time 't_1' and reached point 'B' with final velocity 'v' at time 't_2'.

Acceleration in car is $\frac{v-u}{t_2-t_1}$

Deriving units for acceleration:

$$A = \frac{(v-u)}{(t_2-t_1)} = \frac{(m/s)}{s} = \frac{m}{s^2} = \text{m s}^{-2}$$

The SI unit is m s^{-2}.

If $v > u$, then 'a' is positive and the body is in acceleration.

If $v < u$, then 'a' is negative and the body is said to be in retardation.

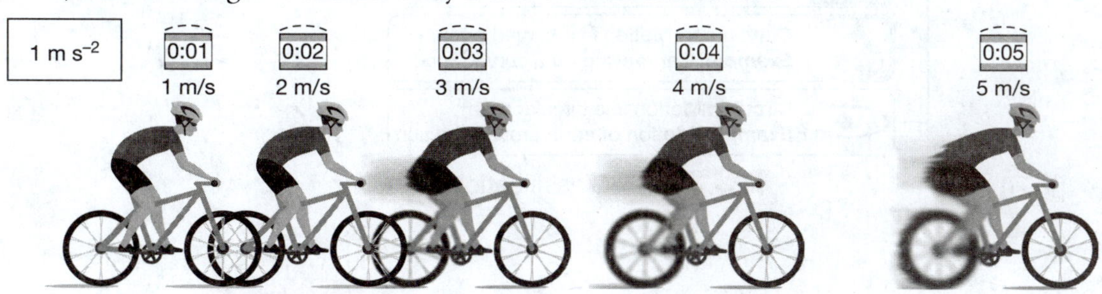

Figure 1.20 A cyclist moving with non-uniform velocity

EXAMPLE 1.22 A motorist started from a position of rest from Warangal and reached Hyderabad in 3 hours. If the distance between the cities is 200 kilometres, what is the average speed of the motorist?

SOLUTION

$u = 0 \text{ m s}^{-1}$

Avg speed = Total distance travelled/Total time taken

1 (kilometer/hour) = 1000(meters)/3600(seconds)

OR

1 (kilometer/hour) = 5/18 (meters/second)

$$v = \frac{200}{3} \text{ kmph (using the formula)}$$

$$= \frac{200}{3} \times \frac{5}{18} \text{ m s}^{-1} = 18.5 \text{ m s}^{-1}$$

Classification of Motion

The motion of bodies can be classified based on two parameters, (i) the path travelled by the body and (ii) the velocity of the body.

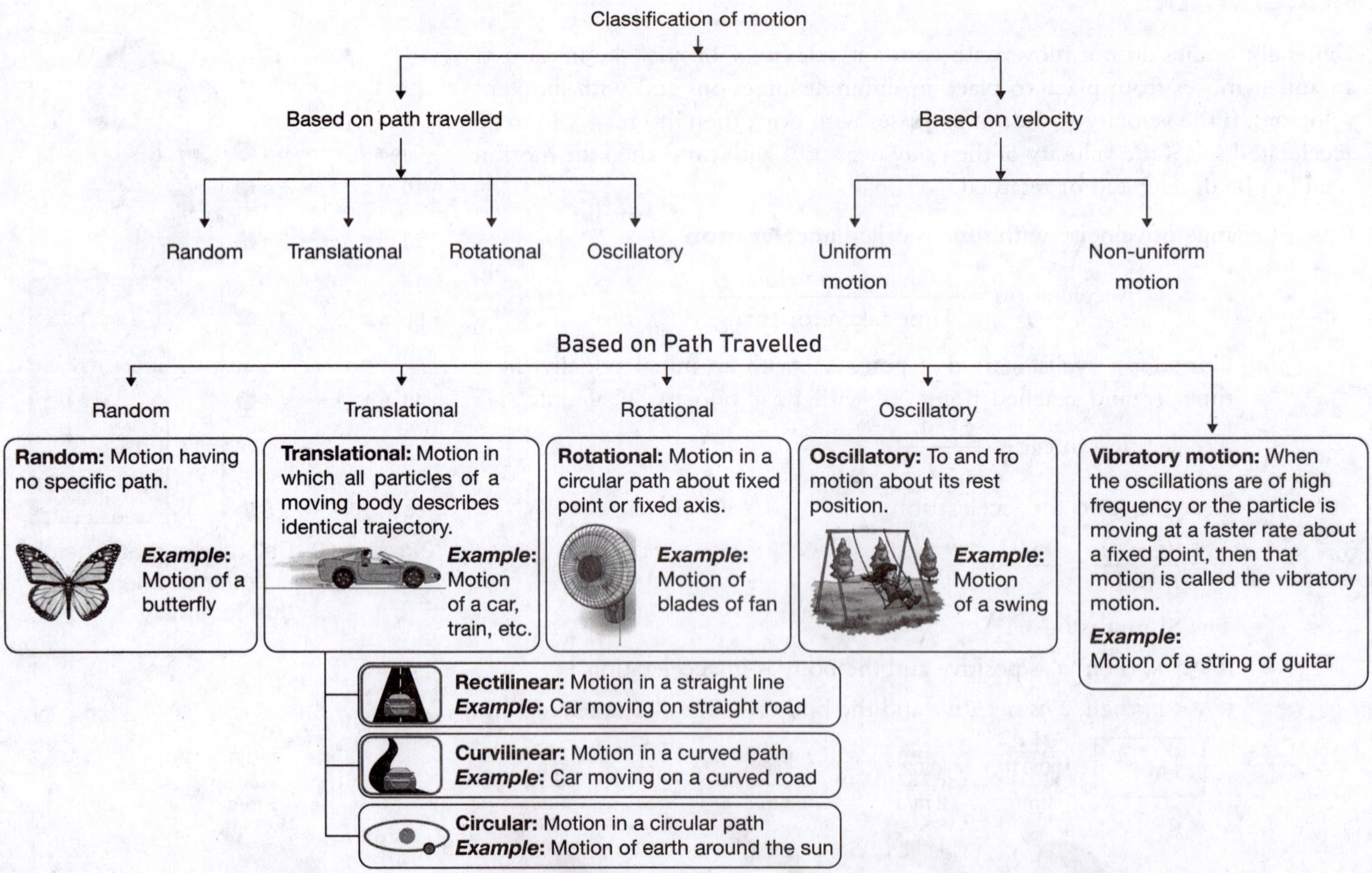

Figure 1.21 Classification of motion

Uniform Motion

If a body travels equal distances in equal intervals of time, then the body is said to be in uniform motion.

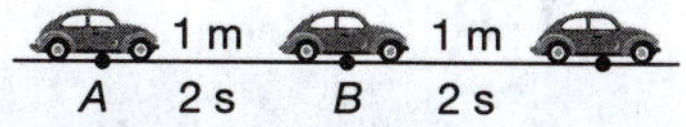

Example: Car moving at a speed of 20 miles per hour.

Non-uniform Motion

If a body travels unequal distances in equal intervals of time, then the body is said to be in non-uniform motion.

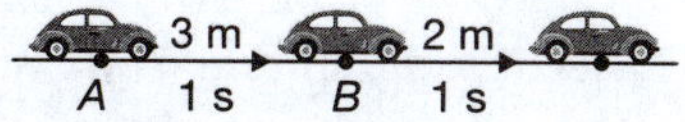

POINTS TO REMEMBER

- ✔ Measurement is essential for maintaining accuracy in our everyday life. It plays an essential role in our lives.
- ✔ Quantities which can be measured physically are called physical quantities.
- ✔ Units which are used to measure large quantities are called multiple units.
- ✔ Whenever we measure width, thickness, depth, distance and height, we are measuring length. The SI unit of length is 'metre'.
- ✔ Everybody in the universe is in motion. In our daily life we see many things moving around us.

DW

PRACTICE QUESTIONS CLASSROOM WING

Very Short Answer Type Questions

Directions for questions from 1 to 5.
Select the correct alternative from the given options.

1. Which of the following is a fundamental quantity?
   (a) Length (b) Area
   (c) Volume (d) Force

2. Which of the following unit is a derived unit?
   (a) Cubic metre (b) Newton
   (c) Metre^2 (d) All of these

3. The unit of electric current is denoted by
   (a) I (b) E
   (c) A (d) a

4. Prefix used for 10^{-3} is
   (a) Milli (b) Micro
   (c) Mega (d) Kilo

5. Prefixes used for negative powers of 10 are called
   (a) Units (b) Multiples
   (c) Submultiples (d) Standards

Directions for questions from 6 to 15.
Fill in the blanks.

6. To measure irregular areas ______ paper is used.
7. 2 decades are equal to ______ years.
8. 5 centimetres are equal to ______ metres.
9. ______ grams make 0.2 kilograms.
10. 5 milliseconds is equal to ______.
11. The ratio of the SI unit of mass to its CGS unit is ______.
12. A thread of length 20 cm is made into square, then the length of its side is ______.
13. Ratio of the SI unit of volume to the SI unit of area is ______.
14. If the volume of a sphere is $\frac{4}{3}\pi r^3$ where $\pi = \frac{22}{7}$ and r is radius of the sphere, then the radius of the sphere of volume $\frac{704}{21}$ m^3 is ______.
15. ______ grams make 20 milligrams.

Directions for questions from 16 to 20.
Select the correct alternative from the given options.

16. The SI unit of mass is
    (a) kg (b) gram
    (c) second (d) g cm^{-3}

17. Area is measured in
    (a) m^2 (b) cm^2
    (c) mm^2 (d) All of these

18. ______ is used to measure the length of a curved line.
    (a) A thread
    (b) A graph paper
    (c) Water
    (d) None of these

19. Relation between length (ℓ), area (A), volume (V) is
    (a) $V = A\ell$ (b) $V = \frac{A}{\ell}$
    (c) $\ell = VA$ (d) $V = A\ell^2$

20. If the length of a square is 2 cm, then its area in SI system is
    (a) 4 cm^2 (b) 4×10^4 m^2
    (c) 4×10^{-4} m^2 (d) 40 cm^2

Directions for questions from 21 to 25.
Fill in the blanks.

21. The least measurement of time in a wall clock is ______.
22. The thermometer used to measure the minimum and maximum temperatures of a day is called ______ thermometer.
23. The short hand of a clock is at 12 and the minutes hand is 3, then the time at that instant is ______.
24. The relations between kelvin and celsius scales is K = C + 273. The temperature of a body in Kelvin scale is 19 K, if its equivalent temperature in celsius scale is ______.
25. The shape of six's maximum and minimum thermometer is in the shape of the English alphabet ______.

Directions for questions from 26 to 30.
Select the correct alternative from the given options.

26. The angle between the minutes hand and hours hand in a clock, at 12:30 p.m. is

(a) $>0^0$ (b) $>30^0$
(c) $>60^0$ (d) $>90^0$

27. Temperature is a ______ quantity.

(a) Derived (b) Fundamental
(c) Physical (d) Both (b) and (c)

28. Time is a fundamental quantity

(a) Since it is independent of other quantities.
(b) Since it is measured in secondary scale.
(c) Since it is dependent on other quantities.
(d) Since it depends on the mass of the clock.

29. The device used to measure temperature is

(a) Metre scale (b) Barometer
(c) Thermometer (d) Lactometer

30. Which of the following units of temperature is not followed by the word 'degree'?

(a) Celsius (b) Centigrade
(c) Fahrenheit (d) Kelvin

Directions for questions from 31 to 35.
Fill in the blanks.

31. If a body does not change its position, it must be in a state of ______.

32. The CGS unit of distance covered is ______.

33. Acceleration is measured in ______ in SI system.

34. A passenger in a moving bus appears to be in a state of rest with respect to ______.

35. A body is said to be in a state of motion if it changes its ______.

Directions for questions from 36 to 40.
Select the correct alternative from the given options.

36. The SI unit of velocity is

(a) cm s^{-1} s (b) mm s^{-1}
(c) m s^{-1} (d) km h^{-1}

37. Which of the following is different from the others?

(a) Distance covered
(b) Displacement
(c) Velocity
(d) Acceleration

38. Centimetre per second is the unit of

(a) Distance covered
(b) Displacement
(c) Velocity
(d) Acceleration

39. If the velocity of a body decreases gradually with time, then it is said to be in

(a) Acceleration (b) Deceleration
(c) Retardation (d) Both (b) and (c)

40. A bus is moving with uniform velocity

(a) Then its acceleration is non-zero.
(b) Then its acceleration is negative.
(c) Then its acceleration is zero.
(d) Then its acceleration is positive.

Short Answer Type Questions

41. Define physical quantity and give any two examples.

42. Define derived physical quantity and give any two examples.

43. Define multiple units.

44. Define unit and write any three examples.

45. Define fundamental unit and write any two examples.

46. What is the SI unit of density?

47. Write the correct notation for the following.

(a) 2 Kg (b) 4 Newtons
(c) 6 metres (d) 35 Gram
(e) 7 S

48. Match the entries in Column A with entries in Column B.

	Column A		Column B
(A)	SI unit of electric current	(a)	Candela
(B)	CGS unit of time	(b)	Ampere
(C)	SI unit of luminous intensity	(c)	Metre
(D)	SI unit of distance	(d)	Second

49. **Assertion A:** 1 metre can be written as 1 m and not as 1 M.

Reason R: If the unit of physical quantity is not named after a scientist, symbol of the unit should not be denoted with a capital letter.

(a) A and R is correct and R is the correct explanation of A.
(b) A and R is incorrect.
(c) Both A and R is true but 'R' is not the correct explanation of A.
(d) A is true, R is not true.

50. Write the following steps in sequential order to convert centimetres into millimetres.
(a) Convert centimetres into metres by dividing the given value with 100.
(b) Write the given value.
(c) Multiply the result with 1000.
(d) The result of the length given above is in millimetres.

51. If the product of milli and micro is nano and the values of milli and nano are 10^{-3} and 10^{-9}, find the value of micro.

52. If A, B, and C are the units of time, length, and speed, then find the relationship between them.

53. Find the units of density, $\frac{\text{density}}{\text{mass}}$, and $\frac{\text{electric current}}{\text{time}}$.

54. Write the SI unit of the product of force and time.

55. Find the unit of work if work is the product of force and displacement, force $= \text{mass} \times \text{acceleration}$, where acceleration $= \frac{\text{length}}{\text{time}^2}$.

56. Define length.

57. Define mass.

58. Define volume.

59. Define area.

60. Define measurement.

61. Find the value of the ratio of the nanometer to the micrometer.

62. What is the physical quantity measured in cm^2?

63. Arrange the following steps in a sequence to find the area of a leaf.
(a) Find the number of complete boxes and half boxes inside the boundary.
(b) As the area of one box is 1 cm^2, the total area is equal to the sum of full boxes and half boxes areas.
(c) Place it on a graph paper.
(d) Take an irregular shaped leaf.
(e) Draw the outline and remove it from the graph paper.

64. Match the following.

Column A	Column B
(A) Area/length	(a) $metre^{-1}$
(B) Mass/volume	(b) No unit
(C) Length/area	(c) metre
(D) $Length^2$/area	(d) kg m^{-3}

65. **Assertion (A):** m^2 is a derived unit.
Reason (R): Area is a derived quantity.
(a) A and R is correct and R is the correct explanation of A.
(b) A and R is incorrect.
(c) A and R is true but 'R' is not the correct explanation of A.
(d) A is true, R is not true and R is not the correct explanation of A.

66. Pavan is measuring the area of a leaf by using a graph paper and he measured the sum of the areas of full boxes and more than half boxes inside the outline of the leaf which is 25 cm^2. Find the length of the square whose area is equal to the area of the leaf.

67. Ram measured the length of a curved line using a thread. He made a right angled triangle, of base 10 cm and height 20 cm, with the same thread. Find the length of the curved line measured by him.

68. Convert the unit of ratio $\frac{\text{mass} \times \text{area}}{\text{volume}}$ from SI system to CGS system.

69. Find the area of a coloured paper used to stick to a sphere of radius 7 cm.

70. Define time.

71. Define temperature.

72. Match the following.

Column A	Column B
(A) Kelvin	(a) Hotness
(B) Time	(b) Temperature
(C) Temperature	(c) Second

73. **Assertion (A):** Temperature is a fundamental quantity in SI system.
Reason (R): In other systems of measurement only mass, length, and time are fundamental quantities.
(a) A and R is correct and R is the correct explanation of A.

(b) Both A and R is incorrect.
(c) A is true, R is true and 'R' is not the correct explanation of A.
(d) A is true, R is not true.

74. Write the following steps in a sequential order to find the time at a given instant by using a clock.
(a) Observe the position of the hour hand.
(b) Observe the position of the minute hand.
(c) Multiply 1 hour with the number at which the hour hand is located.
(d) Note the number of minutes, considering the gap between two numbers of clocks as 5 minutes.
(e) Find the time.

75. Raju started a piece of work when the hours hand and minutes hand in a wall clock are at 9 and 12, respectively. He completed his work when the hours hand is at a midway between 11 and 12, while the position of the minutes hand is at 6. Find the time taken by him to do the work.

76. Define rest.

77. Define motion.

78. Define displacement.

79. Define velocity.

80. Define acceleration.

81. How can you differentiate between distance and displacement?

82. If the distance covered by a body moving in a circular path of radius (r) is equal to $2\pi r$, find its displacement.

83. How can you say that speed and velocity are different even though their units are the same?

84. How can one say that the tree on the earth is in a state of rest and in a state of motion at the same time?

85. Give any one example in which a body travels with retardation and give a reason for the same.

86. A particle is moving in circular path of radius 7 cm. Find the ratio of its displacement to the distance covered after the completion of a half circle.

87. Find the minimum speed required by a person standing 5 m behind a bus, to catch the bus in one minute which is moving at a speed of 600 m min^{-1}.

88. If a bus moves from A to B and comes back to A, find the displacement and velocity of the body.

89. What is the speed of a body if it covers a distance of 20 m in 4 seconds?

90. Find the acceleration of the car, if it changes its velocity from 20 m s^{-1} to 30 m s^{-1} in 5 seconds.

91. Write the differences between speed and velocity.

92. How do you represent a vector geometrically?

93. Define distance, displacement and speed.

94. A cube of side 2.5 cm weighs 100 g. Calculate the density of the cube.

Essay Type Questions

95. (a) Given that the time taken by an oil dropper to drop 100 oil drops is 800 min, find the time taken to drop 10 oil drops in hours.
(b) On dropping 3 identical bullets into a measuring jar containing a liquid, the level of the liquid increased from 280 cm^3 to 316 cm^3. Then the volume of each bullet is ______ m^3.

96. (a) An object 'X' of volume 200 cm^3 and another object Y of volume 250 cm^3 are taken. If their area is the same, then determine the ratio of their heights.
(b) Four spheres made of different materials but having the same mass, have a radii of 100 mm, 2×10^{-2} m, 30 cm and 10^{-5} km then arrange them in ascending order of their volumes.

PRACTICE QUESTIONS COMPETITION WING

Level 1: Apply Your Concepts

Directions for questions from 1 to 5.
Fill in the blanks.

1. In SI system mass is measured in ______.
2. Unit of ______ is the same in all the systems of measurements.
3. In ______ system there are seven fundamental quantities.
4. Prefix used for factor 10^{-6} is ______.
5. Mega is used for a factor of ______.

Directions for questions from 6 and 7.
Select the correct alternative from the given options.

6. When one of the passengers was traveling on a city bus, his mobile phone slipped from his hands and that fell out of the bus through the window. This was observed by a school boy standing on the road. The path of the mobile phone observed by the school boy is ______.
   (a) circular (b) parabolic
   (c) linear (d) elliptical
7. The number of divisions on a Fahrenheit scale of temperature, having LFP and UFP as 32 °F and 212 °F respectively, is ______.
   (a) 100 (b) 180
   (c) 120 (d) 150

Directions for questions from 8 to 12.
Answer the following questions.

8. The mass of a wooden block of dimensions 1 m × 1 m × 1 m is 500 kg. Calculate the relative density of wooden block.
9. When can we say that a particle in motion is moving with uniform speed?
10. A body is dropped from a height of 50 m. Find the velocity of the body at the end of every second up to 5 seconds if the acceleration due to gravity is 10 m/s^2.
11. What will be the displacement of a body when it travels along the following paths?
    (a) Half circle
    (b) Full circular path?
12. What are the physical quantities that can be measured in m s^{-1}, km, and km h^{-2}?

Directions for questions from 13 to 16.
Fill in the blanks.

13. In case of Vernier calipers, the smallest measurement possible is ______ cm.
14. 1 km^2 = ______ m^2
15. For a Fahrenheit scale of temperature, the LFP is ______ and UFP is ______.
16. The instantaneous velocity of a body which is moving with a uniform velocity of 25 m/s is ______.

Directions for questions from 17 to 21.
Select the correct alternative from the given options.

17. 1 m^3 = ______
    (a) 1 L (b) 10 L
    (c) 100 L (d) 1000 L
18. If 'R' be the radius of the given sphere, then its volume = ______
    (a) $4\pi R$ (b) $4\pi R^2$
    (c) πR^3 (d) πR^3
19. SI unit of temperature is ______.
    (a) °C (b) °F
    (c) K (d) T
20. Distance ______.
    (a) is always positive
    (b) can be negative
    (c) can be zero
    (d) Both (a) and (c)
21. Find out the physical quantity in CGS unit that results on simplifying the expression $1000\ \frac{a^2b^2c^3}{d}$, where a – acceleration, b – displacement, c – time, d – velocity.
    (a) 10,000 cm^3 (b) 1000 cm^3
    (c) 1000 l (d) 1000 g

Directions for question 22
Assertion and Reason-based question

22. Assertion (A): Mercury is used in thermometer to measure a wide range of temperatures.

Reason (R): Mercury has low freezing point (–39°C) and a high boiling point (357°C).

(a) Both A and R are correct, and R is the correct explanation to A.

(b) Both A and R are correct, and R is not the correct explanation to A.

(c) A is correct and R is incorrect.

(d) Both A and R are incorrect.

Directions for questions from 23 to 31.

Answer the following questions.

23. Some amount of water is poured in a measuring jar and the surface of water coincides with 570 cm^3 on it. When a stone is immersed in water completely, the level of the water changes. If the volume of the stone is 70 cm^3, then find the mark on the measuring jar with which the surface of water coincides.

24. Convert 1 litre into mm^3.

25. The relative density of a substance is 3. Find the density of the substance in SI units.

26. Mention the name of the thermometer used by doctors to measure human body temperature. What is the calibration on it?

27. Convert 90 km/h into m/s.

28. A bus starts from rest and moves on a straight road *ABCD*. The distances covered by the bus for the given time intervals are shown in the figure below.

(i) Identify the type of motion of the bus.

(ii) Calculate the change in velocity for every second.

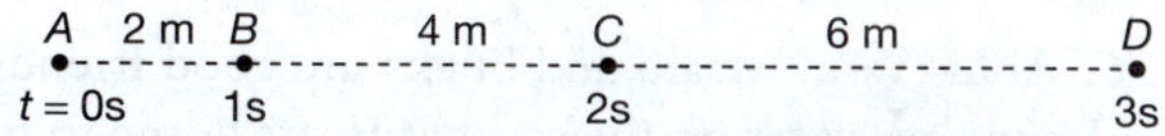

29. An athlete completes two rounds of a circular track of radius 50 m by running and comes back to his initial position. Calculate the distance and displacement of an athlete.

30. A bus starts from rest and covers 50 m in 20 s. Calculate average velocity of the bus.

31. A body moves along a straight path *ABCDE*. The distances covered by a body for the given time intervals are shown in the figure below.

(i) Identify the type of motion of the body.

(ii) Calculate the average velocity of the body.

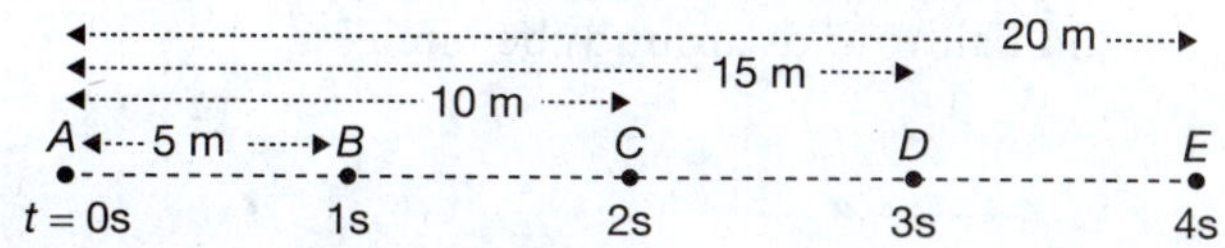

Directions for question 32.

Select the correct alternative from the given options.

32. Jyothi created a temperature scale, in which the reading at room temperature divides the total length of the temperature scale in 2 : 3 ratio from LFP. Find its value on Jyothi's scale, which is the same as Kelvin scale.

(a) 40 K (b) 313 K

(c) 200 K (d) 73 K

Level 2: Review Your Concepts

33. Abhi who is interested in physics measured the volume of an irregular shaped body with concepts given by his physics teacher. When he immersed the body in water contained in a measuring jar, the level of water is increased from 500 ml to 1500 ml. Find the volume of the body and also find the length of the edge of the cube whose volume is equal to the volume of the given irregular shaped body.

34. Keshav observed that the increase in the temperature of a body is given by $T_1 = 2t^2$ for the first 5 minutes and $T_2 = 3t$ for the next 5 minutes, where T_1, T_2 and '*t*' are temperatures in Fahrenheit, Celsius scales and time in minutes, respectively. If the initial temperature of the body is 20°F and the relation between the Celsius and Fahrenheit scale is, then find the temperature of the body after 8 minutes in Celsius scale.

35. Dev is a 12-year-old, studying in 6th class, and has a younger brother Surya whose age is 7-years. Surya is playing by dipping balls in water tub. Dev observed that the level of the water increases when Surya starts dipping the balls one after the other in the water. Then Dev remembered his 6th class topic measurement of volume. He poured water up to the brim of the tub and set up another bigger tub at the bottom of the first tub. He then asked his brother Surya to dip ten identical balls in it so that the overflowed water is collected in the tub at the bottom. Dev calculated volume of overflowed water and found that it was 2 litres. Dev calculated volume of each ball. Which of the following options matches with Dev's calculation?

(a) 2000 *l* (b) 200 *l*

(c) 20 *l* (d) 0.2 *l*

Level 3: Assess Your Concepts

36. Abhi, Vasu, Maahi and Lucky are good friends. During summer vacation they met at Vasu's home to play. Vasu's father is good at mathematics and physics, so he used to play with Vasu and his friends by asking subject-related questions in the middle of their play. He asked a question; "how will you write the weight of your 1 litre water bottle in physics?" Select the correct form of writing the weight from the options given below.
   (a) Abhi wrote 10 n
   (b) Vasu wrote 10 newtons
   (c) Maahi wrote 10.N
   (d) Lucky wrote 10, N.

37. A girl was running in a circular field of radius 10 cm. What will be her displacement when she travels three and half rounds around the circle?

38. The temperature values recorded during the day-time are given in the table below. Convert them into Fahrenheit.

Time	07:00 AM	10:00 AM	01:00 PM
Temperature	25 °C	30 °C	35 °C

39. A boy walks along a circular track of radius 35 m. The distances covered by the boy with respect to time are given below.
   (i) Identify the type of motion of the boy
   (ii) Calculate the speed of the boy.

Time (s)	0	10	20	30	40	50
Distance (m)	0	20	40	60	80	100

AT

ANSWER KEYS

Crossword

Across

2. Distance 3. Volume 5. Velocity 7. Meter 8. Displacement

Down

1. Acceleration 4. Multiple 6. Speed 9. Physical 10. Accuracy

Classroom Wing

Very Short Answer Type Questions

1. (a) 2. (d) 3. (c) 4. (a) 5. (c)
6. graph 7. 20 8. 5×10^{-2} 9. 200 10. 5×10^{-3} s
11. $10^3 : 1$ 12. 5 cm 13. Metre 14. 2 m 15. 20×10^{-3}
16. (a) 17. (d) 18. (a) 19. (a) 20. (c)
21. 1 second 22. Six's maximum and minimum 23. 12 : 15 a.m. (or) 12 : 15 p.m.
24. −254°C 25. U 26. (d) 27. (d) 28. (a)
29. (c) 30. (d) 31. rest 32. centimetre 33. metres per second square
34. another passenger 35. position with respect to time 36. (c)
37. (a) 38. (c) 39. (d) 40. (c)

Short Answer Type Questions

46. kg/m^3 48. (A) → (b), (B) → (d), (C) → (a), (D) → (c) 49. (a)
50. (b)(a)(c)(d) 51. 10^{-6} 52. B = CA 53. A s^{-1} 54. N s
55. kg m^2 s^{-2} 61. 10^{-3} 62. Area 63. (d)(c)(e)(a)(b)
64. (A) → (c), (B) → (d), (C) → (a), (D) → (b) 65. (a) 66. 5 cm
67. 52.3 cm 68. 10 g cm^{-1} 69. 616 cm^2 72. (A) → (b), (B) → (c), (C) → (a)
73. (c) 74. (a), (c), (b), (d), (e) 75. 2.5 hours 82. zero
86. 7 : 11 87. 605 m min^{-1} 88. zero 89. 5 m s^{-1} 90. 2 m s^{-2}
94. 6.4 g/cm^3

Essay Type Questions

95. (a) 1.3 hr (b) 12×10^{-6} m^3 96. (a) $\frac{4}{5}$ (b) $V_4 < V_2 < V_1 < V_3$

Competition Wing

Level 1: Apply Your Concepts

1. kilogram 2. time 3. SI 4. micro 5. 10^6
6. (b) 7. (b) 8. 0.5 13. 0.01 cm 14. 10^6 m^2
15. 32°F; 212°F 16. 25 m/s 17. (d) 18. (c) 19. (c)
20. (a) 21. (b) 22. (a) 23. 640 cm^3 24. 10^6 mm^3
25. 3000 kg/m^3 27. 25 m/s 28. 2 m/s^2 29. 628 m; 0 30. 2.5 m/s
31. 5 m/s 32. (b)

Level 2: Review Your Concepts

33. 10 cm 34. 30°C 35. (d)

Level 3: Assess Your Concepts

36. (c) 37. 20 cm 38. 77 °F, 86 °F, 95 °F, 39. 2 m/s

Hints and Explanations

CLASSROOM WING

Very Short Answer Type Questions

11. $\frac{\text{kg}}{\text{g}} = \frac{10^3 \text{ g}}{\text{g}} = 10^3 : 1$

12. $4 \times \text{side} = 20$

$\text{Side} = \frac{20}{4} = 5 \text{ cm}$

13. $\frac{m^3}{m^2} = \text{metre}$

14. $\frac{4}{3}\pi r^3 = \frac{704}{21}$

$r^3 = \frac{704}{21} \times \frac{3}{4} \times \frac{7}{22}$

$r^3 = 8$

$r = 2 \text{ m}$

15. 20 milligrams = 20×10^{-3} gram (∵ milli = 10^{-3})

16. SI unit of mass is kilogram (kg)

17. Area = length × breadth = side × side

∴ mm^2 or cm^2 or m^2 are the units of area.

18. A thread and scale is used to measure the length of a curved line.

19. Relation between length (ℓ), area (A), volume (V) is $V = A \times \ell$

20. Area = Length × Length

$= 2 \times 10^{-2} \times 2 \times 10^{-2}$

$= 4 \times 10^{-4} \text{ m}^2$

21. The least measurement of time in a wall clock is 1 second.

22. The thermometer used to measure the minimum and maximum temperatures of a day is called Six's maximum minimum thermometer.

23. 12:15 am or 12:15 pm or quarter past 12.

24. $C = K - 273$

$= 19 - 273$

$= -254$

∴ $C = -254°\text{C}$

25. The shape of six's maximum and minimum thermometer is in the shape of the English alphabet *U*.

26. The angle between the minutes hand and hours hand in a clock, at 12:30 p.m. is greater than 90°.

27. Temperature is a fundamental physical quantity.

28. Time is a fundamental quantity since it is independent of other quantities.

29. The device used to measure temperature is Thermometer.

30. Kelvin is the unit of temperature which is not followed by the word 'degree'.

37. Except the distance covered, all the other quantities have direction.

Short Answer Type Questions

41. Quantity which can be measured is called physical quantity.

Example: time, speed.

42. Physical quantity which is dependent on other physical quantities is called derived physical quantity.

$\text{Speed} = \frac{\text{Length}}{\text{Time}}$; $\text{Area} = \text{Length}^2$

43. Prefixes or units used to represent very higher values of physical quantities are called multiples.

44. Standard reference of a physical quantity is called its unit.

Example: Length – metre, time – second and mass – kilogram.

45. Units of fundamental quantities are called fundamental units.

Example: gram, metre.

46. Density is defined as the mass per unit volume.

i.e., $\text{Density} = \frac{\text{Mass}}{\text{Volume}}$

Therefore, the SI unit is kg/m^3

47. (a) 2 kg (b) 4 newtons
(c) 6 metres (d) 35 grams
(e) 7 s

(A) → (b), (B) → (d), (C) → (a), (D) → (c)

48. (A) SI unit of electric current is ampere.
(B) CGS unit of time second.
(C) SI unit of luminous intensity candela.
(D) SI unit of distance is metre.

49. 1 metre can be written as 1 m and not as 1 M as it is not named after a scientist, symbol of the unit should not be denoted with a capital letter.

50. Write the given value. Convert centimetres into metres by dividing the given value with 100. Multiply the result with 1000. The result of the length given above is in millimetres.

51. milli × micro = nano

$10^{-3} \times \text{micro} = 10^{-9}$

$\text{Micro} = 10^{-6}$

52. $\text{Speed} = \dfrac{\text{Length}}{\text{Time}}$

$C = \dfrac{B}{A}$ or $B = CA$

53. $\text{Density} = \dfrac{\text{Mass}}{\text{Volume}} = \dfrac{\text{kg}}{\text{m}^3} = \text{kg m}^{-3}$

$\dfrac{\text{Density}}{\text{Mass}} = \dfrac{\text{kg m}^{-3}}{\text{kg}} = \text{m}^{-3}$

$\dfrac{\text{Electric current}}{\text{Time}} = \dfrac{A}{s} = \text{A s}^{-1}$

54. We have, SI unit of force is newton (N)
SI unit of time is second (s)
Therefore, the SI unit of product of force and time is N s

55. Work = Force × Displacement

$= m \times a \times s = m \times \dfrac{\ell}{t^2} \times \ell = m \dfrac{\ell^2}{t^2}$

$= \text{kg} \dfrac{m^2}{s^2} = \text{kg m}^2\ \text{s}^{-2}$

56. Extent of a body from one end to other end is called length.

57. Amount of matter contained in a body is called mass.

58. Space occupied by a body is called its volume.

59. Measurement of a surface is area.

60. Comparison between known value of a physical quantity to its unknown value is measurement.

61. We have, nanometer $= 10^{-9}$ m

micrometer $= 10^{-6}$ m

Now, the ratio of nanometre and micrometre $= 10^{-9} \times 10^{6} = 10^{-3}$

62. Area is the physical quantity measured in cm^2.

64. (A) → (c), (B) → (d), (C) → (a), (D) → (b)

$\dfrac{\text{Area}}{\text{length}} = \dfrac{\text{length} \times \text{length}}{\text{length}} = \text{length}$, SI unit of length is metre.

$\dfrac{\text{Mass}}{\text{Volume}} = \text{Density}$, SI unit of Density is kg m^{-3}

$\dfrac{\text{length}}{\text{area}} = \dfrac{\text{length}}{\text{length} \times \text{length}} = \dfrac{1}{\text{length}}$

SI unit of $\dfrac{1}{\text{length}}$ is m^{-1}

$\dfrac{\text{length}^2}{\text{Area}} = \dfrac{\text{length}^2}{\text{length} \times \text{length}} = 1$

Since it is a constant value, it has no unit

65. m^2 is a derived unit as it is the SI unit of area. Area is a derived quantity.

66. Areas of square = side^2

$25 = \text{side}^2$

∴ side = 5 cm

67. $\text{Hypotenuse} = \sqrt{100+400} = \sqrt{500} = 10\sqrt{5}$ cm

Length of the curved line $= 10 + 20 + 10\sqrt{5}$
$= 52.3$ cm

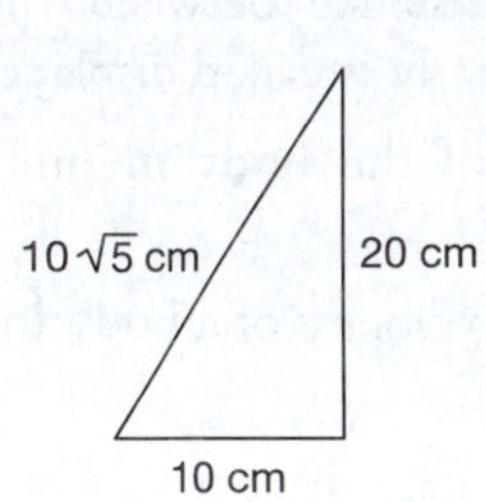

68. $\dfrac{\text{Mass} \times \text{Area}}{\text{Volume}}$

$= \dfrac{\text{kg m}^2}{\text{m}^3} = \text{kg m}^{-1}$

Convertion into CGS unit

kg m^{-1}

$= 10^3\text{g} \times (10^2\ \text{cm})^{-1} = 10\ \text{g cm}^{-1}$

69. $\text{TSA} = 4\pi r^2$

$= 4 \times \dfrac{22}{7} \times 7^2$

$= 616\ \text{cm}^2$

70. Duration between two events is called time.

71. Temperature is the measure of the degree of hotness or coldness of a body.

72. (A) → (b), (B) → (c), (C) → (a)

73. Temperature is a fundamental quantity in SI system, and it is not the fundamental quantity in other systems of unit.

Hence, the correct option is (c).

74. Observe the position of the hour hand.

Observe the position of the minute hand.

Multiply 1 hour with the number at which the hour hand is located.

Note the number of minutes, considering the gap between two numbers of clocks as 5 minutes.

Find the time.

Correct order: a, c, b, d, e

75. $t_1 = 9{:}00$

$t_2 = 11{:}30$

Time taken = 11.30 – 9:00 = 2 hour 30 minutes = 2.5 hours.

76. If a body does not change its position with respect to its surroundings with time, then the body is said to be in a state of rest.

77. If a body changes its position with reference to its surroundings with time, then the body is said to be in a state of motion.

78. The shortest distance between the initial and final positions of a body is called displacement.

79. Displacement of the body in unit time is called its velocity.

80. Change in the velocity of a body in unit time is called its acceleration.

81. Displacement has direction but distance has no direction.

82. If a body travels a distance equal to $2\pi r$ in circular path, it will reach the same position where it started. So, its displacement is zero.

83. Velocity has direction but speed doesnot have any direction, therefore, they are different from each other.

84. With respect to us, trees on the earth are in a state of rest but with respect to other planets, trees on the earth are in a state of motion as the earth rotates around its own axis.

85. When a body projected upwards its velocity decreases, as the gravitational force acts downwards. So, it is said to be moving with retardation.

86. $$\frac{\text{Displacement}}{\text{Distance}} = \frac{2r}{\pi r} = \frac{2 \times 7}{\left(\frac{22}{7}\right) \times 7} = \frac{7}{11}$$

87. 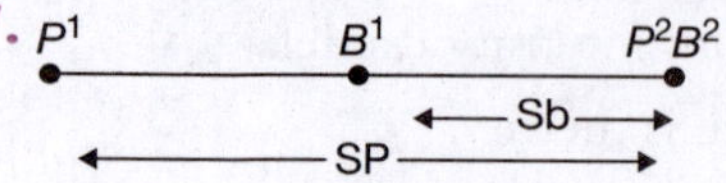

$5 + S_b = V_{p}t$

$S_b = 600 \times 1$

$5 + (600 \times 1) = V_P \times 1$

$V_P = 605 \text{ m min}^{-1}$

88. As the bus comes back to the initial position, its displacement and velocity are zero.

89. $V = \frac{s}{t} = \frac{20}{4} = 5 \text{ m s}^{-1}$

90. $a = \frac{v - u}{t}$

$a = \frac{30 - 20}{5} = 2$

$a = 2 \text{ m s}^{-2}$

91. Differences between speed and velocity

Speed	Velocity
Speed is defined as the rate of distance covered by the body.	Velocity is defined as the rate of displacement covered by the body.
Speed is always positive.	Velocity can have both positive and negative values.
Speed is a scalar quantity.	Velocity is a vector quantity.

92. A vector can be represented by a line segment with an arrow head.

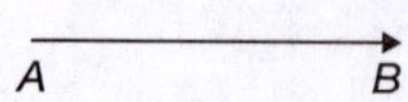

93. Distance is defined as the length of the actual path travelled by a particle in motion. Displacement is defined as the shortest distance between the initial and final positions of a body. Distance travelled by a particle in a unit time is known as speed.

94. Given, Side of the cube, $a = 2.5$ cm

Mass of the cube, $m = 100$ g

Now, the volume of the cube,

$V = a^3 = (2.5)^3 = 15.625\ \text{cm}^3$

Now, the density of the cube,

$$d = \frac{m}{V} = \frac{100}{15.625} = 6.4\ \text{g/cm}^3$$

Essay Type Questions

95. (a) To drop 100 oil drops from a dropper takes 800 min.

100 drops $\rightarrow$ 800 min

$$10\ \text{drops} \rightarrow \frac{10 \times 800}{100}\ \text{min}$$

$$t = \frac{10 \times 8}{1}\ \text{min} = \frac{80}{60}\ \text{hr} = 1.3\ \text{hr}$$

(b) The volume of the 3 bullets = Rise in the water level

$= 316\ \text{cm}^3 - 280\ \text{cm}^3 = 36\ \text{cm}^3$

$\therefore$ The volume of each bullet $= \frac{36}{3}\ \text{cm}^3$

$= 12\ \text{cm}^3 = 12 \times 10^{-6}\ \text{m}^3$

96. (a) They both have equal area. Volume = Area × Height

$$\frac{h_x}{h_y} = \frac{V_x}{V_y} = \frac{200}{250} = \frac{4}{5}$$

(b) Volume of a sphere, $V = \frac{4}{3}\pi r^3$

$V \propto r^3$

$r_1 = 10^2\ \text{mm} = 10^{-1}\ \text{m}$

$r_2 = 2 \times 10^{-2} = 2 \times 10^{-2}\ \text{m}$

$r_3 = 30 \times 10^{-2}\ \text{m} = 3 \times 10^{-1}\ \text{m}$

$r_4 = 10^{-5} \times 10^3\ \text{m} = 10^{-2}\ \text{m}$

$V_4 < V_2 < V_1 < V_3$

COMPETITION WING

Level 1: Apply Your Concepts

6. Parabolic

7. The number of divisions on a Fahrenheit scale of temperature, having LFP and UFP as 32 °F and 212 °F respectively, is,

212 – 32 = 180

8. Given, mass of the wooden block of volume = 500 kg.

Volume of the wooden block = 1 m × 1 m × 1 m = 1 m^3

Therefore, density of wooden block, $d = \frac{\text{mass}}{\text{volume}}$

$= \frac{500}{1}$ kg/m^3 = 500 kg/m^3

We have, density of water, d_w = 1000 kg/m^3

Then, Relative density = $\frac{\text{Density of wooden block}}{\text{Density of water}}$

$= \frac{500}{1000} = 0.5$

9. A body or particle is said to be moving with uniform speed, if it travels equal distances in equal intervals of time.

10. Given, Height, h = 50 m

Acceleration due to gravity = 10 m/s^2

Initial velocity of the body, u = 0

Since the acceleration of the body is 10 m/s^2, the velocity of the body increases by 10 m/s for every second.

If the initial velocity of the body is 0 m/s, then the velocity of the body at t = 1 s is 10 m/s.

Similarly, the velocity of the body at t = 2 s is 20 m/s

the velocity of the body at t = 3 s is 30 m/s

the velocity of the body at t = 4 s is 40 m/s

the velocity of the body at t = 5 s is 50 m/s

11. (a) Displacement = 2 Radius

(b) Displacement = Zero

12. Speed and velocity can be measured in m s^{-1}

Displacement and distance can be measured in km.

Acceleration is measured in km h^{-2}

13. In case of Vernier calipers, the smallest measurement possible is 0.01 cm.

14. 1 km^2 = 1 km × 1 km = 1000 m × 1000 m = 10^6 m^2

15. For a Fahrenheit scale of temperature, the LFP is 32°F and UFP is 212°F.

16. For a body which is moving with a uniform velocity of 25 m/s.

Instantaneous velocity = uniform velocity

Therefore, instantaneous velocity = 25 m/s

17. We know, 1000 cm^3 = 1 L

Therefore, 1 m^3 = $(100\text{ cm})^3$ = 10^6 cm^3 = 1000 × 1000 cm^3 = 1000 L

18. If 'R' be the radius of the given sphere, then its volume $= \frac{4}{3}\pi R^3$.

19. SI unit of temperature is K (kelvin).

20. Distance is always positive.

21. $1000 \frac{a^2b^2c^3}{d} = 1000\text{ cm}^3$

22. Mercury is used in thermometer to measure a wide range of temperatures as it has low freezing point (–39°C) and a high boiling point (357°C).

23. Given,

Initial volume of water, V_1 = 570 cm^3

Volume of the stone, V = 70 cm^3

Final volume of water, V_2 =?

We know, for a measuring jar, volume of the stone, $V = V_2 - V_1$

$\Rightarrow V_2 = V + V_1 = 70 + 570 = 640\text{ cm}^3$

24. We have, 1 litre = 10 cm × 10 cm × 10 cm = 1000 cm^3

Now, 1 cm = 10 mm

Then 1 litre = 1000 × $(10\text{ mm})^3$ = 10^3 × 10^3 mm^3 = 10^6 mm^3

25. Given, Relative density of the substance = 3,

Density of water = 1000 kg/m^3

Density of the substance = Relative density of the substance × density of water

= 3 × 1000

= 3000 kg/m^3

26. Clinical thermometer used by doctors to measure human body temperature. It is calibrated from 35 °C to 43°C.

27. We have, 1 km = 1000 m

1 h = 3600 s

Now, $90 \text{ km/h} = 90 \times \frac{1000}{3600} = 90 \times \frac{5}{18} = 25 \text{ m/s}$

28. Given, for $t = 0$ s to 1 s, distance = 2 m

For $t = 1$ s to 2 s, distance = 4 m

For $t = 2$ s to 3 s, distance = 6 m

(i) The bus covers unequal displacements in equal intervals of time. Therefore, the body is in non-uniform motion.

(ii) Velocity of the bus at $t = 1$ s, $V_1 = \frac{2}{1-0} = 2 \text{ m/s}$

Velocity of the bus at $t = 2$ s, $V_2 = \frac{4}{2-1} = 4 \text{ m/s}$

Velocity of the bus at $t = 3$ s, $V_3 = \frac{6}{3-2} = 6 \text{ m/s}$

Now, the change in velocity for every second, i.e.,

$\text{acceleration} = \frac{4-2}{2-1} = \frac{2}{1} = 2 \text{ m/s}^2$

29. Given,

Radius of a circular track, $r = 50$ m

Circumference of circular track = 2 × 3.14 × 50 m = 314 m

Number of rounds completed by an athlete = 2

Therefore, distance covered by the athlete = 2 × 314 = 628 m

As the athlete is coming back to his initial position after completing two rounds, the displacement of the athlete = 0

30. Given,

Total Displacement of the bus, $s = 50$ m

Time taken, $t = 20$ s

$$\text{Average Velocity} = \frac{\text{Total Displacement}}{\text{Total Time}}$$

$$= \frac{50}{20} = 2.5 \text{ m/s}$$

31. (i) Given, for $t = 1$ s, distance = 5 m

For $t = 2$ s, distance = 10 m

For $t = 3$ s, distance = 15 m

For $t = 4$ s, distance = 20 m

i.e., the displacement of the body for every second is 5 m. Therefore, the body is in uniform motion.

(ii) $\text{Average velocity of the body} = \frac{\text{Total displacement}}{\text{Total time}}$

$$= \frac{20}{4} = 5 \text{ m/s}$$

32. Jyothi created a temperature scale in which reading at the room temperature is dividing the total length of temperature scale into 2 : 3 ratio.

The total length of Jyothi's scale is $2x + 3x = 5x$

$$\frac{2x}{5x} = \frac{K-273}{100}$$

$\therefore K = 273 + 40 = 313$ K in Jyothi's scale

Level 2: Review Your Concepts

33. Volume of an irregular body

= 1500 – 500

= 1000 cm^3

Volume of a cube = 1000 cm^3

Side^3 = 1000

$\therefore$ Side = 10 cm

34. For 1st 5 minutes

$T_1 = 2t^2$

$= 2 \times 25$

$= 50°\text{F}$

Initial temperature = 20°F

After 5 min = 20° + 50° = 70°F

$$\frac{C}{5} = \frac{F-32}{9}$$

$$C = \frac{70-32}{9} \times 5$$

= 21°C

Increase in temperature after next 3 minutes

$T_2 = 3t$

$= 3 \times 3$

$T_2 = 9$

⇒ Increase in temperature is 9°C

Temperature after 8 minutes

= 21 + 9

= 30°C

35. Volume of ten balls = the volume of overflowed water.

10 × volume of each ball = 2 l. Volume of each ball = 0.2 l.

Hence, the correct option is (d).

Level 3: Assess Your Concepts

36. Maahi wrote 10 N.

Hence, the correct option is (c).

37.

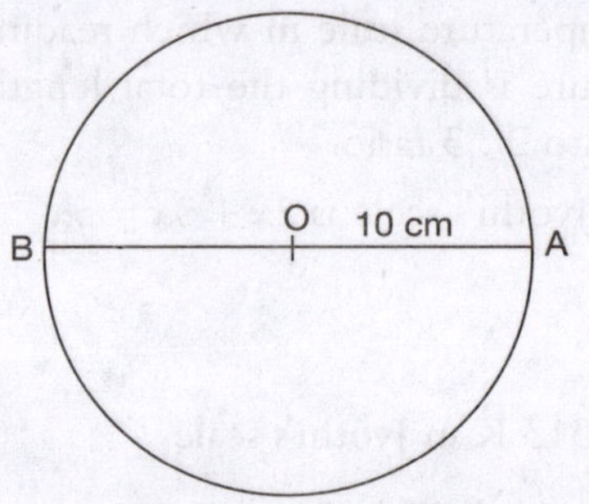

If the girl started running from point A, after three and half rounds she will be at 'B' point.

As displacement is the shortest distance between the initial and final position,

Therefore, displacement = Length of AB.

= 20 cm

38. We have, the relation between Celsius and Fahrenheit scales is given by

$F = (9/5)\ C + 32$

If $C = 25$ °C, then $F = (9/5)\ C + 32$

$\Rightarrow F = [(9/5) \times 25] + 32 = 45 + 32 = 77$ °F

If $C = 30$ °C, then $F = (9/5)\ C + 32$

$\Rightarrow F = [(9/5) \times 30] + 32 = 54 + 32 = 86$ °F

If $C = 34$ °C, then $F = (9/5)\ C + 32$

$\Rightarrow F = [(9/5) \times 35] + 32 = 63 + 32 = 95$ °F

39. (i) Given,

When $t = 10$ s, distance = 20 m

When $t = 20$ s, distance = 40 m

When $t = 30$ s, distance = 60 m

When $t = 40$ s, distance = 80 m

When $t = 50$ s, distance = 100 m

Therefore, the boy walks 20 m every 10 s. i.e., the boy covers equal distances in equal intervals of time. Therefore, the boy is in uniform motion.

(ii) Speed of the boy $= \dfrac{20 - 0}{10 - 0} = 2$ m/s

CHAPTER

2

Force and Pressure

Remember

Before beginning this chapter, you should be able to:

- Recall the basics of motion, attractive, and repulsive forces
- Define rest and motion

Key Ideas

After completing this chapter, you should be able to:

- Understand the physical quantities such as force, pressure and the factors affecting them
- Describe friction, its types, advantages, and disadvantages of it
- Apply the concepts learnt on friction, force to daily life situations.

Scientific Crypt

A Tribute to Blaise Pascal (1623–1662)

Pascal was a French mathematician, physicist, inventor, and philosopher. His earliest mathematical work was on conic sections; he wrote a significant treatise about projective geometry at the age of 16. His work in the fields of hydrodynamics and hydrostatics centered on the principles of hydraulic fluids. His inventions include the hydraulic press and the syringe. He proved that hydrostatic pressure depends not on the weight of the fluid but on the elevation difference.

Pascal performed experiments on Torricellian vacuum and found that the air pressure decreases with altitude i.e., the air pressure on a high mountain must be less than at a lower altitude. In honor of Blaise Pascal, the SI unit of pressure is named as pascal (Pa).

FUN TIME

CROSSWORD

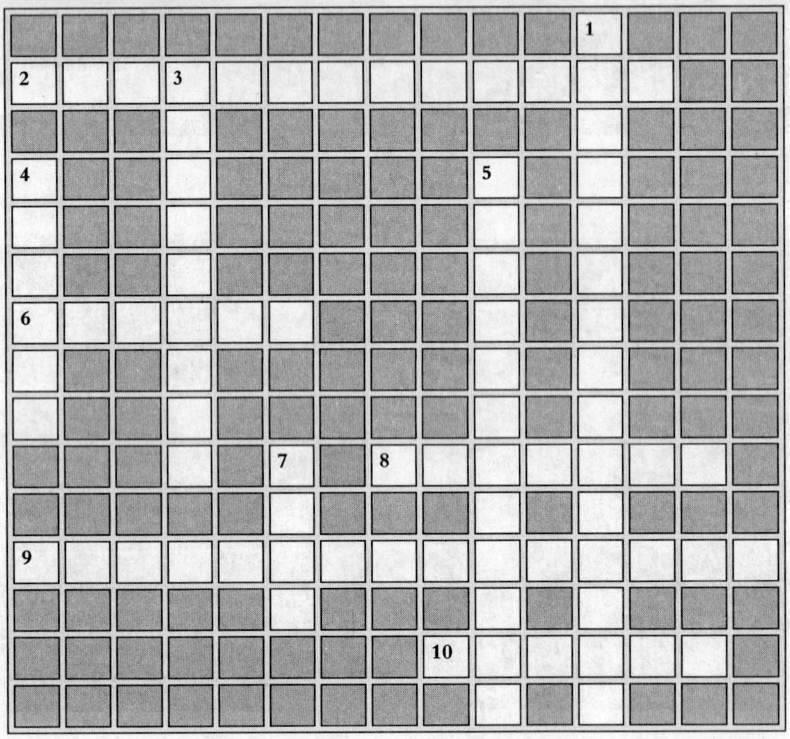

Across

2. Viscous drag is a _______.
6. Necessary thing for the existence of electric force.
8. 10^5 Pa =
9. Force is a _______.
10. What is S.I. unit of a force?

Down

1. Pressure is a _______.
3. What is the mass of 2 gwt of a body?
4. Atmospheric pressure is measured in _______.
5. Pressure acting on a body depends on _______.
7. How much is the lateral pressure difference at a point inside a liquid?

INTRODUCTION

We feel that we are at rest with respect to the other passengers when we travel by a train. But if we look at the window, our perception changes.

We tend to feel that we are moving along with the object on the road side like a tree or a house. The object or a place with respect to which we analyze our position at a certain point of time is known as frame of reference. Frame of reference plays a vital role for conceptualizing the states of rest and motion. With respect to the earth we are at rest but with respect to other planets we are moving.

State of an Object

The state of an object indicates about the rest or movement in them with respect to time.

State of an object with respect to a reference frame at a certain point of time

- State of rest: A body is said to be at rest or stationary position if it does not change its position with respect to its immediate fixed surrounding with the passage of time.
- State of motion: A body is said to be in a state of motion if it changes its position with respect to its immediate fixed surrounding with the passage of time.

Figure 2.1 A dog in the state of rest

Figure 2.2 A dog and a boy in the state of motion

Force

When an object is in a state of rest or motion, a physical cause is required to bring about a change in its state of rest/ motion, like stopping a rolling ball, opening a door, etc. This physical cause is nothing but the force.

Force can be defined as the cause (push, pull, stretch, or squeeze) which changes or tends to change the state of rest, uniform motion, direction of motion, shape, and size of the body.

Types of force

- Contact force: The force which is exerted by an object at the point of contact with another object is called contact force.
- Non-contact force: The force is said to be a non-contact force if the object exerting it is at a distance from the other object on which it is applied.

Figure 2.3 A boy pushing the table by making contact with it

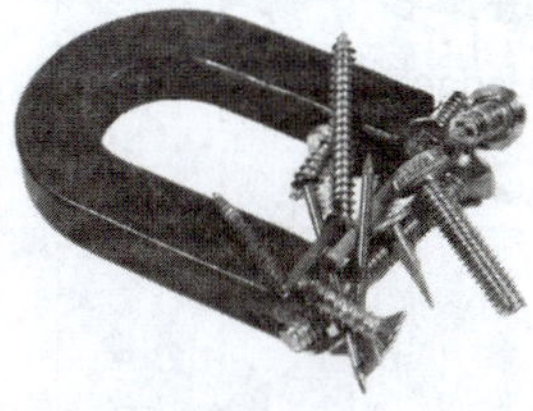

Figure 2.4 Illustration of a horseshoe magnet attracting some chrome balls

Contact force

Muscular force/Mechanical force

The force exerted by an object to make another object move is called mechanical force.

Example: Movement of a sailboat due to the mechanical force exerted by the wind.

1) Fixing a nail into a wall using hammer. Both the hammer and the hammering person exert mechanical force on the nail.
2) Closing or opening a door.
3) Pushing bicycle pedals.

Frictional force

The force which slows down the motion of a moving body when trying to move over the other body.

Example: A rolling ball gradually slows down and finally stops.

1) Sliding of a book on the surface of the table.
2) Dragging a chair.
3) Sliding of coins in carrom board.
4) Applying brakes on the wheels of a moving bike.

Figure 2.5 Movement of sailboat due to wind

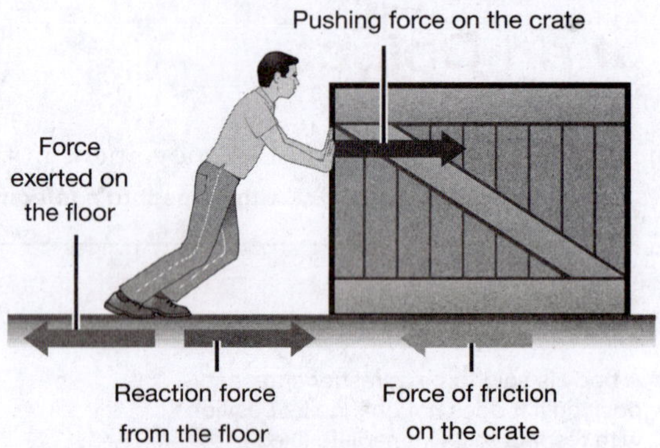

Figure 2.6 Illustration of man pushing crate

Table 2.1 Types of Non-contact force

Magnetic force		Gravitational force	Electrostatic force	
The force exerted by a magnet on another magnet or any other magnetic substance like iron is called magnetic force.		The force of attraction between any two objects due to their masses is called gravitational force.	The force acting between two electrically charged objects is called electrostatic force.	
Magnetic attraction	Magnetic repulsion	Every object in our surrounding is attracted by the earth.	Electrostatic attraction	Electrostatic repulsion
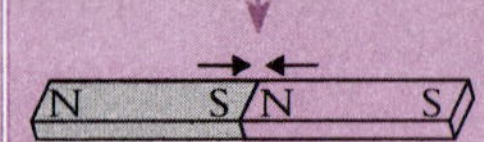	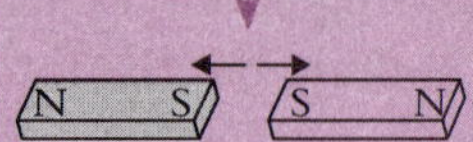	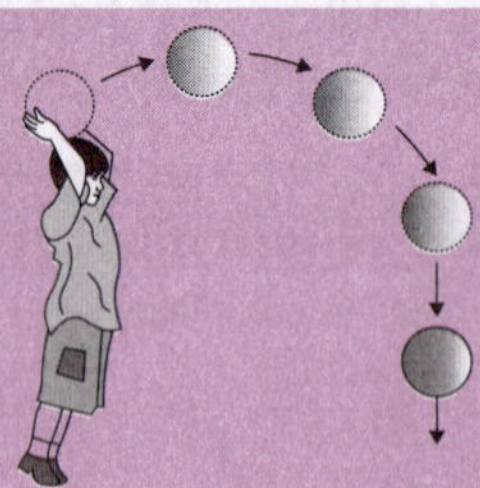	Between two oppositely charged bodies	Between two objects of similar charge
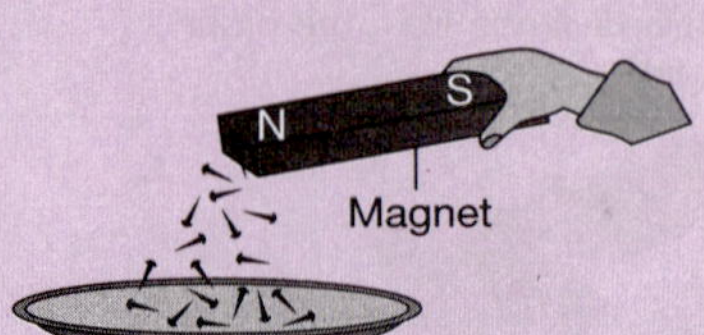				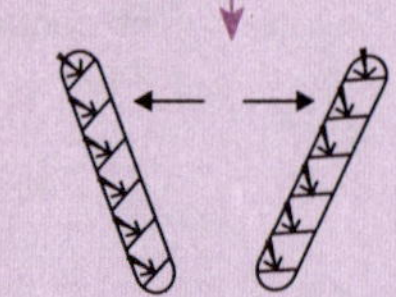 Glass rods rubbed with silk cloth repel each other

A force is represented by two parameters: (a) magnitude and (b) direction. Hence, an arrow (→) is used to interpret a force. The head of the arrow represents the direction of the force.

Units of force

	CGS system	**SI system**
Gravitational →	Gram force (gf) or gram weight (gwt).	Kilogram force (kgf) or kilogram weight (kg wt).
	Gram force is equal to the magnitude of the force exerted by the earth on a mass of one gram in a standard gravitational field.	Gram force is equal to the magnitude of the force exerted by the earth on a mass of one kilogram in a standard gravitational field.
	1 kgf = 10^3 gf	
Absolute →	Dyne	Newton
	One dyne is the force required to accelerate a mass of one gram by 1 cm/s^2.	One newton is the force required to accelerate a mass of 1 kg by 1 m/s^2.
	1 newton = 10^5 dyne	

Relation between kgf and newton (N).

1 kgf = 1 kg × 9.8 m/s(square) = 9.8 N

Hence, it can be concluded that a force of 10 newton is required to lift a mass of 1 kg.

Konnect

- Everything in the universe interacts via fundamental forces.
- The gravitational force has the widest influence as it acts between all masses, but it's the weakest.

Measurement of Force

Spring balance is the instrument which is used to measure force.

Spring balance

- Compression spring balance → ***Principle***: The spring gets compressed when a force acts on it.
- Extension spring balance → ***Principle***: The spring gets stretched when a force acts on it.

Figure 2.7 Compression and extension of a spring balance

Action and Reaction

If a body applies a force on another body, the latter exerts the same amount of force on the former, exactly in the opposite direction. There are two specific types of reaction force.

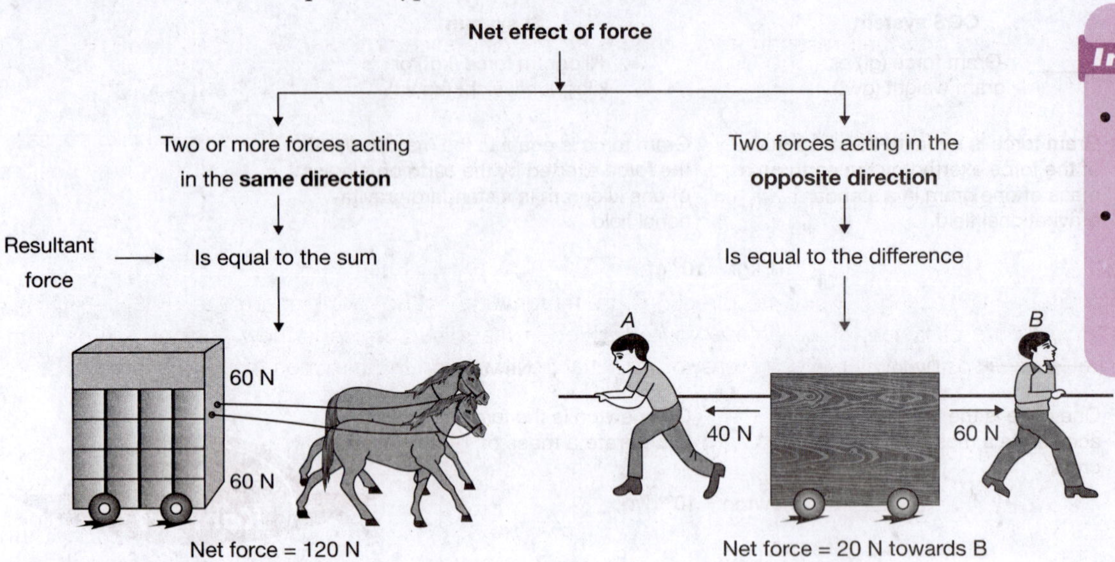

> **Info Bytes!**
> - For every action, there's an equal and opposite reaction.
> - If you tried to push off a wall in outer space, you'd find yourself moving backward.

Table 2.2 Differences between normal reaction and tension force

Normal reaction force	Tension force
This force is equal in magnitude and opposite in direction of the weight of the object when the object is placed on a horizontal surface. Since the weight of the object acts vertically downwards, normal reaction force acts vertically upwards. 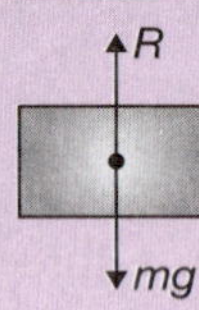	This force is also equal in magnitude and opposite in direction of the weight of the body, but gets generated when an object is suspended by a string. 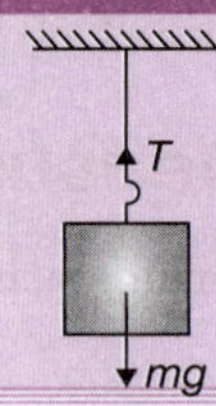

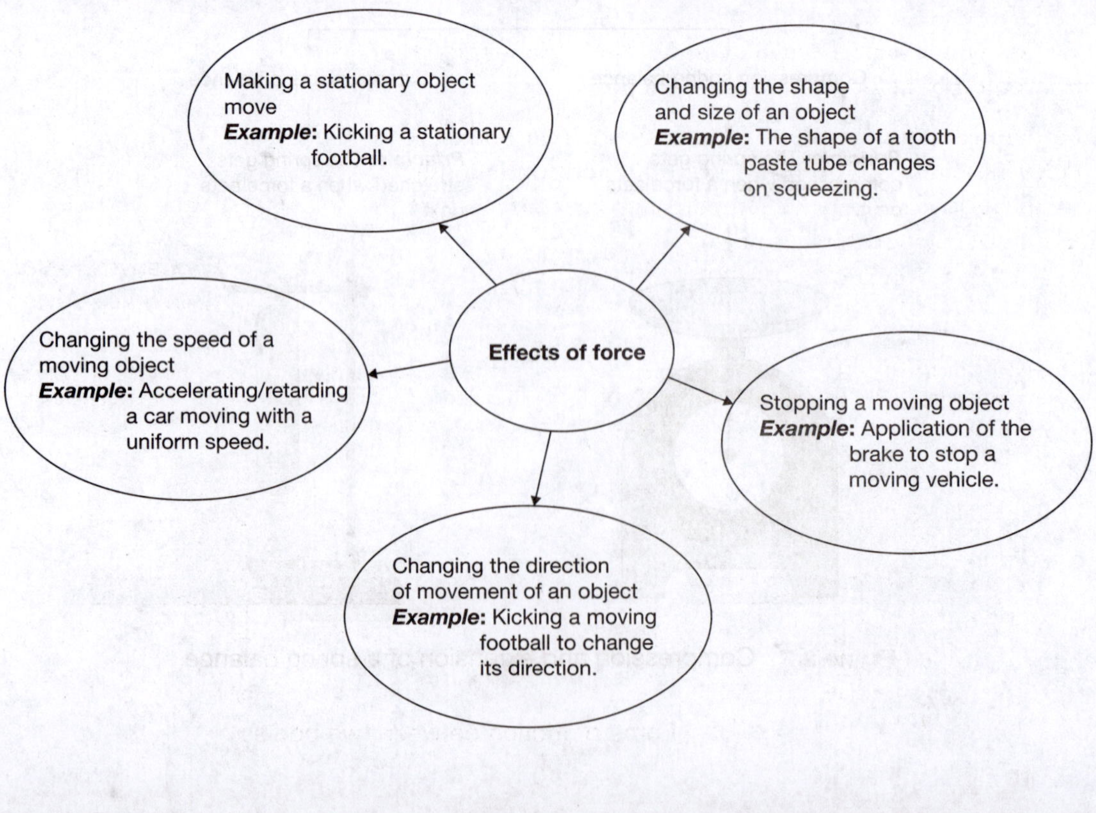

EXAMPLE 2.1 Two constant forces 7 N and 9 N act on a body in opposite directions. Find the resultant force on the body.

SOLUTION

As the two forces are in opposite directions, their resultant force is equal to the difference of those two forces, i.e., $F_R = (9 - 7) = 2$ N and acts in the direction of 9 N force.

EXAMPLE 2.2 A soccer player kicks a ball with a force of 60 N to the east, and another player kicks the same ball with a force of 40 N to the west. If the ball is initially at point *P*, predict its new position and find out the magnitude and direction of the resultant force.

SOLUTION

Since the forces applied to the ball are acting in opposite directions, the magnitude of the resultant force is (60 N – 40 N) = 20 N. The ball will move towards the east due to the greater force applied in that direction, so its new position will be in the eastern direction. So, the ball's new position will be to the east of its initial position, and the direction of the resultant force will also be towards the east.

EXAMPLE 2.3 Two people are trying to lift two different boxes, *A* and *B*, both of the same mass. Person 1 exerts an upward force of 150 N on box *A*, while Person 2 exerts an upward force of 120 N on box *B*. Box *A* starts to rise off the ground. Will box *B* also rise off the ground? Provide a reason for your answer.

SOLUTION

Since both boxes have the same mass, they require the same amount of force to overcome gravity and lift off the ground. The force applied to box *A* is 150 N, which is sufficient to make it rise. However, the force applied to box *B* is only 120 N, which is less than the force required to lift it. Therefore, box *B* will not rise off the ground.

Friction

Now we will learn in detail about a specific contact force named frictional force or friction.

Certain activities which are inevitable in our life, like walking, writing, driving would not be possible without friction.

Friction can be defined as the resisting force between two bodies in contact which prevents either body to move smoothly and continuously. Friction opposes the relative motion of two bodies in contact irrespective of the direction unit of fricional force is newton.

Figure 2.8 Friction prevents spinning of the tyres while driving a car

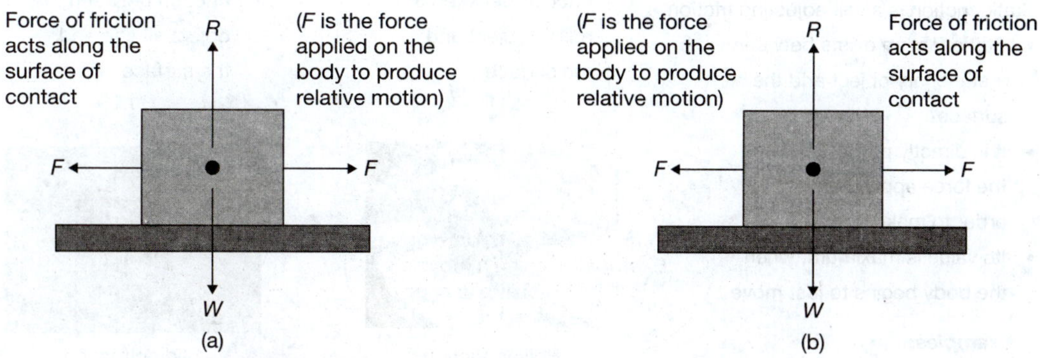

Figure 2.9 Force of friction between two bodies

Advantages of Friction

Advantages of friction

- The vehicles can move due to the friction between road and tyres. Braking system of vehicles works due to the friction between the brake lining and drum of wheel
- ***Writing***: Holding the pencil is possible due to friction. Writing is possible due to the friction between paper and tip of the pen/pencil
- Cutting wood is possible due to the friction between the saw and the wood
- Lighting a matchstick is possible due to friction
- Holding a nail in a wall is possible due to friction
- ***Walking***: We do not slip while walking because of friction between our feet and the ground

Disadvantages of Friction

Disadvantages of friction

- Difficulty in movement
- Wastage of energy to overcome the friction
- Moving parts of any device wear away rapidly
- Loss of energy in the form of heat

A matter existing in any state (solid/liquid/gaseous) exerts frictional force. The order of extent of frictional force exerted by different states of matter is as follows.

Friction between two solids > Friction between a liquid and a solid > Friction between a solid and a gas

Types of Friction

Types of friction

- Acting between a stationary object and the surface
  - **Static friction**
    - Static friction is a self adjusting friction.
      - Static friction exists between a stationary object and the surface.
      - It is directly proportional to the force applied on it in order to make it move.
      - Its value is maximum, when the body begins to just move.

      Examples:
      Flying of aeroplanes.
      Drilling a nail into wall.
      Sliding on a garden slide.
- Acting between a moving object and the surface
  - **Rolling friction**
    - Friction between the rolling object and the surface

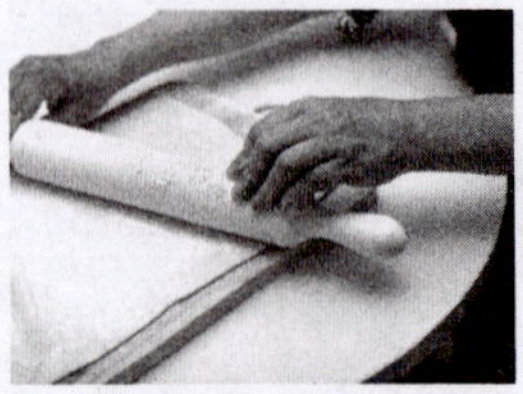

Rolling friction

  - **Sliding friction**
    - Friction between the object sliding and the surface

Sliding friction

The order of different types of frictions for a given pair of surfaces are as follows:

Static friction > Sliding friction > Rolling friction

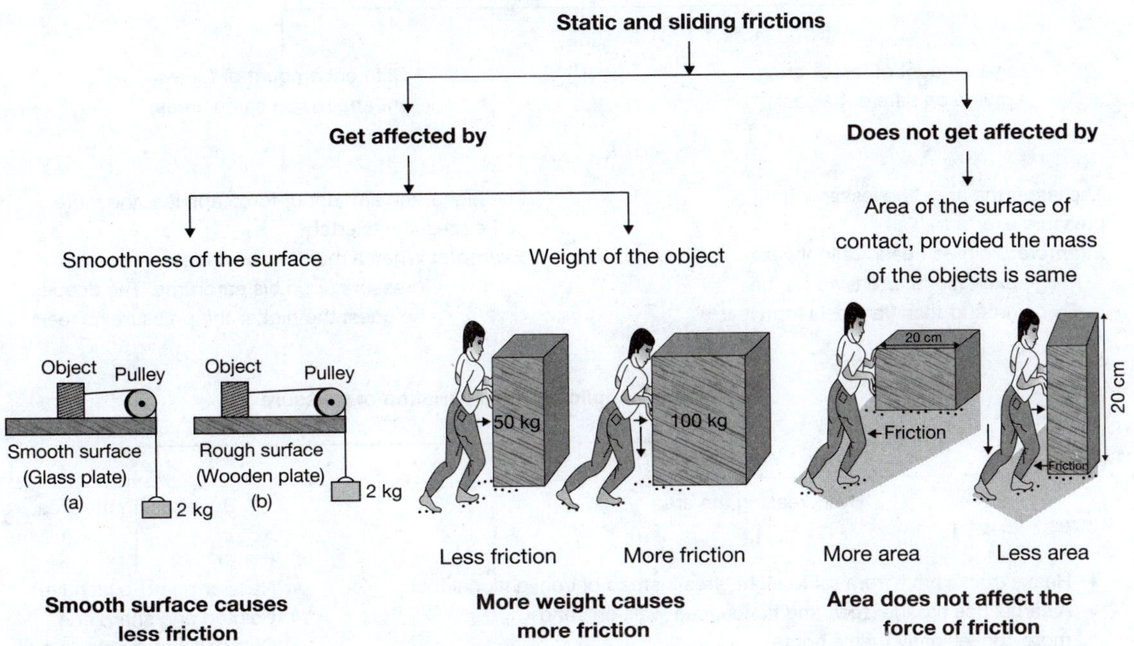

Methods to Reduce Friction

Rolling friction gets affected by smoothness of the surfaces and weight of the object, and increases the area of contact.

Different methods of reducing friction:

(i) Using lubricants
(ii) Using ball bearings between two moving surfaces
(iii) By polishing the surface
(iv) Sprinkling a soft, slippery fine powder on the surface
(v) Use of wheel or rollers since they reduce the surface of contact

Methods to Increase Friction

There are two methods of increasing friction:

(i) by making the surfaces rough
(ii) by increasing the mass of the object that is moving

Pressure

When same amounts of forces are applied on surfaces of different areas, the impact of forces becomes different. This is due to difference in pressure exerted.

Pressure can be defined as the force acting on a unit area of a surface.

$$\text{Pressure } (P) = \frac{\text{Force } (F)}{\text{Area } (A)}$$

Factors Affecting Pressure

Factors affecting pressure

- Same amount of forces are applied on different areas
  - The larger the area, the lesser is the pressure exerted.
    ***Example*:** Pointed heads of footwear exert higher pressure on the ground than flat heels footwear.
- Different amount of forces are applied on same areas
  - The higher the amount of force applied, the more is the pressure exerted.
    ***Example*:** When a man swims under water, feels pressure upon his eardrums. The deeper he goes, the higher the pressure he feels.

Applications of variation of pressure

By increasing the area

- Heavy trucks have from six to eight tyres instead of conventional four.
- A camel has broader feet, and hence, can walk on sand more conveniently than a horse.
- Skiers use long flat skies to slide over the snow.
- Army tanks are made to move over broad steel tracks called caterpillar wheels because of their huge weights.
- Foundations of high rise buildings are wide.
- Porters wear turbans on their heads.
- School bags have broader straps.

By reducing the area

- Nails or board-pins have pointed and sharp end.
- Cutting instruments, like blade, knife, axe, etc., have sharp edges.

Units of pressure

- **Commonly used**: atm (1 atm = 76 cm of mercury column = 1.01 x 10^5 Pa.)
- **CGS**: Dyne/cm^2
- **SI**: Newton (N)/m^2 or Pascal (Pa)

Bigger unit of pressure is kilopascal (kPa)

$$1 \text{ kPa} = 1000 \text{ Pa}$$

$$1 \text{ N/m}^2 = \frac{10^5 \text{ dyne}}{10^4 \text{ cm}^2} = 10 \text{ dyne/cm}^2$$

EXAMPLE 2.4 Minimum 1 kPa pressure is required to carry out an activity. A machine which can apply 10^5 N force is used for this purpose. What should be the maximum area on which this force is required to be applied so that the activity can be carried out?

SOLUTION

1 kPa = 1000 Pa = 1000 N/m^2

Hence, a minimum of 1000 N force is required.

$$\text{Pressure} = \frac{\text{Force}}{\text{Area}} \Rightarrow 1000 = \frac{10^5}{\text{Area}}$$

$\therefore$ Area = 10^2 = 100 m^2

The maximum area on which the force is required to be applied is 100 m^2.

Hence, pressure is inversely proportional to area when the force is kept constant.

EXAMPLE 2.5 5 Pa of pressure is required to be exerted on an area of 250 m^2. A box is placed on that area and the surface of contact is exactly 250 m^2. What should be the mass of the box so that exactly 5 Pa of pressure can be exerted?

SOLUTION

$$\text{Pressure} = \frac{\text{Force}}{\text{Area}}$$

$$5 = \frac{\text{Force}}{250} \quad (1 \text{ Pa} = 1 \text{ N/m}^2)$$

$\therefore$ Required force = 1250 N

Let m be the mass of the object.

$\therefore m \times g = 1250$

$\therefore m \times 10 = 1250$

$$\therefore m = \frac{1250}{10} \text{ kg} = 125 \text{ kg} \qquad (\because g \approx 10 \text{ m s}^{-2})$$

POINTS TO REMEMBER

- ✔ Force can be defined as the cause (push, pull, stretch or squeeze) which changes or tends to change the state of rest, uniform motion, direction of motion, shape and size of the body.
- ✔ Spring balance is the instrument which is used to measure force.
- ✔ If a body applies a force on another body, the latter exerts the same amount of force on the former, exactly in the opposite direction.
- ✔ Friction can be defined as the resisting force between two bodies in contact which prevents either body to move smoothly and continuously
- ✔ Pressure can be defined as the force acting on a unit area of a surface.

PRACTICE QUESTIONS CLASSROOM WING

Very Short Answer Type Questions

Direction for questions from 1 to 5.
Select the correct alternative from the given options.

1. Which of the following acts on a body from a very far distance?
   (a) Electric force (b) Magnetic force
   (c) Gravitational force (d) Frictional force
2. Which of these is not a unit of force?
   (a) Kilogram force (b) Newton
   (c) Gram weight (d) None of these
3. Electric force exists between
   (a) Two masses (b) Two magnets
   (c) Two electrons (d) Two bodies
4. Choose an example from the following where action and reaction pair exists.
   (a) A book placed on a table.
   (b) A person walking on the road.
   (c) A 1 kg mass suspended to a spring balance.
   (d) All the above
5. Choose the incorrect one from the following.
   (a) Electrical forces can be attractive (or) repulsive in nature and they are short range forces.
   (b) Gravitational forces are attractive in nature and they are long range forces.
   (c) Magnetic lines of force cannot exist with a single magnetic pole.
   (d) The energy of flowing water is used to produce necessary force which runs a generator to produce electric current.

Direction for questions from 6 to 10:
Fill in the blanks.

6. Static friction is a _______ force.
7. Air friction can be reduced by _______ the shape of the objects.
8. Friction between highly smooth surfaces is _______.
9. Friction comes into action when there is _______ between the two surfaces.
10. Friction always acts _______ to the surface.

Direction for questions from 11 to 15.
Select the correct alternative from the given options.

11. A child is trying to drag water tin but fails because
    (a) Applied force is not sufficient.
    (b) Applied force is cancelled by frictional force.
    (c) Static friction is not sufficient.
    (d) Both (a) and (b)
12. Which of the following is not possible?
    (a) Sliding friction can be converted into rolling friction.
    (b) Rolling friction increases with area of contact.
    (c) Sliding friction can be converted into static friction.
    (d) None of these
13. Force of friction cannot be reduced by
    (a) Ball bearings
    (b) Lubricants
    (c) Smoothening the surface
    (d) Increasing the weight of body
14. Frictional force causes
    (a) Wear and tear of a machine
    (b) Energy loss in the form of heat
    (c) Motion in a body
    (d) Both (a) and (b)
15. Rohit stepped on a banana peel while walking, so he slipped off
    (a) Due to the less amount of sliding friction under his foot.
    (b) Due to the absence of static friction under his foot.
    (c) Due to the absence of rolling friction of banana peel.
    (d) Due to the presence of kinetic friction under his foot.

Direction for questions from 16 to 20.
Fill in the blanks.

16. The product of pressure and area gives ______.

17. Pressure is inversely proportional to ______.

18. The SI unit of pressure is ______.

19. One atm = ______.

20. 1 N m^{-2} = ______ dyne cm^{-2}

Direction for questions from 21 to 25.
Select the correct alternative from the given options.

21. Which of the following quantities does not have direction?
    (a) Force
    (b) Acceleration
    (c) Pressure
    (d) Velocity

22. Pressure is directly proportional to
    (a) Force (b) Speed
    (c) Area (d) Velocity

23. Sharp edges can apply
    (a) Less pressure than blunt edges.
    (b) Less force than blunt edges.
    (c) More pressure than blunt edges.
    (d) None of these

24. Which of the following water columns exerts the highest pressure on the bottom of the container?
    (a) 10 km (b) 100 m
    (c) 1000 mm (d) 5000 m

25. Which among the following animals generally exerts less pressure on sand so that it moves fast in the desert?
    (a) Dog (b) Elephant
    (c) Horse (d) Camel

Short Answer Type Questions

26. What is force? Mention the effects of force.

27. Distinguish between contact and non−contact forces.

28. What are consequential forces? Give any two examples.

29. Mention the forces that exist in nature.

30. Define rest and motion.

31. Define the gravitational units of force and relate them.

32. Define weight. What is the weight of mass 2 grams in SI system?

33. Write the nature of forces involved in the following cases.
    (a) A cylinder is rolling on the ground.
    (b) A vertically projected stone.

34. Does anybody exist without any force acting on it?

35. Mention the magnitude and direction of the net force for each case. (Take $g = 10$ m s^{-2})

(a)

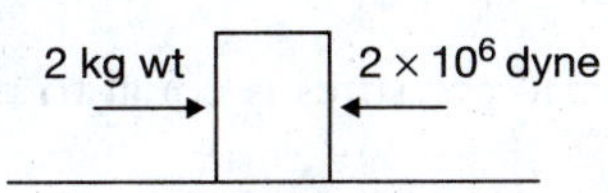

(b)

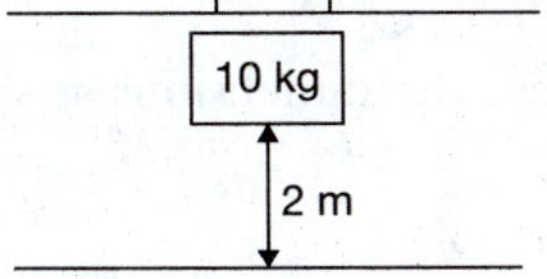

36. Does a situation exist where two forces act on a body without affecting it? Explain with an example.

37. From the figure analyse the situation and explain the nature of forces acting on the following bodies.

(a)

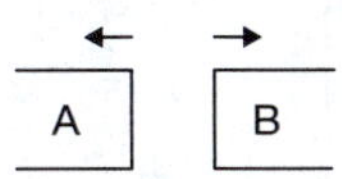

(b)

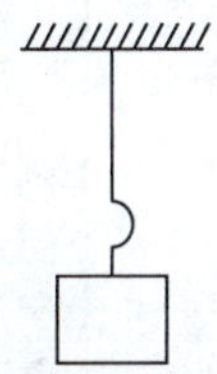

38. Does the forces, like gravitational, electric, and magnetic forces affect each other? If not, why?

39. Is there any difference between mass and weight? If so, what is the difference?

40. Write a situation where action reaction forces do not exist.

41. Write any four advantages of friction.

42. Static friction is a self-adjusting force. Justify the statement.

43. Why are ships, aeroplanes, and sports cars streamlined in shape?

44. Define
    (a) Static friction (b) Dynamic friction
    (c) Rolling friction and (d) Limiting friction

45. On a block of mass 10 kg a child applied a force of 5 N. Explain the position of block and kind of friction acting on it.

46. There are four forces acting on a block as shown in the figure. The magnitude and direction of the net force acting on it is ______.

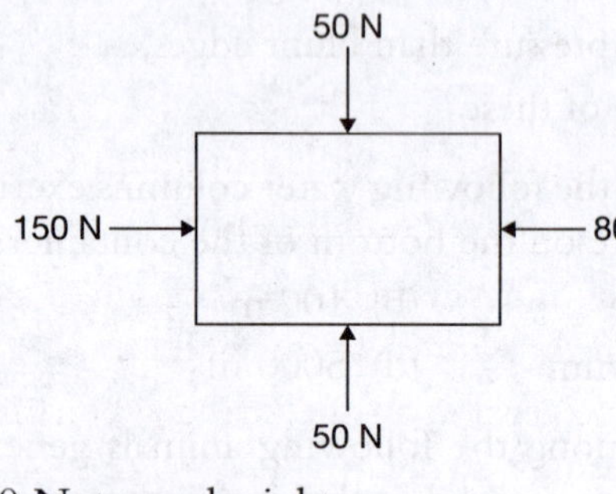

(a) 150 N, towards right
(b) 100 N, upwards
(c) 70 N, towards right
(d) 70 N, towards left

47. A cylindrical vessel is filled with water as shown in the figure. Calculate the difference in pressures due to water at points A and B. (Pressure due to air is negligible, density of water = 1 g cm^{-3})

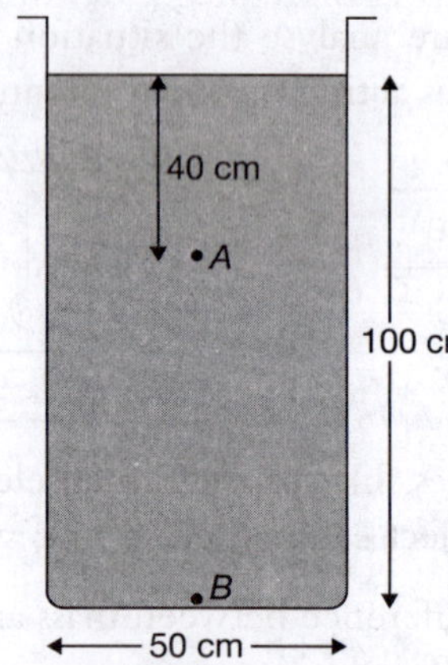

(a) 600 Pa (b) 1200 Pa
(c) 6 Pa (d) 6000 Pa

48. Choose the case where minimum friction acts
(a) When a person walks on the road.
(b) When a person walks on wet marble floor.
(c) When a person walks on sand floor.

49. Friction can be reduced by providing wheels. Explain the statement with an example.

50. Explain how maximum static friction is called limiting friction.

51. What is the purpose of oiling machinery?

52. Lasya is watering the plants in her garden with a pipe of area of cross–section 'A' and observed that the force of water from the pipe is 'F'. Find the change in area of cross section of the pipe to attain a pressure difference which is 1.5 times that of the initial.

53. Explain with an example how frictional force depends on the area of contact.

54.

S. No	Pressure (P)	Force (F)	Area (A)
1.	______ Pa	10 N	5 cm^2
2.	______ atm	5×10^5 N	5 m^2
3.	0.7 Pascal	______ dyne	10 MKS units
4.	8×10^{-5} atm	8 kg m s^{-2}	______ cm^2

55. Define pressure.

56. A camel weighs 20,000 N. The area of its foot is 100 cm^2. How much pressure does it exert on the ground by its single foot?

57. Pressure at the bottom of a sea is much greater than that at its surface. Explain it.

58. When a man swims under water, he feels a pressure on his eardrums. Why?

59. Why porters wear turbans on their heads while carrying heavy loads?

60. Identify the state of a boy with respect to the observer given in the following situations.
(i) The boy is sitting in a bus that is moving and the observer is also sitting in the same bus.
(ii) The boy is sitting in a moving bus the observer is sitting in another bus at rest.
(iii) The boy is standing at a bus stop and the observer is sitting in a moving bus.

61. What is mechanical force? Write two examples of mechanical force.

62. Why does an army tanker have caterpillar wheels rather than ordinary wheels?

63. How many atmospheric pressures is equal to the pressure of 2 kPa?

64. A block of mass 5 kg has the dimensions as shown in the figure.

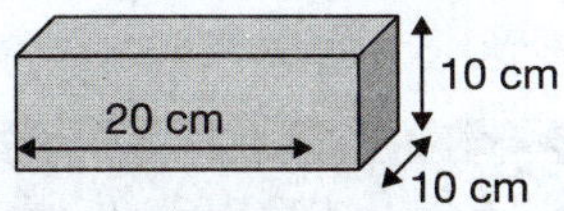

Find the maximum and minimum pressure exerted by the block on the surface of the table on which it is kept. ($g = 10$ ms^{-2})

65. A bunch of five identical balloons can lift a toy of weight 100 N. Find out the pressure inside a single balloon to do this, if the radius of the balloon is $\frac{1}{\sqrt{\pi}}$ m.

66. Find the net force acting on the body in the following cases.

(i)

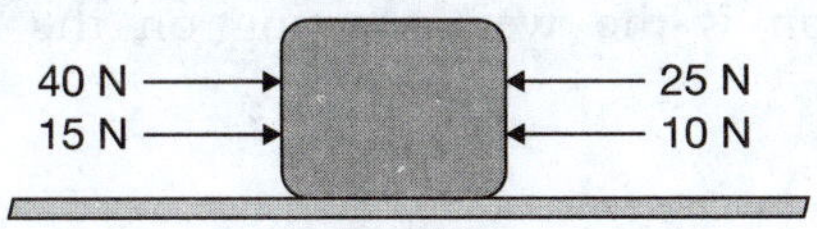

(ii)

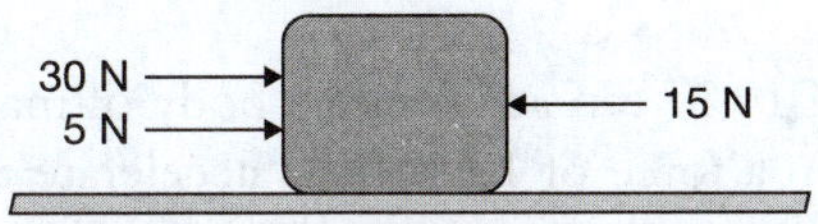

67. A cube of 1 m length is under the pressures given in the figure. Find the magnitude and the direction of the net force on it.

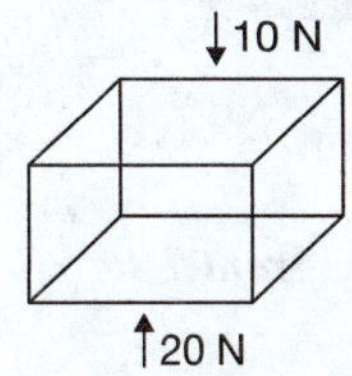

68. A block of dimensions 20 cm × 20 cm × 40 cm has a density of 7 g cm^{-3}. ($g = 10$ ms^{-2})

(i) Find the normal reaction force when the block is kept on the surface of the table.

(ii) Find the tension in the string when the block is hung using a string.

Essay Type Questions

69. (i) What is force? Mention SI and CGS units of force.

(ii) Deduce the relation between the SI and CGS units of force.

(iii) What are the different types of forces that exist in nature?

(iv) What is contact force? Mention the types of contact forces with examples.

70. (i) What is a frictional force? Mention its types.

(ii) Mention the advantages and disadvantages of friction.

(iii) Write the methods to reduce friction.

71. (i) Define pressure. Mention its SI and CGS units.

(ii) What are the factors affecting the pressure?

(iii) Write the applications of variation of pressure when the area is changed.

PRACTICE QUESTIONS COMPETITION WING

Level 1: Apply Your Concepts

Direction for questions from 1 to 5.
Fill in the blanks.

1. If the spring balance graded in gravitational units (CGS system) shows 20 as the reading, then mass of the body is ______ kg.
2. The direction of motion of a tree appears to be ______ when a passenger observes it from a moving train.
3. ______ is the percentage change in pressure when the force is increased by 10% by keeping the area constant.
4. A cylinder of radius 7 cm is made to stand vertically on the surface of the table. ______ is the mass of the cylinder if it exerts a pressure of 10 Pa on the surface of the table. ($g = 10\ ms^{-2}$)
5. One newton is the weight acting on the mass of ______.

Level 2: Review Your Concepts

6. The figure below shows a block with several forces acting on it.
   (i) Find the net force acting on the block.
   (ii) Find the density of the block if its mass is 10 kg.
   (iii) Find the pressure exerted by the block on the surface of the table. ($g = 10\ m/s^{-2}$)

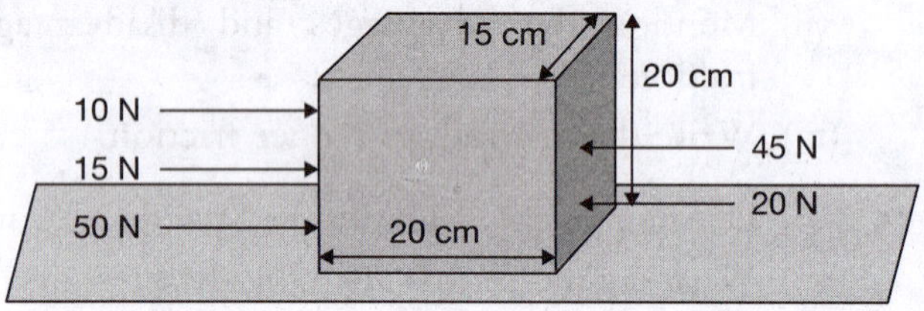

7. If a force of 10 N can accelerate a body of mass '*m*' by $1\ ms^{-2}$, then a force of 100 N can accelerate the same body by ______.
   (a) $10\ ms^{-2}$ (b) $1\ ms^{-2}$
   (c) $100\ ms^{-2}$ (d) $0.1\ ms^{-2}$
8. The force exerted on a moving bike by its engine is 180 N and the roughness of the road applies a retarding force of 5 N on its tyres. Find the force that accelerates the vehicle and also mention the type of friction involved here.
9. Ammu, a second class student of mass 15 kg is sliding over a slide inclined at an angle of 30° but her motion stopped at the middle of the slide. What would be the reason for this?

Level 3: Assess Your Concepts

10. An iron cylinder of base area $7\ cm^2$ and mass 10 kg is melted and reshaped into a rod of area of cross section $1\ cm^2$. Calculate the increase in the pressure exerted on a plane surface when both the cylinder and the rod are made to stand vertically on a plane surface. ($g = 10\ ms^{-2}$)
    (a) 100×10^4 Pa (b) 10×10^4 Pa
    (c) 14.28×10^4 Pa (d) 85.72×10^4 Pa
11. Akash can move an iron block at rest, placed on a metal sheet, by pushing it with a force of 50 N. When a lubricant is applied on the surface of the metal sheet, one fourth of the effort is reduced to do the same activity. The force with which the block can be moved in the second case is ______.
    (a) 25 N (b) 37.5 N
    (c) 12.5 N (d) 50 N
12. A girl can move a stone block at rest, placed on an iron sheet, by applying a force of 60 N. The force reduced to one-third when an oil is applied on the iron sheet. How much force will be required to move a stone block in second case?
13. An incompressible liquid is poured into a u–shaped tube and fitted with pistons as shown in figure. When a block of mass 5 kg is placed on piston–A, balances

the block placed on piston–B. If the area of cross-section of piston–B is 5 times that of piston–A. Then find the mass of the block placed on piston–B. [Hint: The pressure exerted by the piston–A is equal to that of piston–B]

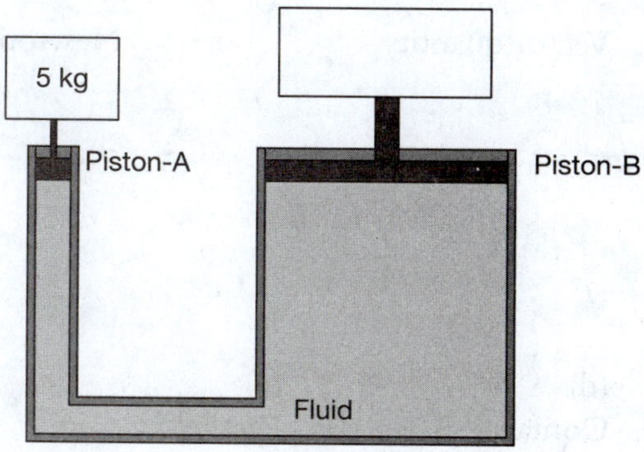

14. A silver cube of base area of 30 m^2 and mass 2 kg is melted and changed into a cuboid of area of cross section 2 m^2. Calculate, how much pressure is increased on a plane surface when both the cube and cuboid made vertically stand.

AT

ANSWER KEYS

Crossword

Across

2. Contact force 6. Charge 8. One atm 9. Vector quantity 10. Newton

Down

1. Scalar quantity 3. Two grams 4. Pascal 5. Surface area 7. Zero

Classroom Wing

Very Short Answer Type Questions

1. (c) 2. (d) 3. (c) 4. (d) 5. (c)
6. Self-adjusting 7. Streamlining 8. high 9. Contact 10. Parallel
11. (d) 12. (c) 13. (d) 14. (d) 15. (a)
16. thrust 17. area 18. pascal (or) N m^{-2} 19. 10^5 Pa
20. 10 21. (c) 22. (a) 23. (c) 24. (a)
25. (d)

Short Answer Type Questions

31. 1 gf = 10^{-3} kgf 32. 0.02 N 34. No 35. (a) Zero (b) 100 N
36. Yes 37. (a) magnetic poles (or) electric charges and (b) Weight and tension
38. No 39. Yes 45. No, the block does not move, static friction.
46. (c) 47. (d) 48. (b) 52. $\frac{3}{5}$ A_1
54. 20,000 Pa, 1 atm, 7×10^5 dyne, 10^{-4} cm^2 56. 5×10^5 Pa
63. 2×10^{-2} atm 64. 2500 Pa 65. 5 Pa 66. (i) 20 N; (ii) 20 N
67. 10 N 68. (i) 11.2 N; (ii) 11.2 N

Competition Wing

Level 1: Apply Your Concepts

1. 0.02 kg 2. Opposite 3. 10% 4. 15.4 g 5. 0.1 kg

Level 2: Review Your Concepts

6. (i) 10 N; (ii) 1666.6 kg/m^3; (iii) 3333.33 Pa 7. (a) 8. 175 N, Rolling friction
9. Net force is zero

Level 3: Assess Your Concepts

10. (d) 11. (b) 12. 40 N 13. 25 kg 14. 46.6 Pa

Hints and Explanations

CLASSROOM WING

Very Short Answer Type Questions

11. The child fails to pull the water tin because the applied force is less than the static friction acting between the suface of body and the surface on which it is placed.

Hence, the correct option is (d).

12. Sliding friction cannot be converted to static friction.

Hence, the correct option is (c).

13. Force of friction cannot be reduced by increasing the weight of the body because increasing weight increases the interlocking between the two surfaces in contact.

Hence, the correct option is (d).

14. Friction itself is a force which opposes the relative motion so it cannot bring a body into motion.

Hence, the correct option is (d).

15. Rohit slipped because the kinetic or sliding friction is less than the required amount of force.

Hence, the correct option is (a).

17. Area on which the force is exerted.

Hence, the correct answer is area.

21. Pressure do not have a single direction therefore it is called a tensor.

Hence, the correct option is (c).

22. Pressure increases with increase in force, therefore pressure directly proportional to the force acting on unit area.

Hence, the correct option is (a).

23. Sharper the edges, lesser will be the area on which the force is exerted. Sharp edges can apply More pressure than blunt edges.

Hence, the correct option is (c).

24. Higher the height of the water column greater will be the weight acting at the bottom of the container.

Hence, the correct option is (a).

25. Camel exerts less pressure on the surface of the desert compared to other animals given in the options because thier feet are wider at the bottom. If area increases the pressure acting on the surface

Hence, the correct option is (d).

Short Answer Type Questions

26. Force is defined as push or pull on a body.

Causes of force:

(a) A force can cause a motion in a stationary object.

(b) A force can stop the moving objects or slow them down.

(c) A force can make a moving object move faster.

(d) A force can change the direction of moving objects.

(e) A force can change the shape of objects.

27.

Contact forces	Non–contact forces
All forces which act on a body directly or through a connector are called contact forces.	The forces which do not make direct contact with a body but act through space are called non–contact forces.
Examples: Frictional force, muscular force.	***Examples:*** Gravitational force, magnetic force.

28. The consequential force can be defined as a force which is called into play, when a force is applied on an object.

Examples:

(a) When a cricket ball is made to roll on the ground by applying force, it stops after covering a certain distance, although, no force is applied to stop it. It is because the force of friction which is called consequential force.

(b) When we stretch a spring or a rubber band by applying force, the consequential force of tension acts on it.

29. (a) Mechanical force

(b) Gravitational force

(c) Magnetic force

(d) Electrical force

(e) Nuclear force

30. A body is said to be at rest if it does not change its position with respect to its immediate fixed surroundings with the passage of time.

A body is said to be in motion if it changes its position with respect to immediate fixed surroundings with the passage of time.

31. Gram force is equal to the force on a mass of one gram in a standard gravitational field.

Kilogram force is equal to the force on a mass of one kilogram in a standard gravitational field.

$1 \text{ gf} = 980 \text{ dyne} = 980 \times 10^{-5} \text{ N} = 9.8 \times 10^{-3} \text{ N}$

$1 \text{ gf} = 10^{-3} \text{ kgf}$

32. Weight: The force by which an object is attracted towards earth is called weight.

Weight $= mg = 2 \times 10^{-3} \times 10 = 0.02$ N $\quad [\because F = ma]$

33. (a) Contact force–friction; Non contact force–Gravitation

(b) Muscular force – a contact force

Gravitation force – a non–contact force

Air resistance – frictional force – a contact force

34. No, a body can exist with zero net force acting on it. Here more than two forces act on it but the resultant of all the forces can be zero.

35. (a) 2 kg wt = 20 N

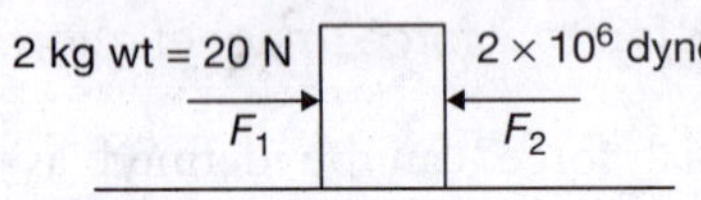

As $F_1 = F_2$, the net force acting on the body is zero and it has no direction.

(b)

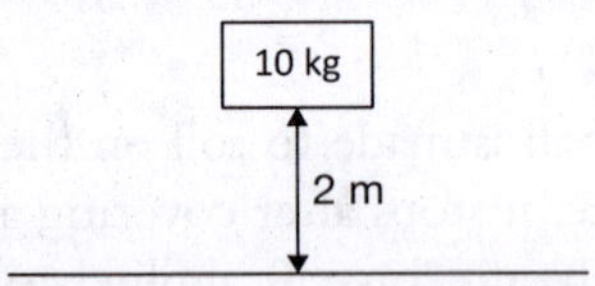

Only weight acts downwards if air resistance is negligible.

Here, weight acts downwards and its magnitude is $10 \times 10 = 100$ N

36. Yes, it is possible when two equal forces act in the opposite direction, i.e., net force acting on the body is zero.

37. (a) A, B may be two magnetic south or magnetic north poles and the force between them is magnetic force (repulsion).

(OR)

A, B may be similar electrically charged bodies, like two positive or two negative charges so that they repel each other, with electric forces.

(b) Two forces are acting on the body they are (i) weight acting downward, i.e., $w = mg$ and (ii) Tension 'T' acting along the thread in upward direction.

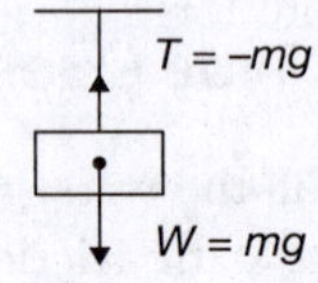

38. No, these forces do not show any affect on each other because the electric force develops due to the presence of charge; the gravitational forces develop due to the mass and magnetic forces develop only between magnetic poles.

39. Yes, mass and weight are different from each other.

(1) Mass means matter contained in a body and weight means the magnitude of gravitational pull acting on the body.

(2) Mass is measured in kilograms and weight in newtons in SI system.

40. When a body is under uniform circular motion the centripetal force and centrifugal force act on the same body. So, these are not called action– reaction forces. Because action–reaction forces must act on different bodies.

41. Advantages of friction:

(1) The tyres of different kinds of vehicles are provided with deep grooves so that they offer large friction with the surface of road and do not slip.

(2) Friction holds nails and screws in the wooden furniture.

(3) Knot from silk thread slips easily but not from the jute thread, because jute offers more friction than silk.

(4) The moving vehicles can be stopped due to force of friction between the brake shoes against the moving wheel rims.

42.

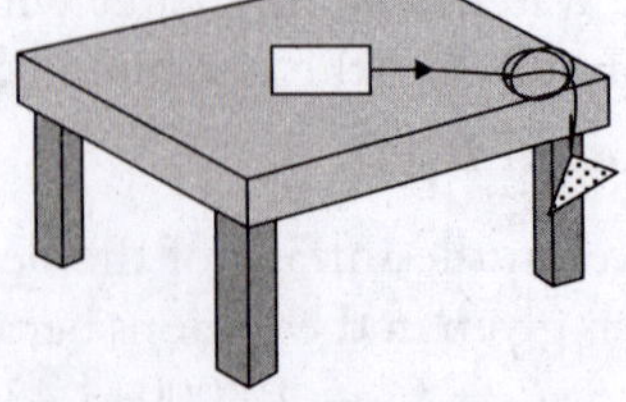

Consider a block of mass 'm' connected to a thread which runs over a pulley and the other end of it is connected to a pan. If we keep on adding small weights, the block does not start sliding at the first attempt. The block starts moving only when the weights in the pan balance and are slightly greater than the frictional force (limiting friction) between the block and table. Since static friction itself will change or self–adjust to provide an equal and opposite force till the force applied to the object is less than or equal to maximum static friction.

43. To reduce friction due to air ships, aeroplanes, and sports cars are streamlined.

44. (a) **Static friction:** The frictional force applied by the surface when the body is at rest is called static friction.

(b) **Dynamic friction:** The frictional force applied by the surface when the body is in motion is called dynamic friction.

(c) **Rolling friction:** The frictional force applied by the surface when the body is in rolling motion is called rolling friction.

(d) **Limiting friction:** The maximum static friction is called limiting friction.

45. No, the block does not move because for 5 N applied force the same amount of static friction force acts on the body in opposite direction. Therefore, the net force acting on the body is zero.

46. Since the upward and downward forces are equal in magnitude but opposite in direction, the net vertical force acting on the body becomes zero and the body does not move either in upward or in downward direction.

Net horizontal force acting on the body is:

F = 150 – 80 = 70 N and in the direction of greater force i.e. towards right side. Therefore, the body moves towards right.

47. Given, depth of point A, $h_A = 100$ cm $= 1$ m

depth of point B, $h_B = 40$ cm $= 0.4$ m

density of water, $d = 1\ \text{gcm}^{-3} = 1000\ \text{kgm}^{-3}$

$$\text{Pressure, } P = \frac{F}{A} = \frac{mg}{A} = \frac{\text{volume} \times \text{density} \times g}{\text{area of cross section}}$$

$$= \frac{\pi r^2 h \times d \times g}{\pi r^2} = hdg$$

At 'A', $P_A = h_A dg = 1 \times 1000 \times 10 = 10{,}000$ pa

At 'B', $P_B = h_B dg = 0.4 \times 1000 \times 10 = 4000$ pa

The difference in pressure, $P_B - P_A$ = 10,000 – 4,000 = 6,000 Pa

48. Option (b) is correct because a person walking on the wet marble floor experiences minimum frictional force, so he has more scope to slip on the floor.

49. For example, a suitcase, when dragged on floor, will experience a large amount of friction but If wheels are provided to it, a very small amount of force is required to move it, because force of friction decreases.

50. Let a heavy wooden box be placed on a floor, it being pushed by a person. The static frictional force developed between the wooden box and floor balances the force applied in pushing the box. If two persons try to push it the box does not move as the static frictional force increases in order to balance the force of pushing it. If the pushing force is further increased, at one stage, the static frictional force reaches a maximum value at which it cannot increase any further. This maximum value of static frictional force is called limiting friction. If the applied force on the wooden box is more than limiting friction, then the box starts moving.

51. To reduce friction between the working parts of the machine oil is used.

52. $P_1 = \frac{F_1}{A_1}$, $P_2 = P_1 + 1.5P_1 = 2.5P_1$

$$P_2 = 2.5\ P_1 = \frac{2.5F_1}{A_1} \Rightarrow P_2 = \frac{F_1}{\left(\frac{A_1}{2.5}\right)}$$

$$\Rightarrow A_1 - A_2 = \frac{3A_1}{5}$$

53. A sharp knife and blunt knife are used to cut vegetables. Sharp knife applies more pressure on vegetables than blunt knife because as area of contact between two surfaces increase then friction between them also increases.

54. $P = \frac{F}{A} \Rightarrow$

(1) $P = \frac{10\ \text{N}}{5 \times 10^{-4}\text{m}^2} = 20000$ Pa

(2) $P = \frac{5 \times 10^5\ \text{N}}{5\ \text{m}^2} = 10^5$ Pa = 1 atm

($\because$ 10^5 pascal = 1 atm)

(3) $P = \frac{F}{A} \Rightarrow F = P \times A = 0.7 \times 10$

$= 7$ N $= 7 \times 10^5$ dyne

($\because$ 1 N = 10^5 dyne)

(4) $\text{P} = \frac{F}{A} \Rightarrow \text{A} = \frac{F}{P} = \frac{8}{8} = 1\ \text{m}^2 = 1 \times 10^{-4}\ \text{cm}^2$

($\because$ 1 m = 100 cm)

55. Thrust acting on unit surface area is called pressure.

56. $W = 20{,}000$ N

Weight acting at its single foot

$$= \frac{20{,}000}{4} = 5000 \text{ N}$$

Area $= 100 \text{ cm}^2 = 10^2 \times 10^{-4} \text{ m}^2$

$= 10^{-2} \text{ m}^2$

$$\text{Pressure} = \frac{\text{weight}}{\text{area}} = \frac{5000}{10^{-2}}$$

$= 5 \times 10^5$ Pa

57. The force acting on surface water is only atmospheric pressure but in the bottom of the sea the weight of water is the force acting on the bottom. Since '*P*' is proportional and to '*F*' pressure at the bottom of the sea is much greater than that at its surface.

58. When a man swims under water, he feels pressure because the pressure inside increases with depth. Therefore, the deeper he goes, the greater is the pressure on his ear drums.

59. To increase the area of contact porters wear turbans on their heads for carrying heavy loads.

60. (i) Since the position of the boy with respect to his surroundings, is not changing with respect to time, the boy is said to be at rest.

(ii) Since the position of the boy changes with respect to observer, therefore, the boy is said to be in motion.

(iii) Since the position of the boy changes with respect to observer, therefore, the boy is said to be in motion.

61. **Mechanical force:** The force that involves the interaction (contact) between two bodies which can change the condition of any of the bodies.

Examples:

(1) Fixing a nail into a wall using a hammer. Both the hammer and the hammering person exert mechanical force on the nail.

(2) Closing or opening a door.

62. Army tankers are usually very heavy and they apply a heavy pressure on the ground. Hence, they are made to move over broad steel tracks called caterpillar wheels of tankers rather than ordinary wheels. The steel tracks increase the surface area which reduces the pressure on the ground, and hence, avoid sinking of the wheels in the ground.

63. $2 \text{ kPa} = 2000 \text{ Pa} = 2000 \times \frac{\text{N}}{\text{m}^2} = 2000 \text{ Pa}$

$= 2 \times 10^{+3} \times 10^{-5} \text{ atm} = 2 \times 10^{-2} \text{ atm}$

64. Given, Mass, $m = 5$ kg

Length, $l = 20$ cm

Breadth, $b = 10$ cm

Height, $h = 10$ cm

We have, Pressure, $P = \frac{\text{Force}}{\text{Area}}$

For maximum pressure, the area should be minimum.

Therefore, Max. Pressure

$$= \frac{\text{Weight of the body}}{\text{Area of small surface of the block}} = \frac{mg}{10 \text{ cm} \times 10 \text{ cm}}$$

$$= \frac{5 \times 10}{0.1 \text{ m} \times 0.1 \text{ m}} = \frac{50}{0.01} = 5000 \text{ Pa}$$

For minimum pressure, the area should be maximum.

Therefore, Min. Pressure

$$= \frac{\text{Weight of the body}}{\text{Area of big surface of the block}} = \frac{mg}{20 \text{ cm} \times 10 \text{ cm}}$$

$$= \frac{5 \times 10}{0.2 \text{ m} \times 0.1 \text{ m}} = \frac{50}{0.02} = 2500 \text{ Pa}$$

65. Number of balloons = 5

Weight of the toy = 100 N

$W = n(P \times A)$

$$P = \frac{W}{nA} = \frac{100}{5 \times 4\pi r^2} = \frac{100}{5 \times 4 \times \pi \times \frac{1}{\pi}} = 5 \text{ Pa}$$

66. (i) There are two forces acting towards the right side and two forces acting towards the left side.

Therefore, the net force, $F = (40 + 15) - (25 + 10)$

$= 55 - 35 = 20$ N

(ii) There are two forces acting towards the right side and one force acting towards the left side.

Therefore, the net force, $F = (30 + 5) - (15)$

$= 35 - 15 = 20$ N

67. $(20 - 10) = F_{\text{net}} \times \text{Area}$

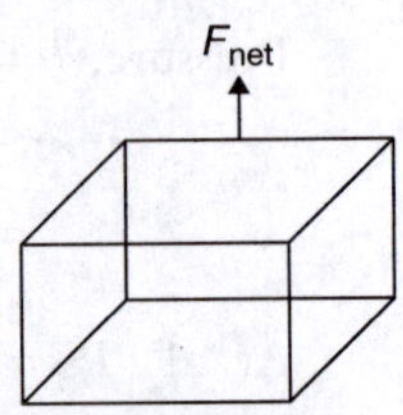

$$F_{\text{net}} = \frac{10}{1 \text{ m}^2} = 10 \text{ N}$$

vertically upwards

68. Given, Length, $l = 20$ cm

Breadth, $b = 20$ cm

Height, $h = 40$ cm

Density, $d = 7 \text{ g cm}^{-3}$

(i) When the block is kept on the surface of the table, the normal reaction force is equal to the weight of the block.

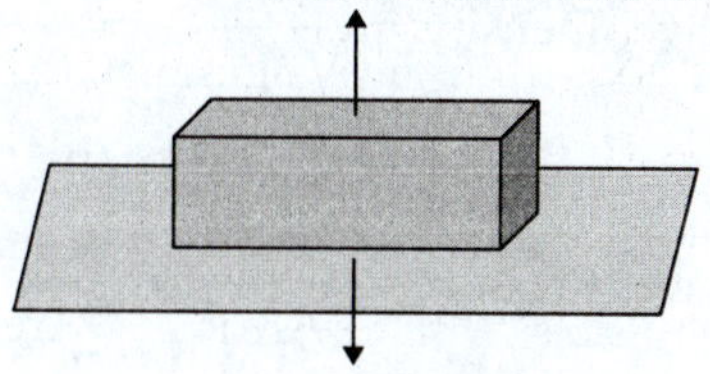

Therefore,

Normal reaction force = Mass of the block × g

= Volume of the block × Density × g

= (20 cm × 20 cm × 40 cm) × 7 g cm^{-3} × 10 × 100 cm s^{-2}

= 112000000 dyne = 11.2 N

(ii) When the block is hung using a string, the tension in the string is equal to the weight of the block.

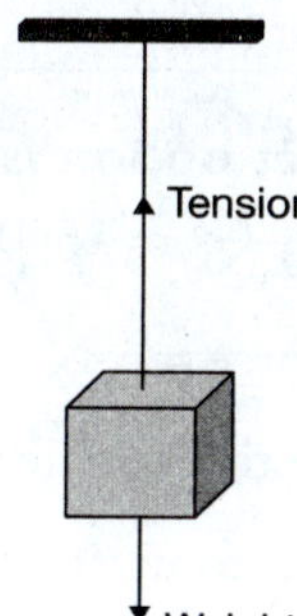

Therefore, Tension in the string = Mass of the block × g

= 11.2 N

Essay Type Questions

69. (i) **Force:** Force can be defined as the cause (push, pull, stretch, or squeeze) which changes or tends to change the state of rest, uniform motion, direction of motion, shape, and size of the body.

SI unit of force: newton (N)

CGS unit of force: dyne

(ii) We have, SI unit of force: newton (N)

1 newton = 1 kg × 1 m s^{-2}

= 1000 g × 100 cm s^{-2}

(Since 1 kg = 1000 g and 1 m = 100 cm)

= 10^5 g cm s^{-2}

= 10^5 dyne

Therefore, 1 newton = 10^5 dyne

(iii) **Contact force:** The force which is exerted by an object at the point of contact with another object is called contact force.

Types of contact forces:

(i) Mechanical force

Ex: Closing or opening a door, Pushing bicycle pedals.

(ii) Frictional force

Ex: Dragging a chair, Sliding coins on a carrom board.

70. **Frictional force:** The force which opposes the motion of a moving body when trying to move over the other body.

Refer to page no. 2.9.

71. (i) Pressure is defined as the force acting on a unit area of a surface.

SI unit: N/m^2, pascal (Pa)

CGS unit: $dyne/cm^2$

(ii) Factors affecting the pressure:

(a) The larger the area, the lesser the pressure exerted.

(b) The higher the amount of force applied, the more the pressure exerted.

(iii) Applications of variation of pressure when the area is changed:

(a) By increasing the area

- Heavy trucks have from six to eight tyres instead of conventional four.
- A camel has broader feet, and hence, can walk on sand more conveniently than a horse.
- Skiers use long flat skies to slide over the snow.
- Army tanks are made to move over broad steel tracks called caterpillar wheels because of their huge weights.
- Foundations of high-rise buildings are wide.
- Porters wear turbans on their heads.
- School bags have broader straps.

(b) By reducing the area

- Nails or board-pins have pointed and sharp end.
- Cutting instruments, like blade, knife, axe, etc., have sharp edges.

COMPETITION WING

Level 1: Apply Your Concepts

1. 20 gf

Mass = 20 grams = 0.02 kg

2. Opposite to the direction of train

3. Take Initial force, $F_1 = F$

Final force, $F_2 = F + 10\%$ of $F = F + 0.1\ F = 1.1\ F$

Initial area, $A_1 = A$

Final area, $A_2 = A$

We have, Pressure $= \dfrac{\text{Force}}{\text{Area}}$

Now, Initial pressure $= \dfrac{F_1}{A_1} = \dfrac{F}{A}$

Final pressure $= \dfrac{F_2}{A_2} = \dfrac{1.1\text{ F}}{A}$

Percentage change in pressure

$= \dfrac{\text{Final pressure} - \text{initial pressure}}{\text{initial pressure}} \times 100$

$= \dfrac{1.1\left(F/A\right) - \left(F/A\right)}{\left(F/A\right)}$

$= (1.1 - 1) \times 100 = 0.1 \times 100 = 10\ \%$

4. Given, Radius of cylinder, $r = 7$ cm

Pressure, $P = 10$ Pa

$g = 10\ \text{ms}^{-2}$

We have, Pressure $= \dfrac{\text{Force}}{\text{Area}} = \dfrac{\text{Mass} \times g}{\pi r^2}$

$\Rightarrow 10 = \dfrac{\text{Mass} \times 10}{\frac{22}{7} \times 0.07^2}$

$\Rightarrow \text{Mass} = \dfrac{\frac{22}{7} \times 0.07^2 \times 10}{10} = 0.0154\ \text{kg} = 15.4\ \text{g}$

Level 2: Review Your Concepts

6. (i) There are three forces acting on the right side and two forces on the left side. Therefore,

Net force = (10 + 15 + 50) – (45 + 20) = 75 – 65 = 10 N

(ii) Given, Length, $l = 20$ cm

Breadth, $b = 15$ cm

Height, $h = 20$ cm

Mass, $m = 10$ kg

We have, Density $= \dfrac{\text{Mass}}{\text{Volume}} = \dfrac{10}{0.2 \times 0.15 \times 0.2}$

$= 1666.6\ \text{kg/m}^3$

(iii) We have, Pressure $= \dfrac{\text{Force}}{\text{Area}} = \dfrac{\text{Weight}}{\text{Area}}$

Pressure $= \dfrac{10 \times 10}{0.2 \times 0.15} = 3333.33$ Pa

7. Given $F_1 = 10$ N

$a_1 = 1\ \text{ms}^{-2}$

$F_2 = 100$ N

$a_2 = ?$

Since mass is same, $\dfrac{F_1}{F_2} = \dfrac{a_1}{a_2}$

$\therefore \dfrac{10}{100} = \dfrac{1}{a_2} \Rightarrow a_2 = 10\ \text{ms}^{-2}$

Hence, the correct option is (a).

8. Applied force = 180 N

Rolling frictional force = 5 N

Net force acting on the vehicle = 180 – 5 = 175 N

9. Because here the net force acting on ammu is zero.

Level 3: Assess Your Concepts

10. Given, mass of cylinder, $m_c = 10$ kg

Base area of the cylinder,

$A_c = 7\ \text{cm}^2 = 7 \times \left(10^{-2}\right)^2 = 7 \times 10^{-4}\ \text{m}^2$

Pressure due to cylinder.

$P_c = \dfrac{F_c}{A_c} = \dfrac{m_c g}{A_c} = \dfrac{10 \times 10}{7 \times 10^{-4}} = 14.28 \times 10^4$ Pa

Mass of the rod, $m_r = 10$ kg

Base area of the rod,

$A_r = 1\ \text{cm}^2 = 1 \times \left(10^{-2}\right)^2 = 10^{-4}\ \text{m}^2$

Pressure due to rod.

$P_r = \dfrac{F_r}{A_r} = \dfrac{m_r g}{A_r} = \dfrac{10 \times 10}{10^{-4}} = 100 \times 10^4$ Pa

Increase in pressure,

$P_r - P_c = (100 - 14.28) \times 10^4$ Pa

Hence, the correct option is (d).

11. Initial force applied to move the block, $F = 50$ N

When the lubricant is applied, one fourth of the effort is reduced.

Therefore, the force applied to move the block is

$$F' = F - \frac{F}{4} = 50 - \frac{50}{4}$$

$$= 50 - 12.5 = 37.5 \text{ N}$$

Hence, the correct option is (b).

12. Force required to move the block = 60 N

When an oil is applied on the iron sheet, one-third force of effort is reduced.

Force applied to move the block

$$F = F - \frac{F}{3}$$

$$= 60 - \frac{60}{3}$$

$$= \frac{180 - 60}{3}$$

$$= 40\text{N}$$

13. Mass of block on piston-A, $m_A = 5$ kg

Take area of cross-section of piston-A = A_A

Then, area of cross-section of piston-B = $5A_A$

Given that the pressure exerted by the piston–A is equal to that of piston–B.

I.e., $\frac{F_A}{A_A} = \frac{F_B}{A_B}$

$$\Rightarrow \frac{m_A g}{A_A} = \frac{m_B g}{A_B} \Rightarrow \frac{m_A}{A_A} = \frac{m_B}{A_B}$$

$$\Rightarrow \frac{5}{A_A} = \frac{m_B}{5A_B} \Rightarrow 5 = \frac{m_B}{5} \Rightarrow m_B = 25 \text{ kg}$$

14. Mass of cube = 2 kg

Base area of cube = $30\,\text{m}^2$

Pressure due to cube

$$P_c = \frac{F_c}{A_c} = \frac{m_c g}{A_c} = \frac{10 \times 10}{30} = \frac{100}{30}$$

Mass of cuboid,

Base area of cuboid (cb),

$A = 2\text{m}^2$

Pressure due to the rod

$$p = \frac{FL_{cb}}{A_{cb}} = \frac{m_{cb}}{A_r} = \frac{10 \times 10}{2} = \frac{100}{2}$$

Pressure due to $P_{cb} - P_c$

$$= \frac{100}{2} - \frac{100}{30}$$

$$= 46.6 \text{ Pa}$$

[illegible] the [illegible]

[illegible] the acceleration [illegible]

[illegible] [illegible] of [illegible]

CHAPTER 3

Work and Energy

Remember

Before beginning this chapter, you should be able to:

- Recall the concept of force, action, and reaction
- Describe types of friction

Key Ideas

After completing this chapter, you should be able to:

- Define the concept of work done
- Explain energy, its types, and units
- Explain the relation between work and energy
- Calculate the work done or energy spent in simple daily life situations
- Understand the need to conserve energy
- Describe various ways to save energy

Scientific Crypt

A Tribute to James Prescott Joule (1818–1889)

James Prescott Joule was an English physicist, mathematician, and brewer, born in Salford, Lancashire. Joule studied the nature of heat and discovered the relationship between heat energy and mechanical work. This led to the development of the first law of thermodynamics. He worked with Lord Kelvin to develop an absolute thermodynamic temperature scale, which came to be called the Kelvin scale. The experiments and measurements with his electric motor led Joule to estimate the mechanical equivalent of heat as 4.1868 joules per calorie of work to raise the temperature of one gram of water by one Kelvin. The SI derived unit of energy, the joule, is named in his honor.

FUN TIME

CROSSWORD

Across

4. Entities from where we obtain energy like sun, water that flows, wind, fossil fuel, biomass, sea wave, and the nucleus of an atom.
5. It is ________ work done when the force acting and the displacement are in opposite directions.
6. When two dry bodies are rubbed together, this form of ________ energy is produced.
8. Friction between clouds generates electrical energy during this event, which gets converted to light and sound energy.

Down

1. Newton's ________ law states that if a body applies a force on another body, the latter exerts the same amount of force on the former, exactly in the opposite direction.
2. Gravitational form of energy calculated based on the work done to lift an object to a certain height.
3. Traditional sources of energy as opposed to newer or more sustainable options.
7. Defined as the capacity of doing work and can exist in various forms.

INTRODUCTION

In our day-to-day life we perform many activities, like playing, reading, thinking, carrying luggage, driving, sleeping, etc.

But the activities mentioned above do not come under the purview of work in science.

Work Done

Work done is when a force is applied on a stationary/moving object.

The object is set in motion.

(or)

The shape and size of the object is changed.

(or)

The direction of the moving object is changed.

Some activities which will strengthen your concept about work done are illustrated below.

Konnect

Work, as a concept in physics, is entirely different from our everyday understanding. In physics, you can be exerting force and still doing zero work, like when you push against a wall, and it doesn't move.

Work is being done when the boy is climbing the stairs

Change in the shape and size of a tin is a kind of work

No work is done while standing with heavy luggage

No work is said to be done if there is no displacement in the position of the car to which the force is applied

No work is done if the force applied on both sides is equal

Figure 3.1 Activities illustrating 'work done' and 'work not done'

Calculation of the Amount of Work Done

Work done depends on two parameters:

1. The amount of force applied on the object.
2. The displacement (shortest distance covered in the direction of force) of the object.

Hence, work can be defined as the product of force applied on the object and the displacement of the object.

Work done is negative if the force acting and the displacement are in opposite direction.

Work done = Force × Displacement
(W = F × s)

↓

Unit of work

CGS

F × s
= dyne × cm = dyne – cm = **erg**

When 1 dyne force is applied on an object and the object gets displaced by 1 cm, then 1 erg of work is said to be done.

SI

F × s
= newton × m = newton – m = **Joule**

When 1 N force is applied on an object and the object gets displaced by 1 m, then 1 joule of work is said to be done.

Relation between Joule and erg

$$1 \text{ joule} = 1 \text{ N} \times 1 \text{ m} = 10^5 \text{ dyne} \times 100 \text{ cm}$$
$$= 10^7 \text{ dyne} - \text{cm}$$
$$= 10^7 \text{ erg}$$

EXAMPLE 3.1 A man pushes a lawn mower through a distance of 20 m in the direction of the force he applies. If the force exerted by the man is 25 N, what is the work done by him in moving the lawn mower?

SOLUTION

Force = F = 25 N; Displacement = s = 20 m

Work = $F \times s$ = 25 × 20

Therefore, Work done by the man = 500 J.

Energy

Energy is defined as the capacity of doing work. Energy can exist in various forms. Major forms of energy are discussed below with the help of flowcharts.

Energy

↓

Universe comprises

Matter

Matter is any physical substance that exists in nature. They have mass and occupy space

Energy

Energy is the ability or capacity to do the work

Different Forms of Energy

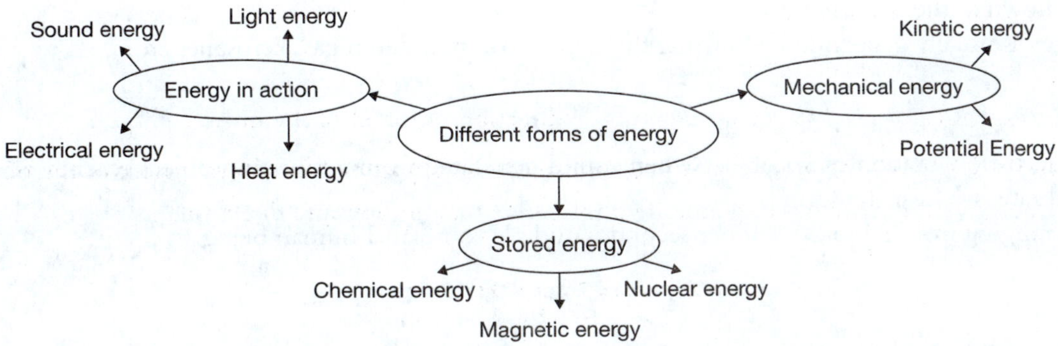

Mechanical energy

Potential energy: The energy possessed by a body as a result of its position or condition is called potential energy.
***Example*:** A raised weight, a compressed spring possess potential energy.

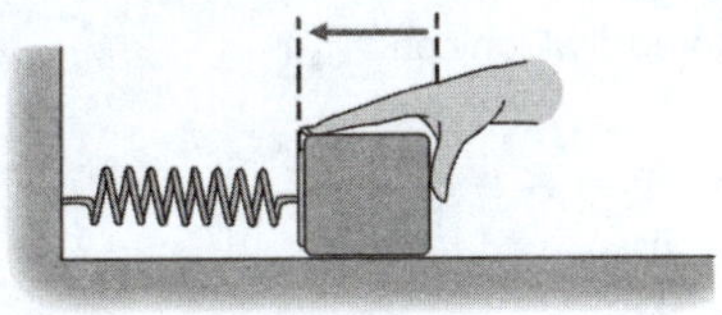

Kinetic energy: The energy possessed by a body due to its motion is called kinetic energy.
***Example*:** A soft rubber ball thrown with a high speed can injure a person, a storm can uproot a tree.

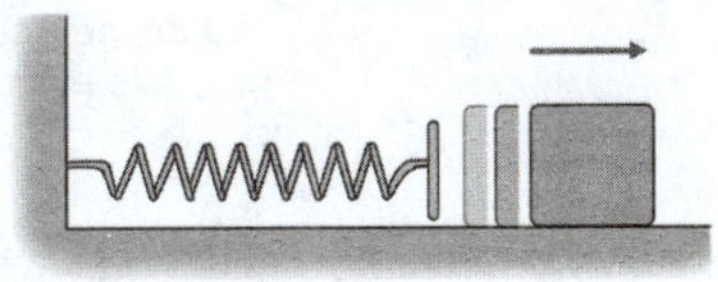

Gravitational potential energy: The energy stored when an object is lifted above the surface is called gravitational potential energy.

Elastic potential energy: The energy stored when an object is stretched or compressed or bent is called elastic potential energy.

Gravitational potential energy is calculated based on the work done to lift an object to a certain height.

Work = Force × displacement = weight of the body × displacement = $m \times g \times h$

m = The mass of the body
g = Acceleration due to gravity
h = The height to which the object is lifted

The unit of energy is same as the unit of work.

CGS → Erg

SI → Joule

Info Bytes!

The concept of energy is so vital that Richard Feynman, a renowned physicist, once remarked, 'All things are made of atoms, and in all atoms is energy. It is energy which makes the world go round, literally and figuratively.'

Energy in Action

Electrical energy

- When two dry bodies are rubbed together, electrical energy is produced.
- During lightening, friction between clouds generate electrical energy which gets converted to light and sound energy.

Heat energy

- It is also known as thermal energy.
- Heat energy is usually generated by burning fuels, like coal, petroleum gas, kerosene, etc.

Sound energy

- It is produced by vibration of an object when sound generated from a vibrating object reaches our ear drum and make it vibrate, we hear the sound.
- Vibration ranging from 20 to 20,000 per second is audible to normal human being.

Light energy

- We can see any object due to the presence of light energy. Light energy travels in a straight path.
- The incident light energy gets reflected from an object and reaches our eyes and enables us to see the object.

Stored Energy

Stored energy

Chemical energy

- It gets stored in a substance, like food, fuel, etc., during their formation due to different chemical reactions.
- In a dry cell, chemical energy is stored which can generate electricity.

Magnetic energy

- A magnet attracts the magnetic substance. When a magnetic substance is attracted towards a magnet, some work is done which is possible because of the energy stored in a magnet. This energy is known as magnetic energy.
- Magnetic energy is used to separate magnetic impurities from non-magnetic ore or to separate magnetic ore from non-magnetic impurities.

Nuclear energy

Nuclear energy can be utilized in two different ways.

- By splitting the nucleus of an atom and thereby converting it into a new element, a lot of energy can be released.
- By the fusion (combination) of two or more atoms, a new element can be formed with the release of huge amount of energy.

Transformation of Energy

The conversion of energy from one form into another is a very common phenomenon in our surrounding. Plants convert light energy into chemical energy through photosynthesis. While driving a car, fuels, like petrol, diesel, etc., are used to supply power to the engine. Hence, chemical energy is finally converted into kinetic energy in the car.

When light rays are converged with the help of a **magnifying lens**, a tiny spot of sunlight can be created on a piece of paper. If we hold the paper and the **magnifying lens** in that position for some time, the paper starts burning. This is an example of the conversion of light energy into heat energy.

Some of the examples for the conversion of one form of energy to another are shown as follows:

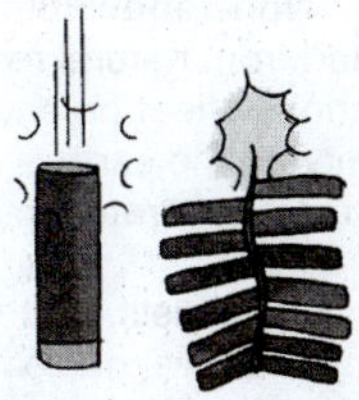

(a) Bursting of fireworks (Chemical energy → Heat, light and sound energy)

(b) Electric bulb (Electrical energy → Light energy)

(c) Loudspeaker (Electrical energy → Sound energy)

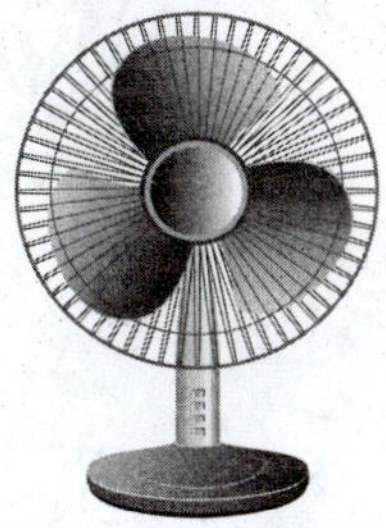

(d) Table fan (Electrical energy → Kinetic energy)

(e) Physical exercise (Chemical energy of food → Muscular energy)

Figure 3.2 Examples of day-to-day phenomena that involve conversion of energy

The table given below represents the conversion of one form of energy into another form in different devices.

Table 3.1 Conversion of energy

Device	Initial form of energy	Final form of energy
Fluorescent tubes and bulb	Electrical	Light
Door bell	Electrical	Sound
Electrical motor	Electrical	Mechanical
Heater	Electrical	Heat
Microphone	Sound	Electrical
Electromagnet	Electrical	Magnetic
Washing machine	Electrical	Mechanical
Generator	Mechanical	Electrical
Solar cell	Light	Electrical
Combustion of fuel	Chemical	Heat
Photovoltaic cell	Light	Electrical
Steam engine	Heat	Electrical
Television	Electrical	Sound and light
Campfires	Chemical	Heat and light

Sources of Energy

There are various sources of entities from where we obtain energy like sun, water that flows, wind, fossil fuel, biomass, sea wave, nucleus of an atom, etc.

They can be broadly classified into two categories based on their specific characteristics.

1. Renewable sources of energy
2. Non-renewable sources of energy

Renewable

- Generated from natural resources
- Environment friendly
- Available abundantly
- Gets regenerated naturally and easily

Examples: Solar, geothermal, wind, tidal energies, energy obtained from flowing water, biomass.

Non-renewable

- Generated from natural resources
- Have serious effect on envir
- Availability on the earth is limited
- Cannot be regenerated in a short span of time

Examples: Fossil fuels, petroleum, natural gas, nuclear energy.

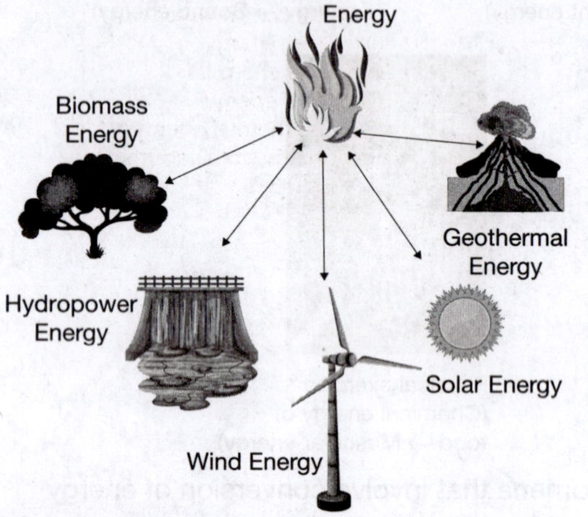

Figure 3.3 Renewable sources of energy

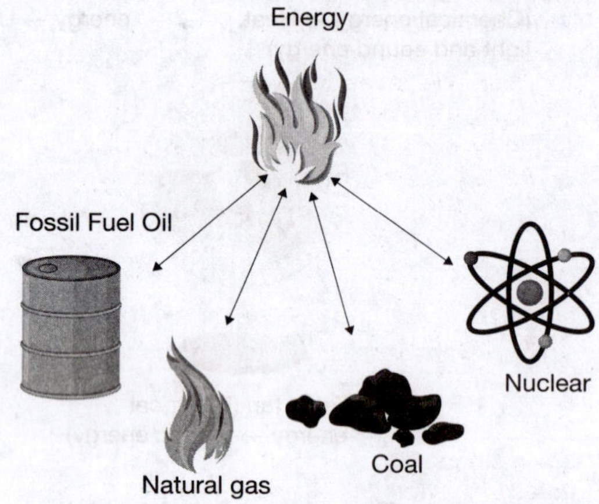

Figure 3.4 Non-renewable sources of energy

Renewable Source of Energy

Renewable sources of energy

Geothermal energy is the thermal energy generated and stored inside the earth and used by converting the heat energy to electrical energy.

Solar energy is obtained from the sun in the form of heat and light and harnessed by the devices, like solar heater, solar electric cell, etc.

Tidal energy is obtained from the sea waves which constantly hit the sea shore. Kinetic energy of sea waves help in rotating turbines, and thus, electrical energy is produced.

Energy obtained from bio mass: Biomass is a fuel obtained from organic materials, like dried leaves, cow dung, etc. Biomass is converted to biogas which contains methane (64%), CO_2 and H_2, and hence, it is a clean, cost effective fuel. Chemical energy stored in biomass gets converted to heat energy on burning and is widely used in villages.

Energy from flowing water: Potential energy of water collected in dams gets converted to kinetic energy when the water is made to flow. This kinetic energy is converted to electrical energy by using turbines. The electricity obtained is known as hydro-electricity.

Wind energy is obtained by converting the kinetic energy of moving air (wind) into electrical energy by using a generator which can be used to pump out underground water, grinding of grains, like wheat, grams, etc.

Non-Renewable Source of Energy

Non-renewable energy

Chemical energy stored in them gets converted to heat energy. Either this heat energy is directly used or electricity is generated from this heat energy.
Fossil fuels
Example: Coal, petroleum, natural gas.

Nuclear energy of radioactive elements is mainly used for production of electricity. This energy is also used in various other fields, like nuclear weapons, medical treatment, controlling insects and pests, etc.
Nuclear energy
Example: Radioactive elements, like uranium.

Sources of energy can also be classified as conventional and non-conventional sources.

Sources of energy

Conventional

The sources of energy which have been used since a long time ago.

(i) Fossil fuel (We get heat and electrical energy)
(ii) Water (We get electrical energy, i.e., hydel power)
(iii) Nuclear energy (We get electrical energy)

Non-conventional

These sources of energy are yet in the process of development over the past few years.

(i) Solar energy
(ii) Tidal energy
(iii) Wind energy
(iv) Geothermal energy
(v) Energy obtained from biomass

Energy Chain

Solar energy

↓

Green plants: Solar energy is stored in the form of chemical energy

↓

Animals (Herbivores) Get energy from plants

↓

Animals (Carnivores) Get energy from other animals

Green plants and Animals (Herbivores) → **Animals (Omnivores)** Get energy from plants and animals

Konnect

The energy chain for a light bulb: Electrical energy (from the power grid) → Thermal energy (in the filament) → Light energy emitted as visible light.

Saving Energy

Measures to be Adopted to Save Energy

- Using efficient electrical appliances like refrigerators, air conditioners.
- Using advanced laptops/computers instead of standard CRT computers.
- Using microwave oven instead of conventional ovens
- Regular maintenance of the appliances so that they consume less energy
- Judicious use of fossil fuels
- Judicious use of electrical appliances
- Using electronic resources for communication instead of paper
- Using solar cooker, solar heater, etc.
- Using laptops/computers instead of standard computers

EXAMPLE 3.2 Find the work done to move an object of mass 5 kg to a height of 15 m from the ground (Take $g = 10\ ms^{-2}$).

SOLUTION

Work done $= mgh = 5 \times 10 \times 15 = 750$ J.

EXAMPLE 3.3 Calculate the amount of force (in N) required to displace an object by 2 m in the direction of force. Work done in this process is 5 kJ.

SOLUTION

Work = Force × Displacement

$5 \times 1000 = F \times 2$

$\therefore F = \frac{5000}{2} = 2500$ N force is applied.

EXAMPLE 3.4 A boy lifted a small carton of 2 kg mass from the ground and placed it on his head. If the height of the boy is (1.5 m), then calculate the work done (Take $g = 10$ m/s^2).

SOLUTION

Work = Force × Displacement

= Weight of the carton × Height of the boy

$= 2 \times 10 \times 1.5 = 30$ Joule

EXAMPLE 3.5 When a force of 4 N is applied on the object placed at one end of the table such that it reaches the other end of the table as shown in the figure, work done in this process is 3.92 Joules, then calculate the length of the table.

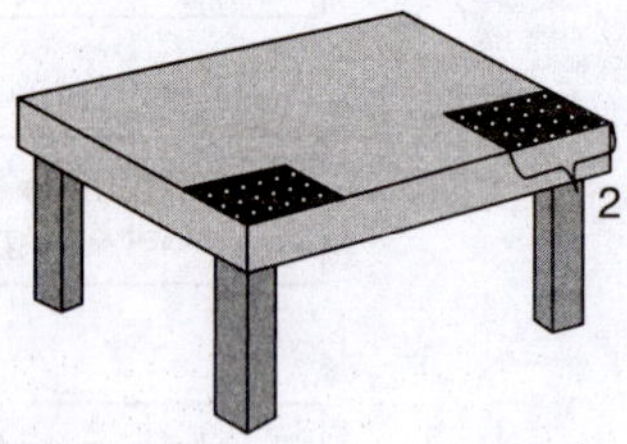

SOLUTION

Work = Force × Displacement

$\therefore 3.92 = 4 \times s$

$s = \frac{3.92}{4} = 0.98$ m

The length of the object is 2 cm = 0.02 m

The length of the table = (0.98 + 0.02) m = 1 m

POINTS TO REMEMBER

- ✔ Work can be defined as the product of force applied on the object and the displacement of the object.
- ✔ If a body applies a force on another body, the latter exerts the same amount of force on the former, exactly in the opposite direction.
- ✔ Energy is defined as the capacity of doing work. Energy can exist in various forms.
- ✔ There are various sources of entities from where we obtain energy like sun, water that flows, wind, fossil fuel, biomass, sea wave, nucleus of an atom, etc.
- ✔ Sources of energy can also be classified as conventional and non-conventional sources.

PRACTICE QUESTIONS CLASSROOM WING

Very Short Answer Type Questions

Direction for questions from 1 to 5.
Select the correct alternative from the given options.

1. Choose the correct one from the following.
   (a) Biogas is a mixture of methane (65%), carbon dioxide and hydrogen.
   (b) An apple on a tree has only potential energy.
   (c) A compressed spring has an elastic potential energy.
   (d) All the above

2. Pick out the incorrect one from the following.
   (a) The chemical energy in fossil fuels is not a form of potential energy.
   (b) Sun, wind, and water come under renewable sources.
   (c) Burning of candle converts wax into light.
   (d) Photosynthesis converts solar energy into chemical energy of food.

3. Find out an example from the following that transforms sound energy into electrical energy.
   (a) Microphone (b) Door bell
   (c) Photosynthesis (d) Loud speaker

4. The ultimate source of energy is
   (a) Bio-gas (b) Solar energy
   (c) Fossil fuels (d) All of these

5. According to the Law of Conservation of Energy, as energy changes from one form to another form, the total energy of that system
   (a) Keeps increasing
   (b) Keeps decreasing
   (c) Increases for some time then remains constant.
   (d) None of these

Short Answer Type Questions

6. Identify the statement from the following in which work is being done according to physics.
   (a) A boy is sitting and solving math problems
   (b) A man is pushing a heavy stone, but it is not moving.
   (c) A porter is keeping a heavy load on his head and walking.
   (d) A girl is holding her school bag and walks upstairs.

7. If a force of 150 N is applied on a body to do a work of 75 J. Find the displacement of the body.

8. What is biomass? How can we obtain energy from biomass?

9. Discuss briefly about the types of energies in stored form.

10. Fill the blanks in the table given below.

Device	Initial form of energy	Final form of energy
Heater	Electrical	___________
Generator	___________	Electrical
Solar cell	Light	___________
Electromagnet	___________	Magnetic
Combustion of fuel	___________	Heat

11. Give any five examples that show transformation of electrical energy into various forms of energy.

12. Aladdin is climbing a tree. Explain how his energy varies?

13. Jasmine is running away from a monster with a speed of 5 m s^{-1}. If her weight is 100 N, then find out the energy spent by Jasmine to escape the monster. (Take g = 10 m s^{-2}; energy possessed by a body in motion = 1/2 mv^2 where m = mass of the body, v = velocity)

14. Calculate the work done and energy spent in the following two cases.
   (a) Smitha has been reading a book since 1 hour.
   (b) A child is pushing a car and the car's displacement is zero.

15. The work done by a boy in lifting his bag up to a height of 2 m is 200 J. Find the mass of his bag (Take g = 10 m s^{-2}).

16. Prakash bought an electric bulb which is rated as 70 W. He knows the fact that a 70 W bulb consumes 70 joules of electrical energy per second. The energy consumed by it per second is ________ ergs.
   (a) 700 (b) 70×10^7
   (c) 7×10^7 (d) 70×10^5

17. Can we draw 100% work from the energy spent on an event? If not, give the reason.

18. Suresh carried a bag containing 25 mangoes from the ground floor to the 5th floor by distributing 5 mangoes at each floor. If he starts distribution from the first floor and each mango weighs 200 g, then calculate the total work done by the person.
   (Height of each floor is 4 m, g = 10 ms^{-2})
   (a) 600 J (b) 1600 J
   (c) 1000 J (d) 60 J

19. What is the lowest limit of frequency range that is audible to human beings?

20. Distinguish between conventional and non-conventional sources of energy.

21. Two persons A and B are pushing two metal blocks that are identical. Person A applies a force of 100 N and moves the block through 1 m. Person B applies a force of 50 m and moves the block through 2 m. Compare the work done by the persons A and B if the person B takes double time than that of person A.

22. An iron ball of mass 2 kg is dropped from a height of 70 m. Calculate the work done by the gravitational force. (g = 10 m/s^2)

23. Divyansh sat on a tree at a height of 2 metres. If he weighs 200 newtons, then what is the energy possessed by him in that situation.

Essay Type Questions

24. (a) What is a source of energy?
   (i) How can we classify different sources of energy?
   (ii) Write the characteristics and examples of Sources of energy.

   (b) Write a short note on
   (i) Solar energy (ii) Wind energy
   (ii) Chemical energy (iv) Nuclear energy

PRACTICE QUESTIONS COMPETITION WING

Level 1: Apply Your Concepts

Direction for questions from 1 to 5.
Fill in the blanks.

1. The product of force and displacement is _______.
2. As the height of a body increases, its _______ also increases.
3. A plastic comb rubbed over dry hair attracts pieces of paper due to its _______.
4. In the universe _______ and _______ are conserved.
5. When one newton of force displaces a body through a distance of 1 m, then the energy spent on it is _______.

Level 2: Review Your Concepts

6. A block with several forces acting on it is shown in the figure below. If the net force moves the block through 50 cm, then find the work done on the block.

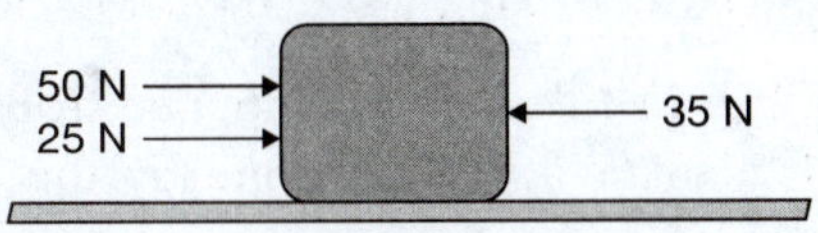

7. A force of 175 N is applied on a body and the body moves. While the body is in motion, a constant frictional force of 45 N on it.
   (i) Calculate the net force acting on the body
   (ii) Calculate the work done on the body if it moves through 10 cm.

8. A horse pulled a cart from position A to position B through C and came back to position C as shown in figure. What is the work done by the horse, if the force applied by the horse is 100 N?

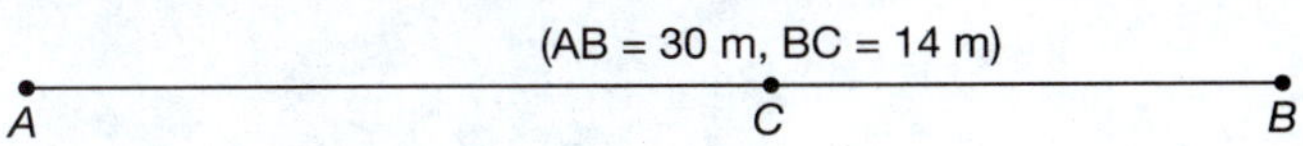

(a) 4400 J (b) 3000 J
(c) 1400 J (d) 1600 J

9. A person of mass 40 kg picked up a bag of mangoes and climbed ten steps. If the bag contains ten mangoes, each of mass 0.5 kg and the height of each step is 10 cm, then find the work done by the person in carrying that till tenth step (Take $g = 10 \text{ m s}^{-2}$).

10. A rice bag of 100 kg is lifted up by four workers to a height of 10 m from the ground. Find the work done by each worker (Assume that four workers muscular energies are equal).

11. Ramu is rolling a gas cylinder from A to C through B as shown in the adjoining figure by applying a force of 100 N. Calculate the total work done by him.

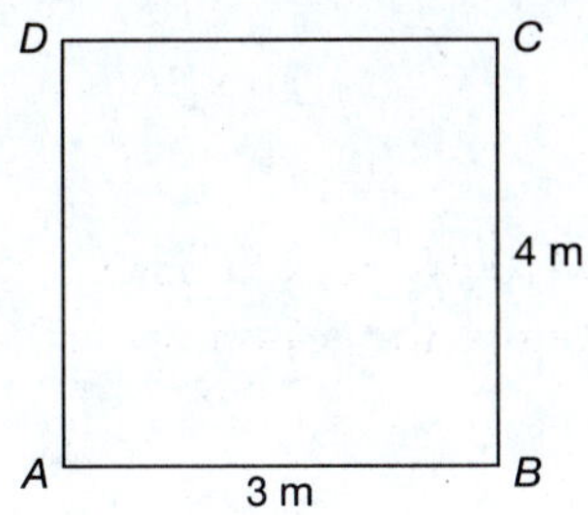

(a) 700 J (b) 400 J
(c) 500 J (d) 300 J

12. A body is moved along the sides of a triangle ABC once in anticlockwise direction by applying different forces along different sides as represented in the figure. The total displacement of the body and work done by the forces are _______ and ______ respectively.

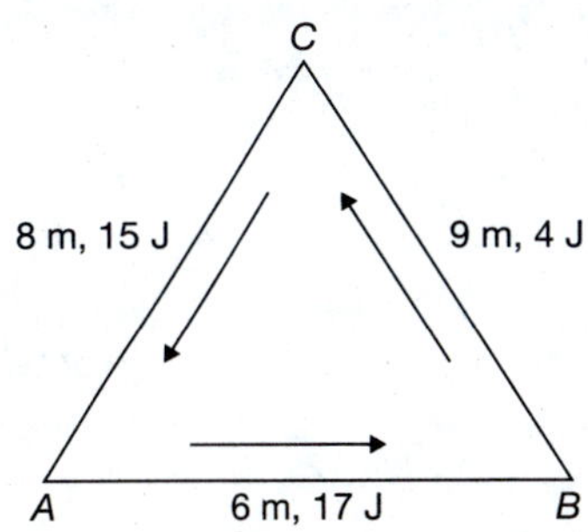

(a) 23 m, 26 J (b) 15 m, 21 J
(c) 25 m, 32 J (d) 0 m, 258 J

Level 3: Assess Your Concepts

13. An aeroplane of mass 5000 kg flying at a constant height of 560 meter from the ground with the speed of 360 ms^{-1}. Calculate the energy possessed by the aero plane.

14. A rubber ball of mass 500 *g* is dropped from a height of 10 m. When it hits the ground, 50% of its energy transformed into heat and sound energy. Find the height to which the ball is raised after the first bounce. ($g = 10$ m/s^2)

[**Hint:** Energy is conserved i.e.; the potential energy of a body can be converted into kinetic energy as well as other forms of energy. Energy = work done]

15. A force of 12 N is applied on an iron scale placed at one end of the floor such that it reaches the other end and work done is 10 joules. Calculate the length of the floor. (Length of scale: 30 cm)

AT

ANSWER KEYS

Crossword

Across

4. Sources 5. Negative 6. Electrical 8. Lightening

Down

1. Third 2. Potential 3. Conventional 7. Energy

Classroom Wing

Very Short Answer Type Questions

1. (d) 2. (c) 3. (a) 4. (b) 5. (d)

Short Answer Type Questions

7. 0.5 m 13. 125 J 14. (a) Zero (b) Zero 15. 10 Kg 16. (b)
17. cannot draw 100% work 18. (a) 19. 20 Hz 22. 1400 J
23. 400 J

Competition Wing

Level 1: Apply Your Concepts

1. work done 2. potential energy 3. electrical energy 4. mass, energy 5. one joule

Level 2: Review Your Concepts

6. 20 J 7. (i) 130 N; (ii) 13 J 8. (a) 9. 450 J 10. 25×10^2 J
11. (a) 12. (d) 14. 5 m

Level 3: Assess Your Concepts

13. 342×10^6 J 14. 3.75×10^4 J 15. 1.13 m

Hints and Explanations

CLASSROOM WING

Very Short Answer Type Questions

1. (a) Biogas is a mixture of methane (65%), carbon dioxide and hydrogen.
   (b) An apple on a tree has only potential energy.
   (c) A compressed spring has an elastic potential energy.
   (d) All the given statements are correct.
   Hence, the correct choice is (d).
2. Burning of thread in the candle gives light but not wax.
3. Microphone converts sound signals to electrical signals.
4. Solar energy is called the ultimate source of energy because it is the renewable source of energy which available in abuntant.
5. According to law of conservation of energy, as energy changes from one form to another the total energy of that system remains constant.

Short Answer Type Questions

6. We know that the work is said to be done when a force acts on a body, and the body moves in the direction of force.
   From the given options, only in option (d), the girl applies force on the bag and the bag moves in the upward direction (opposite to the direction of gravitational force).
7. Given, force, $F = 150$ N
   Work, $W = 75$ J
   We have, Work (W) = Force (F) × Displacement (s)
   $\Rightarrow 75 = 150 \text{ N} \times \text{Displacement } (s)$
   $\Rightarrow \text{Displacement } (s) = \frac{75}{150} = \frac{1}{2} = 0.5 \text{ m}$
8. Biomass is a fuel obtained from organic materials, like dried leaves, cow dung, etc.
   Biomass is converted to biogas which contains methane (64%), CO_2 and H_2, and hence, it is a clean, cost-effective fuel. Chemical energy stored in biomass gets converted to heat energy on burning and is widely used in villages.
9. Chemical energy, magnetic energy and nuclear energy all these come under the category of stored energy.
   (i) The energy stored in the matter is called chemical energy.
   (ii) Magnet can attract iron particles, so it is a form of stored energy.
   (iii) Energy stored inside some elements like uranium is nuclear energy. Some elements can change into another element by releasing a lot of energy in the form of heat. This large energy is called nuclear (or) atomic energy. This energy is used to generate electricity.
10. (i) Heater converts electrical energy into **heat energy**.
    (ii) Generator converts **mechanical energy** into electrical energy.
    (iii) Solar cell converts light energy into **electrical energy**.
    (iv) Electromagnet converts **electrical energy** into magnetic energy.
    (v) Combustion of fuel converts **chemical** energy into heat energy.
11. (a) Electromagnet converts electrical energy into magnetic energy.
    (b) Mixer grinder converts electrical energy into mechanical energy.
    (c) Door bell converts electrical energy into sound.
    (d) Tube and bulbs convert electrical energy into light energy.
    (e) Heater converts electrical energy into thermal energy.
12. While climbing a tree Alladdin's height increases from the ground. The potential energy is directly proportional to height of the body from the ground. Therefore, potential energy of Allauddin increases gradually.
13. $V = 5 \text{ m s}^{-1}$
    $W = mg = 100$ N
    $m = 10$ kg
    Kinetic energy $= 1/2\, mv^2$
    $= 1/2 \times 10 \times (5)^2$
    $= 125$ J

14. (a) Reading is a kind of mental work; so physical work done by Smitha in reading a book is zero, therefore, mechanical energy spent on it is also zero.

(b) A child cannot displace a car with his push, so there is no displacement. Therefore, work done and energy spent are zero.

15. $W = 200$ J

$h = 2$ m

$W = mgh = m \times 10 \times 2$

20 m $= 200$

$m = 10$ kg

16. 70 joule = 70 newton meters = 70×10^5 dynes $\times$ 100 cm = 70×10^7 dyne cm

Therefore, 70 joules = 70×10^7 erg

Hence, the correct option is (b).

17. We cannot draw 100% work from the energy spent on an event. Some amount of energy is lost in the other forms of energy.

18. We have, work done $W = F \times s = mg \times h$ (m – mass of the bag, h – height of each floor)

When the bag is in the ground floor,

$m = 25 \times 200 = 5000$ g $= 5$ kg

When the bag is taken to the first floor,

$m = 5$ kg

$h = 4$ m

$g = 10$ ms^{-2}

Therefore, work done:

$W_1 = m \times g \times h = 5 \times 10 \times 4 = 200$ J

Since 5 mangoes are given in the first floor, total number of mangoes = 20

When the bag is taken to the second floor,

$m = 20 \times 200 = 4$ kg

$h = 4$ m

Therefore, work done

$W_2 = m \times g \times h = 4 \times 10 \times 4 = 160$ J

Since 5 mangoes are given in the second floor, total number of mangoes = 15

When the bag is taken to the third floor,

$m = 15 \times 200 = 3$ kg

$h = 4$ m

Therefore, work done:

$W_3 = m \times g \times h = 3 \times 10 \times 4 = 120$ J

Since 5 mangoes are given in the third floor, total number of mangoes = 10

When the bag is taken to the fourth floor,

$m = 10 \times 200 = 2$ kg

$h = 4$ m

Therefore, work done

$W_4 = m \times g \times h = 2 \times 10 \times 4 = 80$ J

Since 5 mangoes are given in the fourth floor, total number of mangoes = 5

When the bag is taken to the fifth floor,

$m = 5 \times 200 = 1$ kg

$h = 4$ m

Therefore, work done

$W_5 = m \times g \times h = 1 \times 10 \times 4 = 40$ J

Total work done,

$W_1 + W_2 + W_3 + W_4 + W_5 = 200 + 160 + 120 + 80 + 40 = 600$ J

Hence, the correct answer is option (a)

19. Ultrasonic and infrasonic sounds are the inaudible sounds to human beings.

Ultrasonic sounds have frequencies greater than 20 Hz (i.e., > 20,0000 vibrations per second).

Infrasonic sounds have frequencies lesser than 20 Hz (i.e., < 20 vibrations per second).

20.

Conventional sources of energy	Non-conventional sources of energy
(1) The sources of energy which have been in use for a long time. ***Example:*** coal, water, fire wood, charcoal, petroleum, etc.	(1) The resources which are yet in the process of development over the past few years. ***Example:*** sun, wind, water tides, geothermal, etc.
(2) They are exhaustible except water.	(2) They are inexhaustible.
(3) They cause pollution.	(3) They are pollution-free.
(4) Generation of energy is expensive.	(4) Generation of energy is less expensive in long run but initial costs are expensive.

21. Person A:

Given, Force applied, $F_A = 100$ N

Displacement, $s = 1$ m

Work done by $A = F_A \times s = 100 \times 1 = 100$ J

Person B:

Given, Force applied, $F_B = 50$ N

Displacement, $s = 2$ m

Work done by $B = F_B \times s = 50 \times 2 = 100$ J

Work done does not depend on time. Therefore, the work done by the persons A and B are equal.

22. Given, Mass, $m = 2$ kg

Height, $h = 70$ m

$g = 10$ m/s^2

We have, Work done by gravity (W) = Force (F) × Displacement (s)

Here, Force (F) = Weight (w) = Mass (m) × Acceleration due to gravity (g)

$\Rightarrow F = mg = 2 \times 10 = 20$ N

And Displacement (s) = height (h) = 70 m

Then $W = F \times s = 20 \times 70 = 1400$ J

23. Energy required = Potential energy = $mgh = E = 200 \times 2 = 400$ J.

Essay Type Questions

24. (a) A source of energy is that which can provide enough useful energy at a steady rate over a long period of time.

(i) Sources of energy can be broadly classified into two categories based on their specific characteristics.

1. Renewable sources of energy
2. Non-renewable sources of energy

(ii) Renewable sources of energy:

- Generated from natural resources
- Environment friendly
- Available abundantly
- Gets regenerated naturally and easily

Examples: Solar, geothermal, wind, tidal energies, energy obtained from flowing water, biomass.

Non-renewable sources of energy:

- Generated from natural resources
- Have serious effect on environment
- Availability on the earth is limited
- Cannot be regenerated in a short span of time

Examples: Fossil fuels, petroleum, natural gas, nuclear energy.

(b) (i) **Solar energy:** Solar energy is obtained from the sun in the form of heat and light and harnessed by the devices, like solar heater, solar electric cell, etc.

(ii) **Wind energy:** Wind energy is obtained by converting the kinetic energy of moving air (wind) into electrical energy by using a generator which can be used to pump out underground water, grinding of grains, like wheat, grams, etc.

(iii) **Chemical energy:** Chemical energy stored in them gets converted to heat energy. Either this heat energy is directly used, or electricity is generated from this heat energy.

Fossil fuels

Example: Coal, petroleum, natural gas.

(iv) **Nuclear energy:** Nuclear energy of radioactive elements is mainly used for production of electricity. This energy is also used in various other fields, like nuclear weapons, medical treatment, controlling insects and pests, etc.

Nuclear energy

Example: Radioactive elements, like uranium.

COMPETITION WING

Level 2: Review Your Concepts

6. Given, Force (F_1) = 50 N (Right side)
Force (F_2) = 25 N (Right side)
Force (F_3) = 35 N (Left side)
Displacement (s) = 50 cm = 0.5 m
Now, the net force acting on the block,
$F_{net} = (F_1 + F_2) - F_3$
$\Rightarrow F_{net} = (50 + 25) - 35 = 40$ N
We have Work (W) = Net force (F) × Displacement (s)
$\Rightarrow W = 40 \times 0.5 = 20$ J

7. Given, Force applied on the body, $F_1 = 175$ N
Frictional force, $F_2 = 45$ N
Displacement (s) = 10 cm = 0.1 m
(i) Net force, $F = F_1 - F_2$
$\Rightarrow F = 175 - 45 = 130$ N
(ii) Work (W) = Net force (F) × Displacement (s)
$\Rightarrow W = 130 \times 0.1 = 13$ J

8. Initially, the cart is moved from A to B, $s_1 = 30$ m
Next, the cart is moved from B to C, $s_2 = 14$ m
Final displacement of the body,
$s = s_1 - s_2 = 30 - 14 = 16$ m $s = s_1 + s_2 = 44$ m
Force applied by the horse, $F = 100$ N
Work done by the horse,
$W = F \times S = 100 \times 44 = 4400$ J

9.

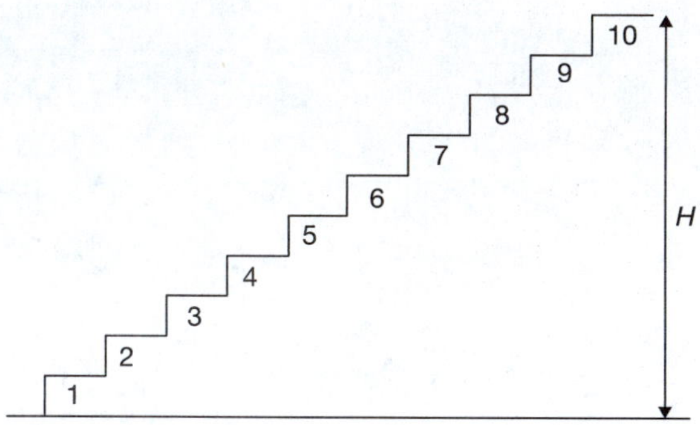

$H = 10 \times 10$ cm = 100 cm = 1 m
$M_P = 40$ kg
$M_m = 0.5$ kg
Work done = $(M_P + 10\ M_m)$ g H
(Gravitational energy)
= $(40 + 10 \times (0.5)) \times 10 \times 1$
= $45 \times 10 = 450$ J

10. Mass = 10^2 kg; $g = 10$ m s^{-2};
$S = 10$ m
Work done by a worker = $\dfrac{mgh}{4} = \dfrac{100 \times 10 \times 10}{4}$
$= 25 \times 10^2$ J

11. Initial displacement of the body, $AB = 3$ m
Subsequent displacement of the body, $BC = 4$ m
Force applied, $F = 100$ N
Work done,
$W = F \times (AB + BC) = 100 \times (3 + 4) = 700$ J
Hence, the correct option is (a).

12. Since the body is coming back to initial position A,
Total displacement of the body, $s = 0$
Total work done (W) = $W_{AB} + W_{BC} + W_{CA}$
$W = (6 \times 17) + (9 \times 4) + (8 \times 15) = 102 + 36 + 120 = 258$ J
Hence, the correct option is (d).

Level 3: Assess Your Concepts

13. Mass of plane = 5000 kg
Height from the ground = 560 meter
Velocity = 360 ms^{-1}
$g = 10$ m/sec
PE = mgh
Potential Energy = Kinetic Energy
PE = mgh = 5000 × 10 m 360
= 18×10^6 J
$$KE = \frac{1}{2}mv^2 = \frac{1}{2} \times 5000 \times 360 \times 360 = 324 \times 10^6\ J$$
Energy possessed by the aero plane = $18 \times 10^6 + 324 + 10^6$
$= 342 \times 10^6$ J

14. Given, mass of the ball, $m = 500$ g
Height, $h = 10$ m
We have, Work done by gravitational force, W = Force × Displacement
Here, Force = Weight of the body = $mg = 0.5 \times 10 = 5$ N
And Displacement = height = 10 m

Then the potential energy of the ball = work done = $(mg) \times h = 5 \times 10 = 50$ J

Given that 50% of the total potential energy is converted into heat and sound energy. Therefore, the remaining 50% of the total energy is converted into kinetic energy that is again converted into potential energy after the first bounce.

Let h_1 be the height reached by the ball after the first bounce.

Then, $mg \times h_1 = 50\%$ of 50 J

$$\Rightarrow 5 \times h_1 = \frac{50}{100} \times 50 = 25 \Rightarrow h_1 = \frac{25}{5} = 5 \text{ m}$$

15. Work = displacement × force

10 = 12 × displacement

$$S = \frac{10}{12} = 0.83 \text{ m}$$

Length of an iron scale = 30 cm

= 0.3 m

Length of the floor = (0.83 + 0.3) m = 1.13 m

CHAPTER

4

The Mechanism of Machines

Remember

Before beginning this chapter, you should be able to:

- Recall various simple machines used in our daily life
- Understand the concept of work and energy

Key Ideas

After completing this chapter, you should be able to:

- Know the types of simple machines
- Learn the new terminology used for levers
- Analyze the efficiency of a simple machine
- Apply concepts learnt to the simple machines used in our daily life.

Scientific Crypt

A Tribute to Archimedes (287-212 BC)

Archimedes of Syracuse was an Ancient Greek mathematician, physicist, engineer, astronomer, and inventor. He is considered the greatest mathematician of ancient history, and one of the greatest of all time. He determined the value of pie (π) to the most accurate approximation at that time. He formulated integral calculus which is an important branch of mathematics and is applied widely in physics. The working mechanism of pulleys and levers was explained by Archimedes when he was 27 years old. He applied geometry to discover the theorems concerning the centre of gravity of plane figures and solids. He formulated Archimedes' principle of buoyancy that explains how bodies float on liquids.

FUN TIME

CROSSWORD

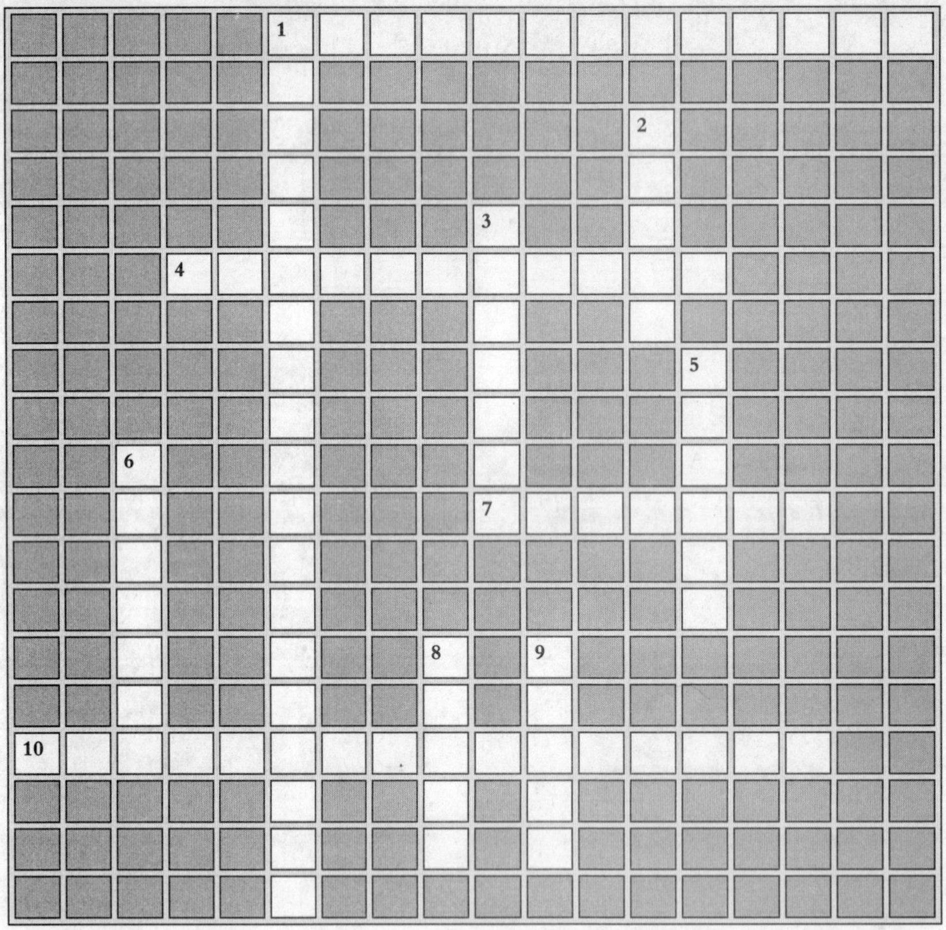

Across

1. Pulley whose axis of rotation is not fixed
4. This is a second order lever
7. Greater the number of pulleys, _______ is the force needed to lift heavy loads.
10. Scissors is an example of _______.

Down

1. Greater the ______, the smaller the effort required to overcome a certain load.
2. Inclined plane wound around
3. Block and tackle means more number of ______
5. This simple machine changes the direction of applied force
6. This can be used both as first and second order lever.
8. Leading edge shape of a speed boat
9. Tap works on the principle of _______

INTRODUCTION

A device which enables us to perform work in an easier way is a machine.

No work is done by a machine on its own. Energy is supplied to the machine by the amount of work performed on it so that work can be carried out in a simpler way.

Simple Machines

Input work is the work done on the machine, while output work is the work done by the machine. For example, the peeler, the knife are examples of simple machines.

Figure 4.1 Peeling potato with a peeler

Info Bytes!

The efficiency of any machine never really reaches 100% due to inherent losses like friction, air resistance, and heat. The closer it is to 100%, the more efficient the machine is.

Since the energy supplied to the machine is partly utilized to overcome the frictional force between the moving parts of the machine, hence, output work is always less than the input work.

Efficiency of a Machine

Efficiency of a machine is the ratio of the work done by the machine (output energy) to the work done on the machine (input energy). Efficiency is generally represented in terms of percentage. It can be mathematically represented as follows:

$$\text{Efficiency} = \frac{\text{Work done by the machine (output energy)}}{\text{Work done on the machine (input energy)}} \times 100$$

If the efficiency of a machine is $x\%$, we can conclude that $(100 - x)\%$ of the energy input is utilized to overcome the frictional force.

The amount of force applied on a simple machine in order to get the work done is called **effort**. The amount of force applied by a simple machine on an object to do the required work is called **load**.

The distance between the point where effort is applied and the fulcrum is called **effort arm**. The distance between the fulcrum and the point at which the load acts is called **load arm**.

Types of Simple Machines

Following are some types of simple machines:

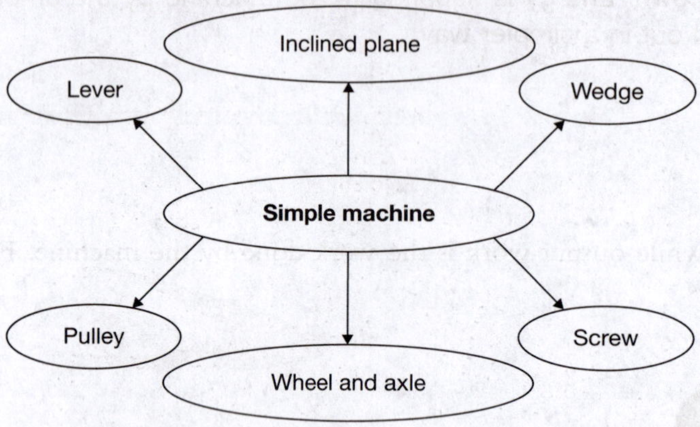

Info Bytes!

The ancient Greek scientist, Archimedes, once said, 'Give me a place to stand, and I shall move the Earth with a lever.'

Lever

A **lever** is a simple machine in which a rigid beam is capable of rotating freely around a fixed point. The fixed point is called fulcrum.

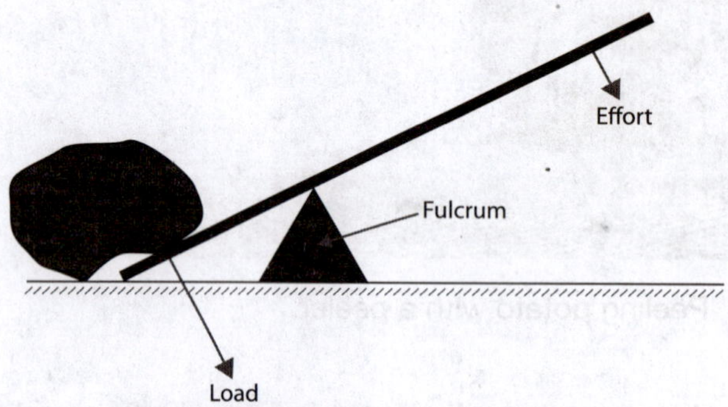

Figure 4.2 Working of a lever

Mechanical advantage of a lever is the ratio of load to effort. Mathematically, it can be represented as follows:

$$\text{Mechanical advantage} = \frac{\text{Load}}{\text{Effort}}$$

This relation is also known as **law of lever**.

Working Principle of Lever

$$\textbf{Load} \times \textbf{Load Arm} = \textbf{Effort} \times \textbf{Effort Arm}$$

The greater the magnitude of load and lesser the magnitude of effort, then higher will be the mechanical advantage.

Class I Lever

- Effort and load are on either side of the fulcrum.
- Mechanical advantage depends on the position of the load effort and fulcrum

Class II Lever

- Fulcrum and effort are on the either side of load.
- Since the effort arm is always longer than the load arm, class II levers have greater mechanical advantage and its value is always more than 1.

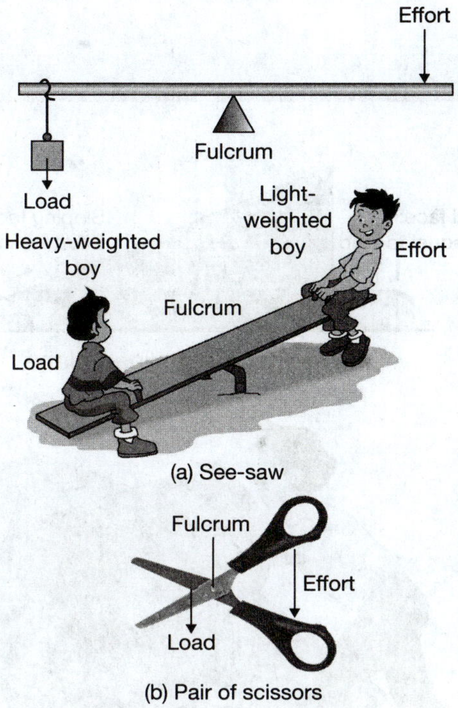

Figure 4.3 Class I Lever

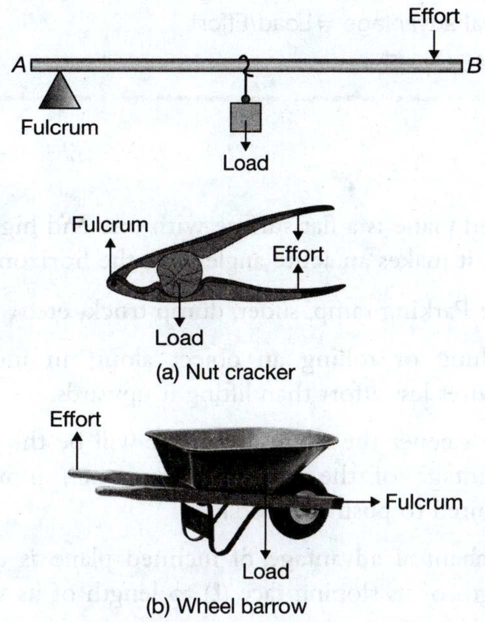

Figure 4.4 Class II Lever

Class III Lever

- Load and fulcrum is on the either side of the effort.
- Since the effort arm is always shorter than the load arm, mechanical advantage of a class III lever is always less than 1.

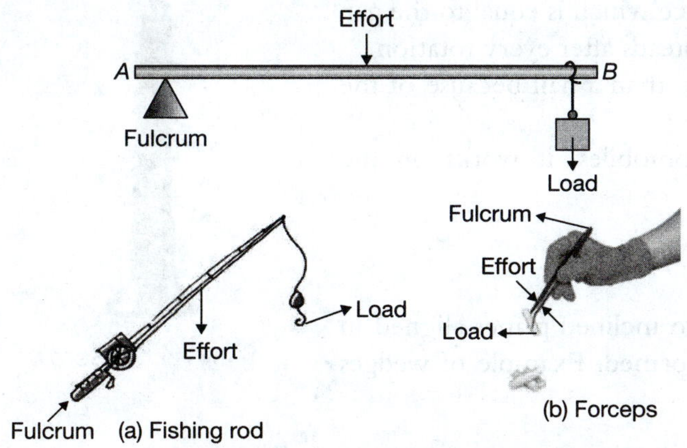

Figure 4.5 Class III Lever

EXAMPLE 4.1 A girl is able to lift a crate containing fruits of 45 N placed at one end of the lever by applying a force of 9 N at the other end. Find the mechanical advantage of the lever.

SOLUTION

Load = 45 N

Effort = 9 N

Mechanical advantage = Load/Effort

$\therefore MA = 45/9 = 5.$

Inclined Plane

An inclined plane is a flat surface with one end higher than the other, i.e., it makes an acute angle with the horizontal plane.

Examples: Parking ramp, slider, dump truck, etc.

1. Pushing or rolling an object along an inclined plane requires less effort than lifting it upwards.
2. The steeper the slope, the lesser will be the mechanical advantage of the inclined plane, i.e., more effort is required to push the load.
3. Mechanical advantage of inclined plane is the ratio of length of its sloping face (ℓ) to length of its vertical face (h). It is given as,

$$MA = \frac{\ell}{h}.$$

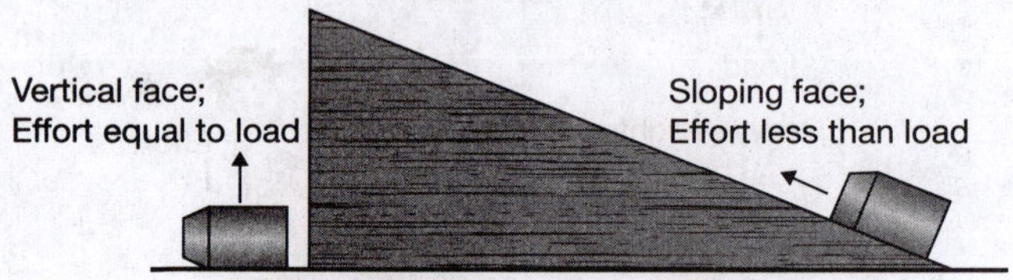

Figure 4.6 An inclined plane

Figure 4.7 Man rolling a drum on inclined plane

Applications of Inclined Plane

Screw

A **screw** is an inclined plane coiled around a nail.

- A screw has a pointed tip and the other end is a flat circular surface with a narrow slit in the middle of the surface.
- The inclined plane wound around the nail is called thread.
- The screw advances a distance which is equal to the gap between two consecutive threads after every rotation.
- A screw has as stronger grip than a nail because of the presence of threads.
- A jack is used to lift automobiles, it works on the principle of a screw.

Figure 4.8 Screw

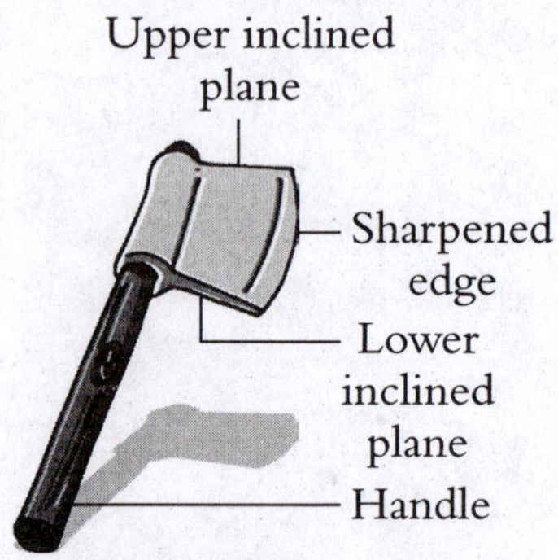

Figure 4.9 Wedge

Wedge

A **wedge** is a combination of two inclined planes aligned in such a way that a sharp edge is formed. Example of wedges are knives, axes, saws, etc.

- It is used to split an object into pieces.
- The thinner the wedge, the higher will be the efficiency of the wedge.

Pulley

A pulley is a circular disc with a grooved rim through which a rope is passed.

- The pulley can rotate around the axle which is present along the central axis of the pulley.
- The axle is fixed to a support called block.

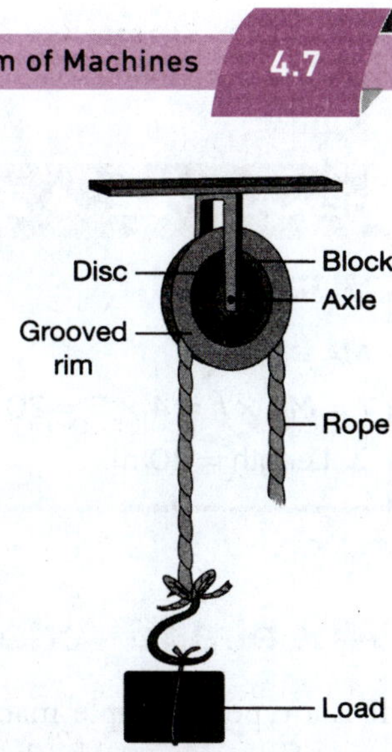

Figure 4.10 A pulley

Single Pulley

- A single pulley or more than one pulley can be used as a simple machine depending on the magnitude of the load required to be lifted. Single pulley can be of two types based on its working principle:

Single Pulley

Fixed Pulley

- Position of axis of rotation is fixed.
- Effort is applied in the downward direction to lift the load in the upward direction.
- Mechanical advantage is equal to 1, since the magnitudes of the load and the effort are the same. Work is simplified by changing the direction of application of effort.
- ***Examples:*** Pulleys are used to draw water from the well, hosting a flat, etc.

Movable Pulley

- Effort is applied in the upward direction.
- One end of the rope is fixed and the effort is applied at the other end. Hence, the load is distributed on both the sides of the rope, and thus, the effort is half of the load. Therefore, mechanical advantage

$$= \frac{\text{load}}{\text{effort}} = \frac{2}{1} = 2$$

- ***Example:*** Construction crane

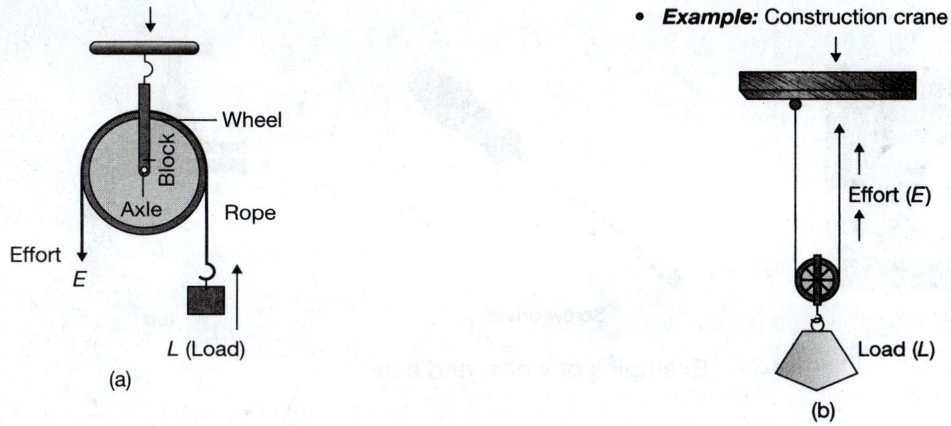

Figure 4.11 Single pulley (a) Fixed pulley (b) Movable pulley

- In order to increase the mechanical advantage, several pulleys are used and the arrangement is called block and tackle.
- The greater the number of pulleys, the higher will be the mechanical advantage.
- Heavy loads can be lifted by this system of pulleys.

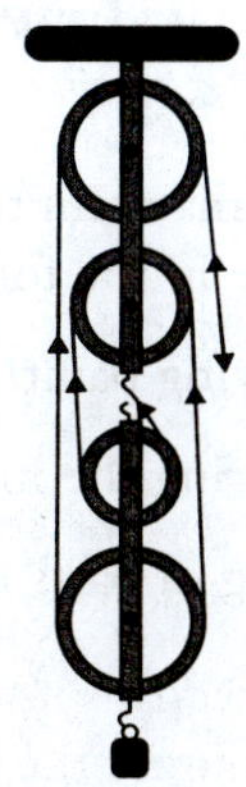

Figure 4.12 A block of pulleys

EXAMPLE 4.2 If the mechanical advantage of an inclined plane is 4 and its height is 5 m, then what will be its length?

SOLUTION

$MA = \ell/h$

$\ell = MA \times h = 4 \times 5 = 20$

$\therefore$ Length = 20 m.

Wheel and Axle

It is a type of simple machine in which a wheel is attached to an axle with a common axis of rotation and both of them rotate together.

An effort is applied either on the wheel or on the axle. Both **wheel** and **axle** work like a lever. The wheel and the axle have a common centre which can be considered as the fulcrum.

The radius of the wheel or axle is considered to be the effort arm depending on which (wheel or axle) the effort is applied and the other radius is the load arm.

Mechanical advantage is the ratio of the effort arm to the load arm. Some common examples are door knobs, screw-driver, tap.

Figure 4.13 Wheel and axle

Door knob

Screw driver

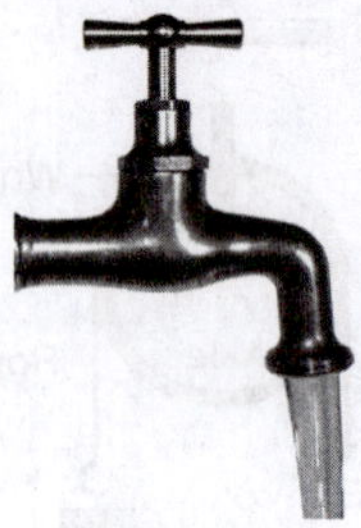

Tap

Figure 4.14 Examples of wheel and axle

Maintenance of a Machine

In order to maintain the functioning and efficiency of a machine we need to take care of the machine in the following ways:

1. Applying paint/rust proof coating helps in preventing from rusting.
2. Covering the machine when not in use helps in protecting from dust.
3. Oiling of parts helps in maintaining efficiency by reducing friction.

Info Bytes!

Regular maintenance of a machine can extend its lifespan by up to 15%.

Figure 4.15 Car mechanic cleaning car wheel brake disk from rust corrosion at automobile repair service station

EXAMPLE 4.3

A machine is operated by an effort of 50 N to lift a load of weight 100 N. Calculate MA.

SOLUTION

$$MA = \frac{\text{Load}}{\text{Effort}} = \frac{100}{50} = 2.$$

EXAMPLE 4.4

An inclined plane of length 8 m is used to lift a load of 20 dynes, by applying an effort of 5 dyne. Find the height of the plane.

SOLUTION

Given, length of the plane, $\ell = 6$ m

Load, $L = 20$ dynes

Effort, $E = 5$ dynes

Let the height of the plane be 'h'.

We know that: $\frac{L}{E} = \frac{\ell}{h}$

$$\Rightarrow h = \ell \times \frac{E}{L} = 8 \times \frac{5}{20} = 2 \text{ m}.$$

EXAMPLE 4.5

A crowbar of length 120 cm is used as a second-order lever to move a rock. If the load arm is 30 cm and the amount of force required to move the rock is 1000 N, find the minimum effort required to move the rock.

SOLUTION

For minimum effort, the effort arm should be maximum which happens when the crowbar is turned about its end and used as a second-order lever.

Use the principle of moments:

Effort × Effort arm = Load × Load arm

Load = 1000 N

Effort arm = 120 cm

Load arm = 30 cm

Effort × 120 = 1000 × 30

$$\therefore \text{Effort} = \frac{1000 \times 30}{120} = 250 \text{ N}.$$

POINTS TO REMEMBER

- ✔ Efficiency of a machine is the ratio of the work done by the machine (output energy) to the work done on the machine (input energy).
- ✔ A lever is a simple machine in which a rigid beam is capable of rotating freely around a fixed point. The fixed point is called fulcrum.
- ✔ Energy is defined as the capacity of doing work. Energy can exist in various forms.
- ✔ A wedge is a combination of two inclined planes aligned in such a way that a sharp edge is formed
- ✔ A pulley is a circular disc with a grooved rim through which a rope is passed.

DW

PRACTICE QUESTIONS CLASSROOM WING

Very Short Answer Type Questions

Direction for questions from 1 to 5.
Fill in the blanks.

1. If MA of a simple machine is greater than 1, then effort arm is ______ than the load arm.
2. For ______ order lever, mechanical advantage (MA) is always greater than 1.
3. For a single movable pulley, MA is ______.
4. Forceps are an example of ______ order lever.
5. If mechanical advantages of two inclined planes A and B are in the ratio of 1 : 3, the slope of A must be ______ than that of B.

Direction for questions from 6 to 10.
Select the correct alternative from the given options.

6. If the effort arm of a lever is twice of its load arm, it is a ______.
   (a) First-order lever (b) Second-order lever
   (c) Third-order lever (d) 1 or 2
7. Which of the following machines is used only to change the direction of input force?
   (a) Inclined plane (b) Single-fixed pulley
   (c) Scissors (d) Screw jack
8. Which of the following is wrong?
   (a) Ist order lever : MA > 1
   (b) IInd order lever : MA > 1
   (c) IIIrd order lever : MA > 1
   (d) single-fixed pulley : MA = 1
9. Which of the following planes cannot be used to push load to a certain height?
   (a) A plane of slope 2
   (b) A plane of slope ∞
   (c) A plane of slope 0
   (d) Both (b) and (c)
10. Regular oiling of parts increases their
    (a) Output work (b) Efficiency
    (c) Mechanical advantage (d) None of these

Short Answer Type Questions

11. Define machine.
12. Define effort.
13. Define load.
14. Define mechanical advantage.
15. Differentiate between single fixed pulley and single movable pulley.
16. If an effort of 10 N is applied on a single-fixed pulley to lift a weight of 10 N, then find out its mechanical advantage.
17. If an inclined plane of length 2 m is used to lift a load of 20 N to a height of 1 m, find the effort required to lift the load to that height using inclined plane.

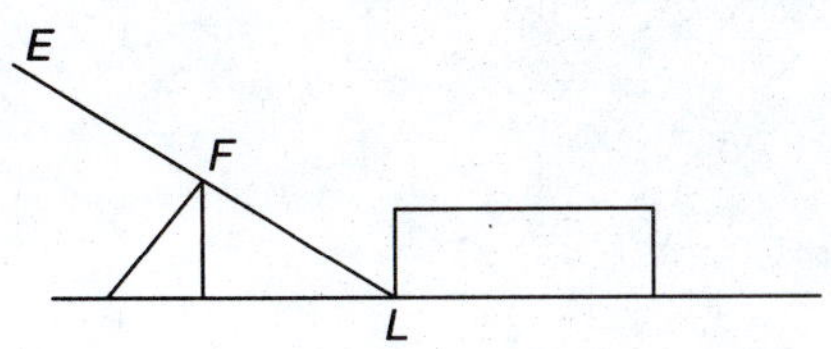

18. A crowbar of length 1 m is used to displace a body. Find its mechanical advantage, if the load arm is 0.25 m.
19. A see-saw of length 2 m is pivoted at 50 cm from one end in a public park. What is the effort applied at the near end to the fulcrum to lift a load of 150 N at the far end to fulcrum?
20. Find the mechanical advantage of the below figure:

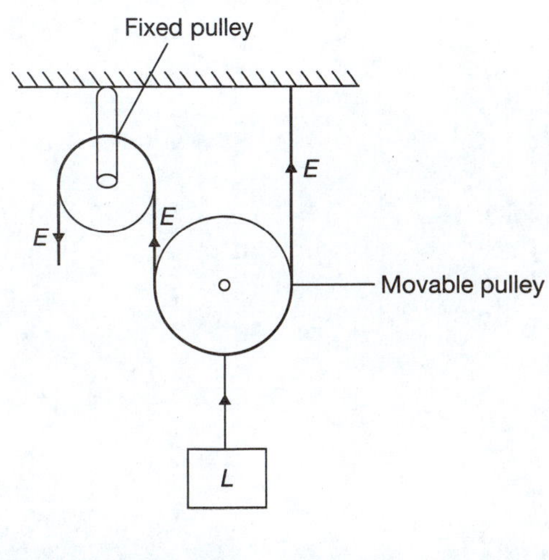

21. A nut is placed in a nut cracker at 5 cm from the fixed end. If the force experienced by the nut is 100 N when a force of 20 N is applied at the free end of the nut cracker, find the length of the nut cracker.

(a) 5 (b) 25 (c) 15 (d) 20

22. Anil has a two-wheeler that weighs 120 kg. After completing his work, he used to park his vehicle in the reg ular parking place which is in connected to the ground with a ramp of inclination 45°. If the length of ramp is 1 m, then calculate the work done by Anil to park the vehicle against gravity. ($g = 10$ m s^{-2})

(a) 10500 J (b) 1005 J
(c) 1050 J (d) 1500 J

23. The efficiency of a rough inclined plane is 80%. Calculate the energy spent in raising a load of 250 N through 1 m.

Essay Type Questions

24. (a) What is a simple machine? Mention different types of simple machines.

(b) What is a lever type simple machine?

(c) Explain the following terms related to levers:

(i) Fulcrum (ii) Load arm
(iii) Effort arm (iv) Mechanical advantage

(d) What is the working principle of levers?

(e) Write the classification of levers with two examples each.

PRACTICE QUESTIONS COMPETITION WING

Level 1: Apply Your Concepts

Direction for questions from 1 to 5.
Fill in the blanks.

1. For an ideal simple machine, work done by a machine equals to _______.
2. A rod which is free to move around a point is called _______.
3. See-saw is an example of _______ order lever.
4. If the mechanical advantage of a lever is equal to 1, then the effort applied on it _______ the load.
5. If the slope of an inclined plane is steeper, the effort required to push a load through it is _______.

Direction for questions from 6 to 10.
Select the correct alternative from the given options.

6. If load is between the fulcrum and effort of a lever, it is called ______ order lever.
   (a) Ist (b) IInd
   (c) IIIrd (d) IVth
7. Efficiency of an ideal machine is _______.
   (a) 0% (b) 50%
   (c) 90% (d) 100%
8. The machine has a mechanical advantage of 3. If an effort of 50 N is applied on the machine, then find the effort used to lift the load.
   (a) 50 N (b) 100 N
   (c) 150 N (d) 30 N
9. The efficiency of a machine is 75%. If 100 J of energy is given to the machine, then find the output of the machine.
   (a) 25 J (b) 75 J
   (c) 50 J (d) 85 J
10. A man uses an inclined plane of length 2 m to raise a load of 1000 N. If he does 2400 J of work, then find the mechanical advantage (Take $g = 10\ ms^{-2}$).
   (a) 0.833 (b) 8.33
   (c) 3.38 (d) 0.338

Level 2: Review Your Concepts

11. To open the lid of a bottle, 50 N force is needed, Siri wanted to open the lid with her maximum effort of 10 N, which of the following openers is suitable for doing it?

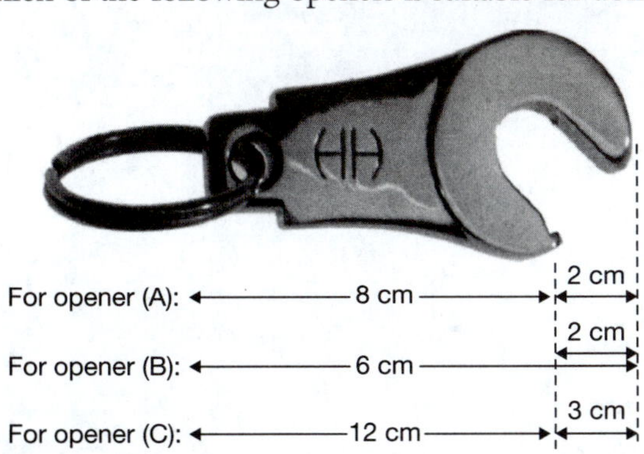

12. Hari and Vamshi constructed houses adjacent to each other, in such a way that the ground floors of both the houses are of height 1 m each from the level of the road. Vamshi built an inclined plane in front of his house so that its length is 50% more than that of Hari's house. Find the ratio of the efforts required to lift the same load to the ground floor of both houses.
13. Hari is studying in 6th standard and is interested in science related experiments. While reading simple machines topic from his text book, he started wondering as to which lever a pen belongs to in its writing position? The length of the pen he is using is 14 cm and he holds it at distance of 4 cm from its nib. If the force applied by Hari to write is 0.02 N, the mechanical advantage of the pen is ___________ and it is acting as a ___________ order lever.
   (a) 5, second (b) 0.25, first
   (c) 2.5, third (d) 0.714, third
14. Ram used a crowbar of length 1.5 m as a IInd order lever to displace a heavy sphere placed on the horizontal surface. If the crowbar applies a force of 240 N on the sphere at a distance of 100 cm from effort, then find the minimum effort applied by Ram to displace it.
15. A tailor purchased a scissors of length 25 cm through online shopping. He sent a feedback to the manufacturer saying 'I cannot cut the Jeans cloth even if I apply my maximum force 83.3 N on it, so please modify it

without changing its length so that I can cut the Jeans cloth at least with my maximum effort.' If you are the manufacturer, how can you modify the scissors as per the feedback given by the tailor? Initially fulcrum is exactly midway between two ends of the scissors and the minimum force required to cut the jeans cloth is 500 N. The position of the load should always be at 7.5 cm from the free end of load arm.

16. The figure shows the combination of single fixed pulley and a single movable pulley. If a load of 100 N is attached to the single movable pulley, the find:

(i) Effort

(ii) Tension T

(iii) Mechanical Advantage

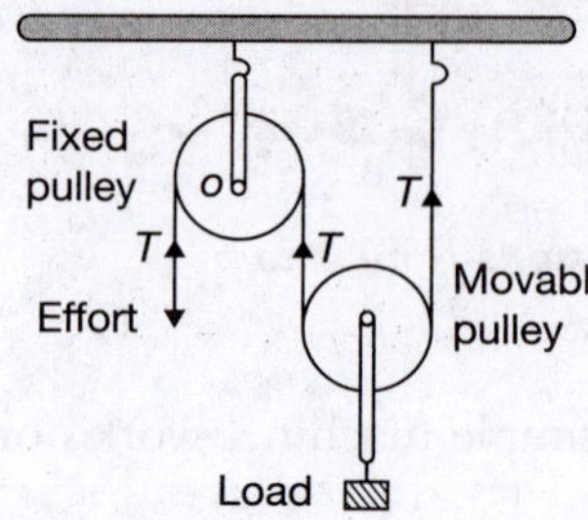

Level 3: Assess Your Concepts

17. A farmer was cutting mangoes from a tree with a long stick of length 2 m. He cut almost all mangoes at the lower branches of the tree and then he aimed to cut the mangoes at higher branches of it. To do this he attached another stick to the top of the first stick so that the overall length increases by 1 m. If the distance between his hands position is the same as before at 40 cm and weight of each mango is 5 N, then calculate the change in mechanical advantage of stick to do this, for the same effort of 20 N.

(a) Mechanical advantage increases by 0.26

(b) Mechanical advantage decreases by 0.0066

(c) Mechanical increases by 0.0066

(d) Mechanical advantage decreases by 1.87

18. Anil has a two-wheeler that weighs 120 kg. After com pleting his work, he used to park his vehicle in the regular parking place which is connected to the ground with a ramp which just covers an open drain of width 4 m. If the length of ramp is 5 m, then find the mechanical advantage of the ramp.

19. A body of mass 10 kg is lifted by using single fixed pulley as well as single movable pulley. Compare the mechanical advantages in lifting the body using both the pulleys.

20. A stone is placed in a stone cracker at 15 cm from fixed end; it experienced the force of 500 N. When force of 100N is applied at the free end of stone cracker, calculate the length of the nut cracker.

21. Calculate the height of the plane if an inclined plane of length 10 m is used to lift a load of 50 dynes, by applying an effort of 15 dynes.

22. A car was parked in 'No parking space' on the road. After some time, the traffic police took the car by lifting it with a rope attached to a pulley arrangement. Calculate the weight of car if its mass is 500 kg.

AT

ANSWER KEYS

Crossword

Across

1. Movable pulley
4. Mango cutter
7. Smaller
10. First order lever

Down

1. Mechanical Advantage
2. Screw
3. Pulley
5. Pulley
6. Crowbar
8. Wedge
9. Screw

Classroom Wing

Very Short Answer Type Questions

1. longer
2. II
3. 2
4. III
5. greater
6. (b)
7. (b)
8. (c)
9. (d)
10. (b)

Short Answer Type Questions

16. 1
17. 10 N
18. 3
19. 450 N
20. 2
21. (b)
22. (c)
23. 312.5 J

Competition Wing

Level 1: Apply Your Concepts

1. Work done on the machine
2. Lever
3. I
4. equals to
5. greater
6. (b)
7. (d)
8. (c)
9. (b)
10. (a)

Level 2: Review Your Concepts

11. $E_A = 10$ N, $E_B = 12.5$ N, $E_C = 10$ N, Either A or C.
12. 3/2
13. (d)
14. 80 N
15. Fulcrum should be shifted to 2.5 cm towards old load position
16. 2

Level 3: Assess Your Concepts

17. (b)
18. 5/3
19. 2
20. 15 cm
21. 3 m
22. 5000 N

Hints and Explanations

CLASSROOM WING

Very Short Answer Type Questions

6. In case of III order lever always the load arm will be greater than the effort arm.
7. Single fixed pulley is used to reverse the direction of application of force.
8. In case of III order lever, always the load arm will be greater than the effort arm. Mechanical advantage is inversely proportional to the load arm therefore it will be always less than 1.
9. Inclined plane of zero inclination is just a horizontal surface which do not bring any change in the effort required to do a work. Slope Infinity means the body has to be lifted to zero height i.e there is no requiremnt of an inclined plane. Therefore, inclined planes of slope infinity or zero cannot be used.
10. Oiling the machinery reduces friction and so there will be less energy lost. Hence, the ouput work also increases and so the efficiency of the machine increases.

Short Answer Type Questions

11. Machine is an object which allows us to do work with less effort than the effort required to do work without a machine.
12. Input force applied on a simple machine is called effort.
13. Output force applied by the simple machine is called load.
14. The ability of a simple machine to multiply the effort applied on it is called its mechanical advantage.
15.

Single fixed pulley	Single movable pulley
Position of axis of rotation is fixed.	Position of the axis is not fixed.
Effort is applied in the downward direction to lift the load in the upward direction.	Effort is applied in the upward direction.
Mechanical advantage is equal to 1 since the magnitudes of the load and the effort are the same.	Mechanical advantage is equal to 2 since the magnitude of the load is double the effort.
Examples: Pulleys are used to draw water from the well, hosting a flat, etc.	Example: Construction crane

(Continued)

16. MA of a single-fixed pulley is always 1.
17. $\text{MA} = \frac{\ell}{h} = \frac{2}{1} = 2$

$\text{MA} = \frac{L}{E}$

$E = \frac{L}{MA} = \frac{20}{2} = 10$

Effort = 10 N

18. $\text{MA} = \frac{\text{Effort arm}}{\text{Load arm}}$

$= \frac{0.75}{0.25} = 3$

19. $\text{MA} = \frac{\text{Effort arm}}{\text{Load arm}}$

$= \frac{50}{150} = \frac{1}{3}$

$\text{MA} = \frac{L}{E}$

$E = \frac{L}{\text{MA}} = 150 \times \frac{3}{1}$

$\therefore$ Effort = 450 N

20. $\text{MA} = \frac{L}{E} = \frac{2E}{E} = 2$

21. $\text{Mechanical advantage} = \frac{\text{Load}}{\text{Effort}} = \frac{\text{Effort arm}}{\text{Load arm}}$

Therefore, $\frac{100}{20} = \frac{\text{Effort arm}}{5}$

$\Rightarrow$ Effort arm = 25 cm

22. AC = 100 cm, BC = BA, $AC^2 = AB^2 + BC^2$

Since inclination is 45°, AB = BC

Therefore, $AC^2 = 2\ AB^2$

$\Rightarrow AB = \sqrt{(10000/2)} = 50 \times 1.4 = 70\text{ cm} = 0.7\text{ m}$

The work done by Anil to park the vehicle against gravity = $mgh = mg \times AB$ (since h = AB)

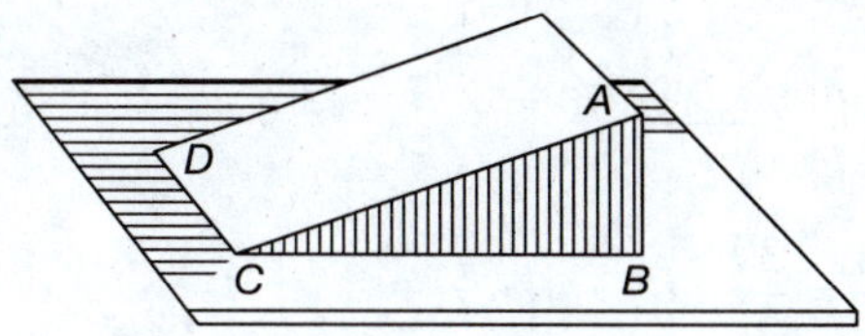

$= 120 \times 10 \times 0.7$

$= 1{,}050$ J

23. Efficiency of the rough inclined plane, $\eta = 80\%$

Load, $L = 250$ N

Displacement of load, $dL = 1$ m

We have, Efficiency, $\eta = \frac{\text{Work output}}{\text{Work input}}$

Now, work output = $L \times dL = 250 \times 1 = 250$ J

Then Work input = $\frac{\text{Work output}}{\text{Efficiency}} = \frac{250}{0.8} = 312.5$ J

Essay Type Questions

24. (a) **Simple machine:** A device which enables us to perform work in an easier way is a machine.

Types of simple machines:

Levers, Pulley, Inclined plane

(b) **Lever:** A lever is a simple machine in which a rigid beam is capable of rotating freely around a fixed point.

(c) (i) **Fulcrum:** The fixed point about which a rigid beam rotates is called fulcrum.

(ii) **Load arm:** The distance between the fulcrum and the load is called load arm.

(iii) **Effort arm:** The distance between the fulcrum and the effort is called effort arm.

(iv) **Mechanical Advantage:** The ratio of effort arm to the load arm is called mechanical advantage.

(d) **Working Principle of Lever:**

Load × Load Arm = Effort × Effort Arm

The greater the magnitude of load and lesser the magnitude of effort, then higher will be the mechanical advantage.

(e) **Classification of levers:**

(i) Class I Lever:

- Effort and load are on either side of the fulcrum.
- Mechanical advantage depends on the position of the load effort and fulcrum.
- Examples: See-saw, scissors

(ii) Class II Lever

- Fulcrum and effort are on the either side of load.
- Since the effort arm is always longer than the load arm, class II levers have greater mechanical advantage, and its value is always more than 1.
- Examples: Nutcracker, wheel barrow

(iii) Class III Lever

- Load and fulcrum is on the either side of the effort.
- Since the effort arm is always shorter than the load arm, mechanical advantage of a class III lever is always less than 1.
- Examples: Fishing rod, forceps

COMPETITION WING

Level 1: Apply Your Concepts

8. Given, $MA = 3$

Effort = 50 N

Load = ?

We have, $MA = \frac{\text{Load}}{\text{Effort}}$

$\Rightarrow 3 = \frac{\text{Load}}{50} \Rightarrow \text{Load} = 3 \times 50 = 150\text{ N}$

Hence, the correct option is (c).

9. Efficiency of the rough inclined plane, $\eta = 75\%$

We have, Efficiency, $\eta = \frac{\text{Work output}}{\text{Work input}}$

Now, work input = 100 J

Then Work output = Efficiency × Work input = 0.75 × 100 = 75 J

Hence, the correct option is (b).

10. Given Length of the inclined plane, $l = 2$ m

Load, $L = 1000$ N (= weight (mg))

Work done = 2400 J (= mgh)

We have, $MA = \frac{\text{Length of the inclined plane } (l)}{\text{Height of vertical side } (h)}$

Now, Work done = mgh = 2400

But mg = 1000 N

Then $(1000)\, h = 2400 \Rightarrow h = \frac{2400}{1000} = 2.4$ m

Now, $MA = \frac{l}{h} = \frac{2}{2.4} = 0.833$

Hence, the correct option is (a).

Level 2: Review Your Concepts

11. $M_A = \frac{10}{2} = 5$

$M_B = \frac{8}{2} = 4$

$M_C = \frac{15}{3} = 5$

$E_A = \frac{L}{MA} = \frac{50}{5} = 10\text{ N}$

$E_B = \frac{L}{MA} = \frac{50}{4} = 12.5\text{ N}$

$E_C = \frac{L}{MA} = \frac{50}{5} = 10\text{ N}$

She can use opener A or C to open the lid.

12. $L_H = L_V = L$

$L_H = 1,\ L_V = 1 + 0.5\,1 = 1.5\,1$

$h_H = hv = H$

$\frac{L}{E} = \frac{\ell}{h}$

$E = \frac{L \times h}{\ell}$

$\frac{E_H}{E_V} = \frac{L_H}{L_V} \times \frac{h_H}{h_V} \times \frac{\ell_V}{\ell_H}$

$= \frac{L}{L} \times \frac{h}{h} \times \frac{1.5\ell}{\ell}$

$\therefore \frac{E_H}{E_V} = \frac{3}{2}$

13. A pen acts as a third order lever in writing position (since the effort is applied at the middle of the fulcrum and the load).

The length of pen = load arm = 14 cm

Effort arm = 10 cm

Mechanical advantage of pen = $\frac{\text{effort arm}}{\text{load arm}}$

$= \frac{10}{14} = 0.714$

14. Crowbar act as IInd order lever as shown below:

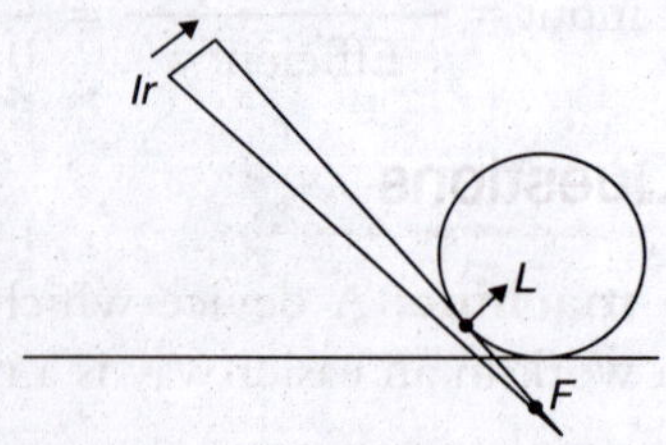

To apply minimum effort, effort should be applied at the top of the crowbar as shown in the figure, then

Effort arm = Length of the crowbar = 1.5 m = 150 cm

Load arm = 150 cm − 100 cm = 50 cm

$\text{MA} = \frac{\text{Effort arm}}{\text{Load arm}} = \frac{150}{50} = 3$

$E = \frac{L}{\text{MA}} = \frac{240}{3} = 80$

Minimum effort = 80 N

15. (i) Before modification:

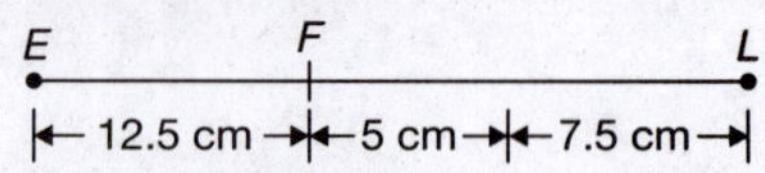

$$MA = \frac{\text{Effort arm}}{\text{Load arm}} = \frac{12.5}{5} = 2.5 \text{ cm}$$

$$\text{Required E} = \frac{L}{MA} = \frac{500}{2.5} = 200 \text{ N}$$

$$\text{Required MA} = \frac{L}{E} = \frac{500}{83.3} = 6$$

(ii) After modification

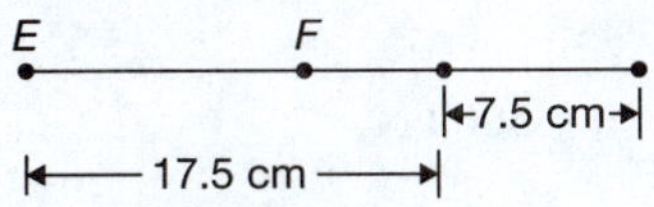

$$MA = \frac{\text{Effort arm}}{\text{Load arm}}$$

$$6 = \frac{x}{17.5 - x}$$

⇒ New effort arm = 15 cm

New load arm = 17.5 – 15 = 2.5 cm

Fulcrum should be shifted to 2.5 cm towards old load position.

16. Given, Load, $L = 100$ N

From figure, $T + T =$ Load

$\Rightarrow 2T = 100 \text{ N} \Rightarrow T = \frac{100}{2} = 50 \text{ N}$

And Effort = T

⇒ Effort = 50 N

We have, Mechanical Advantage = $\frac{\text{Load}}{\text{Effort}} = \frac{100}{50} = 2$

Level 3: Assess Your Concepts

17. Decrease in mechanical advantage of the stick = M.A. of 3 m stick – M.A. of 2 m stick

$$= \frac{40}{200} - \frac{40}{300} = 0.0066$$

Hence, the correct option is (b).

18. $MA = \frac{l}{h}$

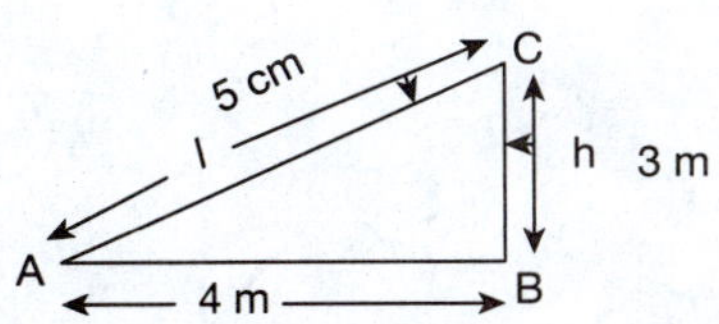

Using Pythogoras theorem,

$AC^2 = AB^2 + BC^2$

$5^2 = 4^2 + BC^2 \Rightarrow BC^2 = 25 - 16 = 9$

$\Rightarrow BC = \sqrt{9} = 3 \therefore h = 3$

$$MA = \frac{l}{h} = \frac{5}{3}$$

19.

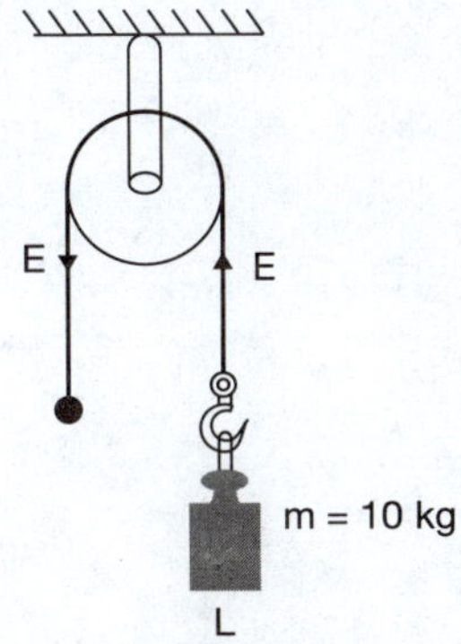

L = E

$$MA = \frac{L}{E}$$

$$= \frac{E}{E} = 1$$

$MA_1 = 1$

$MA_2 = 2MA_1$

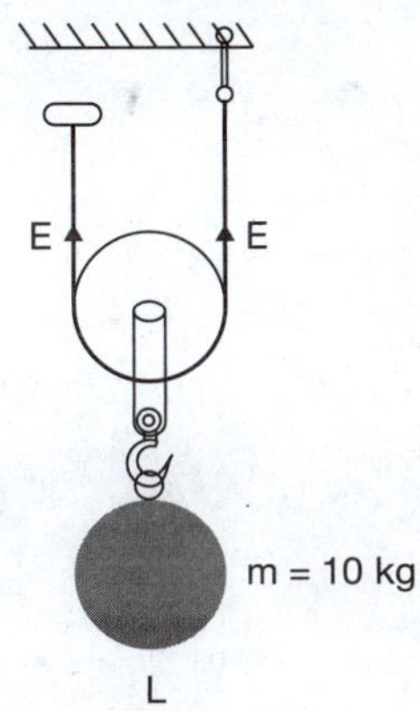

L = E + E

L = 2E

$$M = \frac{L}{E} = \frac{2E}{E}$$

$MA_2 = 2$

20. Mechanical advantage $= \frac{\text{Load}}{\text{effort}}$

$$= \frac{\text{effort arm}}{\text{load arm}}$$

Therefore, $\frac{500}{200} = \frac{\text{Effort arm}}{15}$

$$\text{Effort arm} = \frac{500 \times 15}{200}$$

$$= 10 \times \frac{15}{50} = 15 \text{ cm}$$

21. Length of plane, l = 10m

Load, L = 50 dynes

Effort, E = 15 dynes

Height of plane be 'h'

$$\frac{L}{E} = \frac{l}{h}$$

$$h = l \times \frac{E}{L}$$

$$= 10 \times \frac{15}{50}$$

$$= 3 \text{ m}$$

22. Weight = mg

$mg = 500 \times 10 = 5000$ N

CHAPTER 5

Light

Remember

Before beginning this chapter, you should be able to:

- Know the different sources of light
- Describe the phenomena of day and night

Key Ideas

After completing this chapter, you should be able to:

- Understand various sources of light and optical media
- Explain rectilinear propagation of light and its applications
- Define the laws of reflection
- Discuss applications of light in daily life

A Tribute to Galileo Galilei (1564–1642)

Galileo Galilei was an Italian astronomer, physicist and engineer. He has been called the father of observational astronomy, modern-era classical physics, the scientific method, and modern science. He invented the thermoscope and various military compasses and used the telescope for scientific observations of celestial objects. His contributions to observational astronomy include telescopic confirmation of the phases of Venus, observation of the four largest satellites of Jupiter, observation of Saturn's rings, and analysis of lunar craters and sunspots. Galileo made the first telescope with about 3x magnification. He later made improved versions with up to about 30x magnification. With a Galilean telescope, the observer could see magnified, upright images on the Earth—it was what is commonly known as a terrestrial telescope or a spyglass.

FUN TIME

CROSSWORD

Across

2. A smooth polished surface that reflects light rays back into the same medium.
3. A ray of light that strikes a surface, particularly a mirror.
5. A dark region formed on a screen when an opaque object obstructs light.
7. A ray of light that bounces off a surface.
8. The phenomenon where light bounces back from a smooth polished surface.
10. A perpendicular line drawn at the point where light strikes a surface.

Down

1. An object or entity that emits light.
3. The specific point on a surface, such as a mirror, where light strikes.
4. A tube bent twice at right angles allowing one to see over obstacles.
6. Straight-line propagation of light, key in phenomena like shadows and eclipses.
9. The measurement between two rays or lines, especially in terms of light interaction with surfaces.

INTRODUCTION

Presence of light can be felt anywhere, even though it is an invisible form of energy. Things around us are visible because of light. This is because of the fact that light from a light source falls on an object and then reflects back into our eye. Light is an essential form of energy which plays a vital role in our daily life.

Sources of Light

A source of light is an object/entity that emits light. Following is a chart describing the classification of various sources of light. In the absence of light, a person is unable to see things clearly that are present in a dark room.

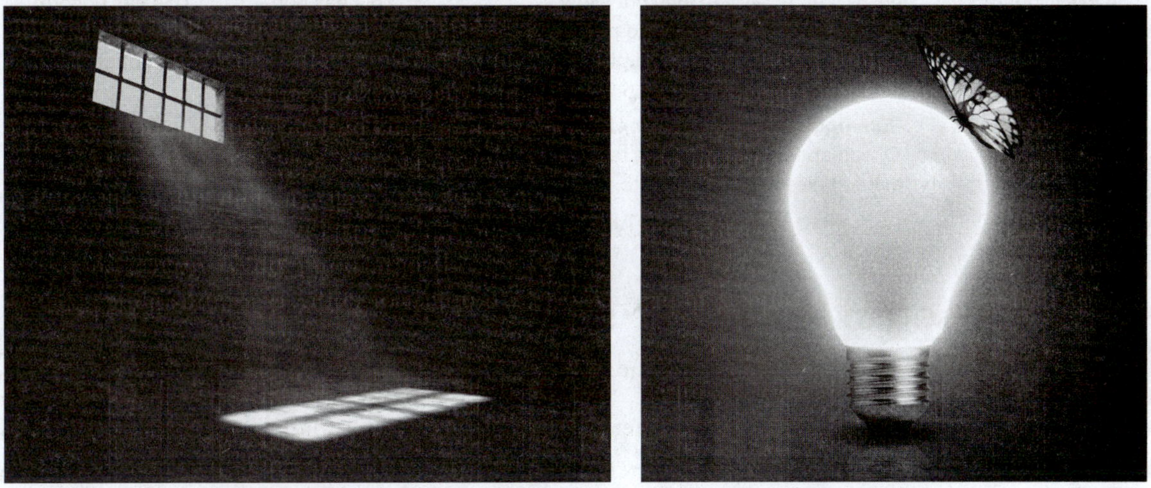

Figure 5.1 Sources of light (natural light and artificial light)

There are two types of sources of light, natural sources and artificial sources, which are further divided basis upon size, coldness/hotness, emission of light, and existence.

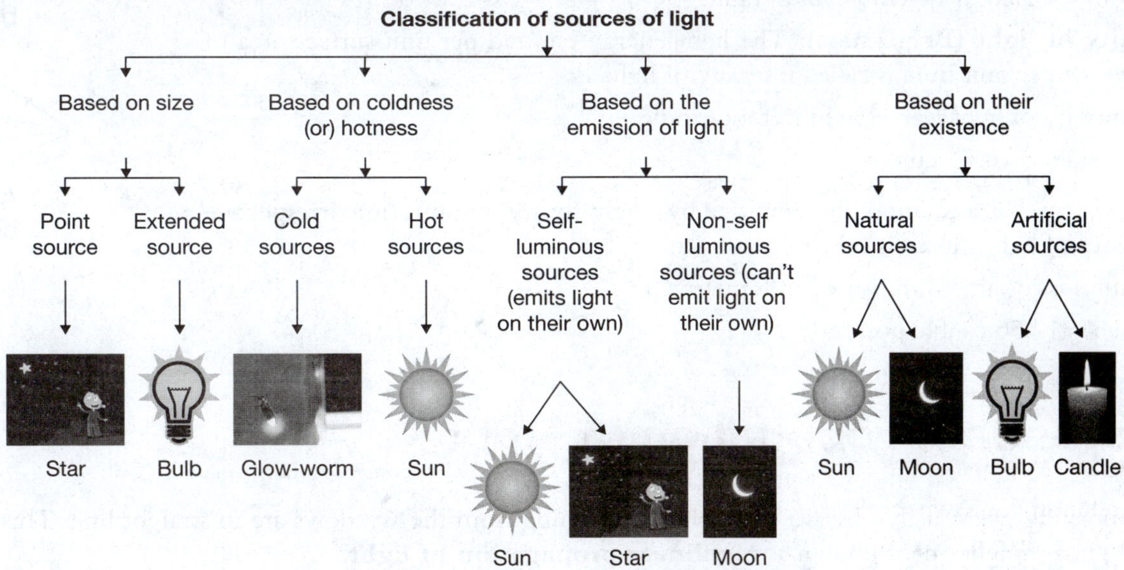

Figure 5.2 Classification of sources of light

Types of Optical Media

Light travels from its source through the media that come on its way. Following is a flowchart describing the classification of optical media.

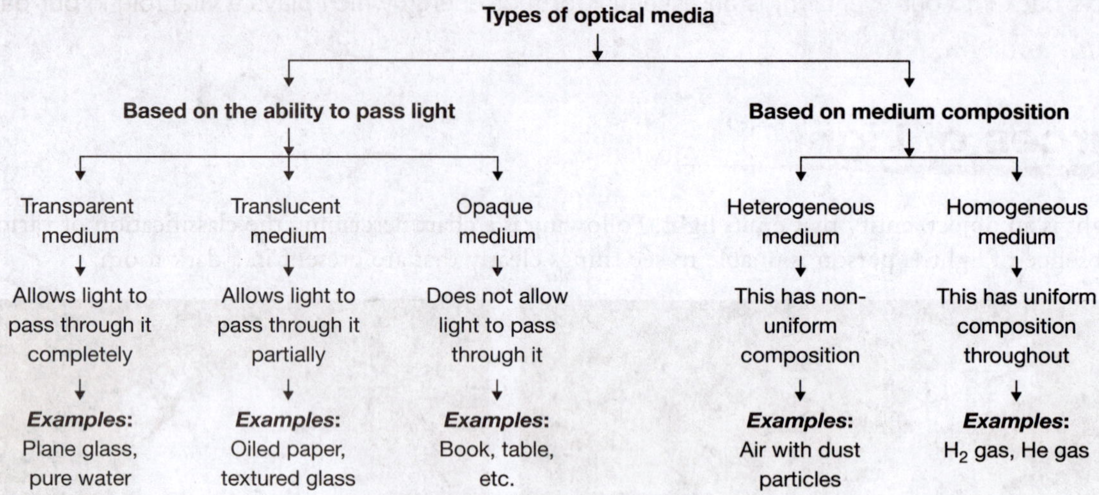

Figure 5.3 Types of optical media

General Terms Used in Light

Let us understand some basic terms related to light in the following points.

1. **Ray of light:** The path along which the light energy travels is called ray of light.
2. **Beam of light:** A collection of a large number of light rays is called beam of light.
3. **Convergent beam of light:** A collection of light rays from different directions that meet at a point is called convergent beam of light.
4. **Divergent beam of light:** A collection of light rays from a point to different directions is called divergent beam of light.
5. **Intensity of light (Brightness):** The light energy emitted per unit surface area of light source per unit time is called intensity of light.

   The intensity of light is measured in foot candle.

   1 foot candle = 10.76 Lux.
6. **Luminosity:** The amount of light emitted by a light source per unit time irrespective of the area of light source is called luminosity.

   The luminosity value is measured in lumens.

   1 Lumen = 12.56 candle power.

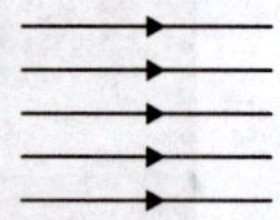

Figure 5.4 Beam of light

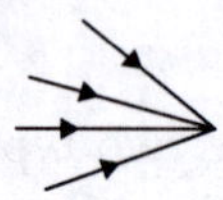

Figure 5.5 A convergent beam of light

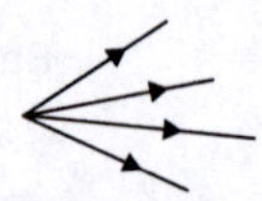

Figure 5.6 A divergent beam of light

Rectilinear Propagation of Light

In the early morning, we usually observe that light rays coming from the windows are in straight line. This property of light travelling in a straight line is known as **rectilinear propagation of light**.

A simple activity is described below to better understand rectilinear propagation of light.

Activity

Aim: To prove that light travels in a straight line.

Apparatus: Candle, match box, three cardboards with a hole.

Principle: Opaque body obstructing the path of light.

Construction and working: Arrange the candle and cardboards in front of a wall as shown in the figure below.

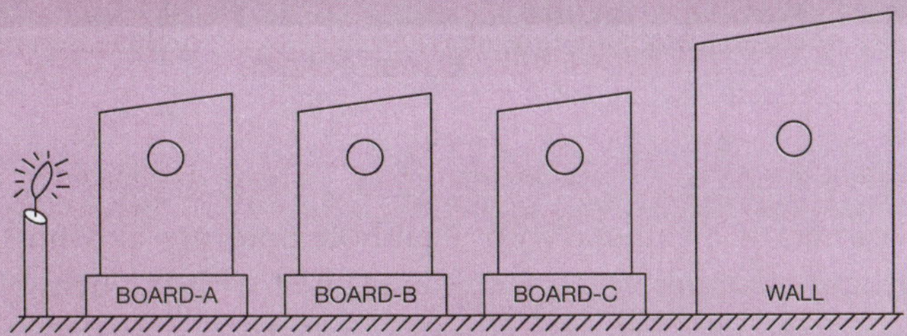

Figure 5.7 Arrangement of candles and cardboards to demonstrate rectilinear propagation of light

Light energy from candle passes through the holes of cardboards and it is incident on the wall as shown in figure.

Precautions:

1. If any of these holes in the three cardboards is not at same level of the lighted candle, then we cannot see light on the wall.
2. The candle and holes of cardboards all should lie at the same height and along a straight line.

Results: Since the light is seen on the wall, this shows that light travels in straight line.

Applications of Rectilinear Propagation of Light

Rectilinear propagation of light finds applications in working of a pinhole camera, formation of shadows, phenomena of eclipses, etc. Rectilinear propagation of light is applied in two most prominent natural phenomena like formation of shadows and eclipses. Let us understand each of them in detail below.

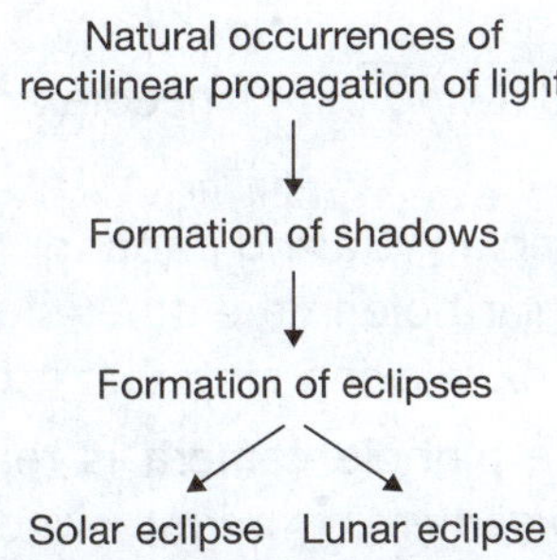

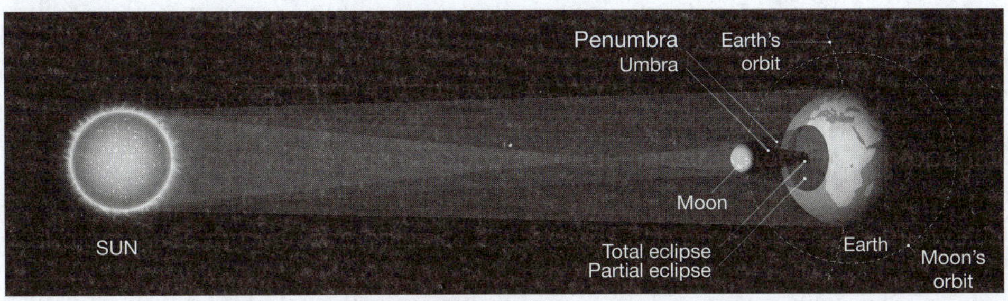

Figure 5.8 Solar eclipse

Figure 5.9 Lunar eclipse

Pinhole Camera

As the name suggests, a pinhole camera is a camera with a pinhole aperture and no lens. The property of rectilinear propagation of light is used in working of a pinhole camera is explained with the help of an activity given below.

Activity

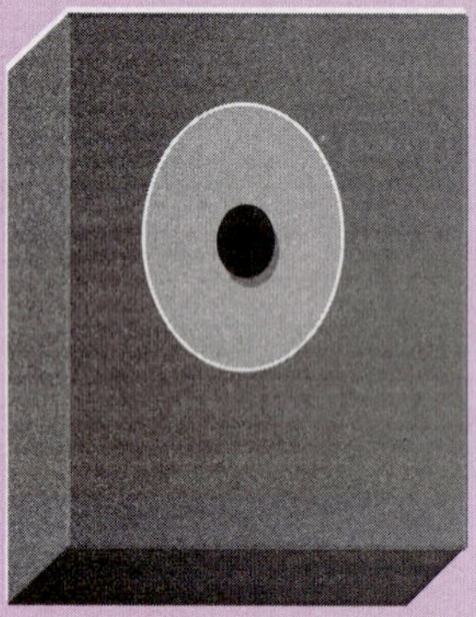

Figure 5.10 A pinhole camera

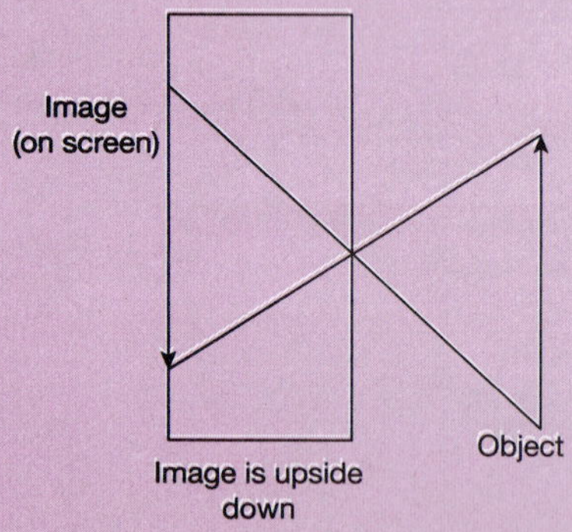

Figure 5.11 Image formation through a pinhole camera

Aim: To construct a simple pinhole camera.

Apparatus: A shoe box, black chart paper/aluminium foil, cello tape, scissors, a square piece of tracing/butter paper.

Principle: The working of a pinhole camera is based on the rectilinear propagation of light.

Construction and working:

1. Make sure that no light can get into the shoe box once the lid is on so tape up any rips and joints.
2. Make two holes in opposite sides of the shoe box so that you can see through them.
3. Cut out a square of sugar paper or tin foil. Make sure that it is bigger than the circular hole and then tape it to the inside of the box so that the hole is covered.
4. Take a drawing pin or needle and carefully make a hole in the centre of the foil.
5. Cut a piece of tracing paper or grease-proof paper which is bigger than the rectangular hole in the other side of your box. Tape the paper to the inside of the box, making sure that it covers the hole. This will act like the screen.
6. Now, the pinhole camera is ready to use. Point the tinfoil end of camera towards something bright (window) and take a look at the screen.
7. The image visible on the screen will be upside down.

Precautions:

1. Paint the inner side of box with black colour.
2. Use high-quality tracing paper for best screen.
3. Although bigger the pinhole, brighter will be the image formed, do not make hole huge in size as too big hole gives blurred image.

Shadow

Dark region is formed on the screen when an opaque object is placed in the path of light, it is called shadow. The darker region of shadow at its centre is called umbra region. The partially dark region of a shadow around the umbra is called penumbra region. Following are the basic requirements to form a shadow.

1. Source of light.
2. Opaque body to obstruct light.
3. Opaque screen to receive the shadow.
   - The darker region of shadow at its centre is called umbra region.
   - The partially dark region of a shadow around the umbra is called penumbra region.
   - For the fixed positions of source of light, for instance take the object and screen, if the source used is an extended source, then the penumbra will be greater than the umbra region as shown in Figure 5.12(a). If the source is a point source, then the umbra region of shadow is greater than the penumbra region as shown in Figure 5.12(b).

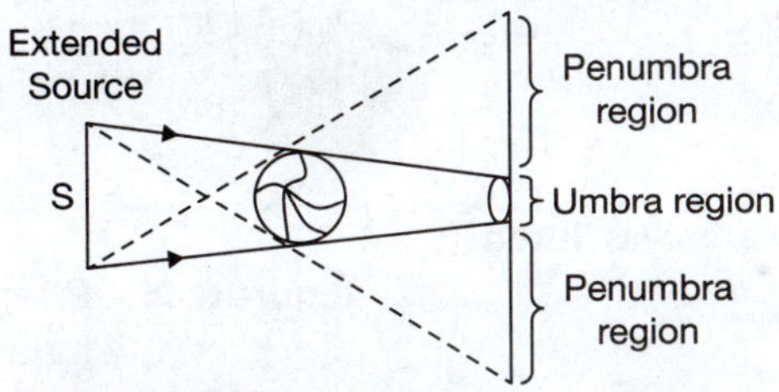

Figure 5.12(a) Formation of shadow by an extended source

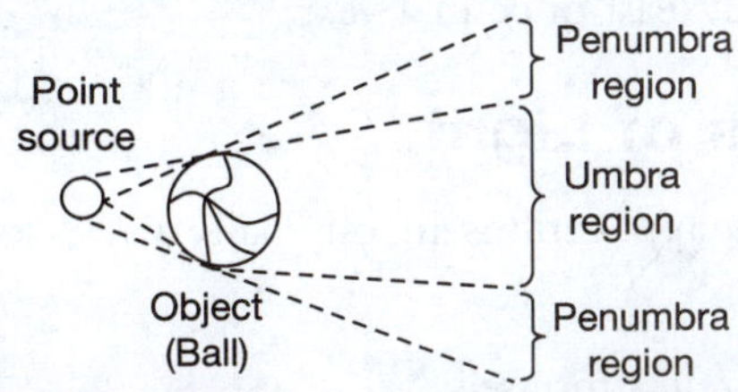

Figure 5.12(b) Formation of shadow by a point source

Some of the examples are given below:

- Birds flying high in the sky do not cast their shadow on the surface of earth.

  From the figure, it is clear that the dark region of shadow is not reaching the earth, therefore the shadow of the bird is not seen on the surface of earth.
- Eclipse is a shadow of a celestial body on the other body.

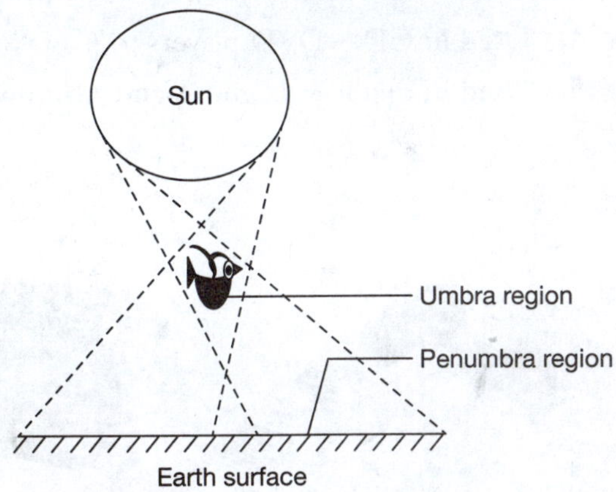

Figure 5.13 Shadow formed by a bird flying high in the sky

Solar Eclipse

- While moon revolves around the earth, a situation arises where the moon comes in between the sun and the earth, it is evident that a shadow of moon is formed on a part of earth, it is known as solar eclipse.

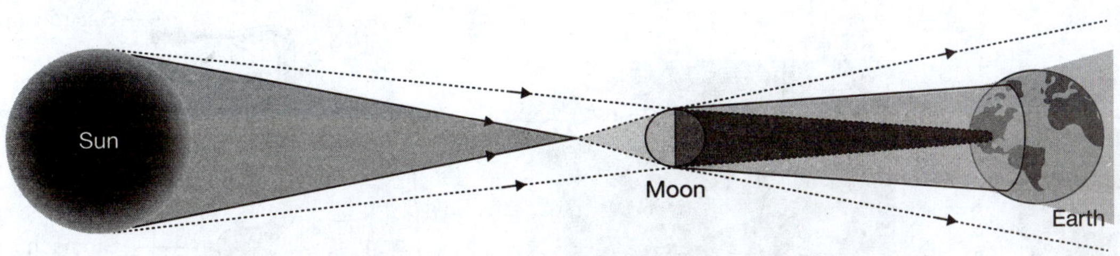

Figure 5.14 Phenomenon of solar eclipse

- This occurs on a day when the moon is not seen, i.e., on full moon day.
- The umbra region of this shadow of moon formed on earth is known as total solar eclipse.

- The penumbra region of this shadow is called partial lunar eclipse.
- People living under the umbra region of shadow could see only the outer rim of the sun due to the presence of moon in between the sun and the earth. This rim of sun is called corona.
- The total solar eclipse lasts for five to ten minutes.

Info Bytes!

During solar eclipse, the earth receives very large amounts of ultraviolet (UV) rays. These rays can even burn the retina of the eye.

Lunar Eclipse

- Lunar eclipse is caused on a full moon light.
- While the sun, the moon and the earth revolve, there arises a situation where all these three come in a straight line with earth at the centre. In this eclipse, the shadow of earth falls on the moon and the moon completely disappears.
- This occurs and lasts for one to two hours.
- This occurs at least once in a year.

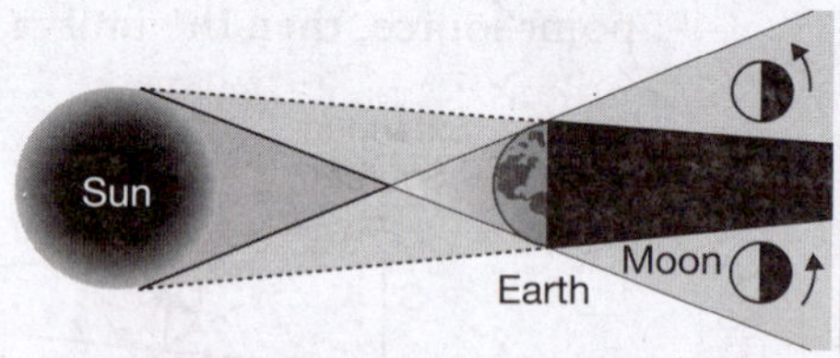

Figure 5.15 Phenomenon of lunar eclipse

Applications of Light

Light finds various applications in our daily lives, some of them are as listed below.

1. Used in a wireless mouse.
2. Used in a barcode reader in a store to find the code and price of product.
3. Used as energy for systems which work on solar energy.
4. Used in CD – DVD players to play your favourite movie, etc.
5. Used in medical diagnosis and treatments, etc.

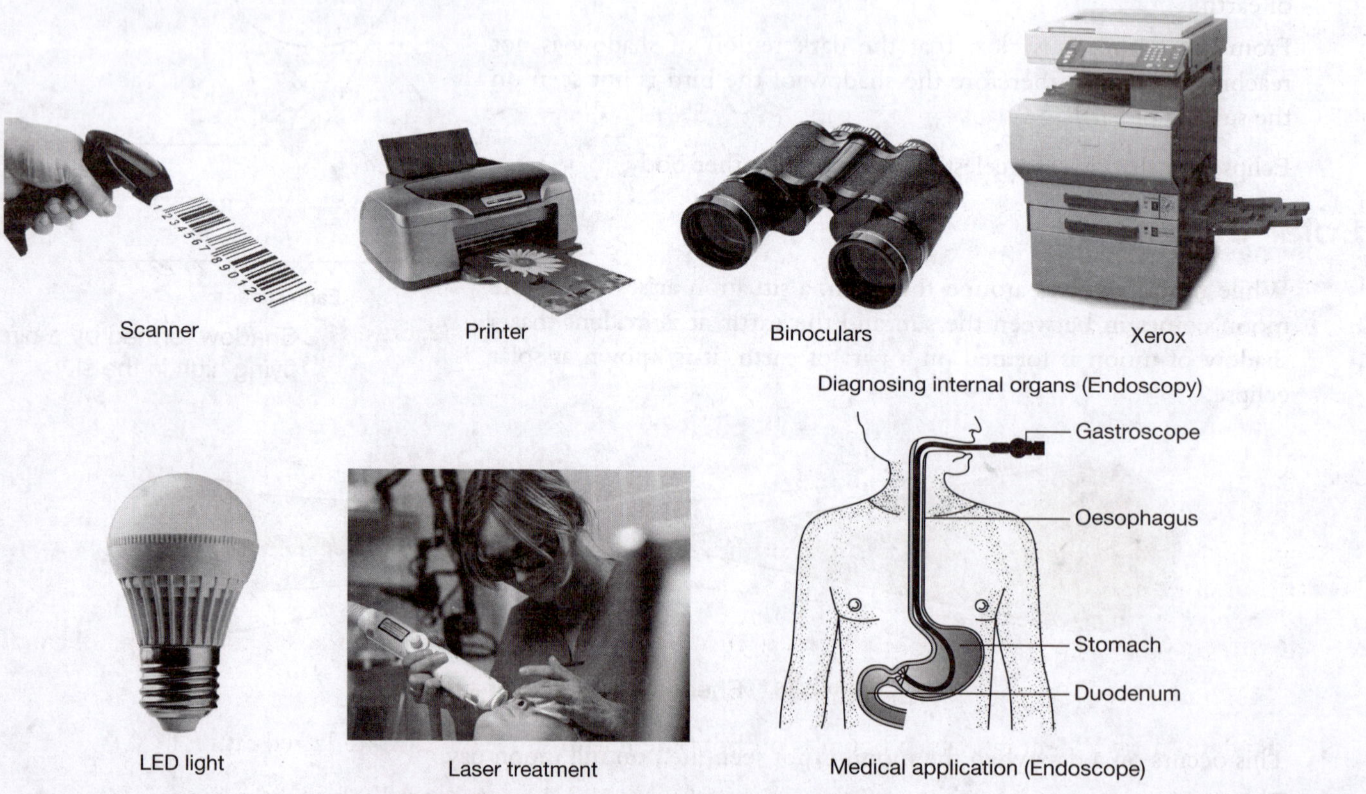

Figure 5.16 Applications of light in technology

EXAMPLE 5.1 Give any two examples for the following terms.

(a) Homogeneous elastic material

(b) Heterogeneous magnetic material

(c) Homogeneous non-magnetic material

(d) Heterogeneous non-elastic material

SOLUTION

(a) Homogeneous elastic material.
Examples: Rubber band, latex.

(b) Heterogeneous magnetic material.
Examples: Magnetite rock, certain ferrite mixtures.

(c) Homogeneous non-magnetic material.
Examples: Copper, aluminum.

(d) Heterogeneous non-elastic material.
Examples: Concrete, composite plastic.

EXAMPLE 5.2 How many Lumens make 37.68 candle power?

SOLUTION

1 Lumen = 12.56 candle power

Number of candle powers

$$n = \frac{37.68}{12.56} = 3.$$

EXAMPLE 5.3 Distinguish between homogeneous and heterogeneous media.

SOLUTION

Homogeneous medium	Heterogeneous medium
An optical medium which has a uniform composition throughout is called homogeneous medium.	An optical medium which has different compositions at different points is called heterogeneous medium.
Examples: Pure water, glass	***Examples:*** Air, impure water

Reflection of Light

The phenomenon of bouncing back of light from a smooth polished surface when light is incident on it is called **reflection of light**. Here are some of the terms used in this reference.

1. **Mirror:** Smooth polished surface which can turn back the light rays into the same medium is called mirror.
2. **Incident ray:** Light ray which is incident on a mirror is known as incident ray.
3. **Reflected ray:** Light ray which bounces off from the mirror surface is called reflected ray.

4. **Point of incidence:** The point on the mirror surface where the incident ray strikes the surface is called point of incidence.
5. **Normal:** The perpendicular line drawn at the point of incidence to the surface of mirror is called normal.
6. **Angle of incidence:** The angle between incident ray and the normal at the point of incidence is called angle of incidence.
7. **Angle of reflection:** The angle between the reflected ray and the normal is called angle of reflection.

In the below figure, *i* is the angle of incidence and *r* is the angle of reflection, *AB* is the incident ray, *BC* is the reflected ray and NN^1 is normal to the reflecting surface.

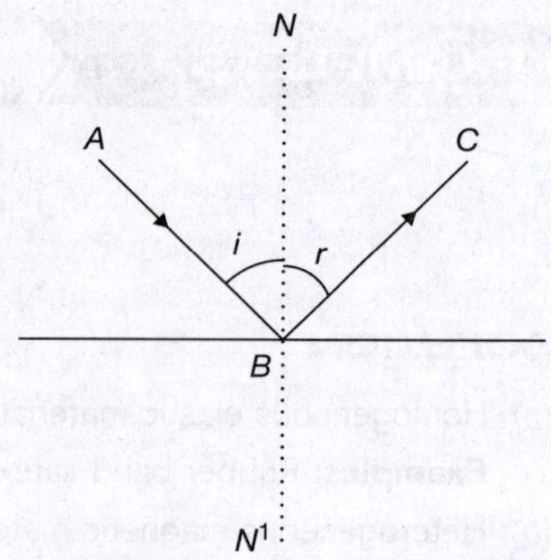

Figure 5.17 Reflection of light by a plane mirror

Types of Reflection

Depending upon the surface on which light is incident, reflection can be of different types.

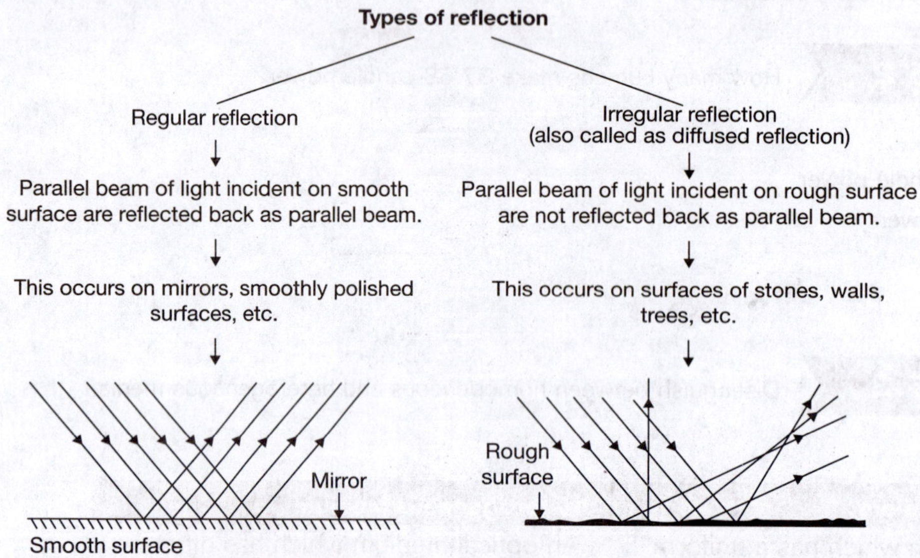

Figure 5.18 Regular and irregular reflections

Laws of Reflection

There are two laws of reflection as stated below:

1. **First law:** The incident ray, reflected ray and the normal lie in the same plane, at the point of incidence. Refer to Fig. 5.19

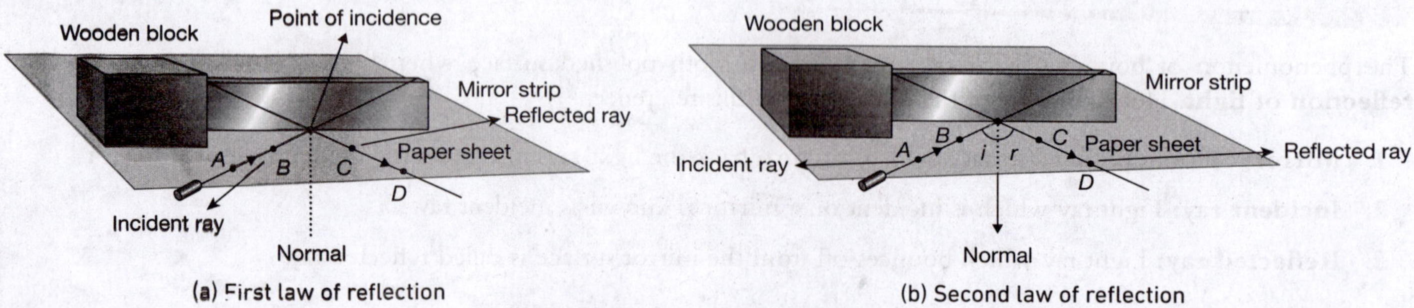

Figure 5.19 Laws of Reflection

2. **Second law:** The angle of incidence is equal to angle of reflection. Let us understand these laws better with the help of figures given below. Refer to Fig. 5.20

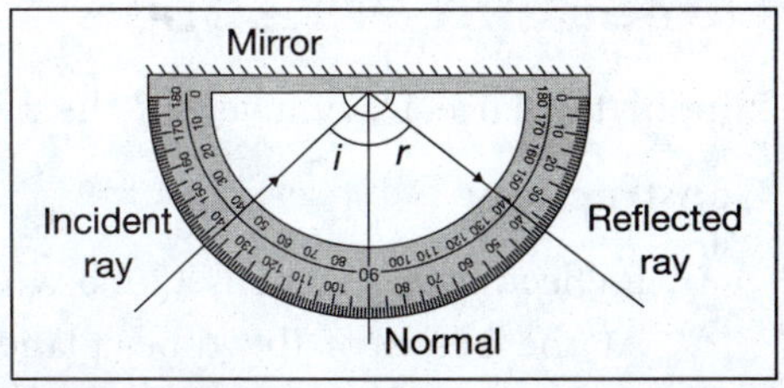

Figure 5.20 Activity to demonstrate second law of reflection

In Figure 5.19(b), mark points A and B on the paper along the incident laser light from the source.

Similarly, mark points C and D on the paper along the reflected light. Draw two straight lines, one through points A and B, the other through points C and D as shown in the figure given below.

Place the protractor on the paper as shown in the above figure.

Angle i = angle of incidence.

Similarly, angle r = angle of reflection.

We will observe that $\angle i = \angle r$, i.e., angle of incidence and angle of reflection are equal.

If a ray falls normally on mirror then angle = 0 and angle $r = 0$. The ray retraces its path. One diagram required.

Angle of deviation = $180° - 2i$

Nature of Image Formed by a Plane Mirror

The image formed by a plane mirror has certain unique properties as given in flowchart below.

Nature of an image formed by a plane mirror

- Image formed is laterally inverted → If we see ourself in the mirror, our left side looks like right side and vice versa as shown in the below figure.
- Distance of an object from the mirror is equal to the distance of image from the mirror. → If you stand in front of a mirror, you will observe that your image and you are at the same distance from the mirror.
- Image formed is virtual and erect → The image seen in the mirror can't be formed on a screen placed in place of mirror.

Figure 5.21 Lateral inversion

Figure 5.22 Image formed by a plane mirror

Uses of Plane Mirror

Plane mirrors are used in a variety of ways as given below:

Uses of plane mirrors

- Used as looking glasses
- Used in reflecting periscope
- Used in solar cookers
- Used in saloons
- Used in kaleidoscope
- Used by architects to show false dimensions

Reflecting Periscope

Hippolyte Marie-Davy invented the periscope.

Construction:

1. Reflecting periscope is a tube which is bent twice at right angles.
2. At the bends of the tube, plane mirrors are arranged such that they make an angle of 45° with the frame of tube as shown in the figure.

Working:

1. Light rays from an object at a higher level enter the tube and it undergoes reflection twice at the two mirrors arranged in the periscope.
2. Finally, the image of an object is seen at the lower end of the periscope.

Use: A person hidden behind a wall could be able to see the other side of the wall using the reflecting periscope.

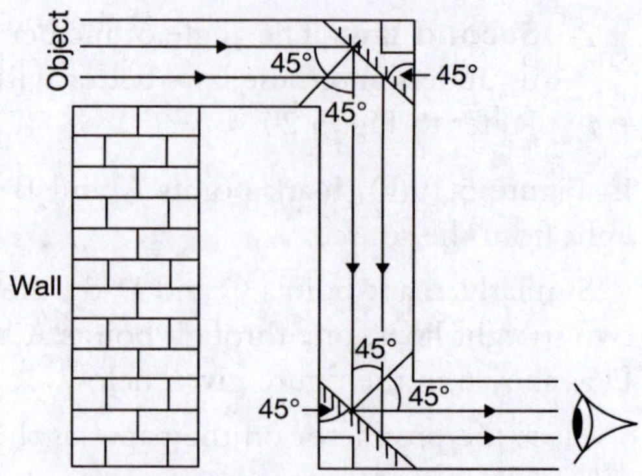

Figure 5.23 Reflecting periscope

Info Bytes!

Light travels in air with a speed $3 \times 10^8\ ms^{-1}$ and sun light reaches the earth's surface in 8 minutes.

Mirrors Placed at An Angle

How many images are observed by two plane mirrors placed at an angle? Imagine yourself positioned between two mirrors placed parallel to each other. How many images are observed?

The number of images observed by two plane mirrors depend on the angle between them. If two plane mirrors are placed at an angle θ, then the number of images observed (n) is/are given by,

$$n = \frac{360°}{\theta}; \quad \text{if } \frac{360°}{\theta} \text{ is odd}$$

$$n = \frac{360°}{\theta} - 1; \quad \text{if } \frac{360°}{\theta} \text{ is even}$$

It is to be noted that the number of images observed by two plane mirrors placed at an angle is always 'odd'.

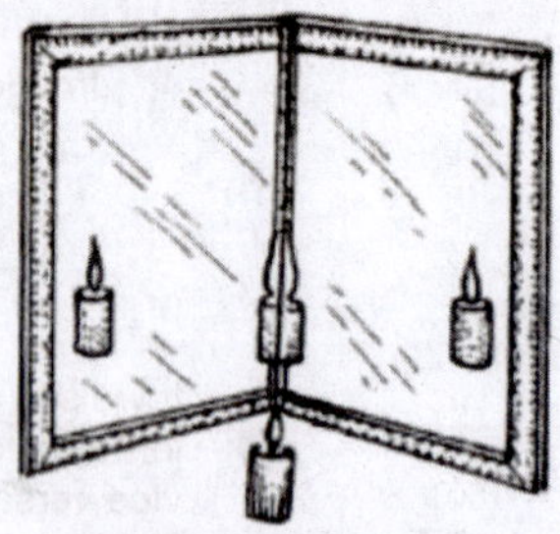

Figure 5.24 Mirrors placed at an angle

EXAMPLE 5.4

When two mirrors are inclined at an angle of 60° with each other, find the glancing angles and angle of deviations at both the mirrors if the angle of incidence of a light ray is 45°. Draw its ray diagram.

SOLUTION

$i_1 = r_1 = 45°$

$i_2 = r_2 = 15°$

Glancing angle at $M_1 = 90° - i_1 = 90° - 45°$

$= 45°$

Glancing angle at $M_2 = 90° - i_2 = 90° - 15°$

$= 75°$

Angle of deviation at $M_1 = 180° - 2i_1 = 90°$

Angle of deviation at $M_2 = 180° - 2i_2 = 150°$.

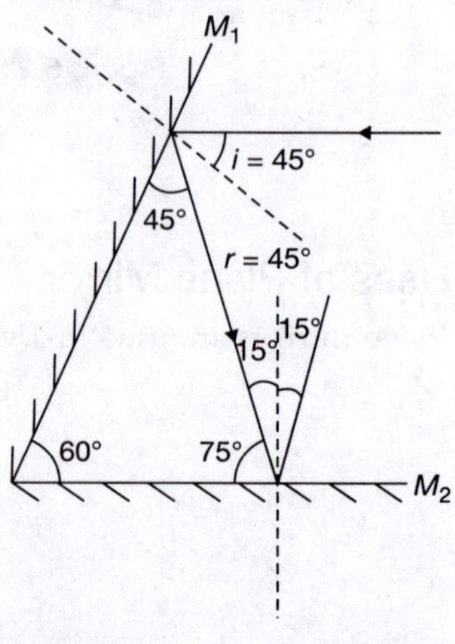

EXAMPLE 5.5

If the angle made by a light ray with the plane of a plane mirror is 22.5°, then find the angle of reflection.

SOLUTION

$i = 90° - 22.5° = 67.5°$ then $\angle r = 67.5°$ (as we know, $\angle i = \angle r$)

EXAMPLE 5.6

Vinay wrote the word 'REFLECTION' on a paper and placed it in front of a plane mirror (as shown in figure) and noticed how the letters of the word appear in the mirror. Write down the mirror image of it.

SOLUTION

As the image formed by a plane mirror is laterally inverted, the image of letters REFLECTION appears as shown in the figure.

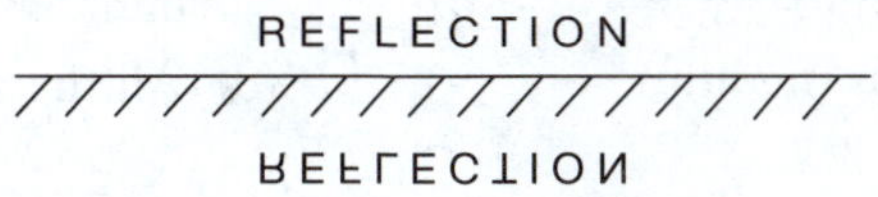

EXAMPLE 5.7

Find the value of x in the adjoining figure.

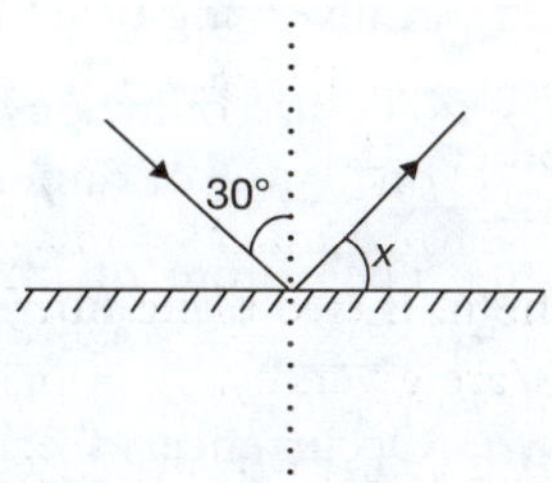

SOLUTION

$i = r = 30°$

$x = 90° - 30° = 60°$.

POINTS TO REMEMBER

- ✔ A source of light is an object/entity that emits light. Following is a chart describing the classification of various sources of light.
- ✔ The phenomenon of bouncing back of light from a smooth polished surface when light is incident on it is called reflection of light.
- ✔ Dark region is formed on the screen when an opaque object is placed in the path of light, it is called shadow.
- ✔ Rectilinear propagation of light finds applications in working of a pinhole camera, formation of shadows, phenomena of eclipses, etc.
- ✔ The phenomenon of bouncing back of light from a smooth polished surface when light is incident on it is called reflection of light.

PRACTICE QUESTIONS CLASSROOM WING

Very Short Answer Type Questions

Direction for questions from 1 to 10.
Fill in the blanks.

1. ____ is a homogeneous medium.
2. 1 foot candle = _____ Lux.
3. ______ is a transparent heterogeneous medium
4. ______ is a transparent homogeneous medium.
5. _______ is a translucent material.
6. A converging beam of light forms ______ image.
7. A diverging beam of light forms ______ image.
8. The size of image obtained by pinhole camera depends on _____ of camera.
9. The nature of image obtained in pinhole camera is ______.
10. Occurrence of eclipse and formation of shadows are due to _______.

Direction for questions from 11 to 15.
Select the correct alternative from the given options.

11. Choose the biggest source of light from the following.
    (a) Star (b) Earth
    (c) Moon (d) Glow-worm
12. Pick out the object that obstructs light.
    (a) Ground glass (b) Glass
    (c) Water (d) Cloud
13. Find the odd one out from the following.
    (a) Air (b) Oiled paper
    (c) Glass (d) Water
14. Choose the incorrect one from the following in case of a pinhole camera.
    (a) It works on the principle of rectilinear propagation of light.
    (b) If the size of hole is decreased, then the image formed is more clear.
    (c) If the size of hole is increased, then the image becomes blurred due to super-position of light.
    (d) Pinhole camera is also known as camera obscure (dark chamber).
15. Choose the correct one from the following.
    (a) Lunar eclipse occurs on full moon day.
    (b) Solar eclipse occurs on new moon day.
    (c) Umbra and penumbra are casted by an opaque object under the exposure of extended source of light.
    (d) All the above

Direction for questions from 16 to 30.
Fill in the blanks.

16. Laws of reflection are applicable for _______.
17. Angle of deviation means ____.
18. Angle of incidence means ____.
19. Angle of reflection means _____.
20. Glancing angle of incidence means ______.
21. Glancing angle and angle of incidence are ____ angles.
22. A plane mirror forms ______ image.
23. When two plane mirrors are parallel to each other, the number of images of an object we can see is _____.
24. During reflection of light ______, ____ and _____ remains constant but ____ changes.
25. The formula for angle of deviation in case of plane mirror, d = _____.
26. When two plane mirrors are at the angle 'θ' with each other, the number of images formed are (formula) ____ for odd number of image; _____ for even number of images.
27. When two plane mirrors are at right angle with each other, the number of images viewed is _____.
28. _______ invented the periscope.
29. Reflecting periscopes can be constructed by ____ mirrors.
30. _______ phenomenon is used in a reflecting periscope.

Short Answer Type Questions

31. What is an optical medium? Explain the types in it with two examples based on the amount of light they allow through them.

32. Write the construction of the pinhole camera.

33. Explain the types of eclipse.

34. **Assertion:** Point sources form only umbra.
Reason: Umbra is formed due to the rectilinear propagation of light.
(a) A and R are true and R is the correct explanation of A.
(b) A and R are true but R is not the correct explanation of A.
(c) A is false and R is true.
(d) Both A and R are false.

35. Match the entries of Column with those of Column B

Column A		Column B	
(A)	Mercury	(a)	Optical properties same throughout
(B)	Firefly	(b)	Optically opaque
(C)	Parallel beam	(c)	The angle between light rays is zero
(D)	Homogeneous	(d)	Source of light

36. Distinguish between shadow and image.

37. What are the factors on which the image obtained by the pinhole camera depend?

38. Explain how an opaque paper can be made translucent.

39. What is a shadow and why the house fly does not cast a shadow on the ground while flying?

40. Write the different case of a point and an extended source of light to cast only umbra for an opaque object.

41. State the laws of reflection.

42. What are the characteristics of an image formed by a plane mirror?

43. Distinguish between real and virtual image with an example.

44. If the sum of the angle of incidence and angle of reflection is 90°, then find the values of angle of incidence and angle of reflection.

45. Match the following.

Column A		Column B	
(A)	A plane mirror	(a)	Number of images formed = 3
(B)	Principle used in a periscope	(b)	Reflection of light
(C)	During reflection	(c)	Shows lateral inversion
(D)	If $\theta = 90°$ between two plane mirrors, then	(d)	Intensity changes

46. Why is the plane mirror inclined at 45° in a periscope?

47. **Assertion:** A plane mirror can form a real and inverted image.
Reason: A virtual image is always formed behind the plane mirror.
(a) A and R are true and R is the correct explanation of A.
(b) A and R are true and R is not the correct explanation of A.
(c) A is false and R is true.
(d) A is true and R is false.

48. Draw the diagrams of
(a) Ray of light
(b) Convergent beam of light
(c) Divergent beam of light
(d) Parallel beam of light

49. A light ray is incident on a plane mirror making an angle of 90° with the mirror's surface. The angle of reflection of the light is ________.
(a) 60° (b) 0° (c) 90° (d) 30°

50. Ashok and Ravi stood before a plane mirror at a distance of 3 m from it. Ashok walked 5 steps towards the mirror, each step measuring 30 cm. Ravi walked 8 steps away from the mirror, each step measuring 25 cm. The distance between Ravi and the image of Ashok in the mirror is ________ m.
(a) 5.5 m (b) 4.5 m
(c) 7.5 m (d) 6.5 m

Essay Type Questions

51. (a) Mention in brief the applications and natural occurrences of rectilinear propagation of light.
(b) Draw the ray diagram of a plane mirror that shows the image formation by an extended real object.

PRACTICE QUESTIONS COMPETITION WING

Level 1: Apply Your Concepts

Direction for questions from 1 to 5.
Fill in the blanks.

1. ________ is a self-luminous body.
2. ________ is an example for a cold source of light.
3. _____ gives light from its bio-chemical energy.
4. Optical medium means _______.
5. An optically opaque body casts a _______.

Direction for questions from 6 to 11.
Select the correct alternative from the given options.

6. If angle of incidence of a light ray on a plane mirror is 30°, then
   (a) The angle of reflection is 30°
   (b) The glancing angle of incidence is 60°
   (c) The angle of deviation is 120°
   (d) All of these
7. Choose the incorrect one from the following.
   (a) Periscope forms a real image for a real object.
   (b) Periscopes form a virtual image for a real object.
   (c) Object distance equals to image distance for a plane mirror.
   (d) Both (b) and (c)
8. The number of images formed when two plane mirrors are at 60° with each other is ____.
   (a) 6 (b) 36 (c) 5 (d) 4
9. If the object is placed at a distance of 10 cm from a plane mirror, then the image distance is ____.
   (a) 20 cm (b) 5 cm
   (c) 10 mm (d) 10 cm
10. Two plane mirrors *A* and *B* are kept at an angle of 60° as shown in the figure. A ray of light travelling parallel to plane mirror *B* incident on plane mirror *A*. Find the angle with which a light ray gets reflected from the plane mirror *B*.

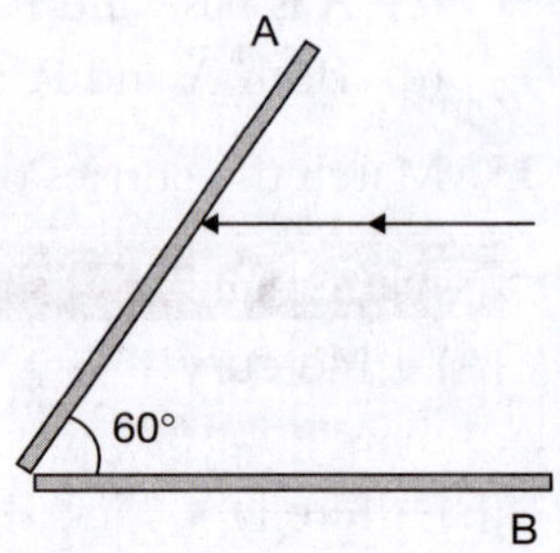

   (a) 120° (b) 15°
   (c) 60° (d) 30°
11. In a reflecting periscope, if a light ray is incident at 45° angle at the first plane mirror, then the angle of deviation of light ray by the periscope is ___.
   (a) 30° (b) 90°
   (c) 180° (d) zero

Level 2: Review Your Concepts

12. Two plane mirrors are arranged perpendicular to each other. If a light ray is incident at 30° on one of the plane mirrors of above arrangement, then find
   (a) Angle of reflection at the second plane mirror.
   (b) Angle of deviation at both the mirrors.
   (c) Number of images that we can observe when one plane mirror is rotated by 30° towards the other.
13. Two plane mirrors *A* and *B* are kept parallel to each other as shown in the figure. A light ray is incident on mirror *A* which makes an angle 30° with its plane. Find the angle of incidence and angle of refraction of the light ray on mirror *B*.

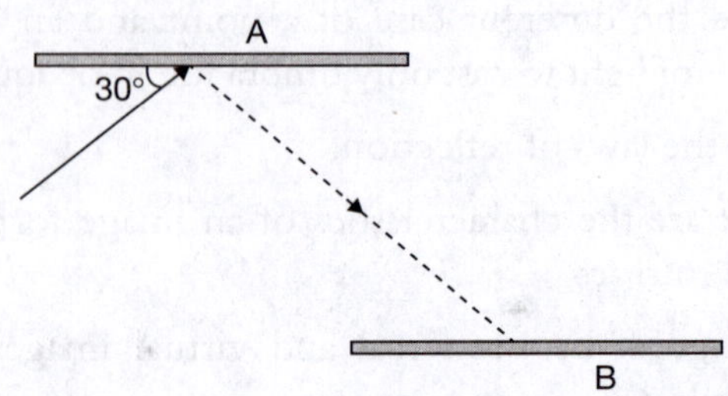

14. Gopi and Bhasker arranged a pair of plane mirrors at an angle of 120° and 30°, respectively. Who will observe more number of images, when an object is viewed through the mirrors at symmetric position?

15. Two plane mirrors are placed parallel to each other, and an object '*O*' is placed exactly midway between the two mirrors as shown in figure. Find the distance between the first images formed in the two mirrors.

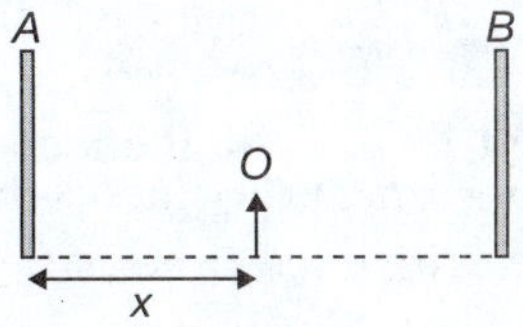

16. Fill in the blanks of the following table.

Angle between two plane mirrors	Number of images observed
30°	________
________	7
60°	________
________	9

17. A light ray is incident on a smooth reflecting surface making an angle of incidence $2i$. If the angle of incidence is doubled, then the deviation of the light ray is equal to ________.

Level 3: Assess Your Concepts

18. Two plane mirrors M and M' are arranged such that their reflecting surfaces face towards a common object placed between them and making an angle of 72° with each other. The number of images of the object placed between the reflecting surfaces of the mirrors is ________.

19. A tall person 'A' and a short person 'B' stood before a plane mirror. 'A' stands 1.25 metres behind 'B'. If the distance between 'B' and the plane mirror is 50 cm, then the distance between 'A' and his image in the mirror is ________.

20. Two friends 'P' and 'Q' stood before a plane mirror at a distance of 5 m from it. 'P' walked 3 steps towards the 15 cm. 'Q' walked 5 steps towards the mirror, reach step measure 20 cm. Calculate the distance between 'P' and the image of 'Q' in the mirror.

21. Calculate how many lumens make 62.8 candle power.

22. Two plane mirror are placed in such a way that their reflecting surface face towards a common object placed between them and make an angle of 120° with each other. Calculate the number of images of object placed between of images of object placed between the reflecting surface of the mirrors.

AT

ANSWER KEYS

Crossword

Across

2. Mirror 3. Incident 5. Shadow 7. Reflected 8. Reflection
10. Normal

Down

1. Source 3. Incidence 4. Periscope 6. Rectilinear 9. Angle

Classroom Wing

Very Short Answer Type Questions

1. Pure water 2. 10.76 3. Air 4. Glass
5. Ground glass (or) tracing paper. 6. A real 7. A virtual 8. Size of the hole
9. Neither a perfect image nor a perfect shadow. 10. Rectilinear propagation of light.
14. (b) 15. (d) 16. All kinds of reflecting surfaces.
17. Angle made by the reflected ray with its original path of light ray.
18. Angle made by the incident ray with the normal.
19. Angle made by the reflected ray with the normal.
20. Angle made by the incident ray with the surface of a reflector. 21. Complementary
22. A virtual 23. Infinity 24. Wavelength, velocity, frequency, intensity (or) brightness.
25. $180° - 2i$ 26. $\left(\frac{360°}{\theta}\right); \left(\frac{360°}{\theta} - 1\right)$ 27. Three
28. Hippolyte Marie – Davy 29. Plane 30. Reflection of light

Short Answer Type Questions

34. (a) 35. (A) → (b), (B) → (d), (C) → (c), (D) → (a)
44. 45° 45. (A) → (c), (b), (B) → (b), (C) → (d), (D) → (a)
47. (c) 49. (b) 50. (d)

Competition Wing

Level 1: Apply Your Concepts

1. Sun (or) Star (or) Glow-worm 2. Glow-worm 3. Glow-worm (or) fire fly
4. A material through which an electromagnetic wave propagates. 5. Dark shadow
6. (d) 7. (a) 8. (c) 9. (d) 10. (d)
11. (d)

Level 2: Review Your Concepts

12. (a) 60° (b) 120°, 60° (c) 5 13. $i = 60°; r = 60°$ 15. $4x$ 16. 11,51.4°, 5, 40°
17. $180 - 8i$

Level 3: Assess Your Concepts

18. 5 19. 3.5 m 20. 8.5 m 21. 5 22. 3

Hints and Explanations

CLASSROOM WING

Very Short Answer Type Questions

1. Pure water is a homogeneous medium.
2. 1 foot candle = 10.76 Lux.
3. Air is a transparent heterogeneous medium.
4. Glass is a transparent homogeneous medium.
5. Ground glass or tracing paper is a translucent material.
6. A converging beam of light forms a real image.
7. A diverging beam of light forms a virtual image.
8. The size of image obtained by pinhole camera depends on size of the hole of camera.
9. The nature of image obtained in pinhole camera is neither a perfect image nor a perfect shadow.
10. Occurrence of eclipse and formation of shadows are due to rectilinear propagation of light.
11. Star
12. Cloud
13. Oiled paper
14. If the size of hole in a pinhole camera is decreased, then the image becomes blurred.
15. (a) Lunar eclipse occurs on full moon day.
    (b) Solar eclipse occurs on new moon day.
    (c) Umbra and penumbra are casted by an opaque object under the exposure of extended source of light.
    (d) All the given statements are correct.
16. Laws of reflection are applicable for all kinds of reflecting surfaces.
17. Angle made by the reflected ray with its original path of light ray.
18. Angle made by the incident ray with the normal
19. Angle made by the reflected ray with the normal
20. Angle made by the incident ray with the surface of a reflector.
21. Glancing angle and angle of incidence are complementary angles.
22. A plane mirror forms a virtual image.
23. When two plane mirrors are parallel to each other, the number of images of an object we can see is infinity.
24. During reflection of light wavelength, velocity, frequency remains constant but intensity (or) brightness changes.
25. The formula for angle of deviation in case of plane mirror, $d = 180 - 2i$.
26. When two plane mirrors are at the angle 'θ' with each other, the number of images formed are (formula) for odd number of image; for even number of images.
27. When two plane mirrors are at right angle with each other, the number of images viewed is 3.
28. Hippolyte Marie – Davy invented the periscope.
29. Reflecting periscopes can be constructed by plane mirrors.
30. Reflection of light phenomenon is used in a reflecting periscope.

Short Answer Type Questions

31. **Optical medium:** The material through which light exhibits its different phenomena is called optical medium. There are three different kinds of optical mediums based on the passage of light. They are
    (a) Transparent medium
    (b) Translucent medium
    (c) Opaque medium
    (a) **Transparent medium:** The medium that allows light to pass through is called transparent medium.
    Examples: Air, glass, pure water.
    (b) **Translucent medium:** The medium through which light rays can pass partially is called translucent medium.
    Examples: Fog, ground glass.
    (c) **Opaque medium:** The medium through which light rays cannot pass at all is called opaque medium.
    Examples: Metal, wood.

32. Construction of a pinhole camera:

Pinhole camera: This is a device which forms a photograph-like image of a stationary bright object on a screen. This works on the rectilinear propagation of light.

A pinhole camera consists of a cubical or cylindrical empty cardboard box with a fine hole on one side and with a paper or glass on the opposite side that acts as a screen. The box is blackened from inside so that any light which falls on its walls directly or indirectly is absorbed. When a stationary bright object (AB) is placed in front of a pinhole camera, an inverted impression (A^1B^1) can be seen on the screen. To take an actual photograph, the pinhole camera is covered with a thick black cloth and the screen is replaced by a photographic film. The camera is faced towards the objects to be photographed and the black cloth is removed only from the side of the pinhole. The film gets exposed to the light coming from the object through the pin hole. The film is developed and printed in studio. The size of the image formed by a pinhole camera depends on the distance of the object in front of the pinhole and the distance of the screen or film behind the pinhole. To compare the size of the image with the size of the object, we define the term magnification.

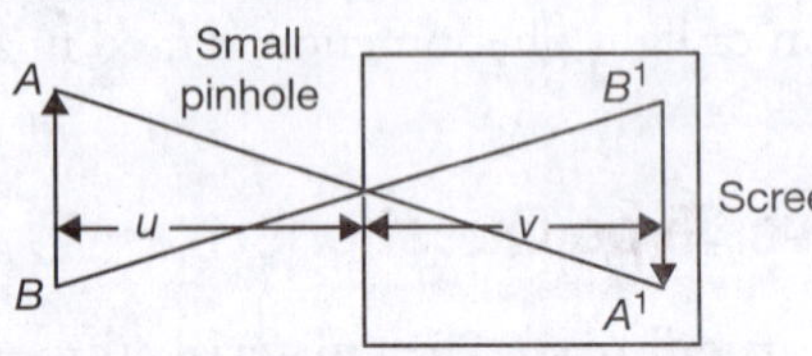

$$\text{Magnification } (m) = \frac{\text{Size of image } (i)}{\text{Size of object } (o)}$$

$$= \frac{\text{Distance of image } (v)}{\text{Distance of object } (u)}$$

$$= \frac{\text{Width of the pinhole camera}}{\text{Object distance}}$$

Note: Normally, we use 'u' to represent object distance and 'v' to represent image distance and both are measured from the optical instrument.

33. **Types of Eclipse:** There are two types of eclipses.

(a) **Solar eclipse:** When the shadow of moon falls on the earth, we cannot see the sun. is called solar eclipse. Solar eclipse occurs only on new moon days. Solar eclipse does not occur on every new moon day.

(b) **Lunar eclipse:** When the shadow of the earth falls on the moon, this is called lunar eclipse. Lunar eclipse always occurs on a full moon night but does not occur on every full moon day.

35. (A) → (b), (B) → (d), (C) → (c), (D) → (a)

36.

Shadow	Image
It is black in colour.	It has many colours.
It is formed due to rectilinear propagation of light.	It is formed due to the point of intersection of reflected (or) extended reflected rays.
The shadow consists of either umbra (or) umbra and penumbra.	Image may be real (or) virtual.

37. (i) The width of the pinhole camera.

(ii) The object distance.

38. A paper is a translucent medium of light. The pores of an opaque paper do not allow any light to get transmitted as some part of it get either absorbed or reflected. On oiling it, the pores get filled with oil, and hence, some part of light can be transmitted while remaining light gets reflected or absorbed. Hence, oiled paper behaves as a translucent object.

39. Shadow is the dark region formed behind an opaque body when it is placed in the path of light.

We cannot find a flying house fly shadow on the ground, because it is formed in the air. Unless we keep a screen there, we cannot find it.

40. (i) For a point source of light, only the umbra is cast.

(ii) For an extended source of light, only the umbra is cast on the screen when the opaque object and screen are close to each other.

41. Laws of reflection:

(i) Angle of incidence = Angle of reflection

(ii) Incident ray, reflected ray and normal at the point of incidence all lie in the same plane.

42. Characteristics of an image formed by a plane mirror:

(i) Image formed is virtual and erect in nature.

(ii) Object distance always equals to the image distance.

(iii) For a real object, the image formed is virtual and vice versa.

(iv) Image shows lateral inversion.

43.

Real image	Virtual image
The point of intersection of reflected rays forms a real image.	The point of intersection of extended reflected rays forms a virtual image.
This can be captured on the screen.	This cannot be captured on the screen.
Example: Images on cinema screen.	Example: Image of an object in a plane mirror.

44. Given, Angle of incidence (i) + Angle of reflection (r) = 90°

i.e., $i + r = 90°$

We have from first law of reflection, $i = r$

Then $2i = 90° \Rightarrow i = \frac{90}{2} = 45°$

Since $i = r$, $r = 45°$

45. (A) → (c), (b); (B) → (b); (C) → (d); (D) → (a)

46. Because it gives maximum field of view of observed object and also to change the direction of light ray by 90° during reflection.

47. A is incorrect and R is correct.

48. (a) Ray of light

(b) Convergent beam of light

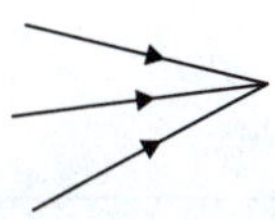

(c) Divergent beam of light

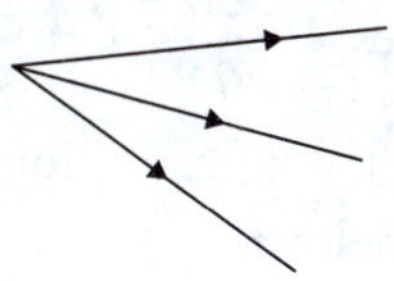

(d) Parallel beam of light

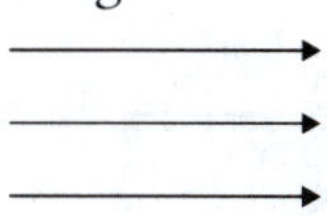

49. If the light ray makes an angle of 90° with the surface of the mirror, then

Angle of incidence = 0°

Therefore, angle of reflection = 0°

50. Initially Ashok and Ravi stand at a distance of 3 m from the mirror.

After Ashok moved 5 steps towards the mirror, then his distance from the mirror = 3 m – 5(30) cm

= 3 m –1.5 m

= 1.5 m.

After Ravi moved away from the mirror, his distance from the mirror = 3 m + 8(25) cm

= 3 m + 2 m = 5 m

Therefore, the distance between Ravi and the image of Ashok

= 1.5 m + 5 m = 6.5 m.

Essay Type Questions

51. (a) Applications of rectilinear propagation of light:

(i) Occurrence of eclipse

(ii) Working of pinhole camera

(iii) Reflecting periscope

(b)

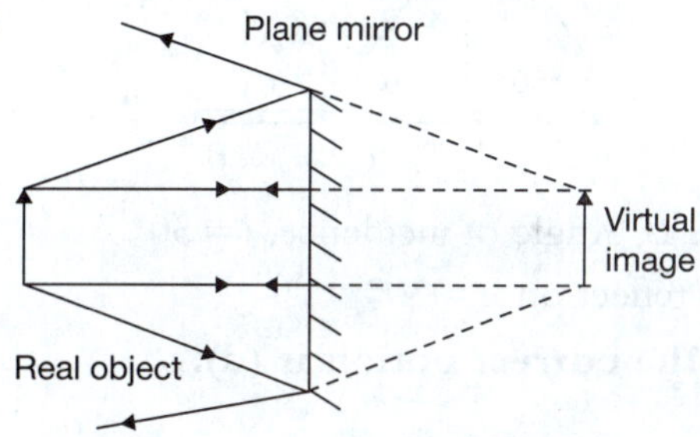

COMPETITION WING

Level 1: Apply Your Concepts

6. Angle of incidence is equal to angle of reflection according to laws of reflection. Glancing angle of incidence is equal to the difference between 90° and angle of incidence. Angle of incidence of deviation is twice the glancing angle of incidence.

7. Periscope forms virtual image of virtual object.

8. $\theta = 60°$

$$n = \frac{360}{\theta} - 1$$

$$= \frac{360}{60} - 1 = 6 - 1 = 5$$

Hence, the correct option is (c).

9. $u = v = 10$ cm

Hence, the correct option is (d).

10. We have the first law of reflection, $i = r$

From the figure below

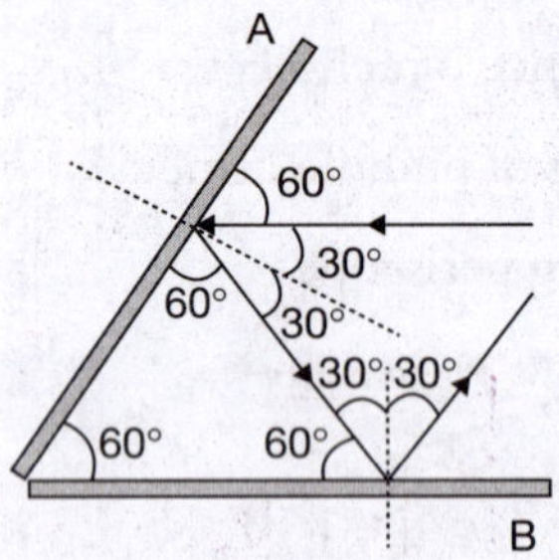

For plane B, Angle of incidence, $i = 30°$

Angle of reflection, $r = 30°$

Hence, the correct option is (d).

11. $i = 45°$

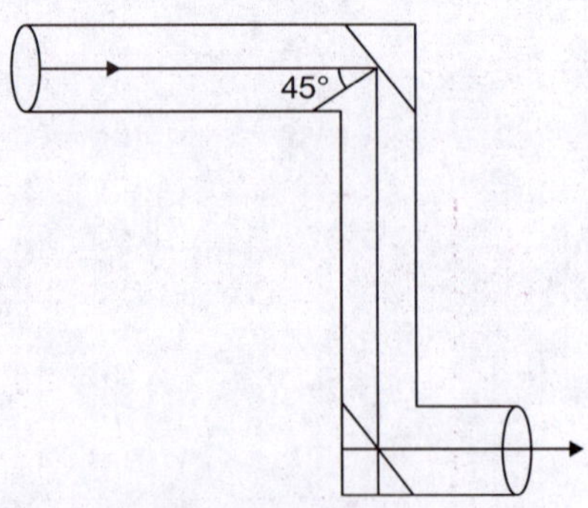

Angle of deviation = zero

Since incident ray is parallel to emergent ray.

Hence, the correct option is (d).

Level 2: Review Your Concepts

12.

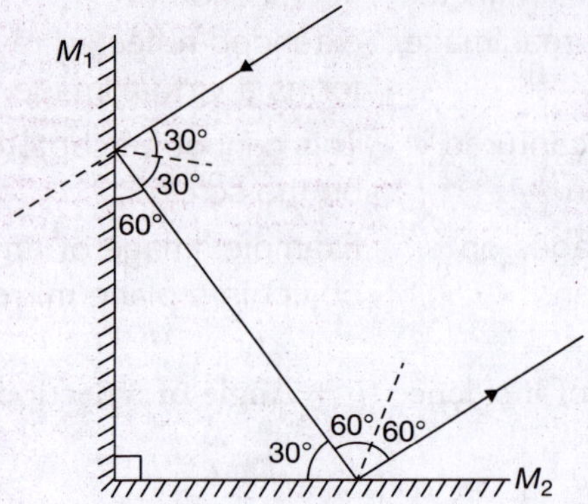

(a) Angle of reflection at the second plane mirror = 60°

(b) Angle of deviation at $M_1 = 180 - 2i$

$= 180 - 2\,(30)$

$= 120°$

Angle of deviation at $M_2 = 180 - 2i$

$= 180 - 2\,(60)$

$= 180 - 120 = 60°$

(c)

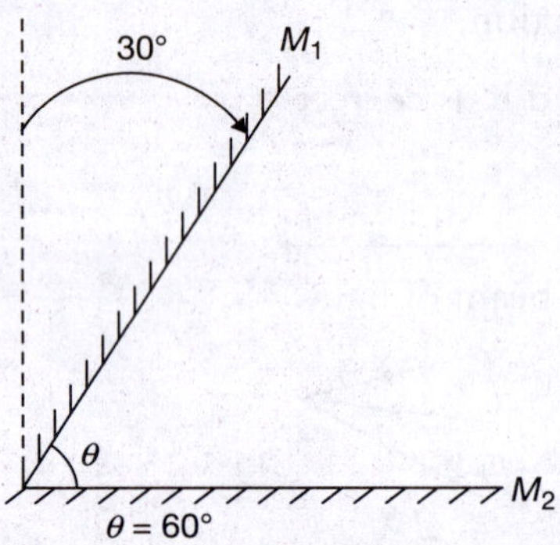

$$\text{Number of images} = \frac{360}{\theta} - 1 = \frac{360}{60} - 1 = 5$$

13. We have the first law of reflection, $i = r$

From the figure below

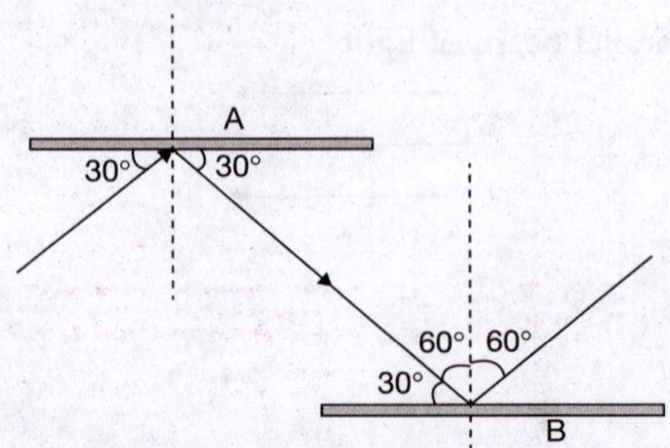

For plane B, angle of incidence, $i = 60°$

Angle of reflection, $r = 60°$

14.

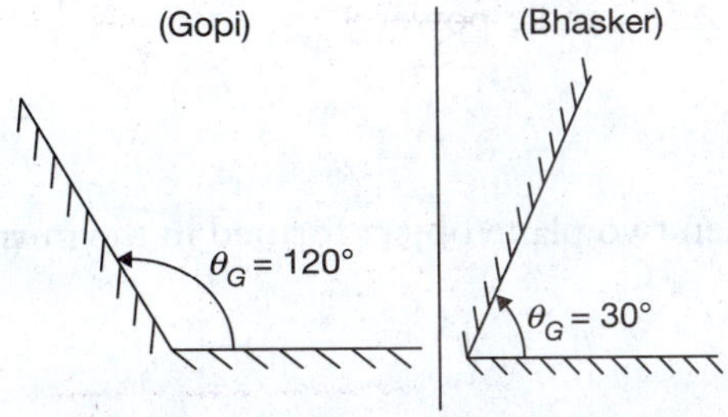

$$n_G = \frac{360}{\theta_G} = \frac{360}{120} = 3$$

$$n_B = \frac{360}{\theta_B} - 1 = \frac{360}{30} - 1 = 12 - 1 = 11$$

$\therefore n_B > n_G$ that means Bhaskar will see more number of images than Gopi.

15. We know that in case of a plane mirror,
Image distance = Object distance = x
Therefore, from the figure,

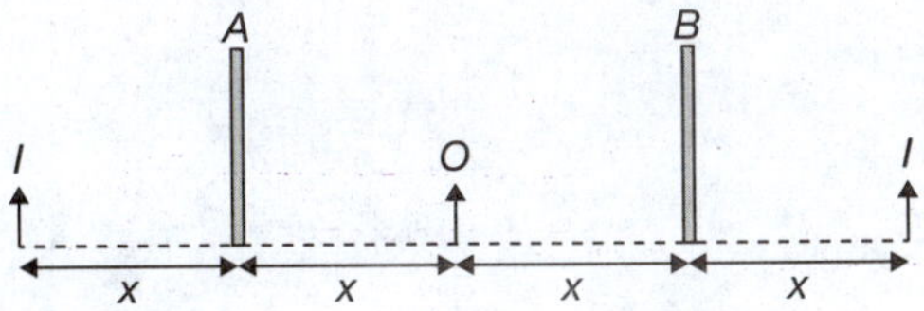

the distance between the images formed by the mirrors A and $B = x + x + x + x = 4x$

16. We have, if two plane mirrors are placed at an angle θ, then the number of images observed (n) is/are given by,

$$n = \frac{360}{\theta}; \quad \text{If } \frac{360}{\theta} \text{ is odd}$$

$$n = \frac{360}{\theta} - 1; \quad \text{If } \frac{360}{\theta} \text{ is even}$$

(i) When $\theta = 30°$, $n = \frac{360}{\theta} = \frac{360}{30} = 12$ (even number)

Then the number of images observed, $n = 12 - 1 = 11$

(ii) when the number of images observed, $n = 7$

i.e., $\frac{360}{\theta} = 7 \Rightarrow \theta = \frac{360}{7} = 51.4°$

(iii) When $\theta = 60°$, $n = \frac{360}{\theta} = \frac{360}{60} = 6$ (even number)

Then the number of images observed, $n = 6 - 1 = 5$

(iv) When the number of images observed, $n = 9$

i.e., $\frac{360}{\theta} = 9 \Rightarrow \theta = \frac{360}{9} = 40°$

Therefore

Angle between two plane mirrors	Number of images observed
30°	11
51.4°	7
60°	5
40°	9

17. Initial angle of incidence = $2i$
Angle of incidence when doubled = $2 \times 2i = 4i$
Therefore, angle of deviation = $180 - (4i + 4i)$
$= 180 - 8i$.

Level 3: Assess Your Concepts

18. Angle between two plane mirrors, $\theta = 72°$
Number of images of the object formed in the mirrors
$= 360/\theta = 360/72 = 5$

19. Distance between the plane mirror and B = 50 cm = 0.5 m

Distance between A and B = 1.25 m.

Therefore, distance between the plane mirror and A = 1.25 m + 0.5 m

= 1.75 m

Therefore, distance between A and his image in the mirror = 2 × 1.75 m

= 3.5 m.

20. Initially 'P' and 'Q' stand at a distance of 5 m from the mirror.

'P' moves 3 step towards mirror his distance from the mirror = 5 m − 3 (15) cm

= 500 m − 45 cm

= 455 cm

After 'Q' moved towards the mirror, his distance from mirror = 5 m −5(20) cm

= 500 cm − 100 cm

= 400 cm

Therefore, the distance between P and image of Q is:

= 455 cm + 400 cm

= 855 cm

= 8.5 m

21. 1 lumen = 12.56 candle power

$$n = \frac{62.5}{12.56} = 5$$

22. Angle between two plane object formed in the mirrors

$$\frac{360}{120} = 3$$

Hence, 3 image are formed.

CHAPTER

6

The Essence of Electricity

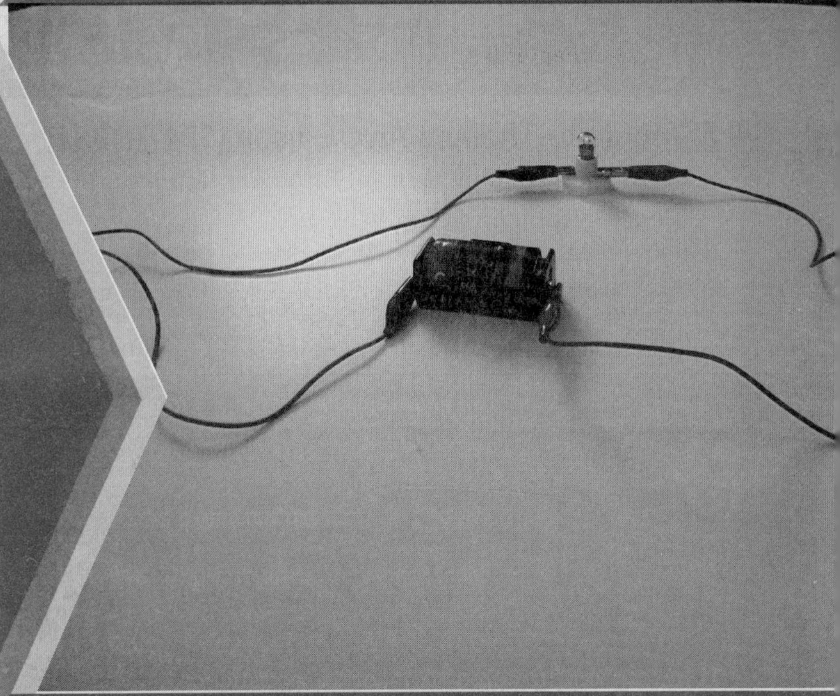

Remember

Before beginning this chapter, you should be able to:

- Know the appliances which work using electrical energy

Key Ideas

After completing this chapter, you should be able to:

- Understand different sources of electrical energy
- Describe few basic electrical components and their uses in a circuit
- Construct a simple electric circuit safely
- Understand the safe use of electrical appliances
- Explain various ways of conserving electrical energy as a part of social responsibility

Scientific Crypt

A Tribute to Thomas Alva Edison (1847–1931)

Thomas Alva Edison was an American inventor. He developed many devices in fields such as electric power generation, mass communication, sound recording, and motion pictures. By the age of 12, he started printing his weekly newspaper "Grand Trunk Herald". In 1879, Edison invented the incandescent electric light bulb.

He started a new laboratory and research facility in West Orange, New Jersey and employed nearly 60 workers. From here he produced the commercial phonograph, the kinetoscope, the Edison storage battery, the electric pen, the mimeograph and micro taximeters. Thus, he patented more than 1000 discoveries. He was appointed president of the U.S Navy Consulting Board.

FUN TIME

CROSSWORD

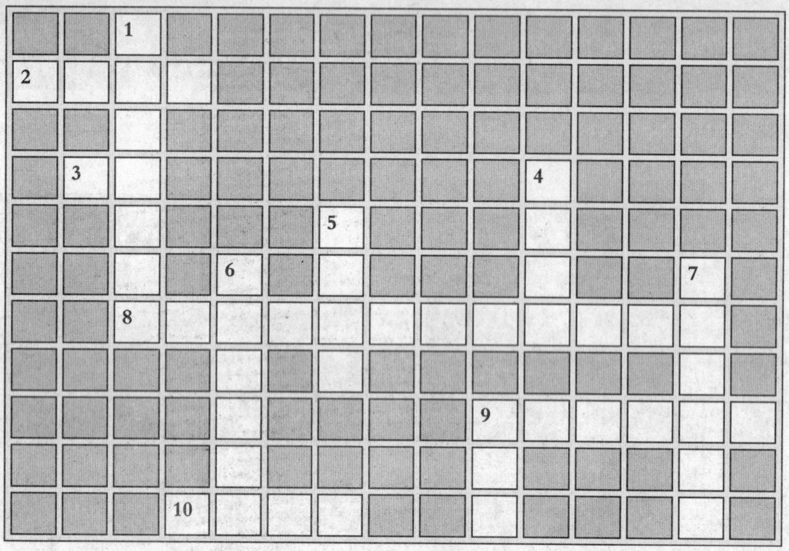

Across

2. What the MCB does if electrical energy in a circuit exceeds the limit.
3. Type of electricity supplied to our home appliances by mains.
8. Part of the distribution network carrying power to consumers.
9. Devices installed in homes to measure electrical energy consumption.
10. An electrical device delivering energy as a result of a chemical reaction.

Down

1. The path through which electrical energy flows.
4. One of the mechanisms where construction helps generate electricity using water turbines.
5. A small wire in the circuit with a low melting point.
6. What can happen to electrical devices with improper usage, like short circuit or high voltages.
7. Electricity is the secondary source of energy which means that this energy is produced from primary sources of energy, such as oil, natural gas, sunlight, etc.
9. Alternative device for a fuse which trips when excess electrical energy passes through.

INTRODUCTION

Discovery of electricity has brought a lot of difference in the lives of the people. Earlier people used wood, charcoal, etc., to cook, warm themselves, whenever and wherever they needed. Energy gained by burning wood or charcoal cannot be supplied over long distances to wherever it is needed. Now people no longer need to worry about producing energy for heating or cooking; all they need to do is just plug-in and switch on.

Sources of Energy

The various sources of energy we use in our day-to-day life are shown as follows.

Figure 6.1 Some-energy producing devices

Importance of Study of Electricity

Electricity is like a common 'language' that all modern appliances can 'speak'. One can cook food with it, run car on it, charge our mobiles, etc. It is the energy for everyone, everywhere and available all the time.

Electricity is the secondary source of energy which means that this energy is produced from primary sources of energy, such as oil, natural gas, sunlight, etc.

1. The usage of electrical appliances has become a part of our lives. So, it is essential to learn about their safe handling.
2. To know about the sources of electricity and the types of sources.
3. To know about the uses and applications of electricity.
4. To gain the knowledge of constructing a simple circuit.

Sources of Electricity

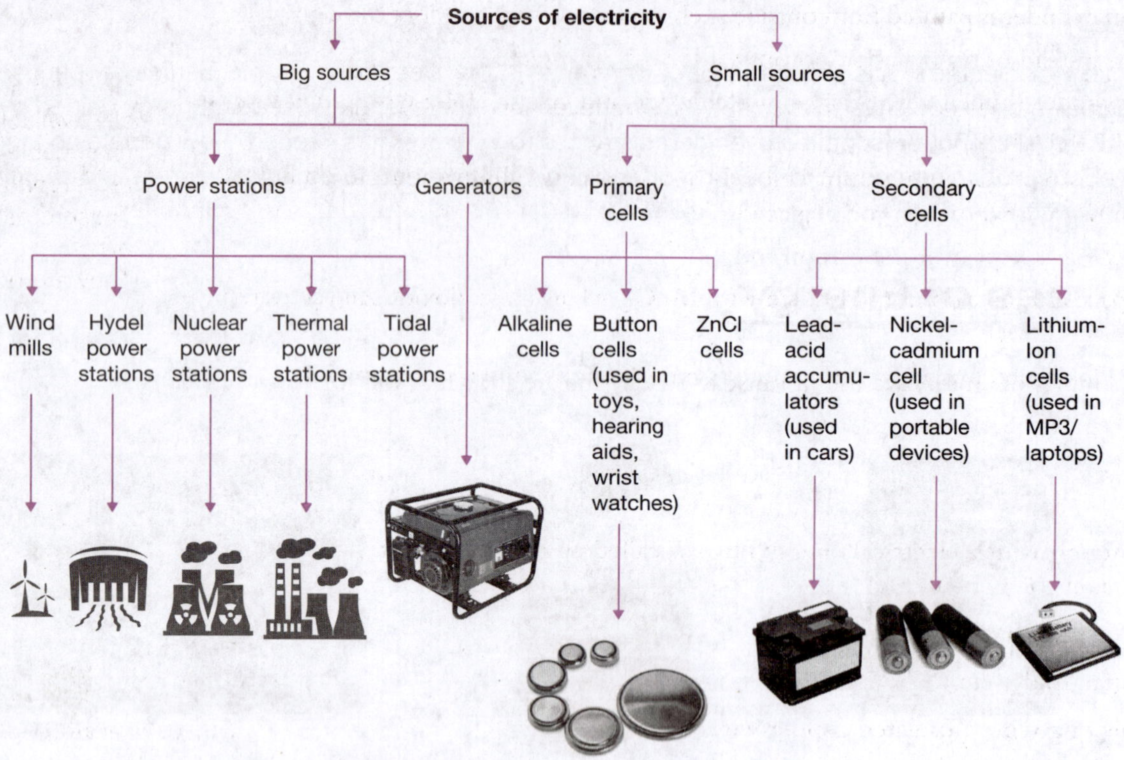

Figure 6.2 Various sources of electricity

Cell

It is an electrical device which delivers electrical energy as a result of a chemical reaction. Cells are further classified into two types i.e., primary cell and secondary cell. Major differences between these are tabulated below:

> **Info Bytes!**
> Secondary cells are also known as accumulators since they can store charge.

Table 6.1 Differences between primary and secondary cells

Primary cell	Secondary cell
Cannot be recharged	Can be recharged
Irreversible chemical reaction takes place in this cell	Reversible chemical reaction takes place in this cell.
These are also known as 'use and throw' type of cells.	These are also known as accumulators.

Dry Cell

A dry cell stores chemical energy to be converted into electrical energy. This is a type of electric battery, majorly used for portable electrical devices.

Dry cell was invented by Georges Leclanche.

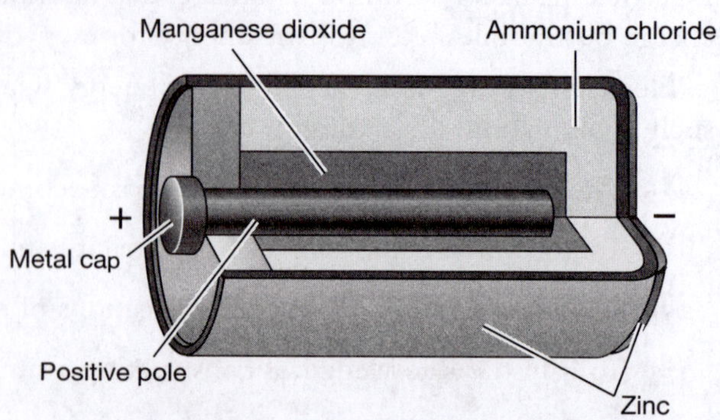

Figure 6.3 Structure of a dry cell

- Dry cells consist of a zinc cylinder placed in a tin cylinder.
- The tin cylinder is painted from outside such that it does not conduct through walls.
- Earlier, instead of tin cylinder, porous cardboard was used.
- Zinc cylinder is filled with ammonium chloride and gelatin along with some water so that a paste is formed.
- Inside this paste of ammonium chloride and gelatin a cylindrical arrangement of muslin bag with a carbon rod is placed.
- A brass cap is kept over the carbon rod.
- The space around carbon rod is filled with MnO_2 (Manganese dioxide) and activated carbon.
- The cell is sealed from top with a porous membrane as shown in Figure 6.3.

Info Bytes!

1. Dry cells are generally available as chargeable and non-rechargeable.
2. These cells are leak proof.
3. They are portable.

Electric Circuit

The path through which electrical energy flows is called an electric circuit. The basic components of a circuit are

1. Source of electricity (battery or cell)
2. Load (fan, bulb, etc.)
3. Connecting wires (insulated copper wires)

Info Bytes!

In India, the government has formed an agency called Indian Standard Bureau which issues certificates to all good quality products. These certified products carry 'ISI' mark.

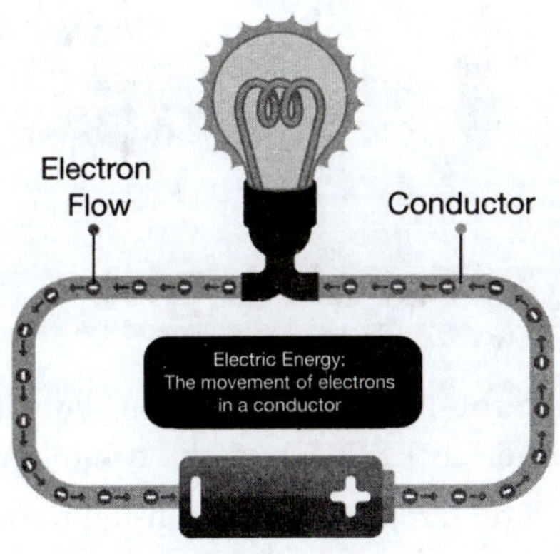

Figure 6.4 Simple electric circuit

Types of Circuits

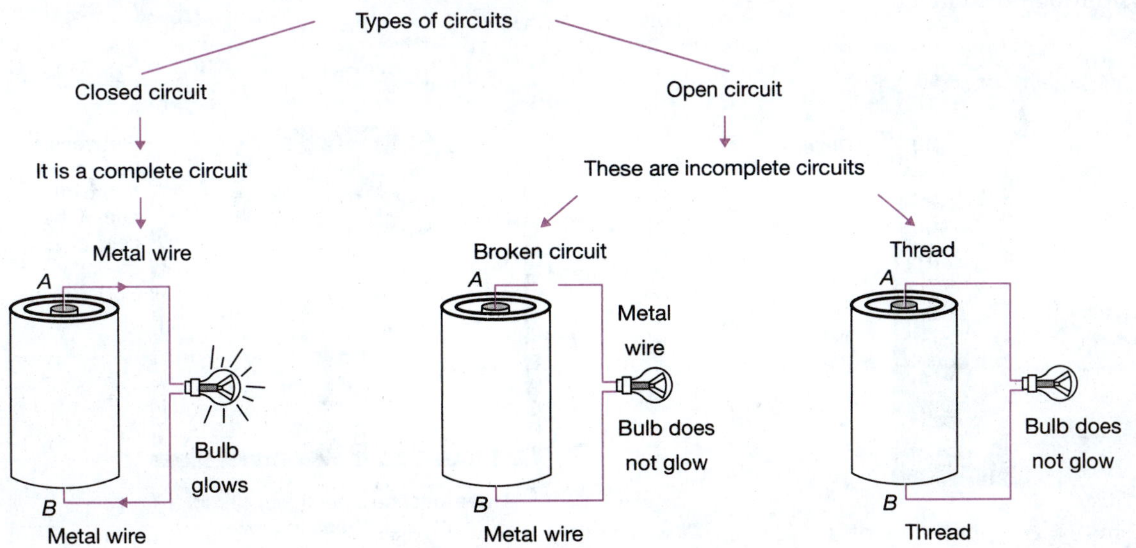

Figure 6.5 Types of circuits

Important Electrical Components and Their Symbols

Table 6.2 Electrical components and their symbols

Component	Symbol
Cell (source of electricity)	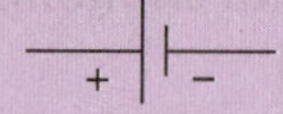
A battery (source of electricity)	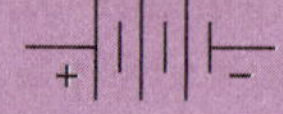
Plug key (switch) in open condition	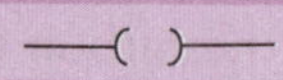
Plug key in closed condition	
Tap key (switch) in open condition	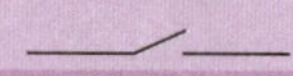
Tap key in closed condition	
Bulb	
Ammeter (electric current measuring device)	
Voltmeter	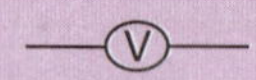
Resistance	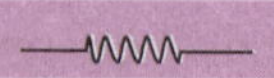
Fuse	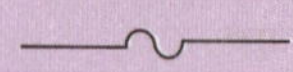
Rheostat	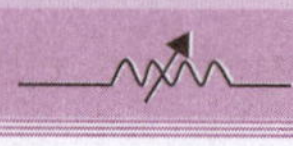

Torch Light

The torch light is an electrical device in which we can find a simple circuit. The torch light consists of a lamp and inside it there is LED. Thus, the torch light is possible to produce light when the LED works.

The circuit in the torch light consists of a cell. One terminal of the cell is connected to a bulb using connecting wire and the other terminal of the cell is connected to one end of the switch. The other end of the switch is connected to the second end of the bulb as shown in the adjoining figure.

Working

The electrical energy delivered by the cell will flow through the bulb when the key is closed. The bulb glows as long as the energy flows through the circuit.

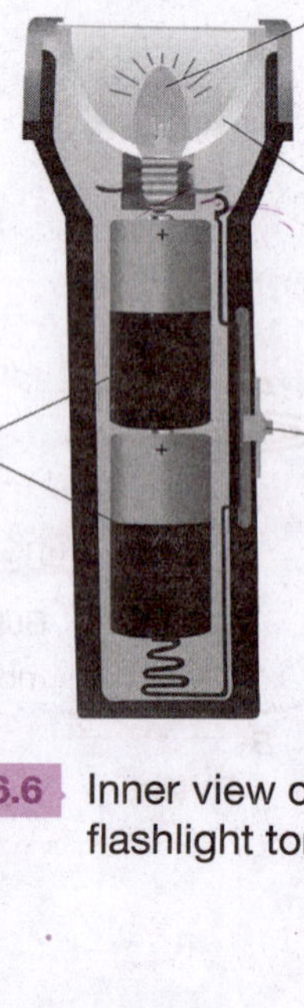

Figure 6.6 Inner view of a flashlight torch

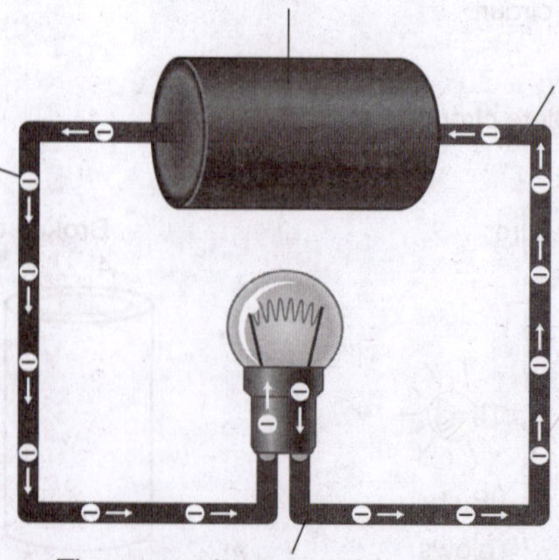

Figure 6.7 Working of an Electric circuit

Konnect

As the number of cells connected in the circuit increases, the brightness of the bulb increases. In the figure given below, the bulb A glows brighter than the bulb B.

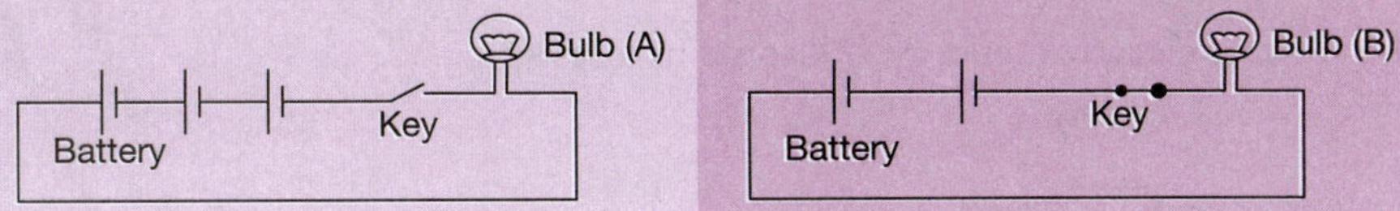

Classification of Materials

We come across many type of materials around us, such as wood, plastic, silk, etc. Among these, only a few materials allow electrical energy to pass through them.

Classification of materials

- Conductors
  These materials allow electrical energy to pass through them.
  - ***Example***: Materials, like iron, gold, steel, water, etc.
  - Applications: These materials are used in the manufacture of electric wires and applications.
- Insulators (or) poor conductors
  These materials do not allow electrical energy to pass through them.
  - ***Example***: Plastic, wood, thread, etc.
  - Applications: These materials can be used in manufacture of handles for electrical appliances to avoid electric shocks.

Effects of Electricity

Two major effects of electric current are heating effect and magnetic effect.

Effects of electricity

- **Heating effect**
  Electrical energy flowing through the circuit for long time will heat the circuit.
  - Electric stove
  - Filament bulb
  - Immersion heater
- **Magnetic effect**
  Any conductor carrying electrical energy behaves like a magnet.
  - Electric bell (Electro magnet)

Electric stove

Filament bulb

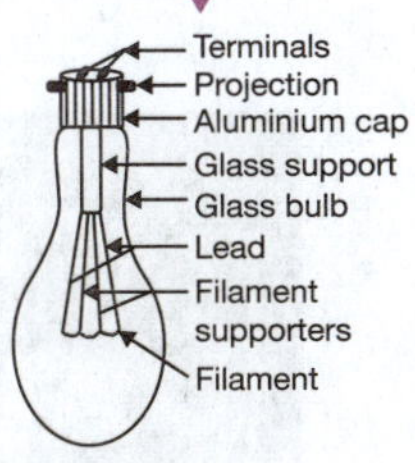

Immersion heater

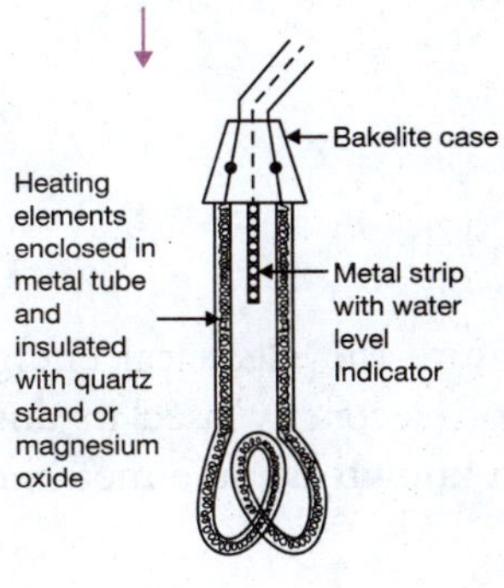

Electric bell (Electro magnet)

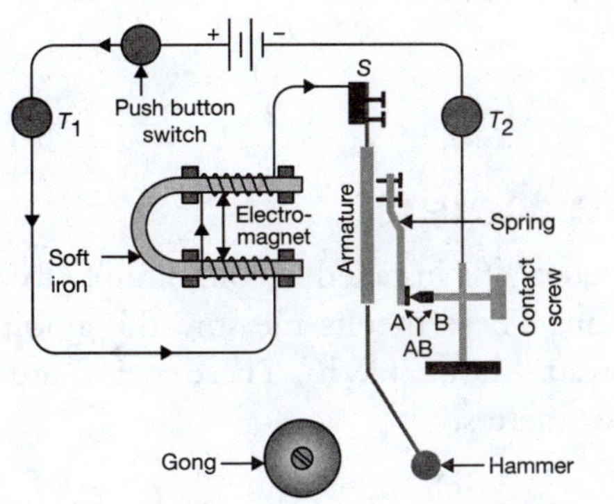

Electricity at Home

Electricity supplied to our home appliances is supplied by AC mains. We generally come across a few terms, such as fuse, MCB, electric meters in our daily life. Now we shall understand their significance.

Resistor

A wire which opposes the flow of electrical energy is known as a resistor.

Symbol of a resistor 

Symbol of Variable Resistor 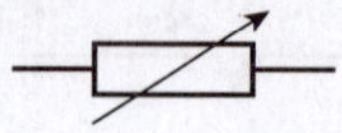

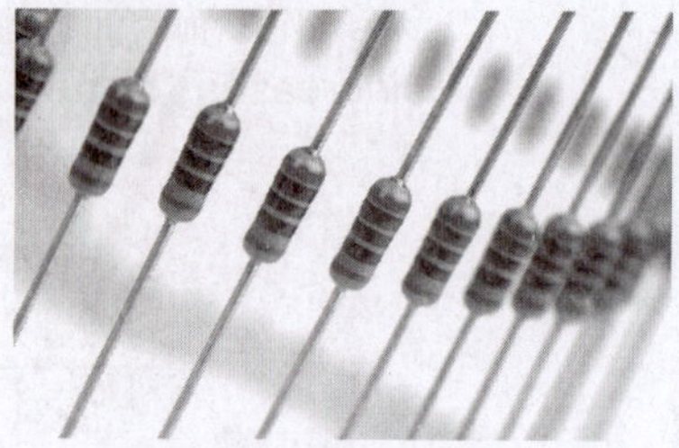

Figure 6.8 A resistor

Fuse

A fuse is a small wire which has low melting point and is included in the circuit. Improper usage of electric devices, like short circuit or high voltages drawn will damage the electrical devices. In such cases, a fuse wire which is included in the circuit gets melted and results in an open circuit. In this way, the devices connected in the circuit are safe.

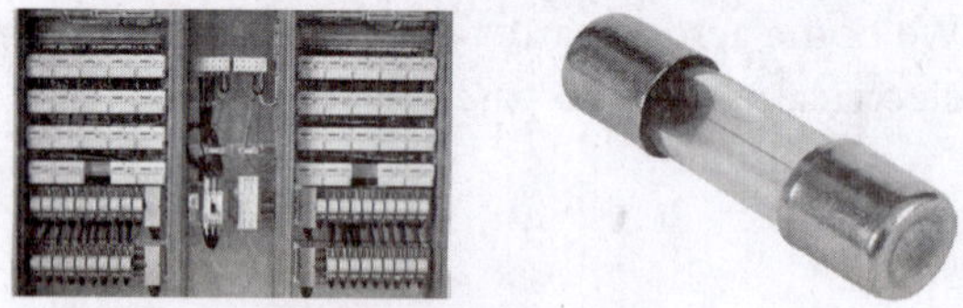

Figure 6.9 Fuse

Miniature Circuit Breaker (MCB)

The fuse is a very good safety device but once blown off it should be replaced with a new one. Alternative device for a fuse is a Miniature Circuit Breaker (MCB). Alternative device for a fuse is a Miniature Circuit Breaker (MCB). This looks like a switch and is used like a fuse.

If the electrical energy passing through a circuit exceeds the limit, the MCB trips down and makes the circuit open. After the problem is rectified, MCB can be easily reset by pushing its switch.

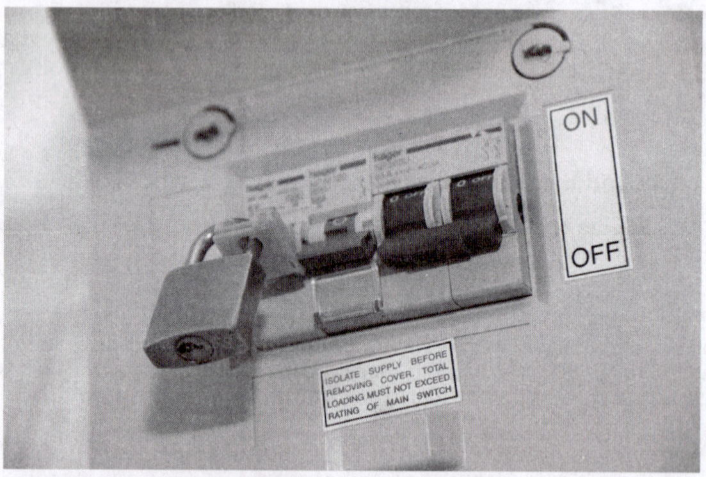

Figure 6.10 MCB (Miniature Circuit Breaker) with padlock on switch

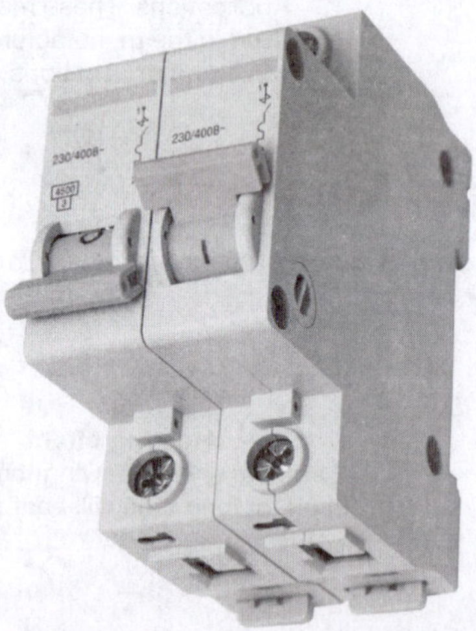

Figure 6.11 A Miniature circuit breaker

Electric Meter

Electric meters are installed in our homes to measure the electrical energy consumption. These meters measure the amount of electricity used in units called kilowatt – hour (kWh). These meters are also known as joule meters or Watt – hour meters.

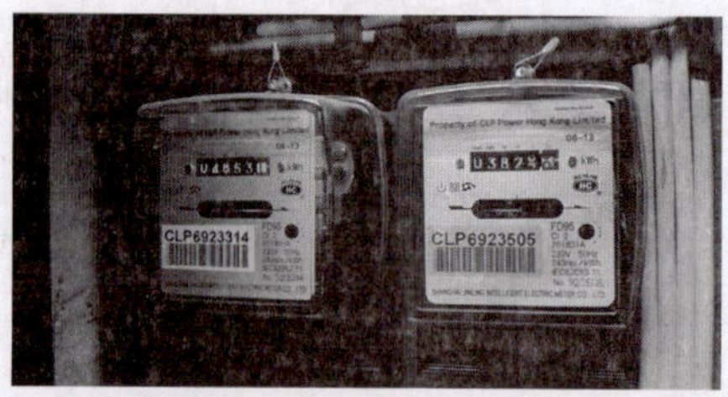

Figure 6.12 Electric meter

Distribution of Electricity

Distribution networks carry power(through wires either on poles or, in many urban areas, underground) to consumers up to the last few miles via transmission or sub-transmission.

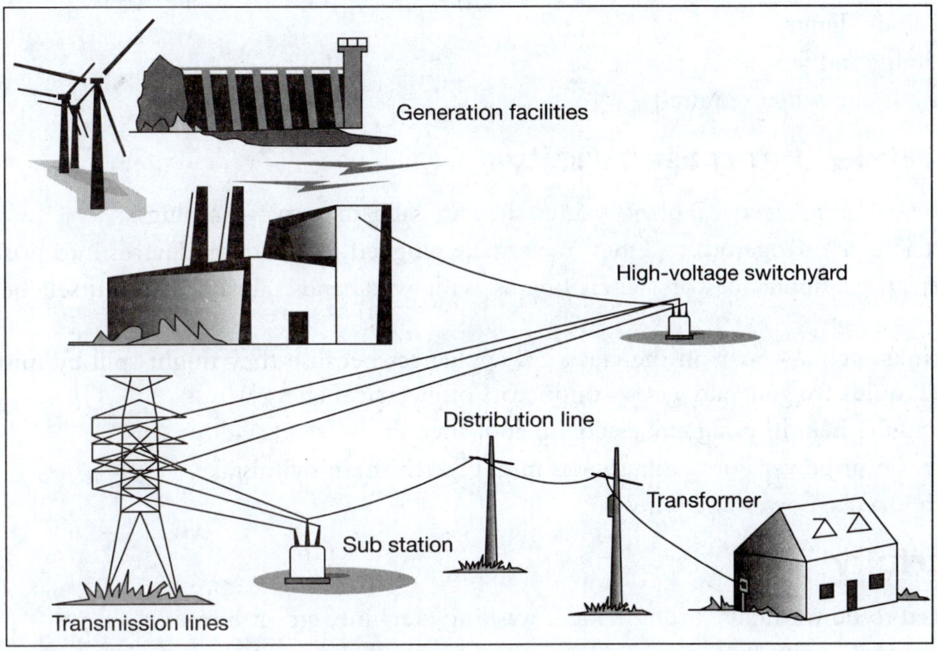

Figure 6.13 (a) Distribution of electricity

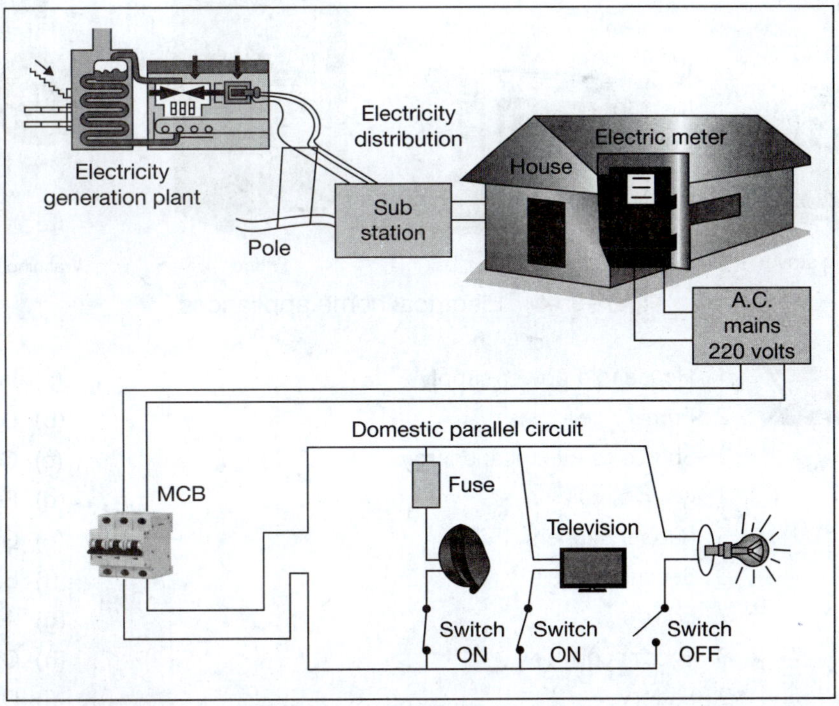

Figure 6.13 (b) Generation, distribution, and uses of electricity

Conservation of Electricity

Electricity is generated using costly mechanisms, such as construction of dams to run water turbines, burning of coal in thermal power plants, etc. Therefore, electricity should be conserved. Some of the methods to conserve electricity are:

1. Avoid using tube lights and filament bulbs by replacing them with CFL (compact fluorescent lamp) bulbs or LED (light emitting diode) lights.
2. Switch off the lights and fans when not in use.
3. Use solar energy as and when required.

Precautions While Using Electricity

- Always use three-pin plug electrical devices since they are safer than two-pin plugs.
- Water and electricity are dangerous together; never take plugged-in electrical devices into wash room.
- Never touch electrical appliances or switch boards with wet hands, always dry yourself before using electrical appliances.
- Never place drinks such as water on the electrical appliances because they might spill by mistake and result in an electric shock (Liquids are generally good conductors of electrical energy).
- Always take an adult's help in using any electrical appliance.
- Never climb trees near power lines because you might touch them by mistake.
- Never play with electric power line wires.

Uses of Electricity

1. Electricity is used to power lights, ovens, fridge, washing machine, etc. at homes.
2. Modern-day communication and transport is facilitated by electricity.
3. Electricity is required for engineering and technical activities.

Electric stove Oven Fridge Washing machine

Figure 6.14 Electrical home appliances

EXAMPLE 6.1

1. Household power supply	(a) Insulators
2. Primary cell	(b) Load
3. Source of electrical energy	(c) Combination of cells
4. Open circuit	(d) Rechargeable
5. Rubber slippers	(e) Good conductor
6. Secondary cell	(f) Bad conductor
7. Iron	(g) A.C mains
8. Thermocol	(h) Open switch
9. Battery	(i) D.C. mains
10. Bulb	(j) Button cell
11. Unit for electric current	(a) Battery
12. Device that measures current	(b) Insulator

13. Material that allows electricity to flow (c) Ammeter
14. A source of direct current (d) Ampere
15. Copper (e) Resistance
16. Circuit component that opposes current flow (f) Conductor
17. Plastic (g) Volt
18. Unit for electric potential (h) Resistor
19. Closed loop for electricity (i) Circuit

SOLUTION

1 – g; 2 – j; 3 – c, g, i, j; 4 – h; 5 – a, f; 6 – d; 7 – e; 8 – a, f; 9 – c; 10 – b; 11 – d; 12 – c; 13 – f; 14 – a; 15 – f; 16 – e; 17 –b; 18 – g; 19 – i

EXAMPLE 6.2 Arrange the following components in a circuit diagram such that the bulb glows.

(a) Cell 1 **(b)** Cell 2 **(c)** Bulb **(d)** Switch

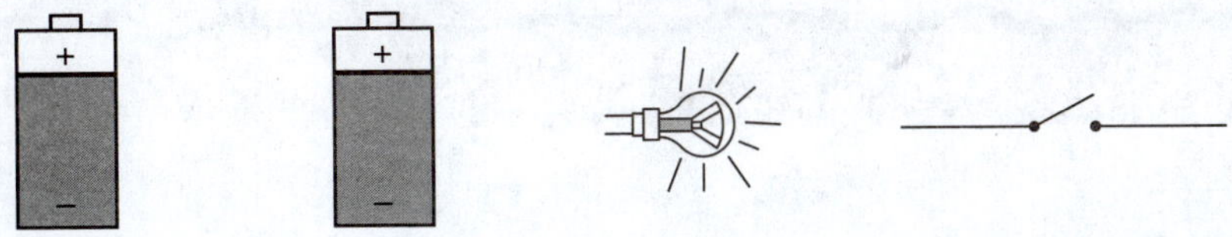

SOLUTION

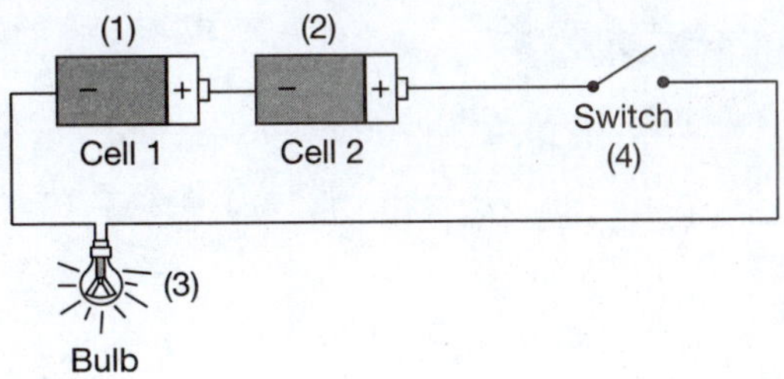

EXAMPLE 6.3 Identify the following symbols:

(a)

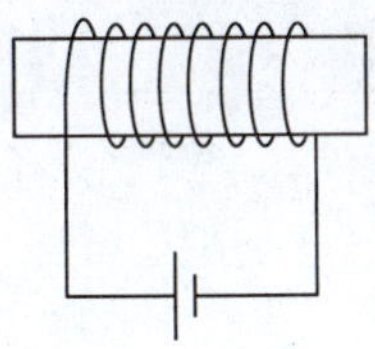

(b)

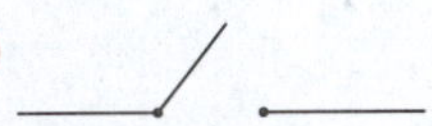

(c)

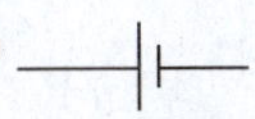

(d)

(e)

(f)

SOLUTION

(a) Electromagnet **(b)** Switch **(c)** Cell
(d) Battery **(e)** Button cells **(f)** Wind mills

POINTS TO REMEMBER

- ✔ Electricity is the secondary source of energy which means that this energy is produced from primary sources of energy, such as oil, natural gas, sunlight, etc.
- ✔ The path through which electrical energy flows is called an electric circuit.
- ✔ Electricity supplied to our home appliances is supplied by AC mains.
- ✔ Electricity is generated using costly mechanisms, such as construction of dams to run water turbines, burning of coal in thermal power plants, etc.
- ✔ Alternative device for a fuse is a Miniature Circuit Breaker (MCB)

DW

PRACTICE QUESTIONS CLASSROOM WING

Very Short Answer Type Questions

Direction for question 1.
Fill in the blank.

1. Tungsten is the material used to manufacture filament of an electric bulb, since it has _____ melting point.

Direction for questions from 2 to 35.
Select the correct alternative from the given options.

2. One unit means ______
   (a) 10 Wh (b) 1 kWh
   (c) 10 W (d) 10 MWh

3. Hydroelectric power plants convert _____ to _____.
   (a) potential energy, electrical energy
   (b) kinetic energy, potential energy
   (c) electrical energy, mechanical
   (d) electrical energy, kinetic energy

4. Thermal power plants convert _____ to _____.
   (a) electrical energy, heat energy
   (b) heat energy, electrical energy
   (c) potential energy, kinetic energy
   (d) kinetic energy, electrical energy

5. In atomic and nuclear power plants, electrical energy is generated using the process of _____.
   (a) Nuclear fission
   (c) Nuclear fusion
   (b) Neither nuclear fission nor nuclear fusion
   (d) Both nuclear fusion and nuclear fission

6. The current supplied to our home is _____.
   (a) Alternating currents (AC)
   (b) Direct current (DC)
   (c) AC and DC
   (d) Only DC

7. The material will act as good conductor of electricity if it has more number of _____.
   (a) Free neutrons (b) Free protons
   (c) Free positrons (d) Free electrons

8. Rechargeable cell/cells among them is/are _____.
   (a) Dry cell (b) Secondary cell
   (c) Primary cell (d) Both (a) and (c)

9. _____ is/are used as electrical source/sources
   (a) Cell (b) Bulb
   (c) AC Mains (d) Both (a) and (c)

10. Which of the following statements is/are incorrect?
    (a) Dry cells are used in torch lights.
    (b) Cells, if not used for long time, gets discharged.
    (c) Dry cells do not contain water in them.
    (d) None of the above

11. Find the odd one out from the following.
    (a) Accumulators (b) Nickel cadmium cells
    (c) Alkaline cells (d) Lithium – ion cells

12. Anode means _____.
    (a) Positive electrode
    (b) Negative electrode
    (c) Cathode
    (d) Electrolyte

13. All electrical gadgets in our house work using electricity from _____.
    (a) AC mains power supply
    (b) Cells
    (c) Batteries
    (d) None of the above

14. Which of the following is the biggest source of electricity?
    (a) Generator
    (b) Wind mill
    (c) Hydel power plant
    (d) Accumulator

15. The heating effect of electric current is used in _____.
    (a) Electric cell (b) Electric bell
    (c) Electric switch (d) Electric hairdryer

16. The electrical component/components used in a circuit to offer variable resistance is/are _____.
    (a) Resistance box
    (b) Rheostat
    (c) Resistance
    (d) Both (a) and (b)

17. Material which allows current to flow through it is _____.
(a) Conductor (b) Insulator
(c) Glass (d) Plastic

18. The symbol of electrical component whose longer vertical line represents positive terminal while short and thick line denotes negative terminal is _____.
(a) Cell (b) Battery
(c) Key (d) Fuse

19. _____ is the device which is used to open or close the circuit.
(a) Key/switch (b) Battery
(c) Fuse (d) Cell

20. Two or more cells joined together to form _____.
(a) Inductor (b) Capacitor
(c) Cell (d) Battery

21. _____ is the symbol of fuse.
(a) 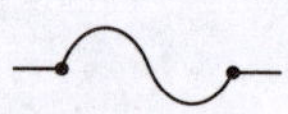 (b) 
(c)  (d) 

22. The safety device used in electric circuit is _____.
(a) Cell (b) Fuse
(c) Capacitor (d) Switch

23. MCB stands for _____.
(a) Minute circuit breaker
(b) Miniature capacity breaker
(c) Miniature circuit breaker
(d) Minimum current breaker

24. Dry cells convert _____ into _____.
(a) mechanical energy, electrical energy
(b) chemical energy, electrical energy
(c) electrical energy, light energy
(d) kinetic energy, mechanical energy

25. _____ effect of electric current is used in rice cooker.
(a) Sound (b) Electrical
(c) Lighting (d) Heating

26. CFL stands for
(a) Common fluorescent light
(b) Compact fluorescent light
(c) Compact fluorescent lamp
(d) Common fluorescent lamp

27. LED stands for
(a) Light emitting device
(b) Light emitting diode
(c) Less electricity device
(d) Long emission diode

28. A person is sensing the electric shock means
(a) Current flow through him
(b) Charge flows through him.
(c) Person is closing the circuit
(d) All the above

29. Electric current is the flow of _____.
(a) Electrons (b) Protons
(c) Neutrons (d) Positrons

30. Fuse wire is generally made of _____
(a) Tin and lead
(b) Copper and lead
(c) Tin and copper
(d) Lead and iron

31. A fuse wire should have _____.
(a) Low melting point and high resistance
(b) High melting point and high resistance
(c) Very high melting point and low resistance
(d) None of the above

32. All wires used in electrical circuits should be covered with _____.
(a) Conducting material
(b) Insulating material
(c) Metal
(d) Semi-conductor

33. The method to reduce consumption of electricity is _____.
(a) To use tube lights instead of CFL's.
(b) Switching off the lights and fans while leaving a room.
(c) By constructing houses with good ventilation.
(d) All the above

34. In which of the following is an electromagnet used?
(a) Compass (b) Loudspeaker
(c) Heater (d) Water tap

35. Which of the following has a filament?
(a) Bulb (b) Battery
(c) Switch (d) Wire

Short Answer Type Questions

36. What are the uses of an insulator?

37. Write few safety rules in using electricity.

38. Is it necessary to save electricity? If so, suggest a few ways to save electricity.

39. Electrical energy _____ through an open circuit.

40. Write the functions of the following components.
    (a) Key
    (b) Cell
    (c) Rheostat
    (d) Ammeter
    (e) Voltmeter

41. What is meant by a fused bulb?

42. Why are handles of electrical tools coated or covered with insulating materials?

43. Match the following.

Column A	Column B
(A) Power station	(a) Button cell
(B) Primary cell	(b) Lithium-ion cell
(C) Fuse	(c) 
(D) Secondary cell	(d) Windmill
(E) Resistor	(e) 
(F) Conductor	(f) Electric bell
(G) Magnetic effect of electric current	(g) Gold
(H) Insulator	(h) Wood

44. How can one find out whether a bulb is fused or not?

45. Is there any standard in India based on which one can rely to buy any electric device. If so, what is it?

46. Complete the following sequence of circuit positive terminal of Cell → Wire → Switch → Bulb → _____ → _____.

Essay Type Questions

47. Namitha is a journalist. She used her pen camera to capture the photographs of a crime that took place on the way to her office. Which of the following is the source of the electrical energy which must be used in the said camera?
    (a) Nickel-cadmium cells
    (b) Lead-acid batteries
    (c) Alkaline cells
    (d) Button cells

PRACTICE QUESTIONS COMPETITION WING

Level 1: Apply Your Concepts

Direction for questions 1 to 5.
Fill in the blanks.

1. ______ are the two terminals of a battery.
2. A dry cell has ______ electrodes.
3. As a precaution, the source of electricity which should not be used while doing experiment is ______.
4. The scientific name of an electric meter used in homes to measure the consumption of electrical energy is ______.
5. The filament in the bulb is made of ______.

Direction for question 6.
Answer the following questions.

6. Choose the correct order of distribution of electricity from the following.
   (a) Power station → Substation → AC mains → MCB → Electrical Appliance
   (b) Power station → AC mains → Substation → MCB → Electrical Appliance
   (c) Power station → Substation → MCB → AC mains → Electrical Appliance
   (d) Substation → Power station → AC mains → MCB → Electrical Appliance

Direction for question 7.
Select the correct alternative from the given options.

7. (a)

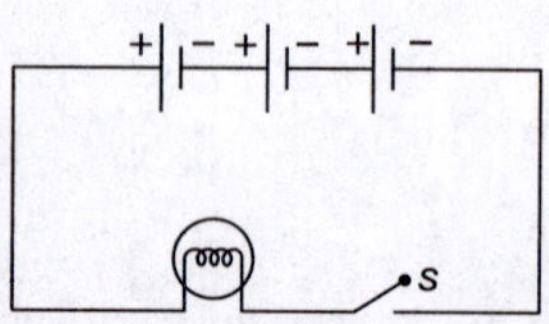

(b)

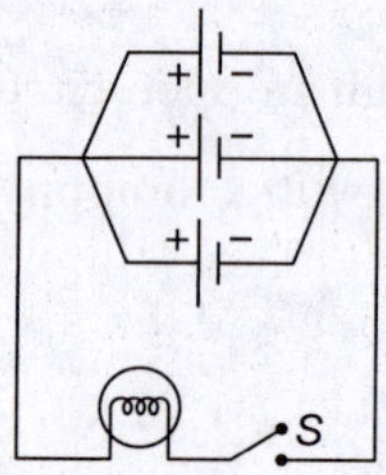

(c)

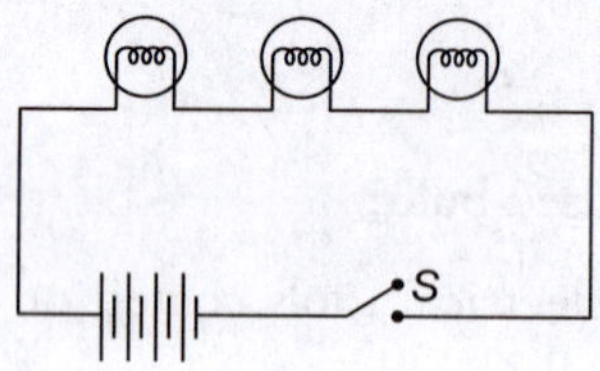

(d)

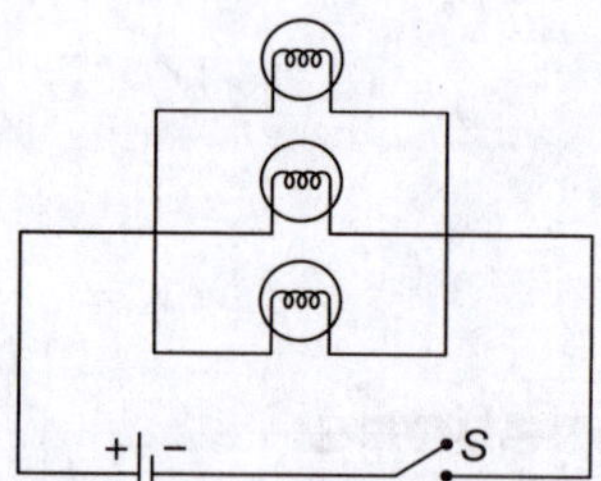

In which of the circuits given above does the bulbs glow brighter? (Assume that all bulbs and cells are identical)

(a) Circuit 'a' (b) Circuit 'b'
(c) Circuit 'c' (d) Circuit 'd'

Level 2: Review Your Concepts

8. **Assertion (A):** The mixy that is running stops suddenly without any damage when there is any voltage fluctuations but the fuse inside it is burned.

   Reason (R): A fuse wire which is included in the circuit gets melted and results in an open circuit. This saves the appliance from damage.

   (a) Both A and R are correct, and R is the correct explanation to A.
   (b) Both A and R are correct, but R is not the correct explanation to A.
   (c) A is correct but R is incorrect.
   (d) Both A and R are incorrect.

9. Have you ever seen an electric cell? If so, how many terminals does it have and how can one differentiate the terminals of a battery?

10. Mohan is a student of class 6. One day, his science teacher taught him electricity. After that, he had many doubts about the electrical appliances and measuring devices that are used in his home. He observed that a wire from an electric pole is connected to a joule meter A, fixed to the wall in the veranda, and from there to a main switch, and then to the main fuse. To this main fuse, a refrigerator, a fan, and a bulb are connected in parallel. Find out the appliance that consumes the least electric power among them.
(a) Bulb (b) Fan
(c) Main switch (4) Refrigerator

Level 3: Assess Your Concepts

11. Mention the effect of electric current with which the following electrical appliances works.
Electric bell, Iron (box), Hair dryer and Bulb
(a) Electric bell – Magnetic effect, Iron box- Heating effect, Hair dryer – Heating effect, Bulb – Heating effect
(b) Electric bell – Magnetic effect, Iron box- Heating effect, Hair dryer – Heating effect, Bulb – lighting effect
(c) Electric bell – Magnetic effect, Iron box- magnetic, Hair dryer – Heating effect, Bulb – Heating effect
(d) Electric bell – Heating, Iron box- Heating effect, Hair dryer – Heating effect, Bulb – Heating effect

12. Maan Singh and Junnu Singh are brothers. One day, Junnu and Maan Singh, as usual, used unauthorized electricity by connecting the wire directly to their nearby electric poles from their respective houses. But unfortunately, Junnu's house got short circuited. Maan Singh realized what could have happened and immediately intimated an electrician to set up a kWh meter and started using electricity in the right way. What do you understand from this?
(a) Using authorized electric connection is safe.
(b) Unauthorized usage of electrical energy might lead to short-circuiting.
(c) Fuses or MCBs used in the electric circuit at home protects the electrical appliances from any unexpected fluctuations in electric current
(d) All the above

13. Name the components labelled as P, Q, R, S, T and U

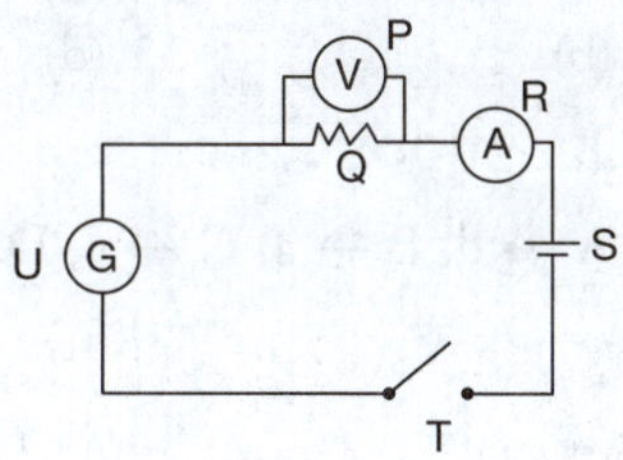

14. How many joules make one kilowatt hour. [1 watt second = 1 joule]

15. Answer the following questions:
(a) Name the material that is used in dry cell to separate cathode from anode.
(b) Draw a correct symbol of fuse.
(c) State two difference between primary and secondary cell

AT

ANSWER KEYS

Crossword

Across

2. Trip 3. AC 8. Transmission 9. Meters 10. Cell

Down

1. Circuit 4. Dams 5. Fuse 6. Damage 7. Energy
9. MCB

Classroom Wing

Very Short Answer Type Questions

1. High	2. (b)	3. (a)	4. (b)	5. (a)
6. (a)	7. (d)	8. (b)	9. (d)	10. (d)
11. (c)	12. (a)	13. (a)	14. (c)	15. (d)
16. (d)	17. (a)	18. (a)	19. (a)	20. (d)
21. (a)	22. (b)	23. (c)	24. (b)	25. (d)
26. (c)	27. (b)	28. (d)	29. (a)	30. (a)
31. (a)	32. (b)	33. (d)	34. (b)	35. (a)

Short Answer Type Questions

39. does not flow 43. A → d, B → a, C → e, D → b, E → c, F → g, G → f, H → h
47. (d)

Competition Wing

Level 1: Apply Your Concepts

1. Electrodes 2. Two 3. AC Mains 4. Kilowatt-hour meter
5. Tungsten 6. (a) 7. (a) 8. (a)

Level 2: Review Your Concepts

8. A – ammeter, B – cell, C – closed key, D – rheostat, E – bulb, F – Voltmeter 10. (a)

Level 3: Assess Your Concepts

11. (a) 12. (d) 14. 3.6×10^6 joule

Hints and Explanations

CLASSROOM WING

Very Short Answer Type Questions

1. Tungsten is the material used to manufacture filament of an electric bulb, since it has high melting point.
2. One unit means 1 kWh.
3. Hydroelectric power plants convert potential energy to electrical energy.
4. Thermal power plants convert heat energy to electrical energy.
5. In atomic and nuclear power plants, electrical energy is generated using the process of nuclear fission.
6. The current supplied to our home is Alternating currents (AC).
7. The material will act as good conductor of electricity if it has a greater number of free electrons.
8. Rechargeable cell/cells among them is/are secondary cell.
9. Cell or AC Mains is/are used as electrical sources.
10. (a) Dry cells are used in torch lights.
    (b) Cells, if not used for long time, gets discharged.
    (c) Dry cells do not contain water in them.
    (d) All the given options are correct.
11. Alkaline cells are use and throw type. The remaining three cell are rechargeable type.
12. Anode means positive electrode.
13. All electrical gadgets in our housework using electricity from AC mains power supply.
14. Hydel power plant is the biggest source of electricity.
15. The heating effect of electric current is used in electric hairdryer.
16. The electrical component/components used in a circuit to offer variable resistance is/are resistance box or rheostat.
17. Material which allows current to flow through it is conductor.
18. The symbol of electrical component whose longer vertical line represents positive terminal while short and thick line denotes negative terminal is Cell.
19. Key/switch is the device which is used to open or close the circuit.
20. Two or more cells joined together to form battery.
21.  is the symbol of fuse.
22. The safety device used in electric circuit is fuse.
23. MCB stands for Miniature Circuit Breaker.
24. Dry cells convert chemical energy into electrical energy.
25. Heating effect of electric current is used in rice cooker.
26. CFL stands for Compact Fluorescent Lamp.
27. LED stands for Light Emitting Diode.
28. A person is sensing the electric shock means current flow through him/charge flows through him/Person is closing the circuit.
29. Electric current is the flow of electrons.
30. Fuse wire is generally made of Tin and lead.
31. A fuse wire should have low melting point and high resistance.
32. All wires used in electrical circuits should be covered with insulating material.
33. The method to reduce consumption of electricity is (1) To use tube lights instead of CFL's (2) Switching off the lights and fans while leaving a room. (3) By constructing houses with good ventilation.
34. Electromagnet used loudspeaker.
35. Bulb has a filament in it.

Short Answer Type Questions

36. Uses of insulator:
    (a) It is used to keep ourselves safe from electricity.
    (b) It is used to make handles and the outer body of the electrical appliances.

37. Safety rules in using electricity:

(a) Always use appliances carrying ISI mark.

(b) For performing any experiments in electricity use only cells and not the mains supply to your household.

(c) Do not put a finger or a metallic wire in the sockets.

(d) Avoid touching switches with wet hands.

38. Yes, it is necessary to save electricity since a lot of investment is involved in generating it.

- Avoid using tube lights and filament bulbs by replacing them with CFL bulbs or LED lights.
- Switch off the lights and fans when not in use.
- Use solar energy as per the requirement.

39. Does not flow.

40. Key – It is used to open or close the circuit

Cell – It supplies current to a circuit

Rheostat – It offers variable resistance in a circuit

Ammeter – It measures current in the circuit

Voltmeter – It measures voltage in the circuit

41. Bulb is said to be fused when its filament is broken. Broken filament cannot complete the circuit; therefore a fused bulb does not glow.

42. All electrical tools are made of metals but covered with plastic or insulating materials so that no leakage current comes in contact with the person who operates them or touches them.

43. (A) Power station → (d) Windmill

(B) Primary cell → (a) Button cell

(C) Fuse → (e) 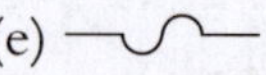

(D) Secondary cell → (b) Lithium-ion cell

(E) Resistor → (c) 

(F) Conductor → (g) Gold

(G) Magnetic effect of electric current → (f) Electric bell

(H) Insulator → (h) Wood

A → d, B → a, C → e, D → b, E → c, F → g, G → f, H → h

44. If the filament of the bulb is broken, then the bulb doesn't glow and is said to be fused.

45. Yes there is a standard ISI mark given by an agency called Indian Standard Bureau formed by the government of India to approve various products. These products are given certification according to the prescribed standards and good quality electrical devices.

46. Wire, negative terminal of cell.

Essay Type Questions

47. Button cells are used in a pen camera.

Hence, the correct option is (d).

COMPETITION WING

Level 1: Apply Your Concepts

6. Power station → Substation → AC mains → MCB → Electrical Appliance

   Hence, the correct option is (a).

7. Circuit A

   Hence, the correct option is (a).

Level 2: Review Your Concepts

8. Both A and R are correct, and R is the correct explanation to A.

   Hence, the correct option is (a).

9. Yes. A cell has two terminals. They are positive and negative terminals. The end which has the brass cap is a positive terminal and the base is the negative terminal.

10. Bulb

    Hence, the correct option is (a).

Level 3: Assess Your Concepts

12. All of these

    Hence, the correct option is (d).

13. P – Voltmeter; Q – Resistor
    R – Ammeter; S – Cell
    T – Switch; U – Galvanometer

14. We have, 1 kilowatt = 10^3 wattt
    1 hour = 3600 second
    1 kilowatt hour = 10^3 wattt × 3600 second
    = $3600 \times 10^3 \times$ watt second
    = 3.6×10^6 joule

15. (a) MnO_2 and Charcoal are used in dry cell to separate cathode from anode.

    (b) 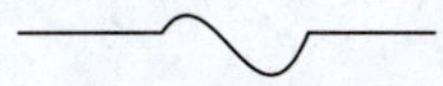

    (c)

Primary cell	Secondary cell
1. It cannot to recharged.	1. It can be recharged
2. Irreversible reaction takes place in this cell	2. Reversible chemical reaction take place in this cell

CHAPTER 7

The Magical Magnetism

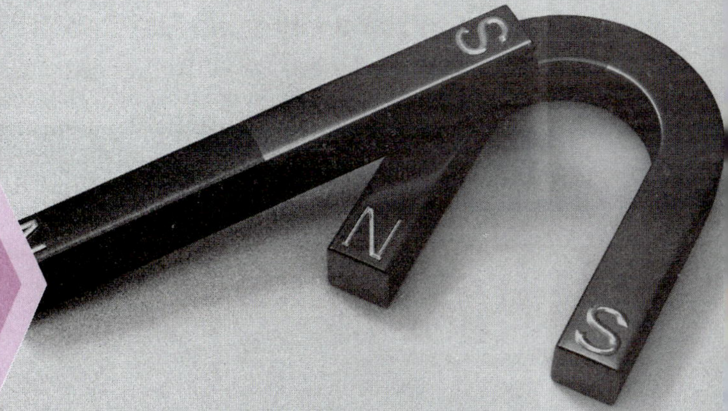

Remember

Before beginning this chapter, you should be able to:

- Recall magnet and its behaviour in various situations
- Identify the cardinal directions

Key Ideas

After completing this chapter, you should be able to:

- Explain few applications in which magnets are used and their working (E.g., compass)
- Understand the methods to magnetize and demagnetize magnetic substances
- Describe the relation between magnet and the Earth

Scientific Crypt

A Tribute to Hans Christian Oersted (1777–1851)

Hans Christian Oersted was a Danish physicist and chemist who discovered that electric currents create magnetic fields, which was the first connection found between electricity and magnetism. He worked as the assistant professor of physics at the university. He published a book on mechanical physics. In 1820, Oersted discovered that a current carrying conductor can deflect a compass needle, confirming a direct relationship between electricity and magnetism. This historic discovery not only accelerated the development of physics, but also resulted in the birth of a new branch in physics called 'electromagnetism'. Oersted made a significant contribution to chemistry by being the first person to successfully produce aluminium in its metallic state.

FUN TIME

CROSSWORD

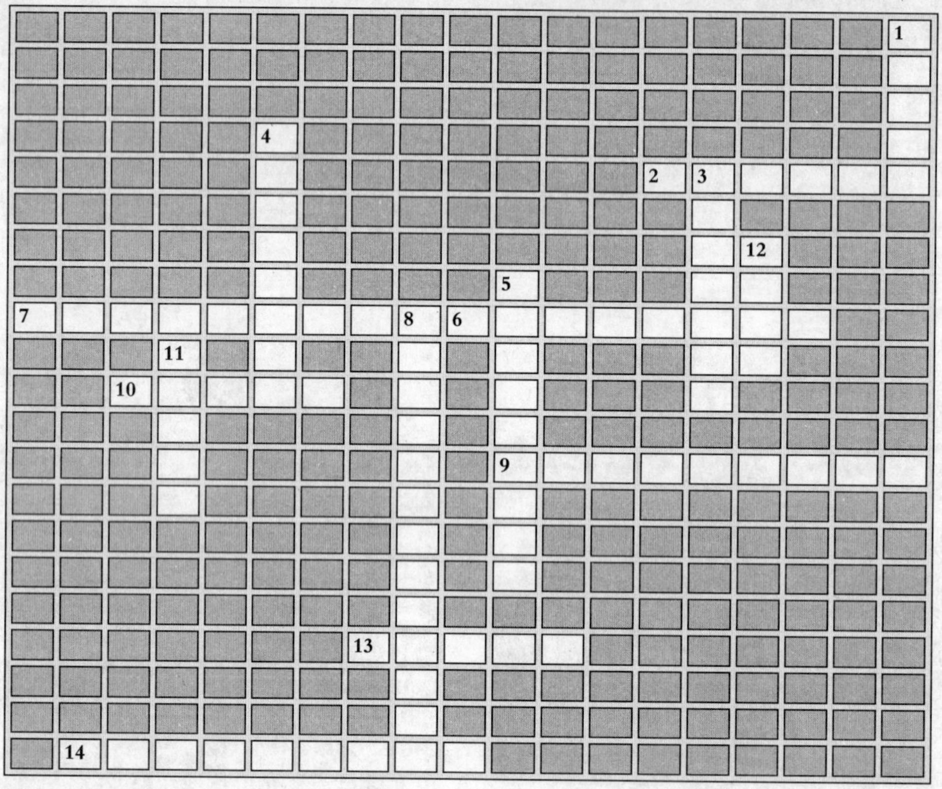

Across

2. Magnetic _______ is the distance between a magnet's North and South poles.
6. _________ strip is found on credit and debit cards, this feature allows them to store user information.
7. Property allowing magnets to attract certain materials.
9. Type of magnetism exhibited by electromagnets due to their use of soft iron.
10. Magnetic _______ is the power by which a magnet can attract or repel other magnets or certain metals.
13. A material commonly used to craft permanent magnets due to its long-lasting magnetic retention.
14. A material that cannot hold magnetism for extended periods.

Down

1. Magnetic _________ is the end of a freely suspended bar magnet that points towards the geographic North.
3. Magnetic _________ is the imaginary line passing through the magnet's center and is perpendicular to its magnetic axis.
4. __________ south is the end of a freely suspended bar magnet that points towards the geographic South.
5. Iron ore from which a magnet's property is derived, enabling it to attract certain materials.
8. The process of making materials magnetic.
11. End points on a magnet where its magnetic power is most concentrated.
12. Magnetic ________ is the imaginary line that runs through the North and South poles of a bar magnet.

INTRODUCTION

Around 800 BCE there was a shepherd called Magnes. While grazing his sheep and walking over a rock, he experienced his shoes with metal base were getting attracted towards the rock. His first thought must be that there might be a spirit in the stone which is pulling him towards itself. This is how the first natural magnet was said to be discovered in a town called magnesia, a district in Asia Minor where large deposits of magnetite were found.

Magnet

A **magnet** is an object constituting an iron ore called magnetite, and thus, it can attract materials, such as iron, cobalt, nickel, etc.

Info Bytes!

In ancient times, the magnetic stone was called lodestone, presently known as magnetite, and it was considered to possess magical powers.

Classification of Magnets

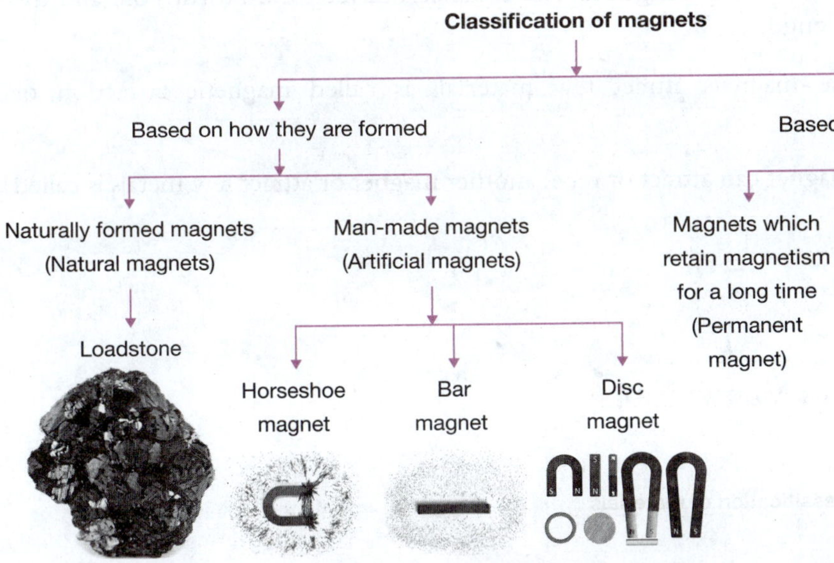

Figure 7.1 Types of magnets

Konnect

If you break a magnet into two pieces, each piece becomes a new magnet with a north and south pole.

Magnetic and Non-Magnetic Materials

Magnetic Materials: Materials that are attracted by a magnet are called magnetic materials or ferromagnetic materials. For example, iron, nickel, cobalt and their alloys.

Non-Magnetic Materials: Materials that are not attracted by a magnet are called non-magnetic materials or ferromagnetic materials. For example, gold, silver, wood, copper, tin, and paper.

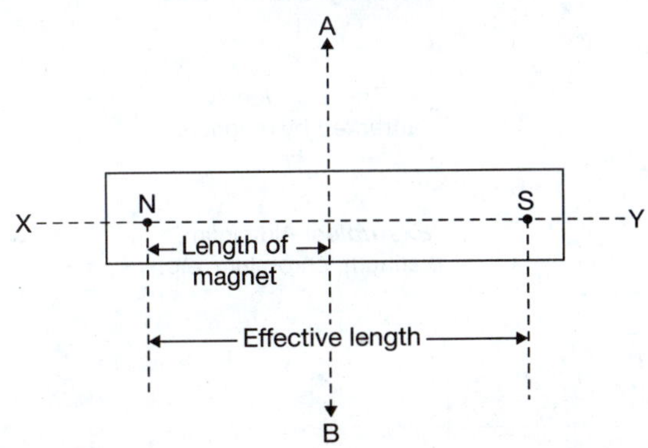

Figure 7.2 Representation of a bar magnet

Different Terms Used in Magnetism

1. **Magnetic Poles:** The end points of a magnet where most of its magnetic power is concentrated are called Poles of a magnet.
2. **Magnetic North Pole:** The point N at the end of the freely suspended bar magnet which points towards the geographic North Pole is called magnetic North Pole.
3. **Magnetic South Pole:** The point S at the end of the freely suspended bar magnet which points towards the geographic South Pole is called magnetic South Pole.
4. **Magnetic Axis:** An imaginary line (XY) passing through the magnetic North Pole and the magnetic South Pole of a bar magnet is called magnetic axis. (Figure 7.2)

> **Info Bytes!**
>
> A mixture of two or more elements, one of which is a metal, is called an alloy.
> ***Example:*** Steel = Iron + Carbon

5. **Magnetic Equator:** An imaginary line (AB) passing through the centre of magnet and perpendicular to the magnetic axis is called magnetic equator. (Figure 7.2)
6. **Length of a Magnet:** It is the distance between one of the poles to the centre of the magnet.
7. **Effective Length (or) Magnetic Length of a Bar Magnet:** The distance between the North Pole and the South Pole of a magnet is called its effective length.
8. **Magnetism:** The property by which the magnets attract few materials is called magnetic attraction or magnetism.
9. **Magnetic Force:** The force with which a magnet can attract or repel another magnet or attract few metals is called magnetic force.

Types of Materials

Classification of Materials (On the Basis of Magnetism)

Classification of materials

- Paramagnetic materials → These are feebly attracted by magnets → ***Examples:*** Aluminum, platinum, chromium, etc.
- Diamagnetic materials → These are repelled by magnets → ***Examples:*** Air, water, copper, bismuth, etc.
- Ferromagnetic materials → These are strongly attracted by magnets → ***Examples:*** Iron, cobalt, nickel, etc.

Properties of Magnet

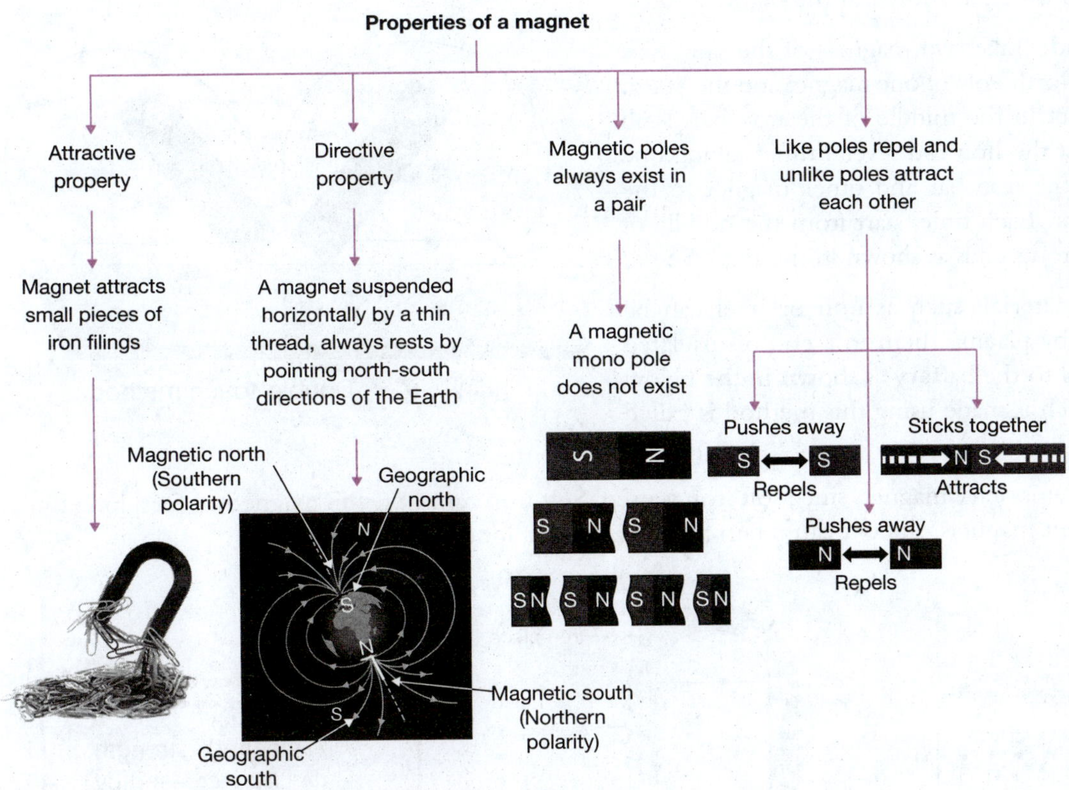

Figure 7.3 Properties of a magnet

Info Bytes!

In 1820, Danish Physicist, Hans Christian Oersted discovered that electric current creates magnetic properties in a substance.

Different Ways of Making a Magnet

Natural magnets are available on Earth but they are weak magnets. Thus, artificial magnets are made from magnetic materials and this process is called **magnetization**.

Following are the different methods to make an artificial magnet:

1. **Magnetic Induction Method:** An ordinary piece of iron behaves like a magnet only when a magnet is kept close to it as shown in the below figure:

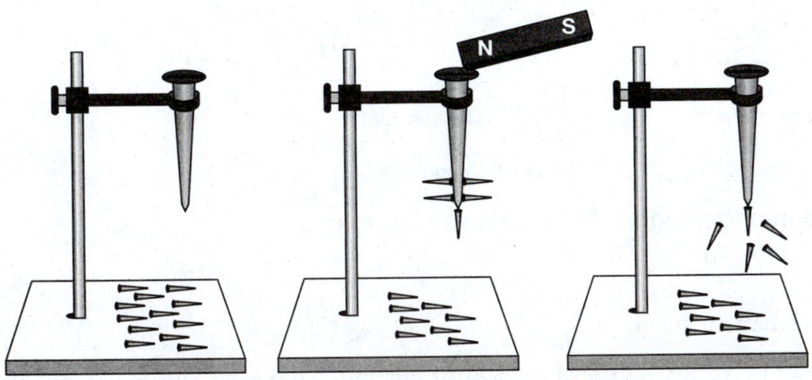

Figure 7.4 Magnetic induction method

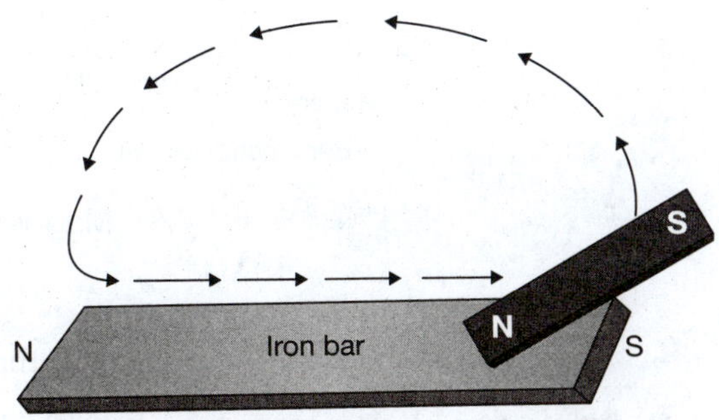

Figure 7.5 Single-touch method

2. **Single-touch Method:** Take a magnet and select its one pole. Use the same pole to rub it on an iron bar only in one direction for several times, as shown in the below figure:

3. **Double-touch Method:** Take two magnets of the same size and strength. Place the North Pole of one magnet and the South Pole of the other magnet in the middle of the iron bar. Rub both the magnets against the iron rod several times taking one magnet to one end of the iron bar and other magnet to the other end of the iron bar. Each time, start from the middle of the iron bar and rub up to its ends as shown in the Fig.7.5.:

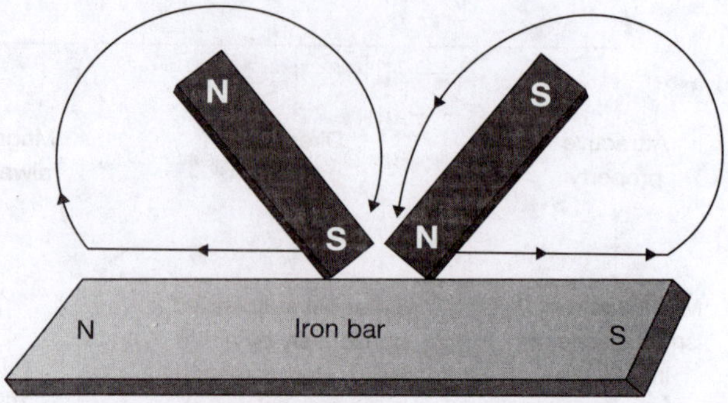

Figure 7.6 Double-touch method

4. **Electrical Method:** Materials such as iron or steel can be magnetized electrically by placing them in a coil of insulated wire which is connected to the battery as shown in the below figure. The magnet which is made using this method is called an electromagnet.

Generally, electromagnets are temporary magnets since soft iron is used. Soft iron cannot retain magnetism for a long time. Steel is used to make permanent magnets, since it can retain magnetism for a long time

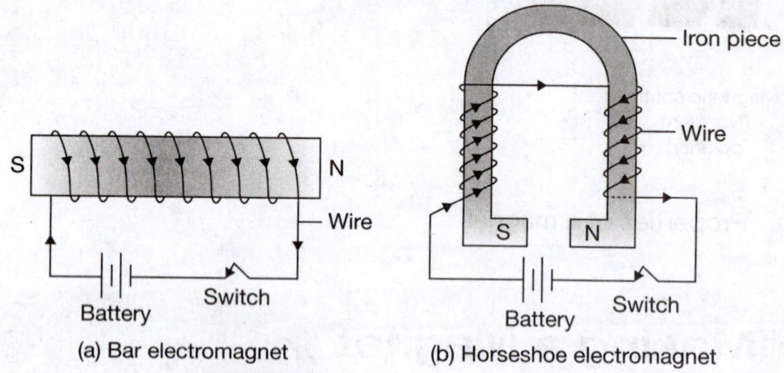

Figure 7.7 Electrical method

Info Bytes!

A magnet's strength can be increased by wrapping it with more coils or by increasing the current flowing through the coil.

Advantages of Electromagnets

1. They can be easily magnetized or demagnetized by turning the current on or off in the coil.

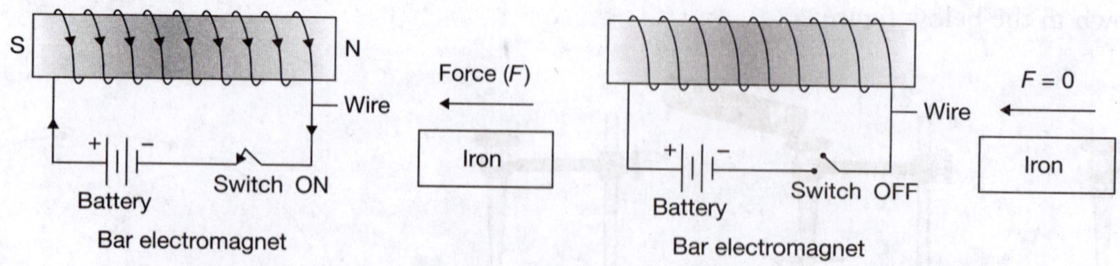

Figure 7.8 Magnetization or demagnetization of an electromagnet

2. These can be made stronger magnets than permanent magnets.

3. Poles of an electromagnet can be interchanged by reversing the direction of current. However, this is not possible in case of permanent magnet.

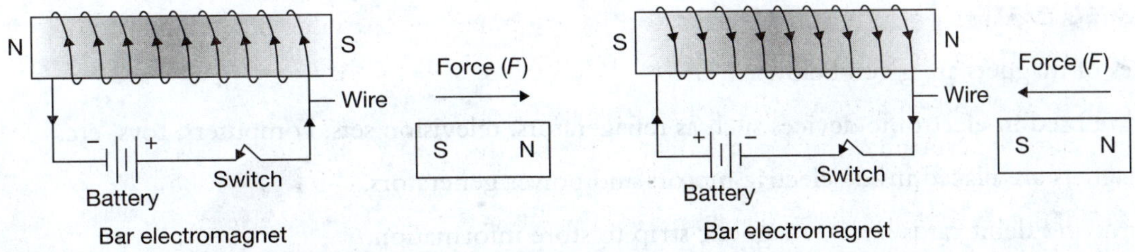

Figure 7.9 Interchanging poles of an electromagnet

4. Increase in the amount of current passing through the coil increases the strength of the electromagnet.
5. Increase in the number of turns of coil increases the strength of the electromagnet.

Uses of Electromagnets

- Loading or unloading heavy loads at shipyards, collecting the iron pieces from the scrap, etc.
- Used to remove small bits of iron lodged in the eyes.
- Used to show directions.
- Used in electric bells, loudspeakers, motors, etc.

Info Bytes!

Earth has a strong magnetic effect because Earth's core is composed of a mixture of iron and nickel.

Methods to Demagnetize a Material

1. Heating
2. Hammering
3. Self-demagnetization (this happens when a magnet is not used for a long time)
4. Passing AC current through coil wound over a magnet
5. Rough handling

Maintenance of Magnets

Magnets which are not in use should be stored in magnetic keepers. Improper care could lead to demagnetization of the magnet. It is observed that **self-demagnetization** takes place if the magnetic poles are left free, that is, magnets tend to lose their magnetism on their own.

Figure 7.10 Magnetic compass

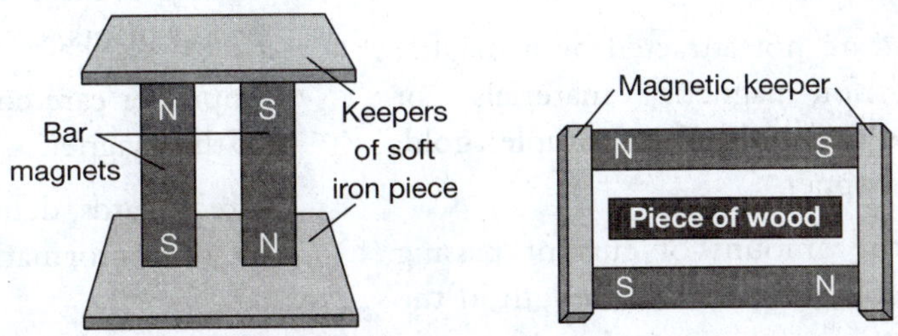

Figure 7.11 Storage of magnets

A magnetic keeper is a cardboard box with one or two soft iron bars. In a magnetic keeper, a pair of bar magnets is placed close to each other and a magnetic keeper is placed at the each end of the magnets.

Uses of Magnets

Some of the uses of magnets are given below:

1. Magnets are used in electronic devices such as refrigerators, television sets, computers, toys, etc.
2. Strong magnets are placed inside electric motors and power generators.
3. Credit cards and debit cards have a magnetic strip to store information.
4. Magnetic poles of a magnet helps in navigating through magnetic compass.
5. Electromagnets have wide industrial and non-industrial applications.

EXAMPLE 7.1 Why does a compass needle point towards the North when held horizontally on the Earth?

SOLUTION

A compass needle points towards the North when held horizontally on the Earth because the compass needle is a small magnet, and it aligns itself with the Earth's magnetic field. The Earth's magnetic south pole attracts the north pole of the compass needle, leading it to point towards the geographic North.

EXAMPLE 7.2 Why do most of the rivers flow towards the east?

SOLUTION

The rivers flowing east is due to the diamagnetic substance of water. So, it always turns perpendicular to the magnetic field of the Earth's magnetic field. This reason is one of the factors in which the direction of the flow of water depends.

POINTS TO REMEMBER

- ✔ A magnet is an object constituting an iron ore called magnetite, and thus, it can attract materials, such as iron, cobalt, nickel, etc.
- ✔ Materials that are not attracted by a magnet are called non-magnetic materials or ferromagnetic materials. For example, gold, silver, wood, copper.
- ✔ Increase in the amount of current passing through the coil increases the strength of the electromagnet.
- ✔ Electricity is generated using costly mechanisms, such as construction of dams to run water turbines, burning of coal in thermal power plants, etc.
- ✔ Improper care could lead to demagnetization of the magnet.
- ✔ Credit cards, debit cards have a magnetic strip to store information.

PRACTICE QUESTIONS CLASSROOM WING

Very Short Answer Type Questions

Direction for question from 1 to 8.
Select the correct alternative from the given options.

1. Mineral from which the first magnet was found is ______.
   (a) Iron (b) Magnus
   (c) Magnetite (d) Magnesia
2. Magnetism was first found around ______.
   (a) 500 BCE (b) 600 BCE
   (c) 700 BCE (d) 800 BCE
3. Lodestone means ______
   (a) Stone which does not attract iron pieces.
   (b) Stone which indicates the north–south direction.
   (c) Stone which behaves like a diamagnetic.
   (d) Substance which is non-magnetic in nature.
4. Which of the following is a non–magnetic substance?
   (a) Nickel (b) Iron
   (c) Cobalt (d) None of these
5. Freely suspended bar magnet comes to rest pointing north – south direction such that
   (a) The North Pole of bar magnet points to geometric North Pole of earth.
   (b) The North Pole of bar magnet points to geometric South Pole of earth.
   (c) The South Pole of bar magnet points to magnetic North Pole of earth.
   (d) The South Pole of bar magnet points to magnetic South Pole of earth.
6. Irrespective of shape, all magnets have ______.
   (a) Only the North Pole
   (b) Only the South Pole
   (c) A large number of poles
   (d) Both the North Pole and the South Pole
7. Dipping a bar magnet into a box of iron filings results in a larger number of iron filings stick to the poles or ends than at the center portion because ______.
   (a) Only ends are dipped in the box
   (b) They are ends of a magnet
   (c) They are easier to attach at the edges than at the centre
   (d) The strength of the magnet is more at the poles
8. **Assertion (A):** When a bar magnet is broken into two pieces, one end of the pieces attracts and the other end of the pieces repels.
   Reason (R): A magnetic monopole does not exist.
   (a) Both A and R are correct, and R is the correct explanation to A.
   (b) Both A and R are correct, but R is not the correct explanation to A.
   (c) A is correct but R is incorrect.
   (d) Both A and R are incorrect.

Short Answer Type Questions

9. Define the following terms.
   (a) Magnetic poles
   (b) Magnetic North Pole
   (c) Magnetic South Pole
   (d) Magnetic axis
   (e) Length of a bar magnet
   (f) Effective length of a bar magnet
   (g) Magnetic equator
10. What are the properties of a bar magnet?
11. What are the advantages of an electromagnet?
12. Mention some of the applications of a magnet.
13. Differentiate a temporary magnet from a permanent magnet.
14. What is meant by dipole in magnetism?
15. What is the use of compass for sailors?
16. Why are the magnets used in earphones or speakers?
17. A boy playing in sand with a magnet notices some dust or particles attracted to magnet. What does this imply?

18. Match the following.

Column A	Column B
(A) Naturally formed magnet	(a) Soft iron
(B) Diamagnetic substance	(b) Hammering
(C) Electromagnet	(c) Water
(D) Demagnetization	(d) Double-touch method
(E) Magnetization	(e) Loadstone

19. Explain with diagrams what happens when a bar magnet is cut into two pieces.

(a) Along its magnetic axis

(b) Along its magnetic equator

20. The north and south poles of a bar magnet are situated 0.4 cm inside from the geometric ends of the magnet. If the geometric length of the magnet is 6 cm, then its effective length is ______ mm.

(a) 48 (b) 52 (c) 56 (d) 54

21. Which of the following arrangements produces a stronger electromagnet and why?

(a)

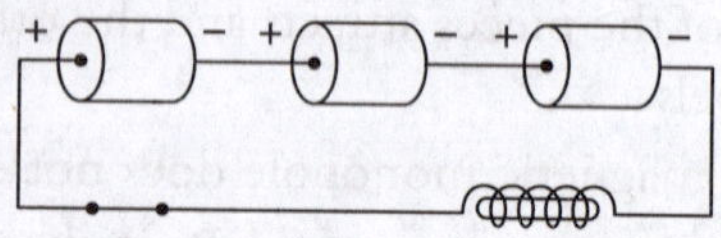

(b)

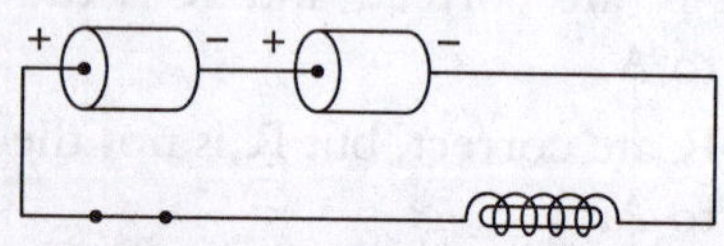

22. Which of the following arrangements produce stronger electromagnet and why?

(a)

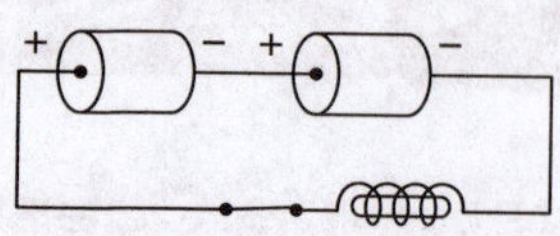

(b)

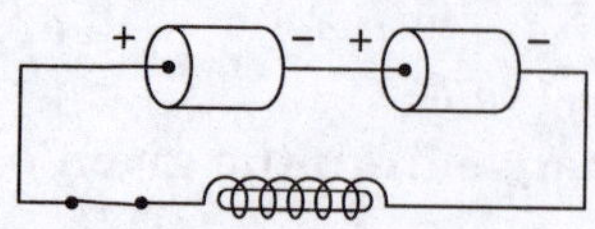

23. Consider a magnet which is hung to the hook of a spring as shown in figure. Then what could be the possible option from the following?

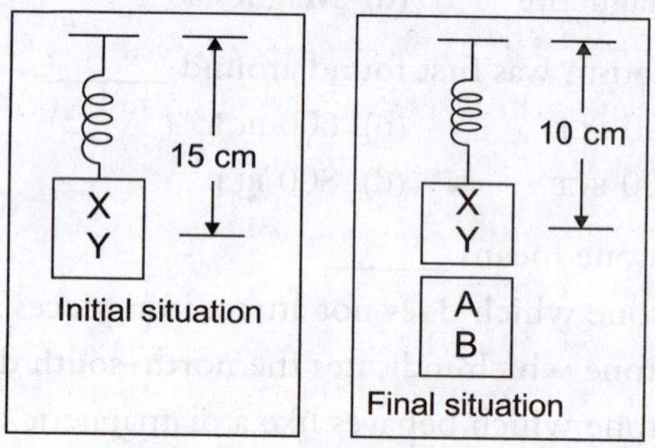

(i) X, A are North Pole and Y, B are South Pole

(ii) X, B are North Pole and Y, A are South Pole

(iii) A, B are South Pole and X, Y are North Pole

(iv) X, A are South Pole and Y, B are North Pole

(a) Only (ii) (b) Only (i)

(c) Both (i) and (ii) (d) Both (ii) and (iii)

Essay Type Questions

24. (a) What is meant by magnetizing a material and how does this happen?

(b) Why does the bar magnet suspended freely aligns itself in the north-south directions?

PRACTICE QUESTIONS COMPETITION WING

Level 1: Apply Your Concepts

Direction for questions from 1 to 5.
Fill in the blanks.

1. Every magnet has both ______.
2. Magnets made by human beings are called ______.
3. Magnetic substances which are strongly attracted by magnets are known as ______.
4. Large deposits of magnetite were found in Asia Minor in a district called ______.
5. The property of attracting iron by a magnet is called ______.

Direction for questions 6 and 7.
Select the correct alternative from the given options.

6. What happens if the material used to make the armature of an electric bell is changed to steel?
   (a) There will not be any change in the ringing of the bell.
   (b) Loudness of the bell ring gradually reduces.
   (c) Loudness of the bell ring gradually increases.
   (d) The hammer hits the gong for once and is likely to stop.
7. What will be the change in the length of each small bar magnet when a bigger bar magnet is cut into 4 equal parts parallel to the equatorial line?
   (a) One-fourth of the initial length
   (b) Half of the initial length
   (c) No change in its length
   (d) One-third of the initial length

Level 2: Review Your Concepts

8. A toy car (made of soft iron) and two bar magnets are arranged as shown in the figure. What would happen if the magnet 'A' is moved towards the car as shown in the figure?

   (a) The car will not have any impact due to the motion of the magnet.
   (b) The car moves away from magnet A.
   (c) The car moves towards magnet A.
   (d) The car moves till it is exactly mid-way between the two magnets.
9. Consider a magnet which is hung by the hook of a spring as shown in figure. Then what could be the possible option from the following to attain the final position shown in figure.

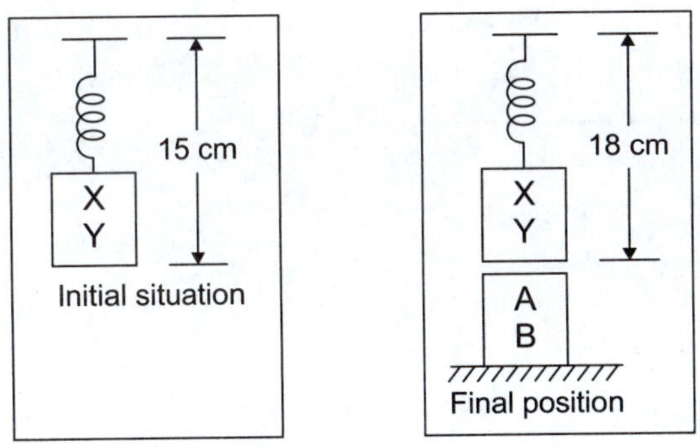

   (a) X, A are North Pole and Y, B are South Pole
   (b) X, B are North Pole and Y, A are South Pole
   (c) X, B are South Pole and Y, A are North Pole
   (d) X, A are South Pole and Y, B are South Pole

Level 3: Assess Your Concepts

10. The effective length of the first magnet is two times that of the second magnet. The effective length of the third magnet is one-third of the first magnet. If the effective length of the second magnet is 7.5 cm, the effective length of the third magnet is ______
(a) 5 cm (b) 15 cm
(c) 2.5 cm (d) 7.5 cm

11. Calculate the effective length of a magnet 'R' if effective length of magnet 'P' is twice of magnet 'Q' and effective length of 'R' is thrice of 'P' and effective length of 'Q' is 10 cm.

12. Define:
(a) Magnetism (b) Effective length

13. Draw and write a note on making a magnet by double torch method.

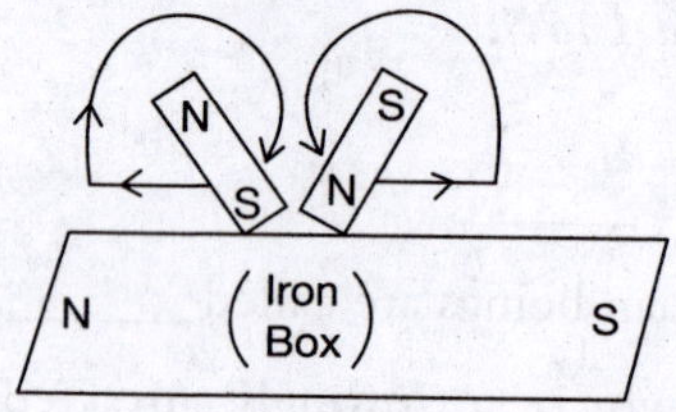

AT

ANSWER KEYS

Crossword

Across

2. Length
6. Magnetic
7. Magnetism
9. Temporary
10. Force
13. Steel
14. Soft iron

Down

1. North
3. Equator
4. Magnetic
5. Magnetite
8. Magnetisation
11. Poles
12. Axis

Classroom Wing

Very Short Answer Type Questions

1. (c)
2. (d)
3. (b)
4. (d)
5. (b)
6. (d)
7. (d)
8. (a)

Short Answer Type Questions

18. A → e, B → c, C → a, D → b, E → d
20. (b)
23. (a)

Competition Wing

Level 1: Apply Your Concepts

1. North and south poles
2. Artificial magnets
3. Ferromagnetic substances
4. Magnesia
5. Magnetism
6. (d)
7. (a)

Level 2: Review Your Concepts

8. (b)
9. (b)

Level 3: Assess Your Concepts

10. (a)
11. 60 cm

Hints and Explanations

CLASSROOM WING

Very Short Answer Type Questions

1. Mineral from which the first magnet was found is Magnetite.

2. Magnetism was first found around 800 BCE.

3. Lodestone means Stone which indicates the north–south direction.

8. Since the magnetic monopole does not exist, when a bar magnet is broken into two pieces, one end of the pieces attracts, and the other end of the pieces repels. Both A and R are correct, and R is the correct explanation to A.

   Hence, the correct option is (a).

Short Answer Type Questions

9. (i) **Magnetic poles:** The end points of a magnet where most of its magnetic power is concentrated are called poles of a magnet.

   (ii) **Magnetic North Pole:** The point N at the end of the freely suspended bar magnet which points towards the geographic North Pole is called magnetic North Pole.

   (iii) **Magnetic South Pole:** The point S at the end of the freely suspended bar magnet which points towards the geographic South Pole is called magnetic South Pole.

   (iv) **Magnetic axis:** An imaginary line passing through the magnetic North Pole and South Pole of a bar magnet is called magnetic axis.

   (v) **Length of a bar magnet:** Total distance from the North Pole to the centre of a magnet or the South Pole to the centre of a magnet is called length of a magnet.

   (vi) **Effective length:** The shortest length between the magnetic North Pole and the magnetic South Pole of a magnet is called effective length of the magnet.

   (vii) **Magnetic equator:** An imaginary line passing through the center of the magnet and perpendicular to the magnetic axis is called magnetic equator.

10. **Properties of a bar magnet:**
    - A magnet attracts small pieces of the iron and this property is called attractive property.
    - A freely-suspended bar magnet aligns itself in north–south direction of the earth and this is known as geographic directive property.
    - Like poles of a magnet repel and the unlike poles attract each other.
    - Magnetic poles always exist in pairs.

11. **Advantages of an electromagnet:**
    - They can be made stronger than any other permanent magnet.
    - These can be magnetized and demagnetized easily.
    - Increasing the amount of current increases the strength of the electromagnet.
    - Poles of an electromagnet can be interchanged by changing the direction of current.

12. **Some of the applications of magnet:**
    - Used in loud speakers, earphones, televisions, etc.
    - Used in magnetic compass, door bells, doors of cupboards, etc.
    - Used in toys.
    - Magnetic tapes used in tape recorders, etc.

13.

Temporary Magnet	Permanent Magnet
These magnets can retain magnetic properties as long as the magnetizing force acts on them.	These magnets do not lose their magnetic properties easily.
These are made up of soft iron.	These are made up of steel, cobalt and nickel.

14. Two poles, i.e., the North Pole and the South Pole separated by some distance is called dipole in magnetism.

15. Sailors travel according to the direction shown in the compass, since the magnetic needle aligns itself in the north-south direction.

16. Sound is produced due to vibration of objects. To produce vibration, you need something that itself vibrates and make air to vibrate. This can be achieved when a current carrying coil is placed near a magnet as arranged in earphones and speakers.

17. Those particles which are attracted to the magnet are small pieces or powder iron or any other magnetic substance. This happens when a magnet attracts magnetic substances.

18. (A) Naturally formed magnet → (e) Loadstone
(B) Diamagnetic substance → (c) Water
(C) Electromagnet → (a) Soft iron
(D) Demagnetization → (b) Hammering
(E) Magnetization → (d) Double-touch method
A → e, B → c, C → a, D → b, E → d

19. (a) (b)

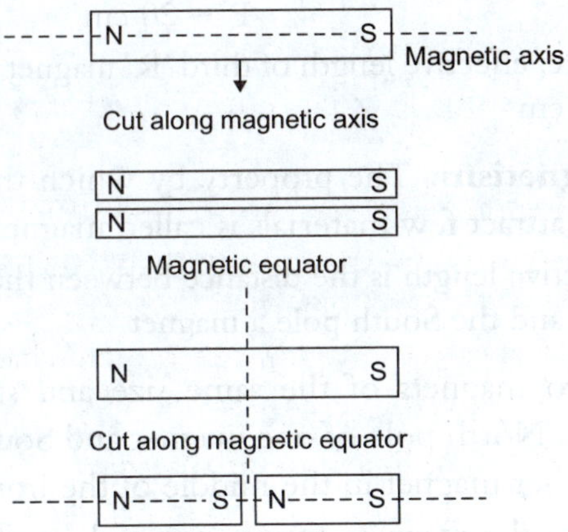

From (a) and (b) we can conclude that new poles exist at cut part of a bar magnet because each molecule acts as a tiny magnet.

20. Geometric length of the magnet = 6 cm.

Therefore, effective length of the magnet = 6 − (2 × (0.4))

= 5.2 cm

= 52 mm.

Hence, the correct option is (b).

21. Circuit in the figure 'a' produces stronger electromagnet than in the figure 'b'. Since in both the circuit the number of turns of wire wound around magnetic materials is of the same, but more cells are included in the circuit 'a'.

22. Circuit in the figure (b) produces a strong electromagnet because the number of turns of wire wound around the magnetic material is more than that in the circuit of figure (a) and the strength of magnet depends directly on the number of turns. Therefore, the magnetic material in circuit 'b' will become a stronger magnet when compared with 'a'.

23. In a pair of magnet, like poles repel and unlike poles attract each other. According to the figure, Y and A should be same poles. Since the distance has decreased from 15 cm to 10 cm, this means that A is repelling *y*.

Thus, X, B are North Pole and Y, A are South Pole.

Essay Type Questions

24. (a) A magnetic substance consists of many dipoles oriented in different directions. These dipoles, while getting magnetized, slowly orient in the direction of the magnetic field applied and this process is called magnetization.

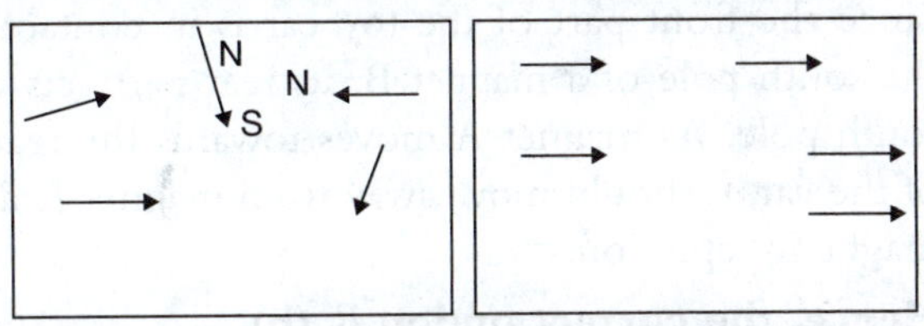

(b) A freely-suspended bar magnet aligns itself in north–south direction because the earth acts like a huge bar magnet with its North Pole facing towards geographic South Pole and magnetic South Pole towards geographic North Pole.

The North Pole of the suspended bar magnet gets attracted towards magnetic South Pole of the earth, i.e., the geographic North Pole.

COMPETITION WING

Level 1: Apply Your Concepts

6. The armature of an electric bell is generally made of soft iron because in an electric bell the armature needs to hit the gong several times as long as the push type switch is in ON condition. This can be achieved if the armature is made of material which has less magnetic retentive property (i.e. the material behaves like magnet only when the current passes through the insulated wire which is wound around it). Due to this temporary magnetism, the hammer hits the gong several times and this is how the bell rings in case of an electric bell. If the armature is made of steel, it exhibits permanent magnetism. Therefore, the hammer hits the gong once and remains in the same position.

   Hence, the correct option is (d).

7. If the bar magnet is cut into four equal parts perpendicular to the axial line, the length of each small magnet becomes ¼ th of the initial length.

   Hence, the correct option is (a).

Level 2: Review Your Concepts

8. Since the front part of the toy car is in contact with the south pole of a magnet B, its rear part acts as the south pole. As magnet A moves towards the rear part of the car, it should move away from magnet A due to magnetic repulsion.

   Hence, the correct option is (b).

9. In the second picture, it is observed that the spring length increased. This shows that the 'Y' part is attracting towards 'A', i.e., 'Y' and 'A' are oppossite poles.

Level 3: Assess Your Concepts

10. Effective length of second magnet = 7.5 cm.

    Therefore, effective length of the first magnet $= 2 \times 7.5$

    $= 15$ cm.

    Therefore, effective length of the third magnet $= 1/3 \times 15$ cm

    $= 5$ cm.

    Hence, the correct option is (a).

11. Effective length of 'Q' = 10 cm

    Effective length of first magnet $= 2 \times 10$

    'P' = 20 cm

    Therefore, effective length of third 'R' magnet is $= 3 \times 20 = 60$ cm

12. (a) **Magnetism:** The property by which the magnets attract few materials is called magnetism.

    (b) Effective length is the distance between the North pole and the South pole a magnet

13. Take two magnets of the same size and strength. Place the North pole of one magnet and South pole of the other magnet in the middle of the iron bar. Rub both the magnets against iron rod several times taking one magnet to one end of the iron bar and other magnet to other end of the iron bar. Start from the middle of iron bar and rub up to its ends

Unit II

Chemistry

In this Unit

CHAPTER

8

Mystery of Matter

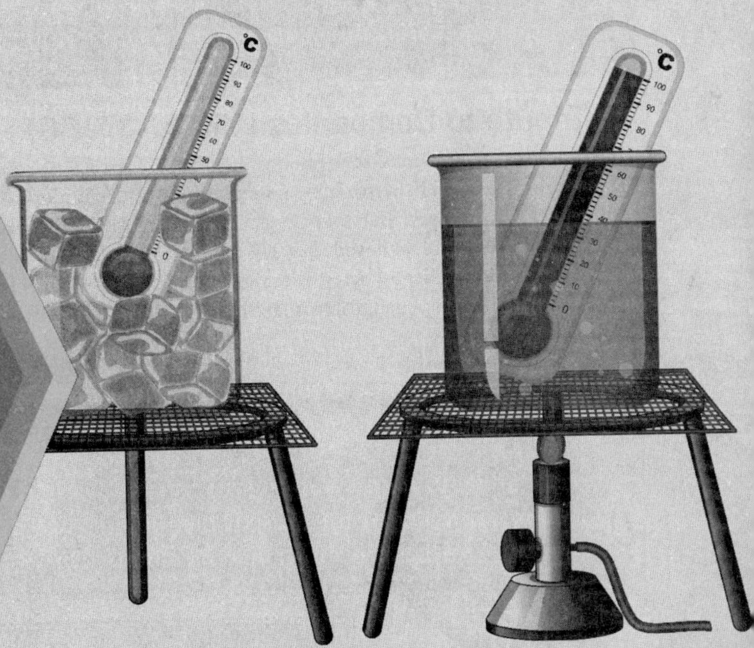

Remember

Before beginning this chapter, you should be able to:

- Classify materials around you
- Identify different states of matter solid, liquid, and gas

Key Ideas

After completing this chapter, you should be able to:

- Understand the classification of materials
- Describe composition of matter
- Explain different states of matter and their interconversion
- Understand mixtures, their types, and methods of separation

Scientific Crypt

A Tribute to Democritus (460BC-370BC)

Democritus, an ancient Greek philosopher, holds a special place in the history of science. His remarkable contributions to the understanding of matter have shaped our knowledge of the tiniest building blocks of the universe. He believed that all matter in the world is made up of tiny, indivisible particles and suggested that these particles are indestructible and unchangeable, making them the fundamental units of matter.

Democritus can be regarded as an extra ordinary thinker whose ideas have stood the test of time and continue to inspire scientists till date. His name would be etched in the history of science for naming the building blocks of matter as 'ATOMOS' along with his fellow philosophers Leucippus and Epicurus. Even centuries after his era, the term 'Atom' derived from 'Atomos' of his times continues to rule the modern-day science in spite of unimaginably huge progress made in Science and emergence of enormous number of branches of science.

FUN TIME

CROSSWORD

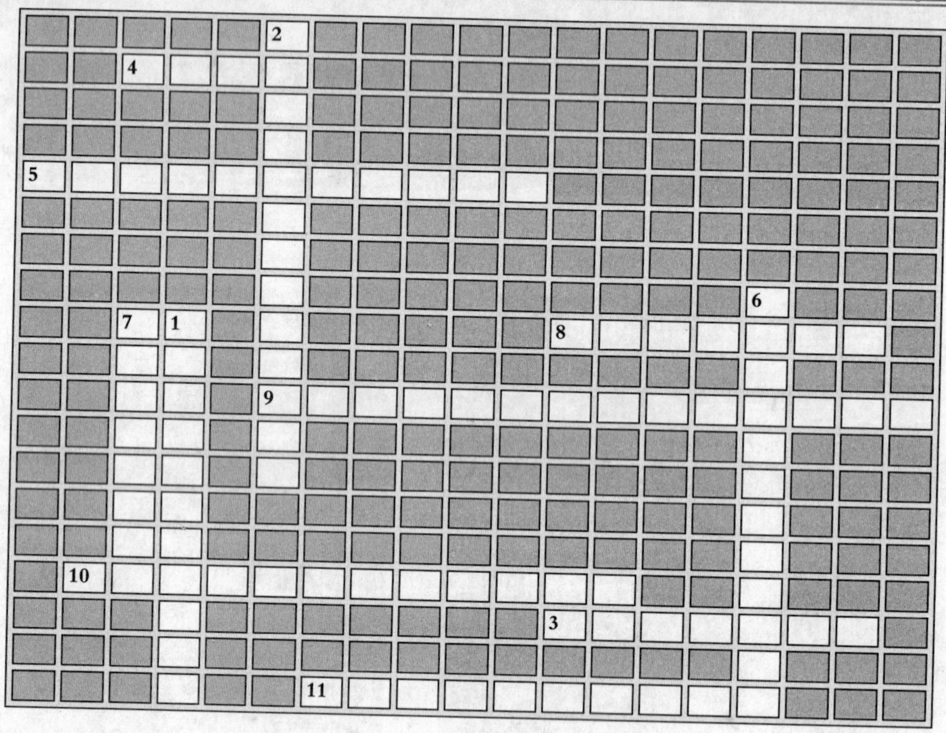

Across

3. Process that helps fine solid particles in a solid-liquid mixture to settle faster with the addition of a chemical.
4. Substances which contain only one kind of molecule are termed as this.
5. Solids that directly changes from solid state to gaseous state
8. The point on temperature scale at which a liquid starts changing into gas or vapour.
9. The spaces between molecules are described by this term.
10. Mixtures with a non-uniform distribution of molecules.
11. Method use for separation of solid from liquid

Down

1. Pouring out the clear liquid after sedimentation without disturbing the sediment.
2. The settling down of suspended, insoluble heavy solid particles in a solid-liquid mixture over time.
6. The process of converting a gas into its liquid state by cooling.
7. Type of forces of attraction among similar molecules of a liquid.

INTRODUCTION

In our day-to-day life, we see many things around us. Some of them might be living like, birds, insects, animals, plants, etc., whereas some other might be non-living like, bus, chair, desk, pen, books, etc. All the things, we observe around us, vary from each other in some way or another. They might have different size, shape, origin, and so on. In this chapter, we will discuss about materials and how to classify them on various basis.

Properties of Materials

The list of objects or entities that we come across in our day-to-day life is infinite; however, it can be classified as living things and non-living things. The non-living things are made up of wide range of materials. The chemistry deals with the study of these materials.

Examples of materials: Wood, glass, steel, metals, leather, concrete, cotton, etc.

These materials differ with respect to various properties. Therefore, the materials can be categorized in many ways on the basis of different parameters.

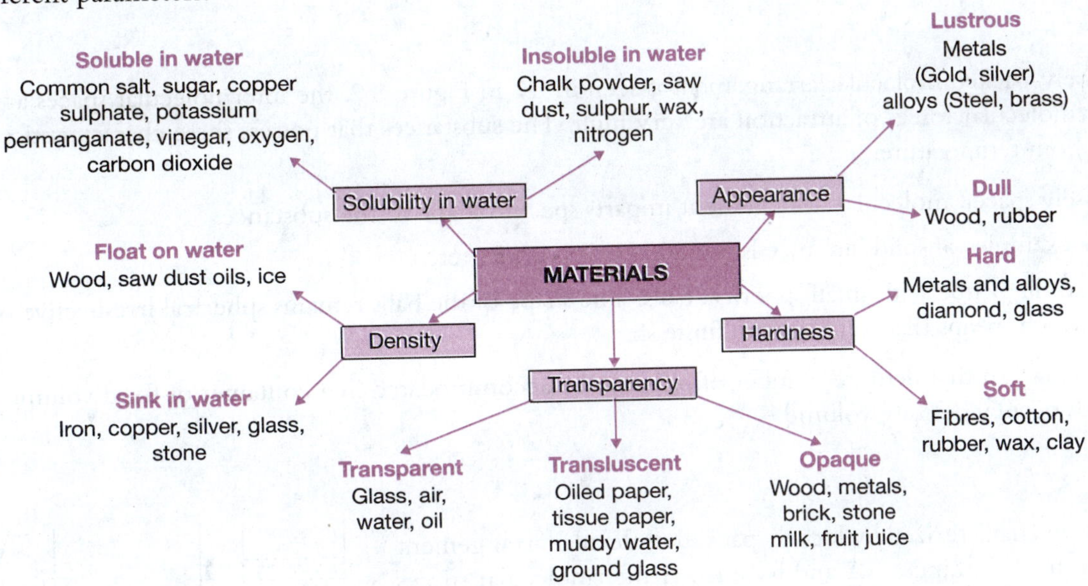

Figure 8.1 Properties of Materials

Matter and Its Composition

The common things that we observe in all the above materials are:

1. They possess mass.
2. They occupy space.

Anything that has mass and occupies space is called **matter**. Matter is made up of small tiny particles which are the building blocks of matter. These are called molecules.

Molecule can be defined as the smallest particle of matter, which can exist independently and retain all the properties of the substance.

Everything we see around us is made up of millions and millions of molecules.

> **Info Bytes!**
> The word 'matter' comes from the Latin word 'materia,' meaning substance or material. All matter is made up of tiny particles. Whether it's a solid, liquid, or gas, these particles are in constant motion, just at different speeds.

States of Matter

Let us now see the various ways in which molecules can be arranged. Molecules are assumed to be hard spheres. How does this arrangement influence the nature of the substances?

The spaces between the molecules are called **intermolecular spaces** and the forces of attraction holding these molecules are called **intermolecular forces of attraction.**

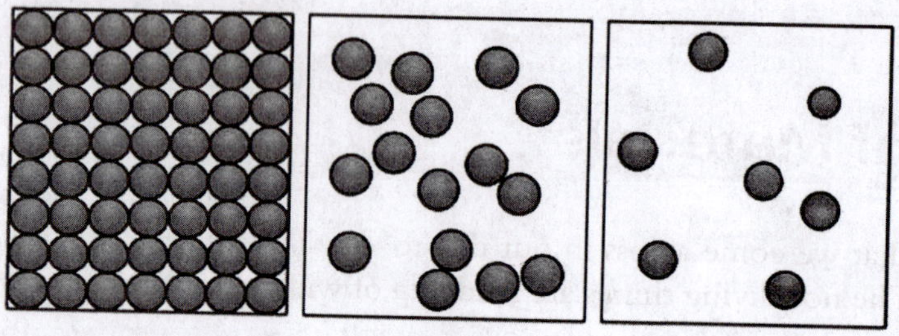

Figure 8.2 Intermolecular spaces in solids, liquids and gases

Solids

- The closely-packed molecular arrangement is seen in 'X' in Figure 8.2, the intermolecular spaces are very less and the intermolecular forces of attraction are very high. The substances that possess these characteristics exist in **solid** state at room temperature.
- This closely spaced molecular arrangement imparts specific shape to the substance.

Some of the examples of solids are metals, woods, chalks, stones, etc.

Example: Try to fill a cube with small spherical balls. The shape of the balls remains spherical irrespective of the shape of the container which means that solid has a definite shape.

- You can also find that definite number of balls can be accommodated in a container of fixed volume which means that solids occupy definite volume.

Liquids

- **Liquids** are characterized by loosely packed molecular arrangement as shown in 'Y' in Figure 8.2 and have larger intermolecular spaces and weaker intermolecular forces of attraction. The molecules have slightly greater freedom of movement.
- Liquids occupy definite volume but do not possess definite shape. *Example:* The same amount of water is taken in three containers A, B, and C (Figure 8.3). In all the cases, water takes the shape of the container. The water fills the same amount of space in all the containers.

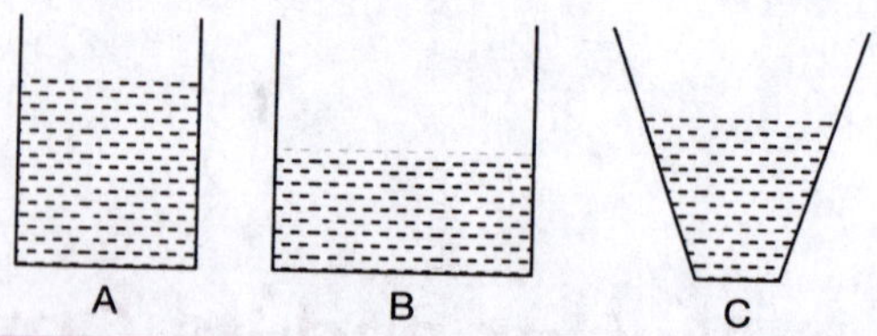

Figure 8.3 Water taking the shape of the container in which it is kept

- In case of liquids, the intermolecular forces of attraction can be of two types. As the liquid is always associated with a solid surface or a container, there exist two kinds of forces of attraction.

The forces of attraction among the molecules of the liquid (similar molecules) is known as **cohesive forces**. The forces of attraction between the molecules of the liquid and the molecules of solid (container or surface; dissimilar molecules) is known as **adhesive forces**.

Example: Water taken in a glass tumbler.

The adhesive forces are stronger than the cohesive forces. Hence, the water sticks the surface of glass.

Gases

- The arrangement shown in 'Z' in Figure 8.2, represents very loosely packed molecular arrangement which is the characteristic of **gases**. The number of molecules is much less than the number of molecules which can be accommodated in the space.
- The intermolecular spaces are very large with negligible intermolecular forces of attraction.

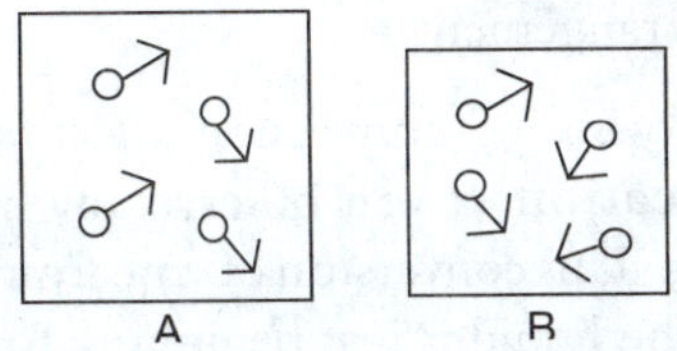

Figure 8.4 Gas filling the entire space of the container it is kept in

Example: 'A' and 'B' are two closed containers (shown in Figure 8.4). The gas in A is transferred to B which is smaller in size than A. In both the containers, the gas fills the entire space. This implies that gases have no definite shape or definite volume.

Table 8.1 Comparison of Properties of Solids, Liquids, and Gases

Property	Solids	Liquids	Gases
Shape	Definite	Not definite, takes the shape of the container	Not definite
Intermolecular forces	Strong	Weaker than solids	Weakest
Compressibility	Cannot be compressed	Compressible to an extent	Easily compressed
Diffusion	Do not diffuse	Diffuse easily	Diffuse easily and quickly
Density	High	Less	Very low

Interconversion of States of Matter

Matter can change its states depending upon the changes in its physical environment. This phenomenon of changing states is often referred as **interconversion of states of matter**. We will understand the changes involved during the interconversion by discussing some of the changes we observed in our daily life.

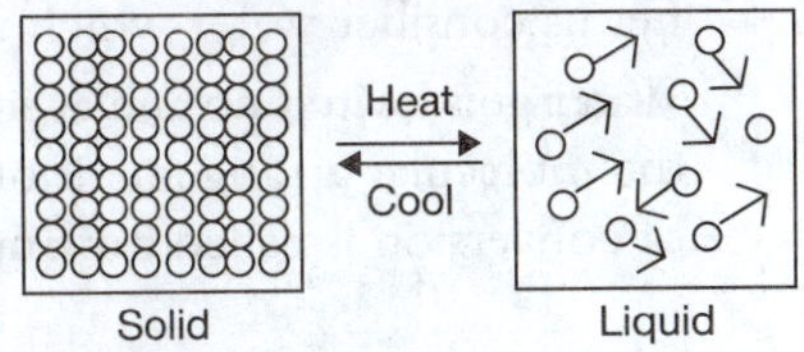

Figure 8.5 Interconversion of solid and liquid states

1. *When an ice block is kept on the table, you find that the ice block is reduced in size and water is formed.*

   Ice block is in solid state. Water is in liquid state. Ice is converted into water as it absorbs some amount of heat from its surroundings. The heat absorbed decreases the forces of attraction between the molecules. The closely packed molecular arrangement changes to a loosely packed molecular arrangement.

Changes occurring during interconversion of solid and liquid states.

(a) Closely packed molecular arrangement ⇌ Loosely packed molecular arrangement

(b) Less intermolecular spaces ⇌ Greater intermolecular spaces

(c) Greater intermolecular forces of attraction ⇌ Lesser intermolecular forces of attraction

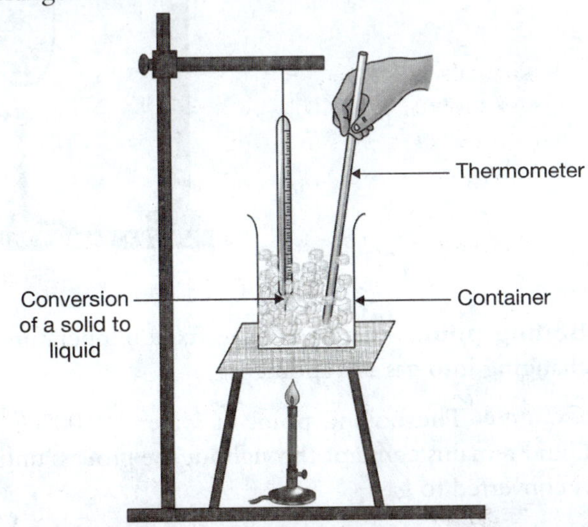

Figure 8.6 Conversion of solid to liquid state by heating

The process of conversion of solid state to liquid state by heating is called **melting** or **fusion**. If you observe any solid, on heating, it becomes hot and melts only on prolonged heating.

This conversion of state from solid to liquid happens at a particular temperature where the solid is just beginning to change into liquid. **Melting point** is defined as the temperature at which a solid starts changing into liquid and the actual conversion of state takes place.

2. *When water is kept in a deep freezer in refrigerator for few hours, it gets solidified to ice.*

   In this case, heat is taken out from water and the intermolecular forces of attraction increases. The loosely-packed molecular arrangement changes to the closely-packed molecular arrangement.

The process of conversion of liquid to solid on cooling is called **freezing** or **solidification**. If you observe any liquid, on cooling, it solidifies only on prolonged freezing. This conversion of state from liquid to solid happens at a particular temperature where the liquid is just beginning to change into solid. **Freezing point** of a liquid is defined as the fixed temperature at which a liquid starts changing into solid and the actual conversion of state takes place.

Konnect

The freezing point of a liquid is equal to the melting point of the solid.

Example: Freezing point of pure water is 0°C which is equal to the melting point of ice.

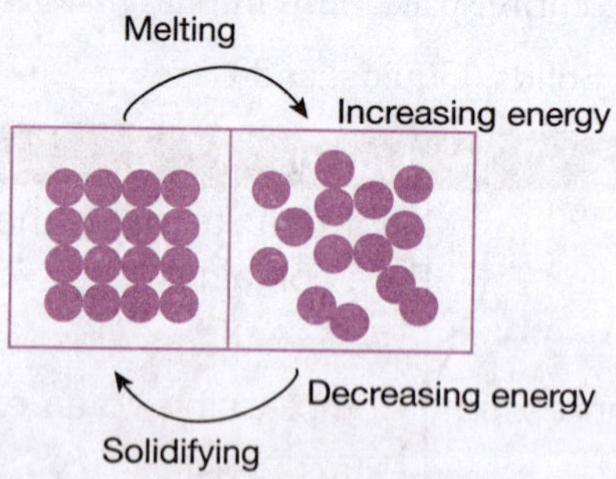

Figure 8.7 Interconversion of solid and liquid states

3. Let us consider water which is subjected to heating.
   Water gets heated up and at some stage, steam comes out of the container. This is because the heat supplied changes the molecular arrangement of the substance from loosely packed to very loosely packed arrangement. This process of conversion is called **boiling**.

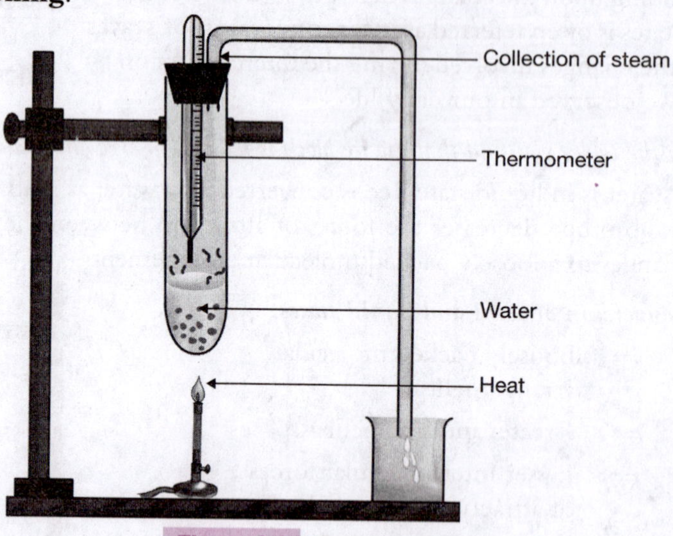

Figure 8.8 Boiling of water

Boiling point is defined as the fixed temperature at which a liquid starts changing into gas or vapour.

Example: The boiling point of water is 100°C. The boiling point of a liquid remains constant throughout the process until when the entire liquid is converted to gas.

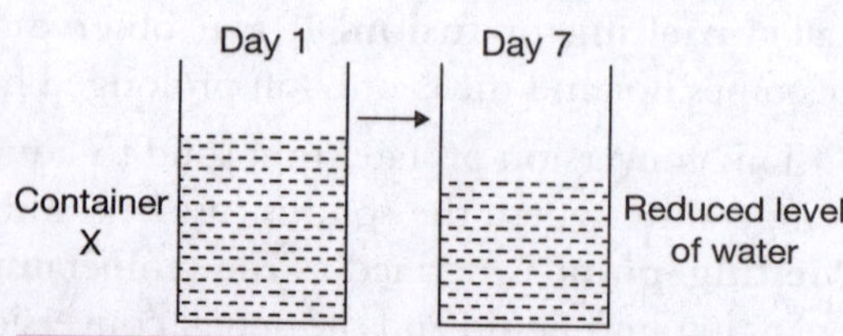

Figure 8.9 Demonstration of process of evaporation

Now, let us assume 50 mL of a liquid is taken in a graduated cylindrical container X. What happens if it is left for few days without heating? You find that the level of water is reduced. That means even without heating, the liquid is converted into gas or vapour. This process is called evaporation. **Evaporation** can be defined as the process of conversion of a liquid to vapour (without heating) at any temperature below the boiling point.

Table 8.2 Differences between Boiling and Evaporation

Boiling	Evaporation
Takes place at a fixed temperature (boiling point).	Takes place at any temperature below the boiling point.
Takes place in the entire bulk of the liquid.	Takes place only at the surface of the liquid.
Fast process	Slow process

4. Let us now carry out an activity:
   Let us keep a beaker containing ice cubes on a table for few minutes. You can find some water droplets on the outer surface of the beaker. Water vapour when comes into contact with ice cold beaker gets cooled and then gets condensed into water drops which get accumulated on the surface of beaker.
   The reverse process of evaporation is called condensation. Vapour on cooling gives the corresponding liquid.

The process of conversion of gas into its liquid state by cooling is called **liquefaction** or **condensation**. The **condensation point** can be defined as the temperature at which a gas changes into its liquid state. The boiling point of a liquid and the condensation point of the gas have the same numerical value.

Example: Condensation point of steam is 100°C which is equal to the boiling point of water.

We know that a solid on heating is generally converted into liquid state. Let us now consider what happens if some amount of solid camphor is heated. You can observe the vapours of camphor coming out. You do not find any liquid substance in the container.

It means that certain solids on heating get converted into their gaseous state directly without passing through the liquid state. This process is called **sublimation**. The solids which undergo this conversion are called **sublimable solids**.

Info Bytes!

Dry ice, or solid carbon dioxide, sublimates directly from a solid to a gas when exposed to air.

Examples: Naphthalene, dry ice, ammonium chloride, iodine.

Sublimation is the process of direct conversion of solid to vapour.

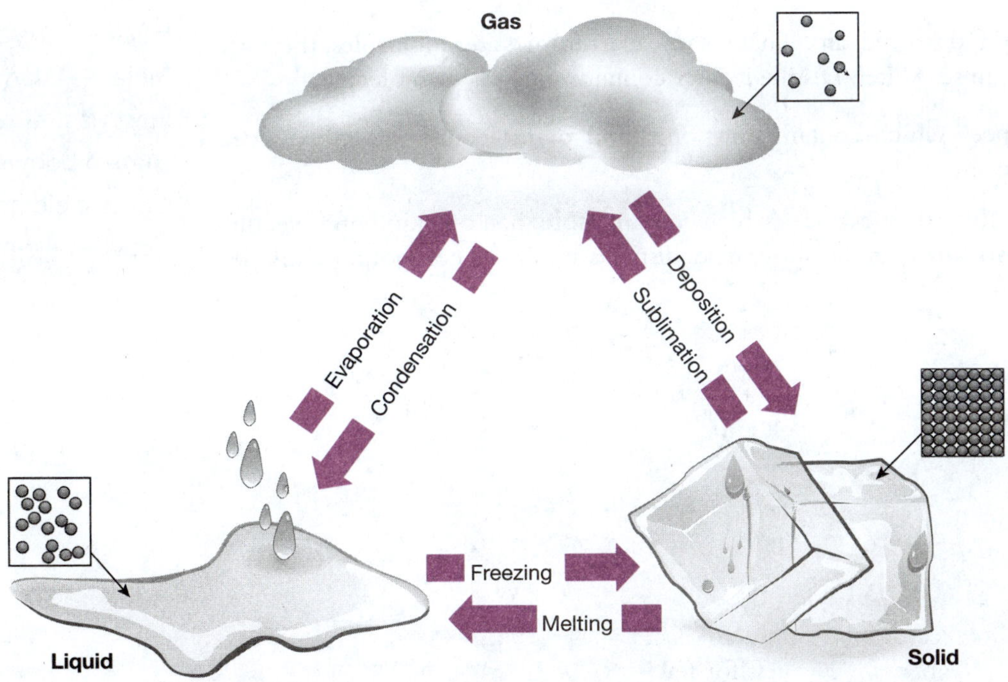

Figure 8.10 States of matter and their interconversion

EXAMPLE 8.1

Two substances *A* and *B* have a single free surface. They are subjected to cooling. After cooling, *A* retains its single free surface while *B* transitions to a state with multiple free surfaces. Comment on the nature of *A* and *B*.

SOLUTION

A and *B* are liquids as they have a single free surface. On cooling, *A* remains in the liquid state, indicating that it does not freeze at the given temperature. However, *B* transitions to a solid state, as it now has multiple free surfaces. That means *B* undergoes freezing. *A* is a liquid below its freezing point at the given conditions, whereas *B* is a typical liquid that solidifies upon cooling.

EXAMPLE 8.2

A solid *A* floats on oil, but sinks in a liquid syrup. And a solid *B* sinks in both oil and syrup. A solid *C* floats both in oil and in the syrup. Draw a comparison among the densities of *A*, *B*, and *C* and justify.

SOLUTION

Since *A* floats on oil, the density of *A* is less than the density of oil. But the density of *A* is more than that of the syrup. Solid *B* sinks in oil and syrup, which means its density is greater than oil and syrup, Solid *C* floats on both oil and syrup, which means its density is less than both oil and syrup. The order of densities of *A*, *B*, and *C* is:

Solid *B* > Oil > Solid *A* > Syrup > Solid *C*.

Composition of Matter

The arrangement of molecules determines the physical state of a substance. However, the composition of a substance determines the nature of the substance.

Let us take the case of sea water and distilled water. We are aware that the sea water tastes salty while the distilled water has a bland taste. What is the reason for this difference in taste?

Sea water contains dissolved salts. That means, apart from water molecules, there are salt molecules also in sea water. Distilled water contains only water molecules.

1. The substances which contain only one kind of molecules are called **pure substances**.
2. Contrary to this, the substances which contain more than one kind of molecules are called **mixtures**. In the above case, distilled water is a compound while sea water is a mixture.

Konnect

Abundant elements

Air → Nitrogen

Earth → Oxygen

Metal → Aluminium

Inert gas → Argon

Human body → Oxygen

Lightest element → Hydrogen

Heaviest element → Uranium

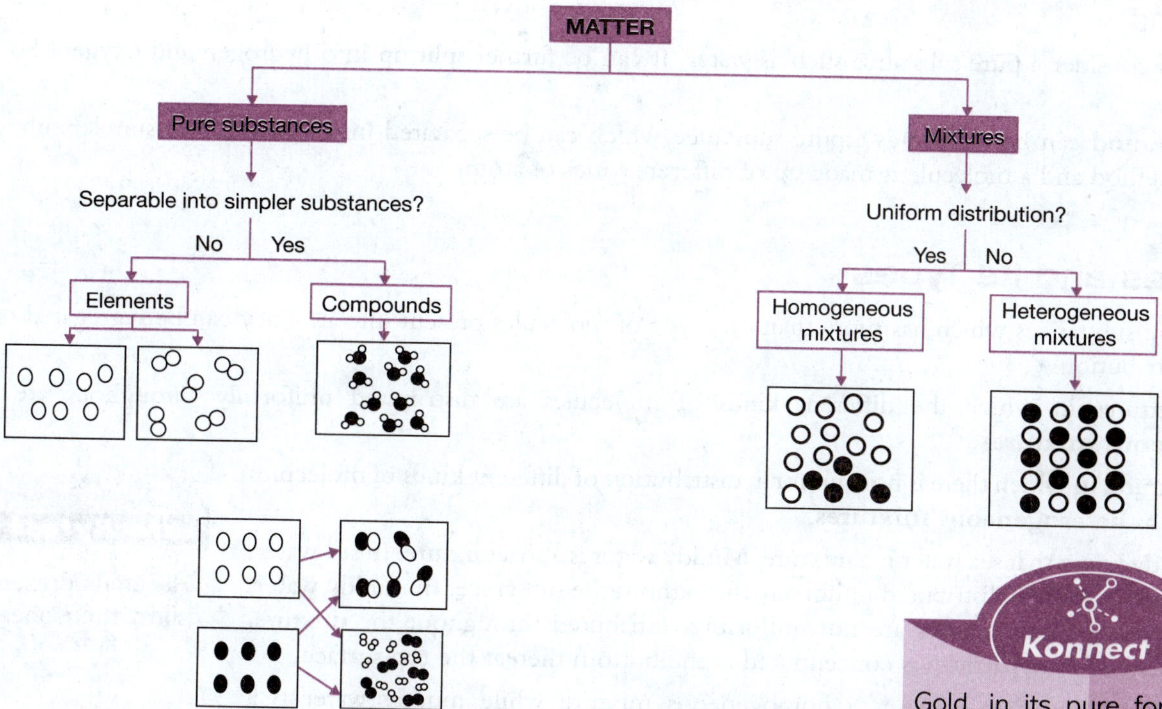

Figure 8.11 Classification of matter

Konnect

Gold, in its pure form, is so soft that you can mold it with your hands.

Pure Substances

As discussed above, pure substances contain only one type of molecules and are absent of any other impurities. They can be further divided into elements and compounds, based on their ability to separate.

Element

The oxygen and hydrogen formed from water cannot be further split up into simpler substances. Such substances are called elements. Elements are the basic substances from which millions of substances are formed.

An **element** can be defined as a pure substance which cannot be separated into simpler substances by any chemical means. Every element is made up of constituent particles called molecules. A molecule is made up of similar kind of atoms.

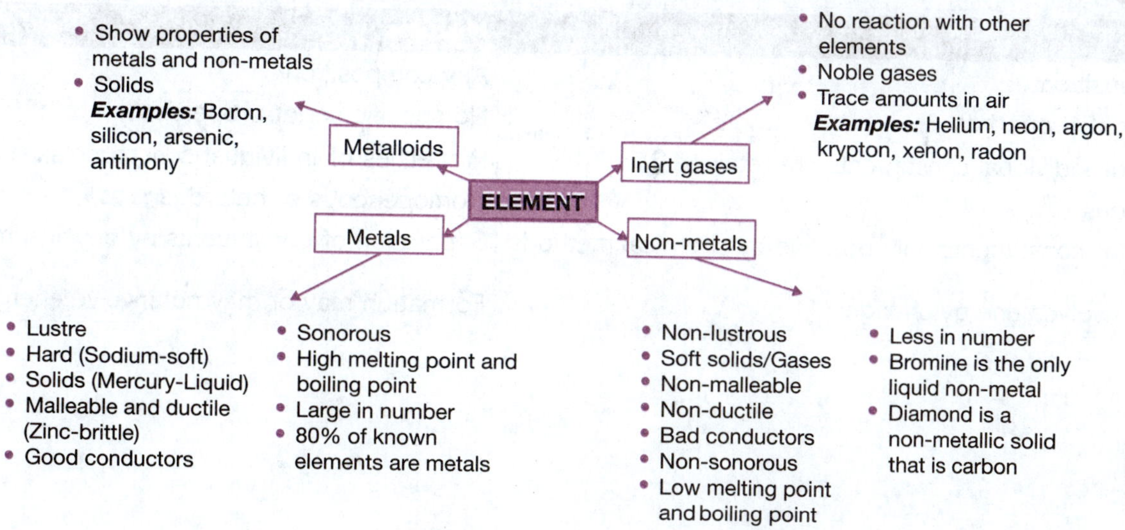

Figure 8.12 Properties of elements

Compound

Now, let us consider a pure substance such as water. It can be further split up into hydrogen and oxygen. So, water is a compound.

A **compound** can be defined as a pure substance which can be separated into two or more simpler substances by a chemical method and a molecule is made up of different kinds of atoms.

Mixtures and its Types

Mixtures are substances which has more than one type of molecules present into it. They can be segregated on the basis of their distribution.

The mixtures in which the different kinds of molecules are distributed uniformly throughout are known as **homogeneous mixtures.**

The mixtures in which there is non-uniform distribution of different kinds of molecules are known as **heterogeneous mixtures.**

Info Bytes!

Helium is present in sun's atmosphere.

We already know that sea water is a mixture. Muddy water is also a mixture. In sea water, the molecules of salt are distributed uniformly throughout the substance. In muddy water, the molecules of mud particles are not uniformly distributed throughout the mixture. More number of mud particles is concentrated at the bottom then at the top surface.

In the above case, sea water is a homogeneous mixture while muddy water is a heterogeneous mixture.

A mixture may contain any number of constituents.

Let us consider a mixture of iron and sulphur. Both are elements.

Let us consider another mixture of oxygen and carbon dioxide used for artificial breathing for patients. Oxygen is an element while carbon dioxide is a compound.

If we consider a solution of common salt in water, both the constituents are compounds.

Depending on the physical states of the constituents, the mixtures can be of various types.

Table 8.3 Differences between compounds and mixtures

Compounds	Mixtures
Fixed composition	Any composition
Specific set of properties	No specific set of properties
Properties of individual constituents not retained	Properties of individual constituents retained
Homogeneous	Homogeneous or heterogeneous
Separation of constituents only possible by chemical methods	Separation of constituents by physical methods
Formation involves energy change	Formation may or may not involve energy change

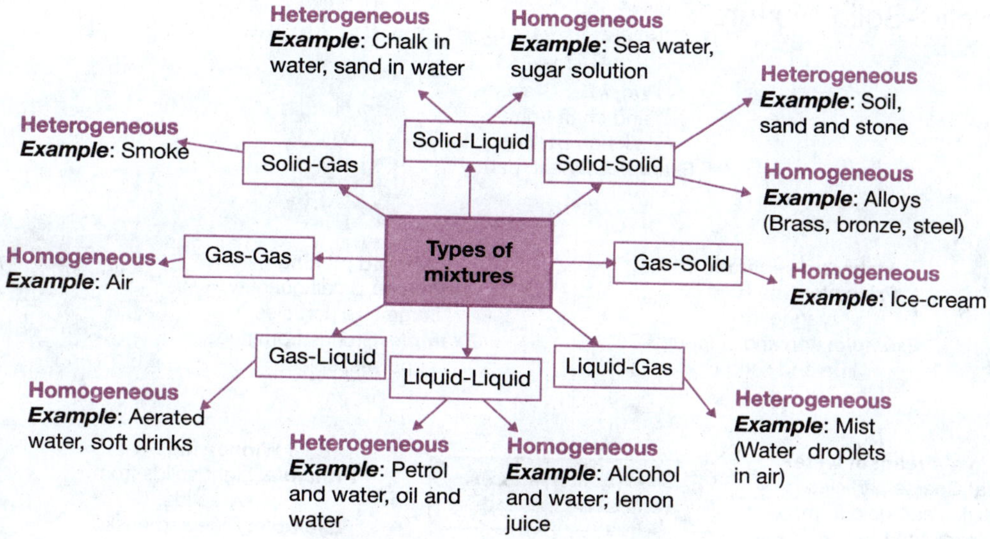

Figure 8.13 Types of mixtures

EXAMPLE 8.3 Sodium is a soft metal and chlorine is a gaseous non-metal but sodium chloride is a brittle solid. Give reason.

SOLUTION

Sodium and chlorine combine chemically to form sodium chloride, which is a compound. In a compound, the constituent elements do not retain their properties. Therefore, sodium chloride gets a new set of properties which is completely different from sodium and chlorine.

Separation of Mixtures

Is water a pure substance or a mixture? Naturally available river water or sea water is not a pure substance. It is a mixture as all these forms of water that contain dissolved salts and gases. You know that water is used for various purposes. Can we use this natural water for all purposes?

No, water required for the preparation of medicines, research laboratories, car batteries, etc., should be completely pure. That means all the dissolved salts should be removed from water. So, separation of mixtures is important.

Uses of Separation of Mixtures:

1. Removal of undesirable and harmful substances from the naturally available substances.
2. Extraction of useful substances from the natural materials.
3. Purification of synthetic substances.

Info Bytes!

A machine for the separation of atoms according to mass was invented by Francis Aston for which he won a Noble prize in Chemistry!

Methods of Separation

The methods of separation of mixtures depend upon:

1. Type of mixture
2. Characteristic properties of the constituents

Separation of Solid–Solid Mixture

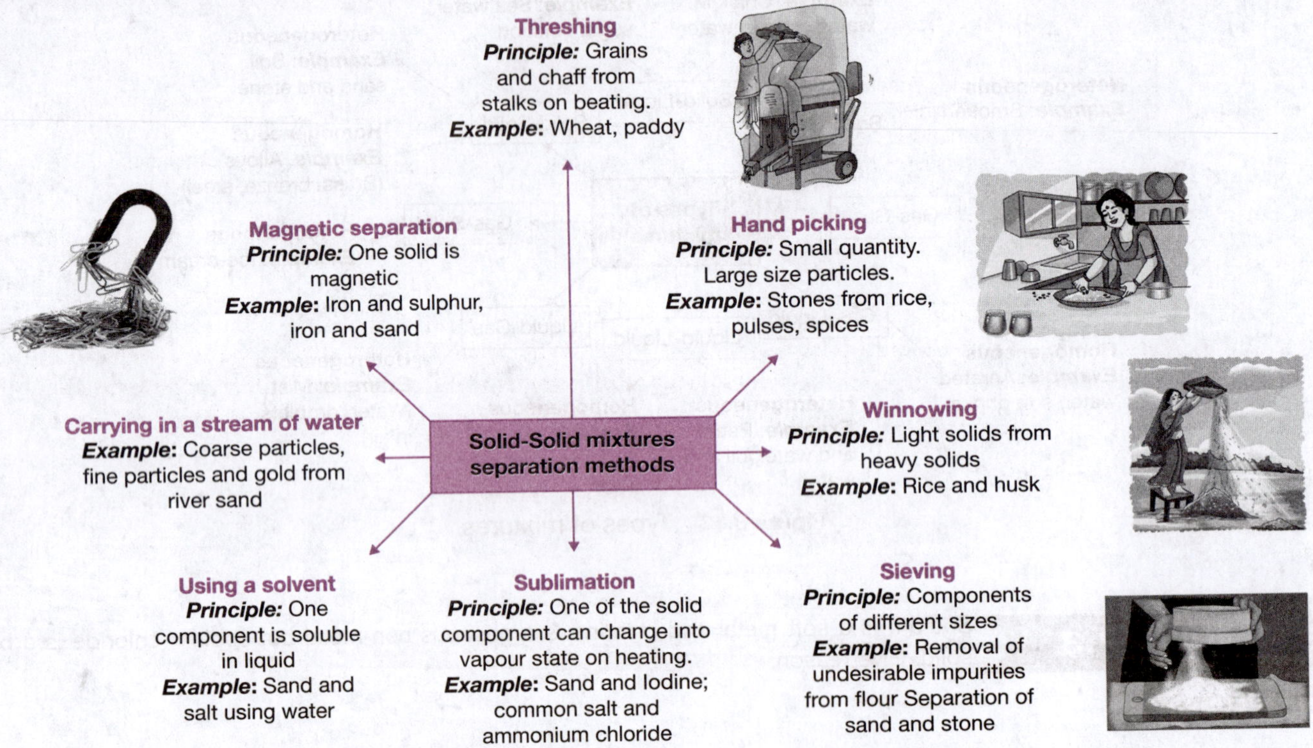

Figure 8.14 Separation of solid-solid mixtures

Separation of Solid–Liquid Mixture

1. **Sedimentation and Decantation:** When muddy water is taken and allowed to stand for some time, the solid mud particles settle down at the bottom. The settling down of suspended, insoluble heavy solid particles in a solid – liquid mixture on long standing is called **sedimentation**. The process of pouring out the clear liquid after sedimentation without disturbing the sediment is called **decantation**.

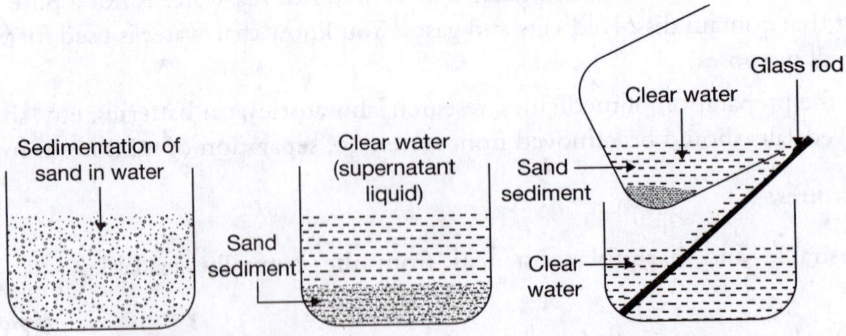

Figure 8.15 Sedimentation and decantation processes

2. **Loading or Coagulation:** The above liquid may still contain some fine particles which do not settle down. This method can be taken up for further settling down of the fine particles. That means, when a river water sample containing sand and clay is taken, the sand settles down on standing. But the clay particles are not heavy enough to settle down. When alum is added, it forms clusters with clay and allows them to settle down. The process of helping fine solid particles in a solid – liquid mixture to settle faster by the addition of special chemical, such as alum is called **loading**.

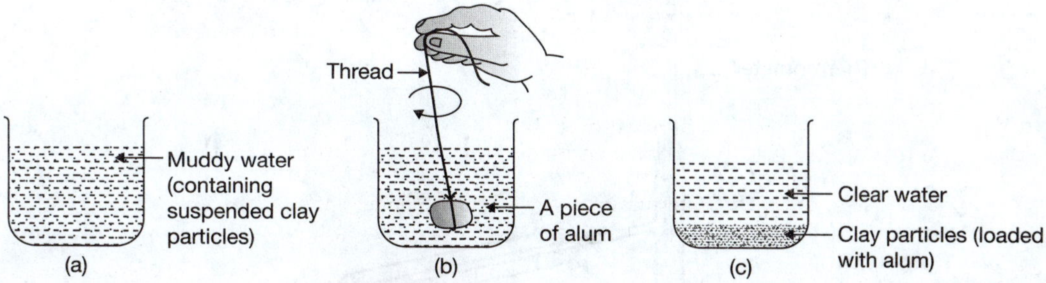

Figure 8.16 Loading process

3. **Filtration:** Very fine solid particles still remain in the water. They can be removed by the process of filtration. The process of separation of solid particles from a liquid when the mixture is allowed to pass through a filter is called **filtration**. Sand, charcoal, cotton, glass-wool, unglazed porcelain and filter paper are the filtering materials. Insoluble solid left on the filter is called **residue**. Liquid which passes through filter is called **filtrate**.

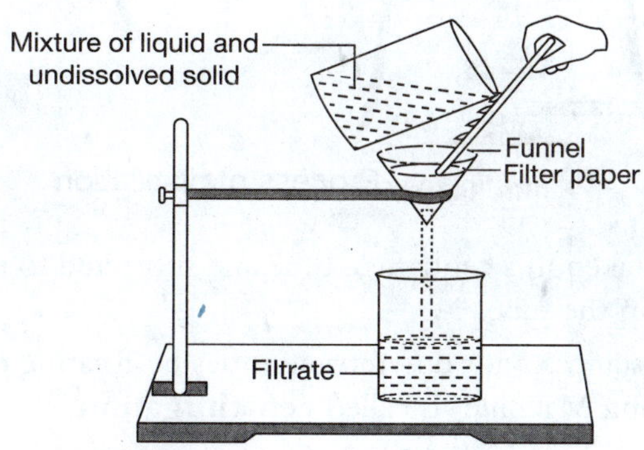

Figure 8.17 Process of filtration

4. **Evaporation:** When salt water is subjected to heating, water gets vaporized leaving behind the crystals of salt. The process of converting a liquid into vapour state either by exposing it to air or by boiling it results in the crystallization of the solid component, is known as **evaporation**.

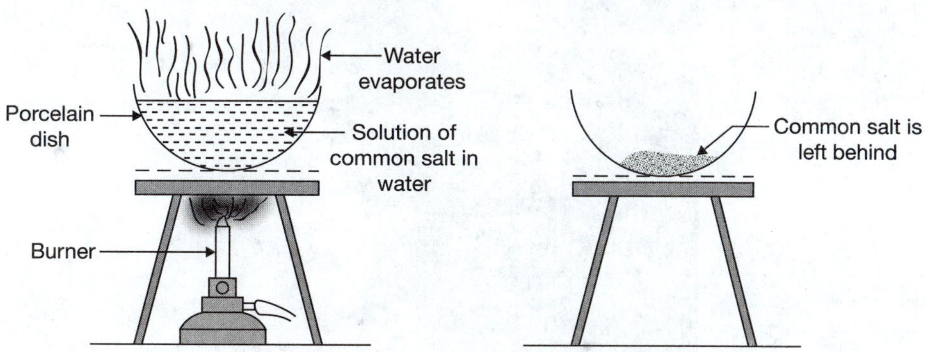

Figure 8.18 Process of evaporation

5. **Distillation:** When the same sea water is taken in a distillation flask fitted with a condenser and is subjected to heating till the boiling point of water, the water is collected in a receiver flask while the salt is left behind in the distillation flask.

Heating of a mixture until when the boiling point of liquid is followed by cooling of vapours results in the recovery of liquid component along with the solid component.

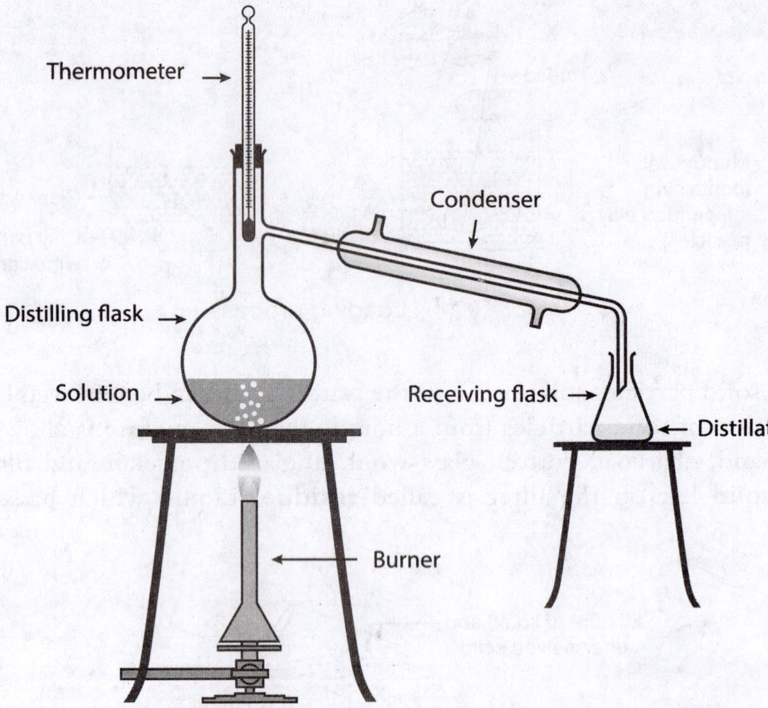

Figure 8.19 Process of distillation

6. **Centrifugation:** When milk is taken in a centrifuge tube and subjected to rotation at high speed, the cream settles down leaving behind the liquid in the tube.

The process of separation of substances with different densities by rotating the mixture at high speed by placing it in a centrifuge machine (Churning Machine) is called **centrifugation**.

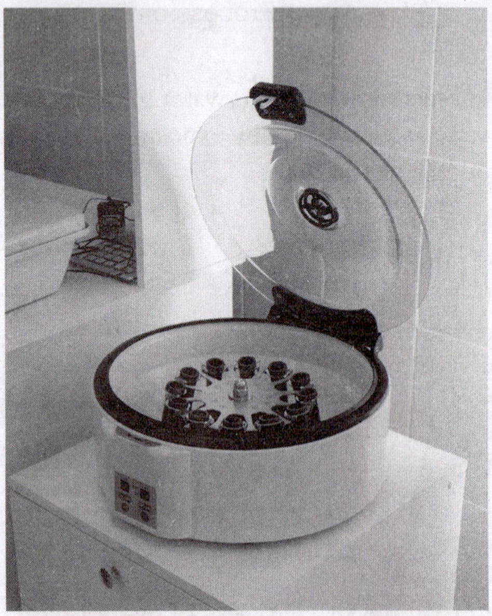

Figure 8.20 Process of centrifugation

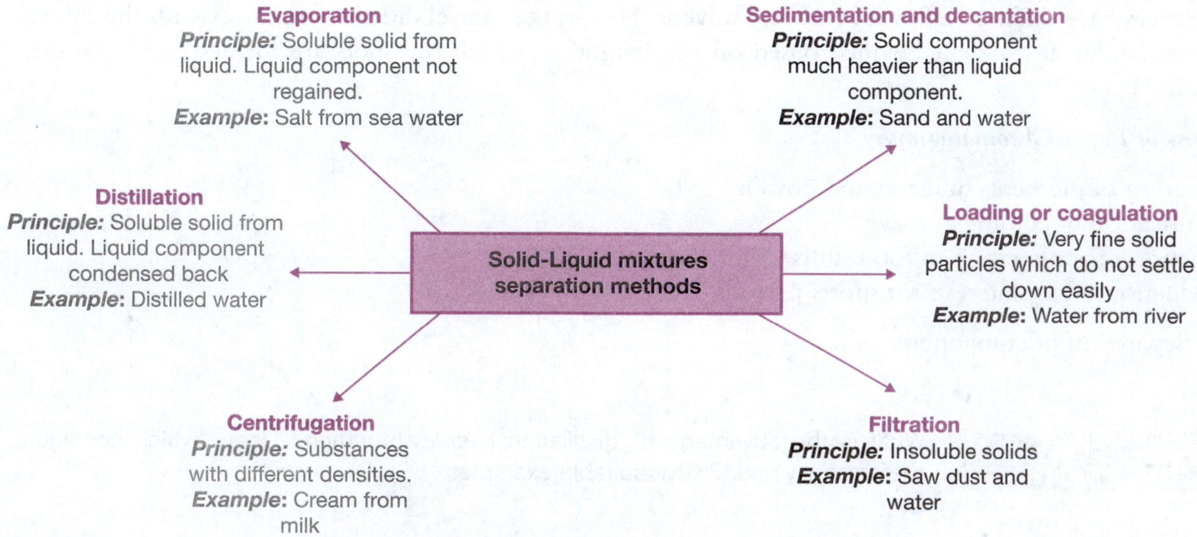

Figure 8.21 Separation of solid-liquid mixtures

Separation of Liquid–Liquid Mixtures

Liquid–liquid mixtures can be of two types. If the constituent liquids are miscible with each other, they form a homogeneous mixtures.

Example: Alcohol + water

Kerosene + Petrol

If the constituent liquids are not miscible with each other, they form a heterogeneous mixtures.

Example: Kerosene + water

Petrol + water

1. **Separating funnel:** When a mixture of oil and water is taken in a separating funnel, oil forms the upper layer and water forms the bottom layer. They can be collected separately.

   Example: Oil and water mixture

   Oil – Upper layer

   Water – Lower layer

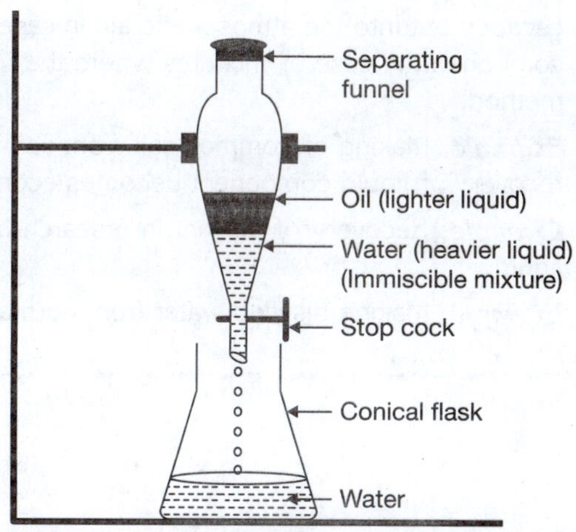

Figure 8.22 Separation of oil and water using separating funnel

2. **Distillation:** The process of separating components based on the difference in the boiling points of the two liquids in a miscible liquid mixture.

   Example: Water and alcohol

   Alcohol – Lower boiling point

   Mixture is heated up to the boiling point of alcohol. Vapour of alcohol is cooled, condensed, and collected in the receiver flask; water is left behind in the distillation flask.

3. **Paper Chromatography:** Though there are different methods of chromatography, **paper chromatography** is the simplest technique used for the separation of coloured components from mixtures. In fact, this is mainly used as an identification method rather than a separation method.

   Process of Paper Chromatography

   A filter paper is suspended in a container with a solvent. The solvent rises on the filter paper. When a mixture containing coloured substances is added to the solvent, these constituents also travel along with the solvent. The various

Konnect

Chromatography is employed for the separation of coloured components from mixture.

substances have different affinities with the solvent. Hence, they travel different distances with the solvent and form coloured spots at different heights. Based on the heights at which the spots are formed, the constituents can be identified.

Applications of Paper Chromatography

- Separation of pigments in leaves and flowers
- Identification of colours in a dye
- Detection of adulteration in food stuffs
- Conduction of doping tests for sports persons

Example: Separation of components of ink.

EXAMPLE 8.4 What is the advantage of distillation over evaporation? Under which conditions, they are preferentially used? Give suitable examples.

SOLUTION

Both evaporation and distillation are based on the same principle of vaporization of the liquid component leaving behind the solid component. But, evaporation results in the recovery of only the solid component. The liquid component vaporizes and escapes out into the atmospheric air. In case of distillation, the liquid component can also be recovered in addition to the solid component. In case of mixtures where the recovery of liquid component is not economically viable, evaporation is a preferred method.

Example: Making of common salt from sea water where recovery of water has no significance. In case of mixtures where the recovery of liquid component becomes economically profitable, distillation is a preferred method.

Example: Recovery of solvent in research laboratories. Distillation is also employed for getting a pure liquid from an impure liquid.

Example: Making distilled water from normal sample of water.

POINTS TO REMEMBER

- Anything that has mass and occupies space is called matter.
- Molecule can be defined as the smallest particle of matter, which can exist independently and retain all the properties of the substance.
- The spaces between the molecules are called intermolecular spaces and the forces of attraction holding these molecules are called intermolecular forces of attraction.
- The forces of attraction among the molecules of the liquid (similar molecules) is known as cohesive forces. The forces of attraction between the molecules of the liquid and the molecules of solid is known as adhesive forces.
- The process of conversion of solid state to liquid state by heating is called melting or fusion.
- Melting point is defined as the temperature at which a solid start changing into liquid and the actual conversion of state takes place.
- The process of conversion of liquid to solid on cooling is called freezing or solidification.
- Freezing point of a liquid is defined as the fixed temperature at which a liquid starts changing into solid and the actual conversion of state takes place. Boiling point is defined as the fixed temperature at which a liquid starts changing into gas or vapour.
- The process of conversion of gas into its liquid state by cooling is called liquefaction or condensation. The condensation point can be defined as the temperature at which a gas changes into its liquid state.
- Certain solids on heating get converted into their gaseous state directly without passing through the liquid state. This process is called sublimation.
- The substances which contain only one kind of molecules are called pure substances. The substances which contain more than one kind of molecules are called mixtures.
- The mixtures in which the different kinds of molecules are distributed uniformly throughout are known as homogeneous mixtures. The mixtures in which there is non-uniform distribution of different kinds of molecules are known as heterogeneous mixtures.
- The settling down of suspended, insoluble heavy solid particles in a solid – liquid mixture on long standing is called sedimentation. The process of pouring out the clear liquid after sedimentation without disturbing the sediment is called decantation.
- The process of helping fine solid particles in a solid – liquid mixture to settle faster by the addition of special chemical, such as alum is called loading.
- The process of separation of solid particles from a liquid when the mixture is allowed to pass through a filter is called filtration.
- The process of separation of substances with different densities by rotating the mixture at high speed by placing it in a centrifuge machine is called centrifugation.

PRACTICE QUESTIONS CLASSROOM WING

Very Short Answer Type Questions

Direction for questions from 1 to 3.
Fill in the blanks.

1. ______ acquires the volume of the container.
2. ______ is the hardest natural material known.
3. The process by which a gas changes into its liquid state is called ______.

Direction for questions from 4 to 10.
Select the correct alternative from the given options.

4. Which among the following is/are pure substance/s?
   (a) 916 gold ornaments
   (b) Coca cola drink in tin can
   (c) Bisleri water
   (d) None of the above
5. Identify the processes associated with an increase in the intermolecular space.
   (a) Freezing of water in deep freezers
   (b) Decrease in the size of naphthalene balls in a cupboard
   (c) Snowfall during winter
   (d) Liquefaction of nitrogen
6. **Assertion (A):** Sodium chloride is a compound.
   Reason (R): Compounds are invariably homogeneous substances.
   Choose the correct option.
   (a) Both A and R are true, and R is the correct explanation for A.
   (b) Both A and R are true, but R is not the correct explanation for A.
   (c) A is true and R is false.
   (d) A is false and R is true.
7. **Assertion (A):** Distilled water can be used in making of medicines.
   Reason (R): Distilled water is a pure substance.
   Choose the correct option.
   (a) Both A and R are true, and R is the correct explanation for A.
   (b) Both A and R are true, but R is not the correct explanation for A.
   (c) A is true and R is false.
   (d) A is false and R is true.
8. Identify a sublimable substance among the following.
   (a) Wax (b) Ice
   (c) Dry ice (d) Steam
9. Identify the odd one among the following.
   (a) Potassium permanganate
   (b) Alum
   (c) Blue vitriol
   (d) Sand
10. Identify the gas which is insoluble in water.
   (a) Oxygen (b) Methane
   (c) Carbon dioxide (d) All of these

Direction for questions from 11 to 20.
Fill in the blanks.

11. ______ cannot be broken down into simpler substances.
12. ______ is the smallest unit of an element.
13. ______ is a liquid metal.
14. ______ do not produce sound when struck.
15. The gaseous elements that do not react chemically with the other elements are known as ______.
16. A ______ is the smallest unit of a compound.
17. ______ can be heterogeneous or homogenous.
18. Brass is a homogeneous mixture of ______ and ______.
19. ______ is the lightest element.
20. ______ and ______ are the most abundant elements present in the earth's crust.

Direction for questions from 21 to 32.
Select the correct alternative from the given options.

21. Identify the liquid non-metal among the following.
   (a) Mercury (b) Iodine
   (c) Bromine (d) None of these
22. Which of the following elements is present in trace amount in the atmospheric air?
   (a) Argon (b) Nitrogen
   (c) Oxygen (d) Ozone
23. Identify the number of noble gases.
   (a) 4 (b) 6
   (c) 8 (d) 10

24. Identify the most abundant class of elements.
(a) Metals (b) Non-metals
(c) Metalloids (d) Inert gases

25. Which among the following elements is abundant in human body?
(a) Iron (b) Calcium
(c) Oxygen (d) Carbon

26. Identify the metal which is non-malleable.
(a) Carbon (b) Zinc
(c) Lead (d) Platinum

27. Which among the following is a soft solid and has high melting point?
(a) Diamond (b) Sodium
(c) Chlorine (d) Sulphur

28. Identify a compound among the following.
(a) Common salt (b) Air
(c) Sugar (d) Diamond

29. Among the following, which is a metalloid?
(a) Antimony (b) Carbon
(c) Iodine (d) Mercury

30. The number of naturally found elements is:
(a) 116 (b) 92
(c) 100 (d) 24

31. Which of the following liquids can form a single layer when added to water?
(a) Alcohol (b) Mustard oil
(c) Kerosene (d) Petrol

32. Which of the following types of mixtures is always homogeneous?
(a) Solid – Liquid (b) Gas – Gas
(c) Liquid – Liquid (d) Solid – Solid

Direction for questions from 33 to 41.

Fill in the blanks.

33. Common salt can be separated from the sea water by the method of ______.

34. A mixture of sodium chloride and ammonium chloride can be separated by ______ method.

35. ______ is the chemical added to water to hasten the process of sedimentation.

36. An apparatus used for the purpose of centrifugation is called ______.

37. In a separating funnel, the ______ liquid forms the upper layer.

38. The components of ink are separated by ______.

39. ______ liquids can be separated from their mixtures by the method of distillation.

40. Solid – solid mixtures are mostly ______.

41. Different sized pearls are separated by jewellers by the process of ______.

Direction for questions from 42 to 48.

Select the correct alternative from the given options.

42. Rice grains and husk can be separated by the method of ______.
(a) Sieving (b) Hand picking
(c) By solvent (d) Winnowing

43. A mixture of chalk and water can be separated by
(a) Sedimentation (b) Filtration
(c) Loading (d) Decantation

44. Centrifugation can be used for the separation of
(a) Components of ink
(b) Sugar from sugar solution
(c) Petrol from crude oil
(d) Cream from milk

45. Distilled water cannot be used for which among the following purposes?
(a) Drinking
(b) Preparation of medicines
(c) Preparation of solutions in industries
(d) None of these

46. Finer clay particles from water can be separated by the process of
(a) Sedimentation (b) Centrifugation
(c) Loading (d) Distillation

47. The process of pouring out the clear water after settling down of the mud particles is called:
(a) Sedimentation (b) Decantation
(c) Distillation (d) Loading

48. Identify the mixture in which the constituents cannot be separated by sublimation.
(a) Naphthalene + Sand
(b) Iodine + Iron
(c) Ammonium chloride + Sand
(d) Sulphur + Sand

Short Answer Type Questions

49. Mixture of iodine and ammonium chloride cannot be separated by sublimation. Why?

50. Give the reason why, generally, solid-solid mixtures are heterogeneous. But alloys are homogeneous.

51. Why Distilled water cannot be used for drinking?

52. Give examples of substances which undergo sublimation.

53. Name two opaque liquids.

54. What is observed when glass and wood are placed in water in two containers? Give reason.

55. Mention the interconversions associated with the following phenomena.
   (a) Wet clothes are hanged on a string.
   (b) Appearance of dew drops on the leaves on winter morning.
   (c) Foggy appearance on a mirror when exhaled air is blown over it.
   (d) Occurrence of snow fall.
   (e) Reduction in size of naphthalene balls when placed in a cupboard.

56. Water plays an important role in the functioning of our body. Give reason.

57. How are animals and plants able to survive in water?

58. When you come out of an AC car, foggy appearance is noticed on the spectacles. Give reason.

59. Name the gaseous non-metallic elements and the solid non-metallic elements.

60. Explain a distinguished characteristic of an atom and a molecule. Based on it, match the following.

(A)	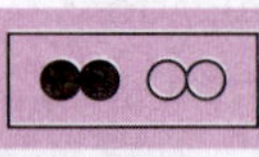	(i)	Elemental molecule
(B)		(ii)	Elemental atom
(C)		(iii)	Mixture of atoms
(D)	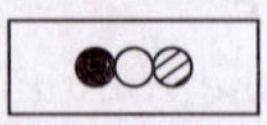	(iv)	Mixture of molecules
(E)	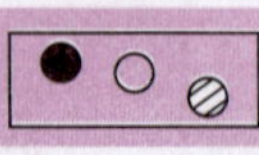	(v)	Compound of two elements
(F)	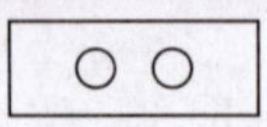	(vi)	Compound of three elements

61. Define the following:
   (a) Element (b) Compound
   (c) Homogenous mixture
   (d) Heterogeneous mixture
   (e) Metalloids
   (f) Noble gases

62. Hot tea when poured into a saucer facilitates easy drinking. Justify.

63. Distinguish between metals and non-metals with respect to the following characteristics:
   (a) Melting and boiling points
   (b) Conductivity
   (c) Malleability

64. Name the metalloids.

65. Distinguish between elements and compounds.

66. Identify the following.
   (a) The gaseous compound of two non-metals required for photosynthesis.
   (b) The compound of two non-metals which exists in all the three states under normal conditions.
   (c) The metal which breaks into pieces on the application of force.
   (d) The metal used in thermometers.
   (e) The inert gas used in advertisement sign boards.

67. How does alum hasten the process of sedimentation?

68. Identify whether the following are elements or compounds or mixtures. Give proper justification.
   (a) Saline water (b) Tincture of iodine
   (c) Distilled water (d) Potable water
   (e) Ozone (f) Sand (silicon dioxide)

69. Mention the purposes for which separation of mixtures is important. Give examples.

70. The principle of separation of a mixture depends on which factors?

71. Sodium chloride is a compound. Is common salt a compound? Justify.

72. Define the following.
   (a) Sedimentation (b) Decantation
   (c) Loading (d) Distillation
   (e) Centrifugation

73. Explain how it is possible to separate gold from river sand.

74. Distinguish between residue and filtrate.

75. Explain the principle involved in centrifugation.

76. Which method is employed for the separation of con stituents from a heterogeneous liquid – liquid mixture? Explain the principle involved.

77. Explain the process of separation of water and alcohol from their mixture.

78. Explain the principle involved in the making of coffee decoction.

79. Why is a diver able to cut through water in a swimming pool?

80. Why ice floats on water?

81. You are provided with a mixture of salt, sand, oil and water. Write the steps involved for the separation of salt, sand and oil from the mixture.

Essay Type Questions

82. (i) Observe the following flow chart and fill in the blanks with suitable process of separation and constituents of mixtures for the given reaction.

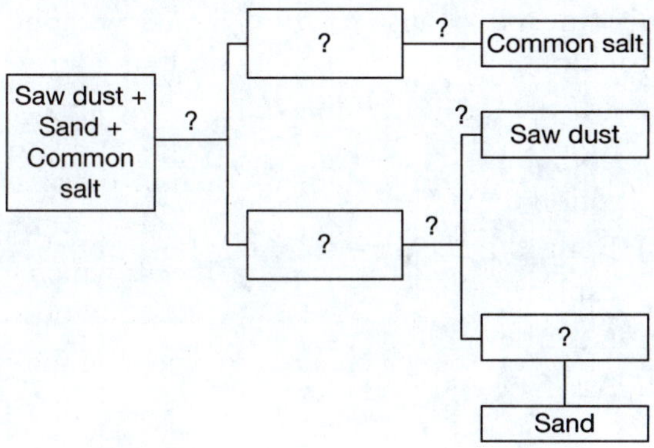

(ii)

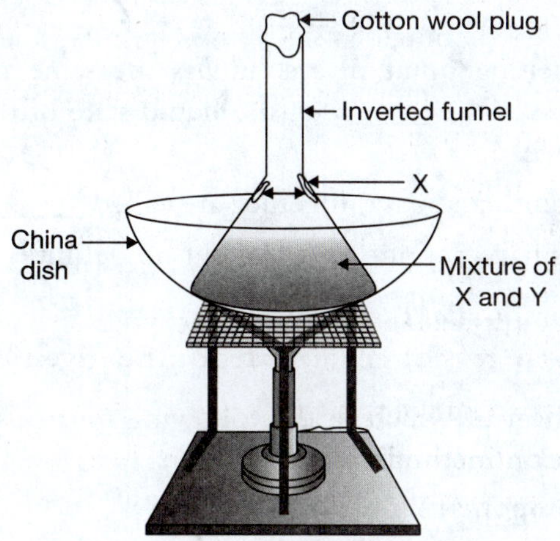

(a) Which method of separation is indicated in the above figure?

(b) A mixture of two components X and Y. X is an element and Y is a compound of two non-metals. Identify X and Y.

PRACTICE QUESTIONS COMPETITION WING

Level 1: Apply Your Concepts

Direction for questions from 1 to 5.
Fill in the blanks.

1. ______ is the process of change of the liquid state into vapour state.

2. ______ is the temperature at which a liquid starts changing into gaseous state.

3. The melting point of a solid has the same numerical value as the ______ of the liquid state of the same substance.

4. The liquids and gases together are called ______.

5. Liquids have definite ______, but no definite ______.

Direction for questions from 6 to 9.
Select the correct alternative from the given options

6. Separation of which of the following given uses centrifugation method?

(a) Components in urine
(b) Water from wet lettuce
(c) Water from wet clothes
(d) All of the above

7. Which of the following mixtures cannot be separated into its components by decanting?

(a) Cornflakes in milk
(b) Oil in water
(c) Bru coffee in boiling water
(d) Mercury in water

8. Assertion (A): Milk is a homogeneous mixture.
Reason (R): Generally homogeneous mixtures appear uniform and consistent throughout, without visible separation.

Choose the correct option.

(a) Both A and R are true, and R is the correct explanation for A.
(b) Both A and R are true, but R is not the correct explanation for A.
(c) A is true and R is false.
(d) A is false and R is true.

9.

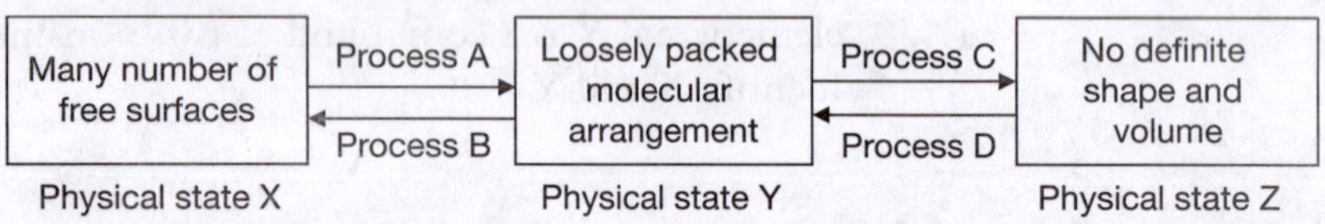

Identify the incorrect option from the following based on the diagram given above:

Option	A	B	C	D
(a)	Melting	Freezing	Boiling	Condensation
(b)	Freezing	Melting	Condensation	Boiling
(c)	Boiling	Melting	Freezing	Condensation
(d)	Melting	Condensation	Boiling	Freezing

Level 2: Review Your Concepts

10. (a) Complete the following table by using the words definite and Indefinite.

Property	Shape	Volume	Mass
Liquids			

(b) A student poured same quantity of liquid into 4 containers as shown.

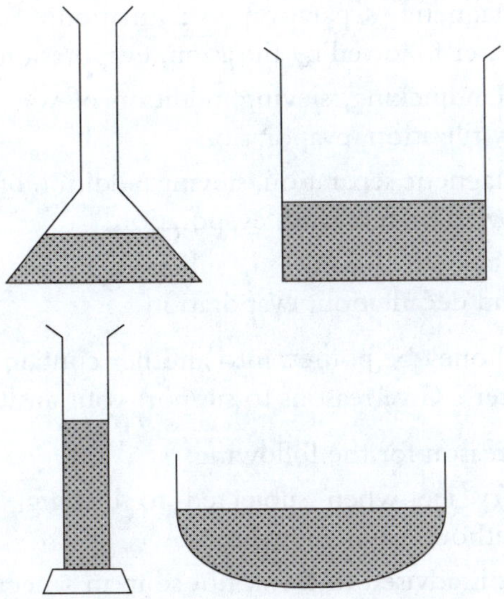

Which of the above given properties of the liquids does this experiment demonstrate? Justify

11. Observe the following figures and draw relevant conclusions regarding the properties of substances represented in the figures.

(a)

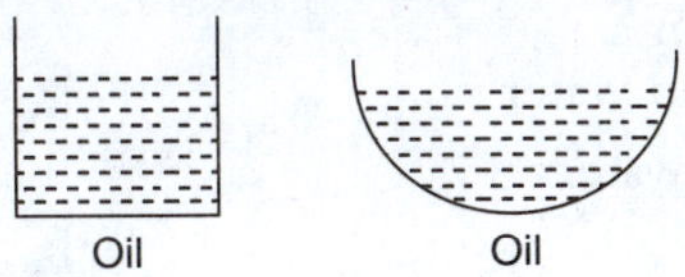

(b)

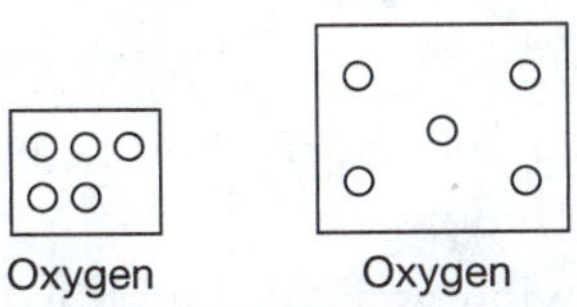

(c)

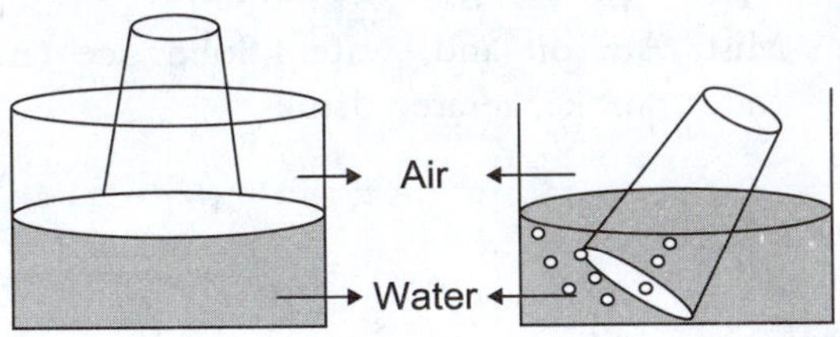

12. Write a suitable term for the following description.

(a) The fragrance of incense stick spreads in the entire space enclosed.

(b) A gas in a larger cylinder can be transferred into a smaller cylinder.

(c) Naphthalene balls reduce in size on long standing.

(d) Ethyl alcohol on heating starts vaporizing at 78°C.

(e) Liquids and gases can spread to larger distances.

13. Identify whether the following sentences are true or false. Also rewrite the false sentences by making suitable corrections.

(a) The constituents of a compound can be separated by physical means.

(b) Boron is a metal.

(c) Xenon is an inert gas.

(d) Atom is the smallest unit of a compound.

(e) Aluminium is the most abundant non-metal in the earth's crust.

14. Write the suitable terms corresponding to the descriptions given below.

(a) The ability of a material to be beaten into thin foils.

(b) The tendency of a material to produce loud ringing sound.

(c) The ability of silver to be drawn into thin wires.

(d) The nature of a substance where the distribution of the different kinds of molecules is not uniform.

(e) A substance in which the constituents can be separated by physical methods.

Level 3: Assess Your Concepts

15. Teacher gave three different objects, *X*, *Y* and *Z* of same mass but made of different materials to Sarita and asked to arrange these objects in the decreasing order of their densities. To find it out, Sarita took a measuring cylinder with 20 ml of water and started putting objects one at a time and measuring the change in the volume. The given diagram shows the changes in water level as each object is put in.

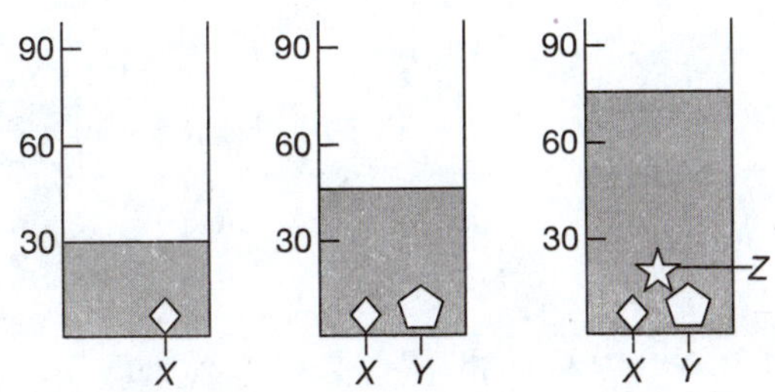

Teacher appreciated Sarita for her correct answer. Based on this information,

a. Can you guess how would have Sarita arranged the objects in the decreasing order of their densities? Justify your answer.

b. Density of which of the object is exactly double that of the other?

16. Study the given flow chart carefully.

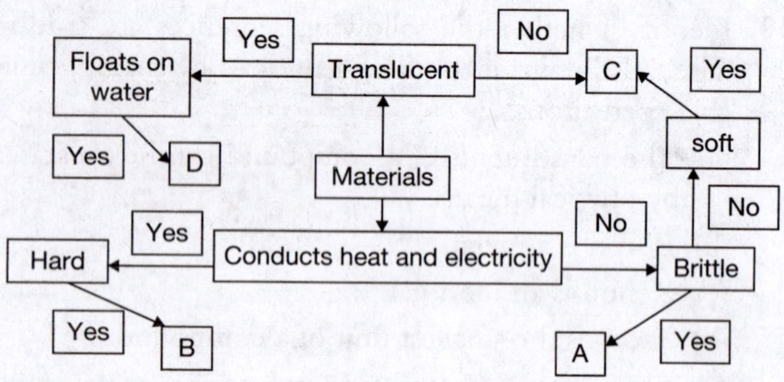

Classify the following given materials into A, B, C and D.

Aluminium pan, plastic comb, flower vase, wooden log, Mirror, iron nails, coins, marbles, plastic paper-clips, fabric, ceramic mug, rubber, Honey, oil paper, ice cubes free of impurities, Wax, vegetable refined oil, sponge, clay pot

(**Note:** some of the given materials may not fall into any category)

17. A mixture of iron filings, saw dust and sugar is available. Explain the methods of separation of these constituents.

18. A mixture contains camphor powder, sand, iron powder and common salt. Identify the separation methods that are employed to separate the constituents from the mixture.

(a) Magnetic separation, sublimation, addition of water followed by filtration, evaporation

(b) Handpicking, sieving, addition of water followed by filtration, evaporation

(c) Magnetic separation, sieving, addition of water followed by filtration, evaporation

(d) Magnetic separation, sublimation, sedimentation and decantation, evaporation

19. 'Can honey be poured into another container as easily as water'? Give reasons to support your answer.

20. Give reason for the following:

(a) Dry ice when subjected to heating, disappears without leaving any liquid.

(b) It is advised to drink hot soup in saucer than that in cup.

21. Answer the following:

(a) Discuss the method by which mixture of naphthalene ball, sand and iron nails can be separated.

(b) Which of the following is an example of homogenous mixture:

(i) Petrol and water

(ii) Aerated water

(iii) Mist

(iv) Chalk in water

22. Answer the following:

(a) Name the material and discuss how it hasten the process of sedimentation.

(b) Identify the following as solid liquid, gas – solid, liquid – gas and gas – gas mixture

Mist, Air, oil and, water. Solid, ice cream, sea water, smoke, aerated drinks

AT

ANSWER KEYS

Crossword

Across

3. Loading	4. Pure	5. Sublimation	8. Boiling	9. Intermolecular
10. Heterogenous	11. Filtration			

Down

1. Decantation	2. Sedimentation	6. Liquefaction	7. Cohesive

Classroom Wing

Very Short Answer Type Questions

1. Gases	2. Diamond	3. condensation	4. (d)	5. (b)	
6. (b)	7. (a)	8. (c)	9. (d)	10. (b)	
11. An element	12. Atom	13. Mercury	14. Non-metals	15. inert gases	
16. molecule	17. Mixtures	18. copper, zinc	19. Hydrogen	20. Oxygen, silicon	
21. (c)	22. (a)	23. (b)	24. (a)	25. (d)	
26. (b)	27. (b)	28. (c)	29. (a)	30. (b)	31. (a)
32. (b)	33. evaporation	34. sublimation	35. Alum	36. centrifuge	
37. lighter	38. chromatography	39. Miscible	40. heterogeneous	41. sieving	42. (d)
43. (b)	44. (d)	45. (a)	46. (c)	47. (b)	48. (d)

Short Answer Type Questions

60. (A) → (iv); (B) → (v); (C) → (i); (D) → (vi); (E) → (iii); (F) → (ii)

Competition Wing

Level 1: Apply Your Concepts

1. Evaporation	2. Boiling point	3. freezing point	4. fluids	5. volume, shape
6. (d)	7. (c)	8. (d)	9. (a)	

Level 2: Review Your Concepts

12. (a) Diffusion; (b) Compressibility; (c) Sublimation; (d) Boiling point; (e) Fluidity
13. (a) False; (b) False; (c) True; (d) False; (e) False
14. (a) Malleability; (b) Sonorousness; (c) Ductility; (d) Heterogenous mixture; (e) Mixture

Level 3: Assess Your Concepts

18. (a)

Hints and Explanations

CLASSROOM WING

Very Short Answer Type Questions

1. Gases acquire the volume of the container.
2. Diamond is the hardest natural material known.
3. The process by which a gas changes into its liquid state is called condensation.
4. All the given options are mixtures.

   Hence, the correct option is (d).
5. Conversion of states of mater associated with solids to gas, solid to liquid and liquid to gas are associated with the increase in the intermolecular spaces. Decrease in the size of naphthalene balls in a cupboard is associated with change of state from solid to gas.

   Hence, the correct option is (b).
6. **Assertion (A):** Sodium chloride is a compound-True.
   Reason (R): Compounds are invariably homogeneous substances-True.
   But (R) is not the correct reason of (A).
   Sodium chloride is a compound as it is formed by the chemical combination of sodium and chlorine. It has its own set of properties and cannot be separated into its constituent elements by physical means.

   Hence, the correct option is (b).
7. **Assertion (A):** Distilled water can be used in making of medicines-True.
   Reason (R): Distilled water is a pure substance-True.
   (R) is the correct explanation of (A).

   Hence, the correct option is (a).
8. Dry ice (solid carbon dioxide) is the sublimable substance.

   Hence, the correct option is (c).
9. Sand is insoluble in water while the other solids are soluble in water.

   Hence, the correct option is (d).
10. Methane is insoluble in water while the other gases are soluble in water.

    Hence, the correct option is (b).
11. An element cannot be broken down into simpler substances.
12. Atom is the smallest unit of an element.
13. Mercury is a liquid metal.
14. Non-metals do not produce sound when struck.
15. The gaseous elements that do not react chemically with the other elements are known as inert gases.
16. A molecule is the smallest unit of a compound.
17. Mixtures can be heterogenous or homogeneous.
18. Brass is a homogeneous mixture of copper and zinc.
19. Hydrogen is the lightest element.
20. Oxygen and silicon are the most abundant elements present in the earth's crust.
21. Bromine is the liquid non-metal.

    Hence, the correct option is (c).
22. Argon, being the inert gas is present in trace amount in the atmospheric air.

    Hence, the correct option is (a).
23. There are six noble gases.

    Hence, the correct option is (b).
24. Metals are the most abundant class of elements.

    Hence, the correct option is (a).
25. Carbon is the most abundant element in human body.

    Hence, the correct option is (d).
26. Zinc is the non-malleable metal.

    Hence, the correct option is (b).
27. Sodium is a metal, and hence has high melting point. But, it is a soft solid unlike other metals which are hard.

    Hence, the correct option is (b).
28. Sugar is a compound among the given ones.

    Hence, the correct option is (c).

29. Antimony is a metalloid among the given elements.

Hence, the correct option is (a).

30. There are 92 naturally found elements.

Hence, the correct option is (b).

31. Alcohol and water form a single layer because they are miscible liquids.

Hence, the correct option is (a).

32. Gas – Gas mixtures are always homogeneous.

Hence, the correct option is (b).

33. Common salt can be separated from the sea water by the method of evaporation.

34. A mixture of sodium chloride and ammonium chloride can be separated by sublimation.

35. Alum is the chemical added to water to hasten the process of sedimentation.

36. An apparatus used for the purpose of centrifugation is called centrifuge.

37. In a separating funnel, the lighter liquid forms the upper layer.

38. The components of ink are separated by chromatography.

39. Miscible liquids can be separated from their mixtures by the method of distillation.

40. Solid – Solid mixtures are mostly heterogenous.

41. Different sized pearls are separated by sieving method.

42. Rice grains and husk can be separated by the method of winnowing.

Hence, the correct option is (d).

43. A mixture of chalk and water can be separated by filtration.

Hence, the correct option is (b).

44. Centrifugation can be used for the separation of cream from milk.

Hence, the correct option is (d).

45. Distilled water cannot be used for drinking purpose.

Hence, the correct option is (a).

46. Finer clay particles from water can be separated by the process of loading.

Hence, the correct option is (c).

47. The process of pouring out the clear water after settling down of the mud particles is called decantation.

Hence, the correct option is (b).

48. The constituents of the mixture of sulphur and sand cannot be separated by sublimation as both the solids are not sublimable.

Hence, the correct option is (d).

Short Answer Type Questions

49. Both Iodine and ammonium chloride are sublimable substances hence their mixture cannot be separated by sublimation.

50. Alloys are homogeneous because they are formed by the uniform mixing of metals in their molten state.

51. Distilled water is pure and free from impurities and dissolved minerals. When consumed, water being a solvent can remove minerals from our body. Therefore, drinking distilled water does not provide minerals to our body but may deplete existing mineral levels over time, potentially leading to deficiencies if consumed long-term. Hence distilled water is not preferred for drinking purposes.

52. Camphor, naphthalene, ammonium chloride, iodine and dry ice are some substances which undergo sublimation.

53. Milk and fruit juice can be considered as opaque liquids.

54. Glass sinks in water and wood floats on water. Glass has a greater density than water. Wood has a lot of pores which are filled with air and its apparent density is lesser than water.

55. (a) Evaporation
(b) Condensation
(c) Condensation
(d) Direct conversion of water vapour into ice crystals at very low temperatures
(e) Sublimation

56. Water is a universal solvent, and so, it can dissolve a wide variety of substances in it. Thus, it acts as a medium for all the metabolic activities taking place in our body.

57. Oxygen and carbon dioxide are soluble in water. Animals and plants can utilize these dissolved gases for respiration and photosynthesis, and hence can survive in water.

58. The temperature remains very low in AC car. The spectacle glasses also remain very cool. When the person at

once gets out of the car, the water vapour in the atmospheric air comes in contact with the spectacles; it cools down and condenses forming very small tiny water droplets. This results in foggy appearance on the spectacles.

59. Fluorine, chlorine, hydrogen, nitrogen, oxygen are the gaseous non-metallic elements. Carbon, silicon, sulphur, phosphorus, and iodine are the solid non-metallic elements.

60. The major difference between an atom and a molecule is that a molecule can exists independently for every element. In case of atoms, only in few elements it can exist independently. (A) → (iv); (B) → (v); (C) → (i); (D) → (vi); (E) → (iii); (F) → (ii)

61. (a) An element can be defined as a pure substance in which a molecule is made up of only one kind of atom and which cannot be split into simpler substances by any chemical means.

(b) A compound can be defined as a pure substance in which a molecule is made up of more than one kind of atom and can be split up into two or more simpler substances.

(c) A homogeneous mixture can be defined as a substance in which there is uniform distribution of molecules of different substances.

(d) A heterogeneous mixture can be defined as a substance in which there is non-uniform distribution of different kinds of molecules in the substance.

(e) Metalloids are the elements which possess some properties of metals and some properties of non-metals.

(f) Noble gases are gaseous elements which do not take part in chemical reactions with any other elements.

62. When hot tea is poured from cup into saucer, more number of molecules occupies the surface as the surface area is large. As a result, evaporation takes place faster, thereby, cooling down the tea to moderate temperature. This facilitates easy drinking.

63. (a) Metals have high melting and boiling points while non-metals have low melting and boiling points.

(b) Metals are good conductors of heat and electricity whereas non-metals are generally bad conductors of heat and electricity.

(c) Metals are highly malleable whereas non-metals are non-malleable.

64. Boron, silicon, arsenic, and antimony are metalloids.

65.

Elements	Compounds
1. Cannot be broken down into simpler substances by any chemical means.	1. Can be broken down into the constituent elements by chemical means.
2. Atom is the smallest unit.	2. Molecule is the smallest unit.
3. Molecule is made up of only one kind of atom.	3. Molecule is made up of more than one kind of atom.

66. (a) Carbon dioxide – Carbon and oxygen are non-metals.

(b) Water – Hydrogen and oxygen are also non-metals.

(c) Usually metals are malleable and ductile. They do not break into pieces on the application of force. However, zinc is a metal which is not malleable. Hence, it becomes brittle and breaks into pieces on the application of force.

(d) Mercury is a liquid metal and is used in thermometers.

(e) Neon is the inert gas used in advertisement sign boards.

67. Alum gets dissolved in water and forms clusters with clay and dust particles making them heavier thereby increasing the rate of sedimentation.

68. (a) Saline water is a mixture as it is a solution of glucose, sodium chloride and potassium chloride in water.

(b) Tincture of iodine is a mixture of iodine and potassium iodide dissolved in alcohol.

(c) Distilled water is a compound as it is pure water devoid of all mineral salts.

(d) Potable water contains dissolved salts in it. Therefore, it is a mixture.

(e) Ozone is an element.

(f) Sand (silicon dioxide) is a compound which contains the elements silicon and oxygen.

69. (a) To get useful substances from naturally available materials.

Example: Common salt from sea water.

(b) For purification of synthetically made compounds.

Example: Distillation of ethyl alcohol.

(c) For removal of impurities from a manufactured substance.

70. The principle exploited for the separation of the constituents of a mixture depends on two factors.

(a) Type of mixture.

(b) Nature of constituents.

71. Sodium chloride is a compound of sodium and chlorine. Though sodium chloride is a major component of common salt, it also contains other components, such as potassium chloride, magnesium chloride, calcium chloride which are there in sea water. Commercially available iodized salt also contains salts of iodine in addition to these components.

72. (a) Sedimentation can be defined as the settling down of suspended, insoluble, heavy solid particles in a solid – liquid mixture.

(b) Decantation can be defined as the process of pouring out the clear liquid without disturbing the sediment.

(c) Loading can be defined as the process of helping the fine solid particles in a solid – liquid mixture to settle faster by the addition of a special chemical, such as alum.

(d) Distillation can be defined as the heating of the solid – liquid or liquid – liquid homogenous mixture to the boiling point of the lower boiling component followed by the subsequent condensation of the liquid resulting in the separation of the constituents of the mixture.

(e) Centrifugation can be defined as the process of separation of substances of different densities in a solid – liquid mixture. This process involves rotating the mixture at high speed which results in the settling down of the heavier solid particles leaving the almost clear liquid at the top.

73. Separation of gold from river sand can be carried out by allowing the sand to a swift stream of water. Sand particles being heavier and coarse settle down while the fine lighter gold particles float.

74. During the process of filtration, the insoluble solid left on the filter is called residue while the liquid which passes through the filter is called filtrate.

75. Centrifugation involves rotation of the solid – liquid mixture at high speed. This rotation creates a centrifugal force which draws the solid particles away from the centre thereby resulting in the settling down of the solid particles at the bottom.

76. Heterogenous liquid – liquid mixture is a mixture of two immiscible liquids which form two layers. The lighter liquid forms the upper layer while the heavier liquid forms the lower layer. They can be separated by taking the mixture in a separating funnel where the liquids get separated into two layers on standing. By opening the nozzle, the liquids in the two layers are separately collected.

77. Water and alcohol are miscible liquids and form a homogenous mixture. Water and alcohol differ widely in their boiling points. Therefore, they can be separated by the process of distillation. Alcohol has lower boiling point, and hence, vaporizes and gets collected in the receiver flask. Water is left behind in the distillation flask as it has a higher boiling point.

78. Coffee powder contains some soluble components and some insoluble component. When hot water is added, the soluble components go into water giving decoction. The insoluble components are filtered off.

79. The diver is able to cut through water in the swimming pool because matter is not continuous, but it is made up of particles which have vacant spaces between them moreover, the attractive forces between molecules of water are not very strong. The diver can easily cut through water by applying force to displace water and occupy its place.

80. Solids generally have higher density than the liquids but ice due to its specific structure has larger interparticle space and hence has lower density than liquid water. As a result ice floats on water.

81. Oil being immiscible and less dense than water will float on top. so it can be easily removed by scooping it out from water.

Sand will sink at the bottom. Salt will dissolve in water, so filter this solution thereby separating the sand particles then let the water evaporate to reclaim the salt.

Essay Type Questions

82. (i)

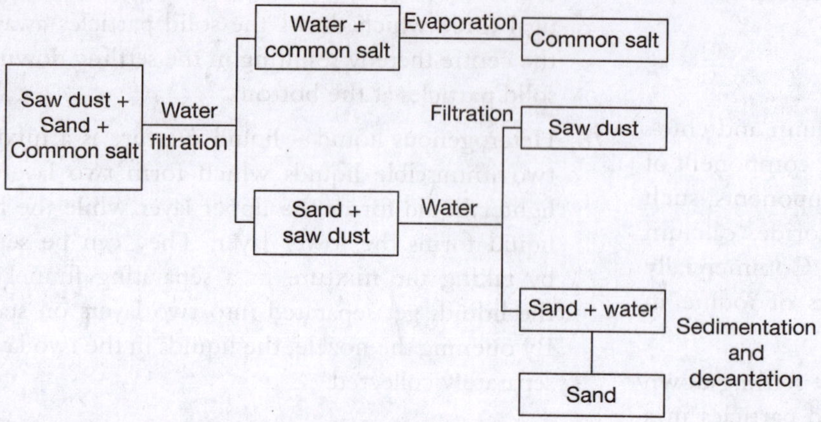

(ii) (a) The figure indicates the separation method of sublimation.

(b) X is an element which undergoes sublimation. Therefore, it should be iodine. Y is sand (silicon dioxide) which is a compound of two non-metals.

COMPETITION WING

Level 1: Apply Your Concepts

1. Evaporation is the process of change of the liquid state into vapour state.
2. Boiling point is the temperature at which a liquid starts changing into gaseous state.
3. The melting point of a solid has the same numerical value as the freezing point of the liquid state of the same substance.
4. The liquids and gases together are called fluids.
5. Liquids have definite volume, but no definite shape.
6. All of the given options use the method of centrifugation for separation.

   Hence, the correct option is (d).
7. Bru coffee in boiling water cannot be separated into its components by decanting as it dissolves in water.

   Hence, the correct option is (c).
8. **Assertion (A):** Milk is a homogeneous mixture-False.

   Reason (R): Generally homogeneous mixtures appear uniform and consistent throughout, without visible separation-True.

   Hence, the correct option is (d).
9. Physical states X, Y, and Z are solid, liquid and gaseous state, respectively.

   A is melting, B is freezing, C is boiling, and D is condensation.

   Hence, the correct option is (a).

Level 2: Review Your Concepts

10. (a) Complete the following table by using the words definite and Indefinite.

Property	Shape	Volume	Mass
Liquids	Indefinite	Definite	Definite

(b) Indefinite shape of the liquids. When the student poured same quantity of liquid into 4 containers of different shapes and sizes, liquid took the shape of the container. This clearly indicates that liquids do not possess any definite shape, but the shape of a liquid will be the shape of the container in which it is taken.

11. (a) Liquids do not have definite shape and they take the shape of the container in which they are taken.

(b) Gases occupy the entire volume of the container.

(c) Water can enter into the tumbler when it is kept in a slanting position. Air comes out as bubbles and water replaces that space. Air and water are forms of matter, and hence occupy certain space.

12. (a) Diffusion
(b) Compressibility
(c) Sublimation
(d) Boiling point
(e) Fluidity

13. (a) False. The constituents of a compound can be separated by chemical means.
(b) False. Boron is a metalloid.
(c) True
(d) False. Molecule is the smallest unit of a compound.
(e) False. Aluminium is the most abundant metal in the earth's crust.

14. (a) Malleability
(b) Sonorousness
(c) Ductility
(d) Heterogenous mixture
(e) Mixture

Level 3: Assess Your Concepts

15. (a) Sarita would have arranged *X*, *Y*, *Z* in the decreasing order of their densities as: $Z > Y > X$.

Reason: Based on the information provided, the volume of *X*, *Y*, *Z* are as follows.

Object	*X*	*Y*	*Z*
Volume	10	15	30

Density of a substance is calculated by dividing mass of the substance with its volume.

Since the objects *X*, *Y*, and *Z* have the same mass, their densities can be determined by comparing their volumes.

The larger the volume of an object for the same mass, the lower its density. Therefore, based on the given volumes (10 for *X*, 15 for *Y*, and 30 for *Z*), the decreasing order of their densities would be $Z > Y > X$.

(b) Volume of *Z* is exactly double that of *Y*. As both *Z* and *Y* are of same mass, density of *Z* will be double that of *Y*

16.

A (Hard, conducts heat and electricity)	Aluminium pan, iron nails, coins
B (Brittle, does not conduct heat and electricity)	Flower vase, mirror, Ceramic mug, clay pot
C (Soft, not translucent and does not conduct electricity)	Rubber, Paperclips, plastic comb, fabric
D (Translucent and floats on water)	Ice cubes free of impurities, wax, vegetable refined oil

17. Iron filings can be separated by magnetic separation method. When water is added to the mixture, sugar becomes soluble in water leaving behind saw dust. When this is filtered, saw dust can be separated as a residue. The filtrate collected is sugar solution. On evaporation of this solution, water is vapourized off and sugar is left behind.

18. Iron powder is separated by using magnet. Camphor powder is separated by sublimation. Water is added to the remaining mixture. Sand being insoluble in water, it can be separated by filtration. Common salt from water is separated by evaporation.

Hence, the correct option is (a).

19. Honey is viscous liquid, and hence has lesser fluidity when compared to water.

20. (a) Dry ice undergoes sublimation due to which it converts directly into vapours and disappears into air without leaving any solid.

(b) When hot soup is poured into the saucer, it will lose heat rapidly that of in cup as rate of evaporation increases with increase in surface area.

21. (a) Mixture of naphthalene ball, sand, and iron nail is separated by sublimation, sieving and by using magnet respectively.

(b)

Homogenous Mixture	Heterogenous Mixture
→ Aerated water	→ Petrol and water
	→ Mist
	→ Chalk in water

22. (a) Alum hasten the process of sedimentation as it gets dissolved in water and forms cluster with day and dust particles, which make them heavier and increases the rate of sedimentation.

(b) Solid – Liquid: Sea water

Gas – Solid: ice – Cream

Liquid – Gas: Mist

Gas – Gas: Air

CHAPTER

9

Language of Chemistry and Changes Around Us

Remember

Before beginning this chapter, you should be able to:

- Know basic concepts of common chemical substances
- Identify different chemical substances like air, clay, water, sand, etc.

Key Ideas

After completing this chapter, you should be able to:

- Describe composition of chemicals and their changes
- Write different chemical formulae of compounds
- Understand different types of changes around us

Scientific Crypt

A Tribute to Jons Jacob Berzelius (1779-1848)

In the vast realm of chemistry, few names shine as brightly as Jons Jacob Berzelius (1779-1848), a Swedish chemist known as the "Architect of Chemical Notation." His pioneering work on modern chemical symbols revolutionized the representation of elements and compounds, thus, laying the foundation for the development of modern chemical notation.

Berzelius compiled an accurate table of atomic weights for 45 of the then known 49 elements which served as evidence for the well-known Dalton's atomic theory. He also contributed to the discovery and characterization of several new chemical elements, including thorium, silicon, cerium, and zirconium. His work in characterizing these elements helped expand our understanding of the periodic table in the subsequent times.

Berzelius's accomplishments as a scientist and educator were widely acknowledged, and his legacy continues to inspire scientists to this day.

FUN TIME

CROSSWORD

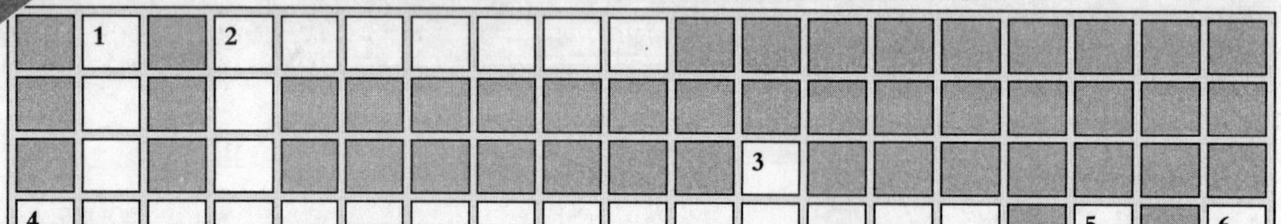

Across

2. 2S represents two atoms of
4. Change of weather from winter to summer
7. Latin name of lead
8. Washing soda
10. Latin name of mercury
11. Phases of moon
12. The number of hydrogen atoms in two molecules of methane

Down

1. The number of atoms present in one molecule of nitric acid
2. Baking soda
3. The name of element with symbol Mn is
5. The change involved in the heating of zinc oxide
6. The name of the compound PbS
9. The number of oxygen atoms present in one molecule of silver nitrate

INTRODUCTION

An interesting fact about the word 'Science' is that it is originated from the Latin word '*scientia*' which means 'knowledge'. Studying science may appear to be strange at first but in reality it is all about finding the reasons behind different phenomena we observe in our daily life. Studying science may help you find answer of some questions like, 'How does a fish breathe in water?' or 'Why the sky appears blue to us?' or 'How we grow from a baby to an adult?' and many more. Chemistry is a branch of science in which we study about the composition, properties and reactions of different substances based on the experimentations and observations. In this chapter we shall study about the classification of substances on the basis of their compositions.

Composition of Chemical Substance

All the things around us are made up of chemical substances. Let us name some chemical substances.

Air, Clay, Water, Sand, Cement, Glass, Paper and many more.

As a matter of fact, the list is endless. We can categorize these substances as follows:

1. Elements
2. Compounds
3. Mixtures

Let us study about these in detail.

Info Bytes!

An element consists of only one type of atom, while a compound consists of atoms of two or more different elements combined in a fixed ratio. For instance, water is a compound made up of two hydrogen atoms and one oxygen atom.

Element

All the substances in nature are made up of elements.

Examples: Water – Made up of Hydrogen and Oxygen

Common salt – Made up of Sodium and Chlorine

Elements are the basic constituents of all materials and are the simplest substances. Let us now have a look at the constituents of elements.

Let us consider an element, sodium. It is a solid substance and it can be cut into smaller and smaller pieces with a knife or blade. When you assume to cut it further into very minute microscopic particles, these particles become further indivisible. These indivisible particles are called **atoms**.

Figure 9.1 Arrangement of atoms in an element of solid state

Atoms are considered to be the basic units of 'EVERYTHING' around us. They are the basic building blocks of matter. If you imagine a huge building, what is it made up of ? The smallest units of the entire structure are bricks. It also applies the same to chemical substances which are made up of atoms.

Do atoms of all elements have independent existence? No, atoms of some elements exist independently. They are metals and inert gases. They are gold, copper, silver, iron, etc. Examples of inert gases are helium, neon, argon, krypton, xenon and radon. The atoms of all these elements exist independently.

Elements are made up of molecules with the same kind of atoms.

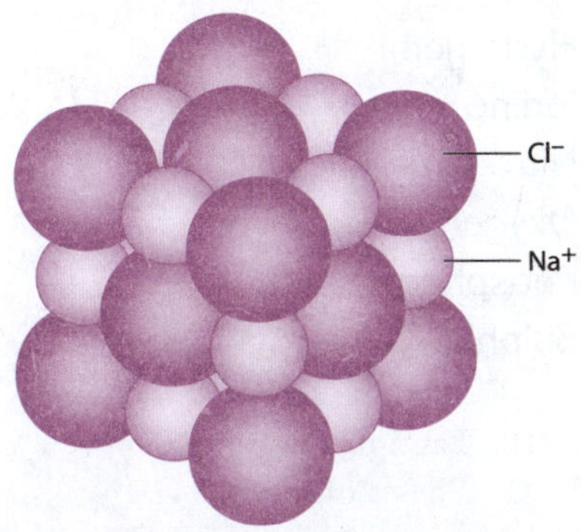

Figure 9.2 Arrangement of atoms in solid NaCl

Compounds

Compounds are made up of molecules with atoms of different elements.

Example: A sodium chloride (NaCl, common salt) molecule is made up of atoms of sodium and chlorine.

There are various numbers of substances or compounds formed among the atoms of different elements.

Atomicity

Atomicity is the number of atoms which make up a molecule of an element. The elements in which the atoms have an independent existence are said to be monoatomic. Some elements have atomicity 'two' which means that a molecule is made up of two atoms. Such elements are said to be diatomic. Most of the diatomic elements are gases.

Examples: Hydrogen, Oxygen, Nitrogen, Fluorine, Chlorine, Bromine (liquid), Iodine (solid).

Some elements have molecules made up of more than two atoms. Those are called **polyatomic elements.**

Table 9.1 Atomicity of some polyatomic elements

Element	Atomicity
Ozone	3
Phosphorus	4
Sulphur	8

Symbols of Elements

In Mathematics, '+' represents addition and '÷' represents division and so on. In similar fashion, all the elements are represented by symbols.

Symbol is defined as the shorthand notation which represents a single atom of an element.

Example: Na → one atom of sodium, 2Na → two atoms of sodium

S → one atom of sulphur, 3S → three atoms of sulphur

The elements are provided with symbols based on their English or Latin names. The element Boron is given the symbol 'B', Carbon is given the symbol 'C'. That means, the first letter of English name is taken as the symbol for that element. All elements are symbolized in capital letters.

What about the symbols for Calcium, Chlorine, Chromium, and so on? All of them start with 'C'. That means, for these elements, the symbols include another alphabet which is spelled prominently in the name along with the first letter. But this second letter is written in lower case keeping the first letter as it is in upper case.

Table 9.2 Some Common Elements with their Symbols

Element	Symbol
Carbon	C
Fluorine	F
Hydrogen	H
Iodine	I
Nitrogen	N
Oxygen	O
Phosphorus	P
Sulphur	S

Table 9.3 Symbols of Elements Starting with Letter 'C'

Element	Symbol
Calcium	Ca
Chlorine	Cl
Chromium	Cr
Cerium	Ce
Cesium	Cs
Cobalt	Co

Here are some elements starting with the letters 'B' and 'C'.

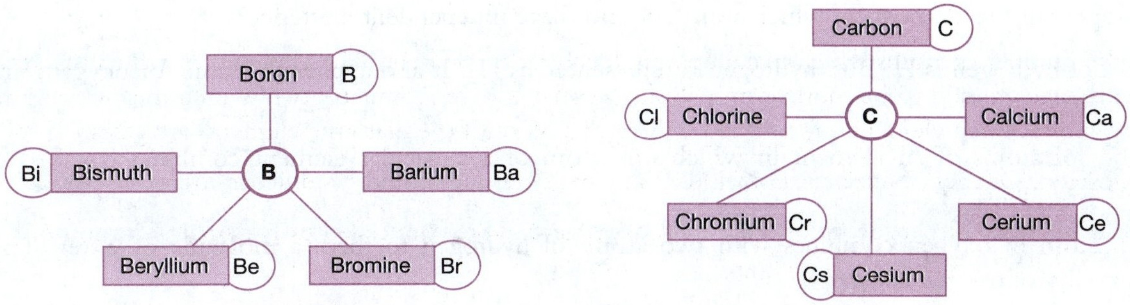

Figure 9.3 Symbols of elements with letters 'B' and 'C'

The symbols of some elements are given below:

Table 9.4 Some Elements with their Symbols

Element	Symbol
Arsenic	As
Astatine	At
Argon	Ar
Germanium	Ge
Gallium	Ga
Helium	He
Halnium	Ha
Hafnium	Hf
Selenium	Se
Silicon	Si
Neon	Ne
Osmium	Os
Platinum	Pt
Palladium	Pd

The symbols for certain elements, like sodium, gold, silver, etc., take a totally different trend. They originate from their Latin names instead of English names. The Latin name for sodium is *natrium* and its symbol is Na.

Some elements starting from their Latin names are given below:

Table 9.5 Elements and their Latin Names

Element Name	Latin Name	Symbol
Sodium	Natrium	Na
Gold	Aurum	Au
Silver	Argentum	Ag
Potassium	Kalium	K
Mercury	Hydrargyrum	Hg
Lead	Plumbum	Pb
Tin	Stannum	Sn
Iron	Ferrum	Fe
Copper	Cuprum	Cu

Structure of Compounds

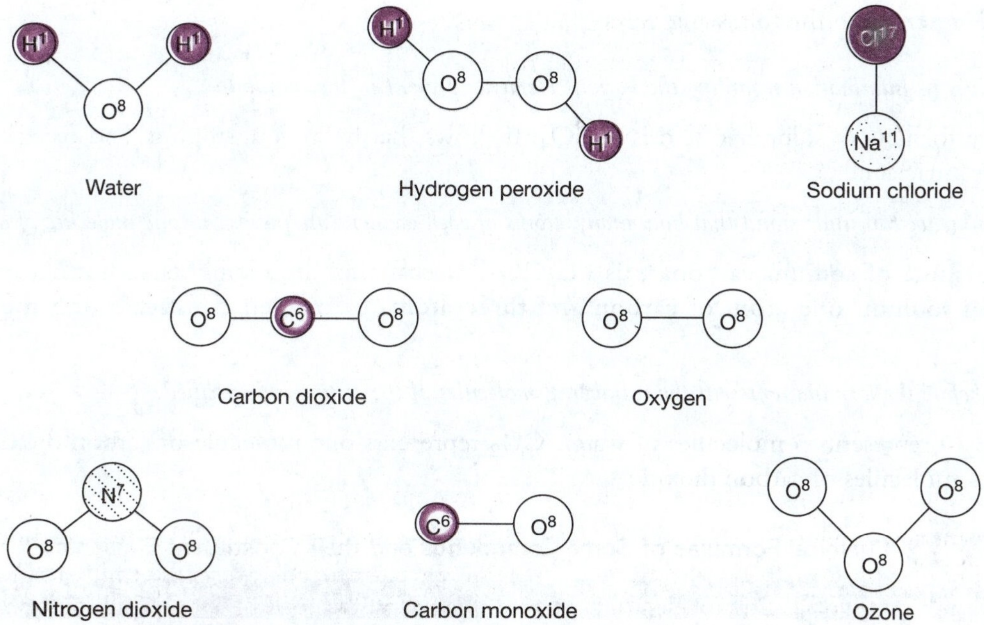

Figure 9.4 Diagrammatic representation of some compounds

EXAMPLE 9.1 Distinguish between the following pairs. Justify.
$2H_2O$ and H_4O_2; 2H and H_2.

SOLUTION

$2H_2O$ represents 2 molecules of water. This is because H_2O is the formula of water and one molecule of water is made up of 2 hydrogen atoms and 1 oxygen atom. H_4O_2, while not a common or stable compound, hypothetically represents 1 molecule made up of 4 hydrogen atoms and 2 oxygen atoms.

2H represents 2 atoms of hydrogen as 'H' is the symbol of hydrogen. H_2 represents one molecule of hydrogen gas.

The number in the subscript represents the number of atoms in a single molecule. The number written as the coefficient represents the number of atoms or molecules as the case may be.

EXAMPLE 9.2 The formula of a compound of a metal with sulphur is written as MS and that of another metal is written as M_2S_3. Give reason. What are the formulae of the compounds of the above metals with bromine?

SOLUTION

In case of a metal having combining capacity 2, the formula of its compound with sulphur is written as MS since the combining capacity of sulphur is also 2. In case of a metal having combining capacity 3, the formula of the compound is written as M_2S_3. Since the combining capacity of bromine is 1, the formulae of the compounds of bromine with the above metals are MBr_2 and MBr_3, respectively.

Combining Capacity

How do we represent the elements in which atom does not have independent existence?

The symbol of hydrogen is H. But, hydrogen is represented as H_2. It also applies the same for oxygen, nitrogen, etc., as O_2, N_2, etc.

The number of atoms of an element in which one atom of a particular element combines is called **combining capacity** of that element.

Example: An atom of oxygen combines with two atoms of hydrogen to form a molecule of water. Therefore, the combining capacity of oxygen is two.

This concept of combining capacity of elements is made useful in deriving the formulae for the compounds.

The combining powers of some important elements are given below.

Table 9.6 Combining Capacities of Some Elements

Element	Combining Capacity	Element	Combining Capacity
Sodium	1	Tin	2
Potassium	1	Oxygen	2
Calcium	2	Sulphur	2
Magnesium	2	Hydrogen	1
Iron	3	Chlorine	1
Lead	2	Nitrogen	3

The atoms of different elements combine in the inverse ratio of their combining powers.

Formulae of Elements and Compounds

A **formula** is defined as the shorthand notation which represents a molecule of an element or a compound. H_2, O_2, N_2, etc., are formulae for hydrogen, oxygen and nitrogen molecules, respectively.

Since the elements exist as molecules, they are represented by formulae. As molecule is the smallest unit of a compound, compounds are represented by formulae. That means the atomicity of the element is written as the subscript.

Fluorine $\rightarrow F_2$

Chlorine $\rightarrow Cl_2$

Bromine $\rightarrow Br_2$

Iodine $\rightarrow I_2$

Ozone $\rightarrow O_3$

Phosphorus $\rightarrow P_4$

O_2 represents one molecule of oxygen.

O_3 represents one molecule of ozone.

$3O_2$ represents three molecules of oxygen.

$2O_3$ represents two molecules of ozone.

Konnect

The chemical formula helps scientists, researchers, and students to predict how different compounds will interact. They are like the 'language' of chemistry.

A molecule is formed by the combination of atoms in a whole number ratio.

Example: Iron oxide is formed from iron and oxygen. The combining capacities of iron and oxygen are 3 and 2, respectively.

Fe and O $\rightarrow$ The formula of iron oxide is Fe_2O_3

That means, the combining capacities of the elements are exchanged and the whole numbers so obtained are written as subscripts for the symbols of the respective elements. If both the elements have equal combining capacities, the subscripts are not mentioned in the formula.

EXAMPLE 9.3 Find out the total number of atoms in the following:

(a) 1 molecule of calcium chloride

(b) 1 molecule of sodium carbonate

(c) 1 molecule of iron(III) oxide

SOLUTION

(a) Calcium chloride → $CaCl_2$ → 3 atoms

(b) Sodium carbonate → Na_2CO_3 → 6 atoms

(c) Iron(III) oxide → Fe_2O_3 → 5 atoms

Changes Around Us

All the substances existing in nature undergo changes. The changes can be categorized on the basis of various parameters.

Apart from these parameters which are described above, there is a vital parameter which plays a more significant role called composition. Composition or to be more precise, **molecular composition**, is the number of atoms of various elements present in a molecule of a substance. During some changes, composition of the substance remains the same whereas in some other changes, the composition of the substance changes.

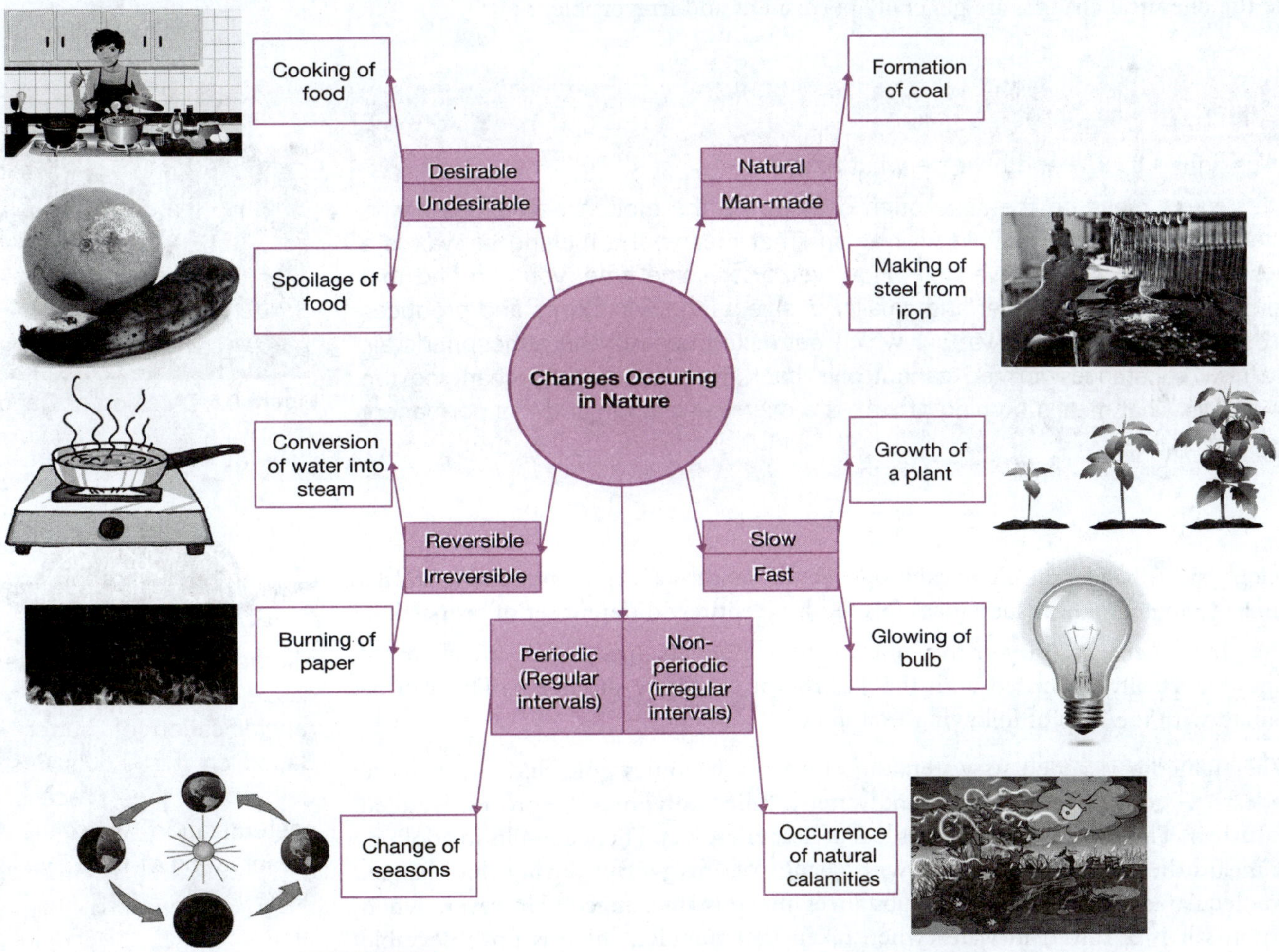

Figure 9.5 Classification of changes occurring in nature

Example: When water is subjected to heating, it is converted into steam. The molecules of water and steam are made up of two atoms of hydrogen and one atom of oxygen. This change does not involve any change in molecular composition. It is called physical change.

Physical Change

A **physical change** is defined as a change in which the molecular composition of the substance remains unchanged and no new substance is formed.

Example: Heating of water gives steam. A molecule of water as well as steam is constituted of two atoms of hydrogen and one atom of oxygen.

Chemical Change

A **chemical change** is defined as a change in which the molecular composition of the substance changes and new substances are formed.

Example: Splitting of water to give hydrogen and oxygen, burning of candle.

Characteristics of Physical and Chemical Changes

Let us now study the other characteristics of physical and chemical changes.

Water when kept in refrigerator, freezes to give ice. Ice when exposed to normal conditions, melts to form water.

That means the above changes are temporary and reversible. Physical changes are generally temporary and reversible, while the chemical changes are generally permanent and irreversible.

Activity

Let us light a candle and observe what happens.

At first, wax melts on the absorption of heat. As the molten wax slides down, it gets solidified to form solid wax again. That means, the melting of wax is a physical change and is reversible. However, after some time, you can find that the candle becomes smaller and smaller in size as the wax burns and produces carbon dioxide and water vapour which get mixed up with the atmospheric air. The new substances formed cannot give back the wax even by changing the conditions. That means burning of wax is a chemical change and it is permanent and irreversible.

Figure 9.6 Melting of Candle

In a physical change, the chemical properties of the substances are not changed. In a chemical change, the new substances formed have entirely different set of properties.

The physical changes may or may not involve energy changes. While the chemical changes are usually associated with the absorption or release of energy. This can be explained with the help of following examples.

When glucose is added to water, the container becomes cold and the glucose disappears. Glucose is called **solute** and water is called **solvent**. The process is called **dissolution**. This process also involves loss of heat energy, and hence results in cooling. That means the change is associated with change of energy. But during this change, the molecular composition of the substances remains unchanged. However, when common salt is dissolved in water when taken in a tumbler, there is no observable heating up or cooling down of the tumbler.

Konnect

Microorganisms (bacteria) cause coagulation of milk, rancidification of butter, etc. Based on this, Louis Pasteur developed the process of pasteurization which is the preservation of food by killing bacteria by heating.

Let us consider burning of fuel. On heating, the substances in fuel combine with oxygen and form new substances (oxides). Heat energy is released during this process. This process is called **combustion**. Not only combustion takes place in this process, but also most of the chemical changes involve either absorption of heat or release of heat.

Info Bytes!

The bursting of crackers involves emission of light in addition to heat!

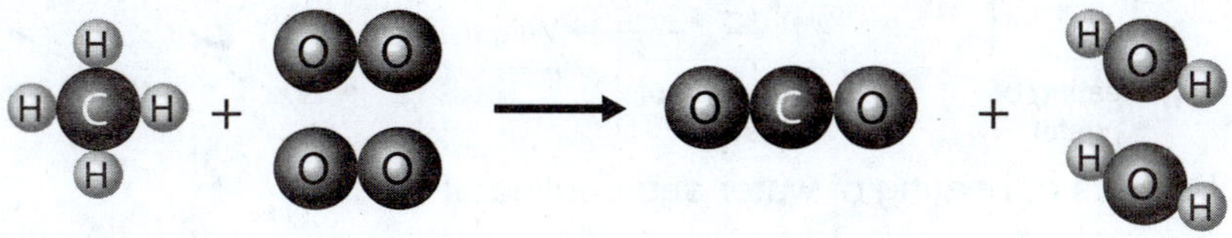

fuel (methane) + oxygen ⟶ carbon dioxide + water

$$CH_4(g) + 2O_2(g) \longrightarrow CO_2(g) + 2H_2O(l)$$

Figure 9.7 Combustion of fuel

What happens when an iron or steel object is left exposed to air for a long time?

You could notice reddish brown flakes on the surface of the object. That reddish brown powdery substance is called **rust** and the process of formation of rust is called **rusting**. The process is so slow that the energy change during this process is not noticed at all.

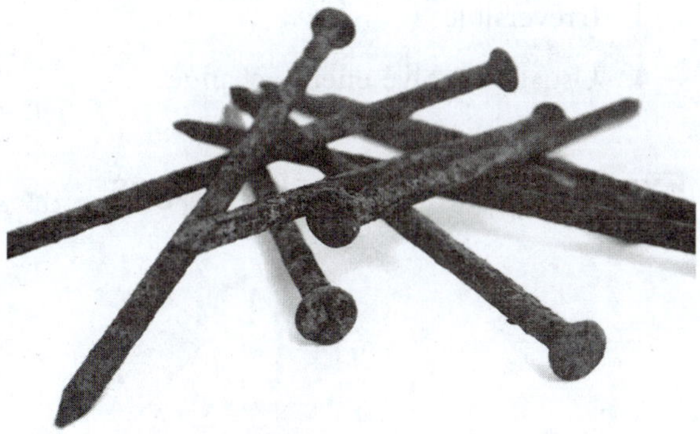

Figure 9.8 Rusted iron nails

Both combustion and rusting come under a chemical change called **oxidation**. Combustion is a fast process while rusting is a slow process. Usually, a chemical change is known as a **chemical reaction**. The original substance is called **reactant** and the new substance formed is called **product**.

Properties of a Physical Change

Properties of a physical change are listed below:

1. No change in molecular composition
2. No formation of new substance
3. Generally reversible
4. May or may not involve energy change

Example of Physical Change

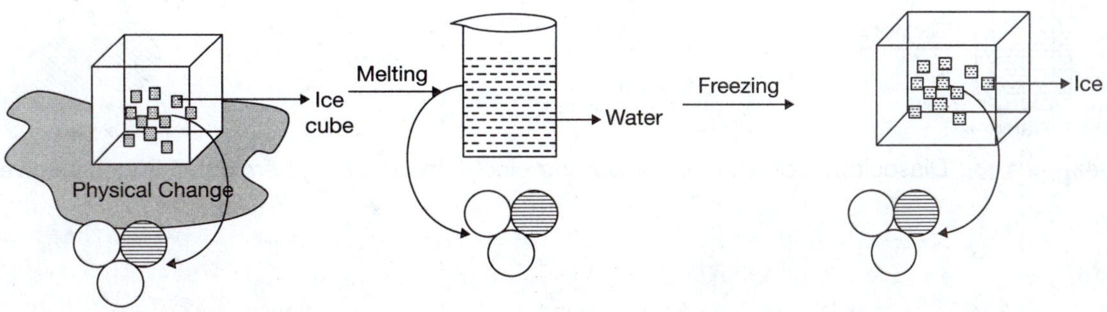

Figure 9.9 Diagrammatic representation of a physical change

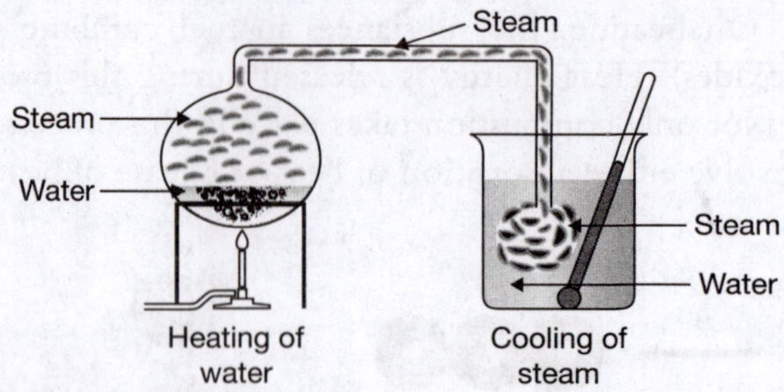

Figure 9.10 Process of heating of water and cooling of steam

Properties of a Chemical Change

Properties of a chemical change are listed below:

1. Change in molecular composition
2. Formation of new substances
3. Irreversible
4. Usually involve energy change

> **Konnect**
>
> Fireflies produce light through a chemical change. They combine oxygen with a substance called luciferin, aided by an enzyme (luciferase) to produce light without any heat.

Examples of Chemical Changes

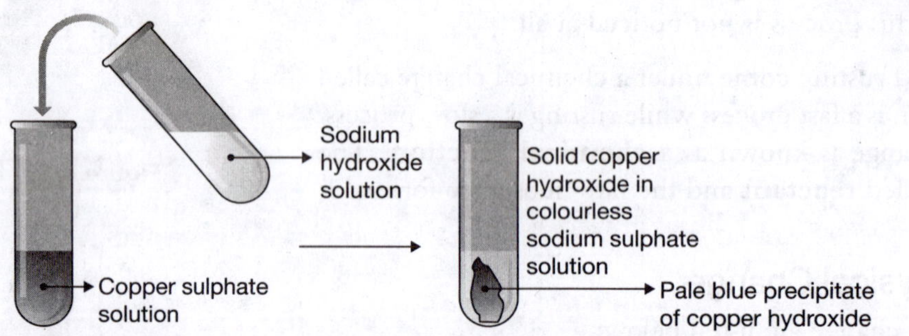

Figure 9.11 Reaction between copper sulphate and sodium hydroxide

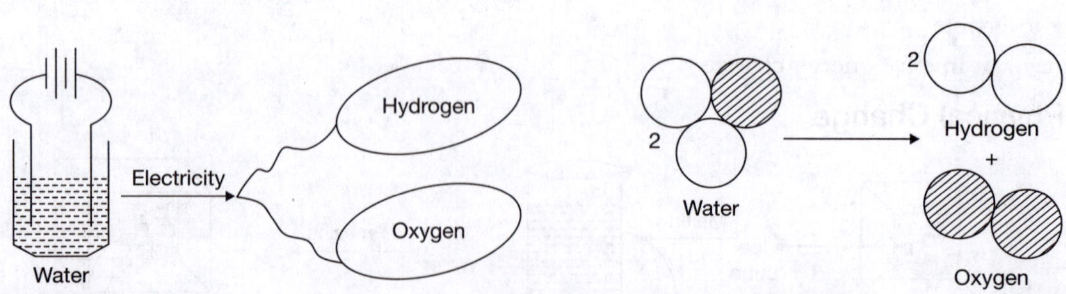

Figure 9.12 Dissociation of water by supplying electricity and the chemical changes involved

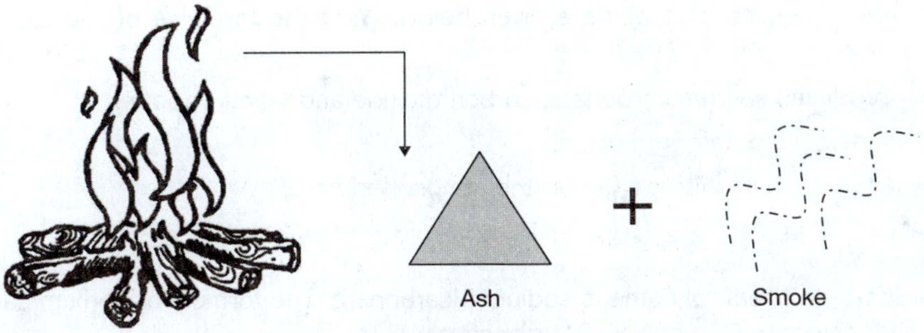

Figure 9.13 Burning of wood

Some examples of physical and chemical changes are given in the following figure.

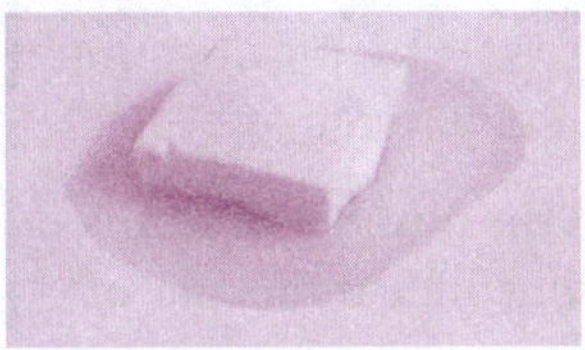

Physical Change
- Melting of butter
- Cutting of wood
- Melting of wax
- Dissolution of salt in water
- Glowing of bulb
- Magnetization of iron
- Making of soda water
- Breaking of glass

Both
- Burning of candle
- Boiling of milk

Chemical Change
- Cooking of food
- Baking of cake
- Rotting of banana
- Burning of cooking gas
- Burning of crackers
- Rusting of iron
- Curdling of milk
- Blackening of silverware
- Germination of seeds
- Ripening of fruits
- Decay of food
- Photosynthesis
- Respiration

Figure 9.14 Examples of physical and chemical changes

Reversible and Irreversible Changes

Heating of lead oxide powder results in the change of colour from yellow to reddish brown, it is a physical change. The change in colour is reversible.

Heating of zinc oxide powder results in the change of colour from white to yellow, it is also a physical change. Heating of mercuric oxide results in the change of colour, it turns into black which is followed by evolution of fumes. Tiny silvery droplets are seen sticking to the cooler parts of the test tube. The change is irreversible. This is because mercuric oxide splits into mercury and oxygen on heating. That means it is a chemical change.

Table 9.9 Difference between Physical and Chemical Change

Property	Physical Change	Chemical Change
Formation of new substance	No	Yes
Reversibility	Reversible	Irreversible
Nature of change	Temporary	Permanent
Amount of energy	Very little amount of energy is absorbed or given out	Huge amount of energy is absorbed or given out

EXAMPLE 9.4 A few chemical changes are given below. Write the formulae of the substances involved in those changes.

(a) Baking soda on strong heating produces sodium carbonate, carbon dioxide and water vapour.

(b) Marble on heating gives calcium oxide and carbon dioxide.

(c) Rust (iron oxide) is formed when iron reacts with oxygen in the atmospheric air.

SOLUTION

(a) Formula of baking soda is $NaHCO_3$. Its chemical name is sodium bicarbonate. The formula of sodium carbonate is Na_2CO_3 and those of carbon dioxide and water are CO_2 and H_2O, respectively.

(b) Marble contains calcium carbonate. Its formula is $CaCO_3$. The formulae of products are CaO (calcium oxide) and CO_2 (carbon dioxide).

(c) Formula of iron and oxygen are Fe and O_2, respectively. The formula of iron oxide formed is Fe_2O_3.

POINTS TO REMEMBER

- ✔ Elements are the basic constituents of all materials and are the simplest substances.
- ✔ Atoms are considered to be the basic units of 'everything' around us.
- ✔ Compounds are made up of molecules with atoms of different elements.
- ✔ Atomicity is the number of atoms which make up a molecule of an element.
- ✔ Some elements have molecules made up of more than two atoms. Those are called polyatomic elements.
- ✔ Symbol is defined as the shorthand notation which represents a single atom of an element.
- ✔ The number of atoms of an element in which one atom of a particular element combines is called combining capacity of that element.
- ✔ A formula is defined as the shorthand notation which represents a molecule of an element or a compound.
- ✔ Molecular composition is the number of atoms of various elements present in a molecule of a substance.
- ✔ A physical change is defined as a change in which the molecular composition of the substance remains unchanged, and no new substance is formed.
- ✔ A chemical change is defined as a change in which the molecular composition of the substance changes and new substances are formed.
- ✔ On heating, the substances in fuel combine with oxygen and form new substances (oxides). Heat energy is released during this process. This process is called combustion.
- ✔ Both combustion and rusting come under a chemical change called oxidation.
- ✔ A chemical change is known as a chemical reaction. The original substance is called reactant and the new substance formed is called product.

PRACTICE QUESTIONS CLASSROOM WING

Very Short Answer Type Questions

Direction for questions from 1 to 3.
Fill in the blanks.

1. Shorthand representation of a single atom of an element is called ________
2. The number of oxygen atoms in one molecule of sulphur trioxide is ______.
3. The Latin name of potassium is ______.

Direction for questions from 4 to 10.
Select the correct alternative from the given options.

4. Which among the following is a polyatomic element?
   (a) Bromine (b) Phosphorous
   (c) Helium (d) Copper
5. The symbol of which among the following elements is derived from its Latin name?
   (a) Zinc (b) Aluminium
   (c) Iron (d) Calcium
6. One molecule of which among the following elements possesses the maximum number of atoms?
   (a) Ozone (b) Sulphur
   (c) Chlorine (d) Nitrogen
7. Which among the following molecules possesses the maximum number of oxygen atoms?
   (a) Carbon dioxide (b) Nitric acid
   (c) Sulphuric acid (d) Calcium oxide
8. Which among the following contains 12 atoms of oxygen?
   (a) 6 molecules of calcium oxide
   (b) 6 molecules of water
   (c) 3 molecules of sodium bicarbonate
   (d) 4 molecules of calcium carbonate
9. The incorrect formula among the following is:
   (a) Mg_2O (b) ZnO
   (c) CaO (d) SO_3
10. The Latin name of silver is ______.
    (a) Aurum (b) Argentum
    (c) Stannum (d) Plumbum

Direction for questions from 11 to 15.
Fill in the blanks.

11. A change which can be reversed is called ______ change.
12. Swinging of clock pendulum is a ______ change.
13. Rusting of iron is a ______ change. (physical/chemical/reversible)
14. Magnetization of iron is a ______ change. (physical/chemical/irreversible).
15. Burning of coal is a ______ change. (physical/chemical)

Direction for questions from 16 to 20.
Select the correct alternative from the given options.

16. The chemical change among the following is:
    (a) Production of sound
    (b) Magnetization of iron
    (c) Curdling of milk
    (d) Melting of ghee
17. Identify the non-periodic change among the following.
    (a) Change of seasons
    (b) Phases of moon
    (c) Beating of heart
    (d) Earthquakes
18. Bursting of crackers is a ______ and ______ change.
    (a) chemical, fast (b) chemical, slow
    (c) physical, fast (d) physical, slow
19. The burning of candle is a:
    (a) Periodic and irreversible change
    (b) Reversible and chemical change
    (c) Non-periodic and reversible change
    (d) Chemical and irreversible change
20. Identify a true statement among the following.
    (a) In a physical change composition changes.
    (b) Chemical change can easily be reversed.
    (c) Physical change is a temporary change.
    (d) In a chemical change no new substance(s) is/are formed.

Short Answer Type Questions

21. Define the following.
(a) Atom
(b) Molecule
(c) Symbol
(d) Formula

22. Write the formulae for the following.
(a) Ozone
(b) Phosphorus
(c) Neon

23. Write the names of the elements with the following symbols.
(a) Fe (b) Zn (c) Al (d) C

24. Find the odd one out among the following sets. Give reasons.
(a) Nitrogen, fluorine, oxygen, hydrogen, ozone.
(b) CaO, NaCl, Co, FeS, KNO_3
(c) Se, K, Cu, Pb, Sl.
(d) Bromine, iodine, carbon, sulphur, silicon.

25. Write the formulae of different compounds formed among the given elements.

Element	Combining power
Ca	2
O	2
Fe	3
S	2
Na	1

26. Identify the combining power of the elements present in the following compounds.
(a) A_2B (b) X_2Y_3 (c) DE_2 (d) G_3H_2

27. Write the compounds of aluminium with the following elements.
Oxygen, Sulphur, Nitrogen.

28. Identify the incorrect formulae and correct them.
(a) CaO_2 (b) Mg_2S_3
(c) FeO_2 (d) PbO
(e) Ca_3S_2 (f) PbS
(g) Zn_2O (h) Fe_2S

29. Classify the following into solids and liquids.
Glucose, Vinegar, Nitric acid, Sodium hydroxide, Baking soda and Sugar.

30. Define atomicity. Based on it match the following.

Column A		Column B	
(A)	$3SO_2$	(a)	Four atoms of oxygen
(B)	7CO	(b)	Eight atoms of oxygen
(C)	$2O_2$	(c)	Six atoms of oxygen
(D)	$2H_2SO_4$	(d)	Five atoms of oxygen
(E)	$5H_2O$	(e)	Twelve atoms of oxygen
(F)	$6NO_2$	(f)	Seven atoms of oxygen

31. On what the symbols of the elements are based?
Match the following elements with their Latin name and symbols.

Elements	Latin name	Symbol
(A) Sodium	(a) Stannum	(i) Sn
(B) Iron	(b) Natrium	(ii) Pb
(C) Gold	(c) Ferrum	(iii) Na
(D) Lead	(d) Aurum	(iv) Fe
(E) Tin	(e) Plumbum	(v) Au

32. Write the symbols for the following elements.
(a) Boron (b) Sulphur
(c) Argon (d) Calcium
(e) Selenium (f) Copper
(g) Lead (h) Barium

33. Give two examples for the following.
(a) Fast changes
(b) Desirable changes
(c) Non-periodic changes
(d) Physical changes
(e) Chemical changes

34. Define the following.
(a) Chemical change
(b) Reversible change
(c) Periodic change
(d) Physical change

35. Classify the following changes as reversible or irreversible changes.
(a) Burning of candle
(b) Glowing of bulb
(c) Freezing of water
(d) Curdling of milk
(e) Burning of paper
(f) Magnetization of iron

36. State the differences between physical change and chemical change.

37. Give reasons for the following.
(a) When magnesium is burnt in air, the weight of white ash obtained is more than magnesium metal.
(b) The weight of rusted iron is more than that of the original metal.

38. Classify the following into physical and chemical changes.
(a) Expansion of metals on heating
(b) Crystallization of salts from their solutions
(c) Blackening of silverware
(d) Ripening of fruits
(e) Cooking of food
(f) Melting of ice

39. (a) Identify the product formed.

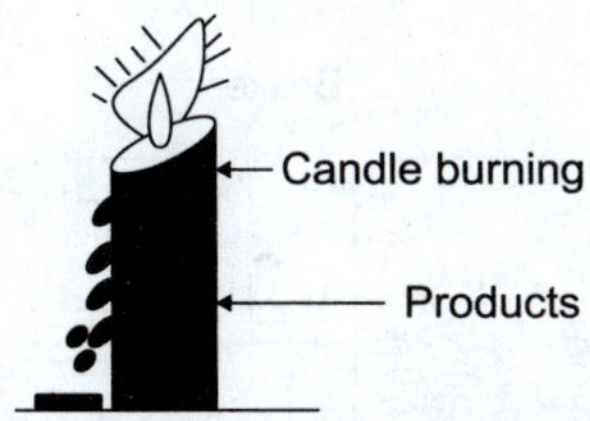

(b) Observe the following figure and identify the change associated with it.

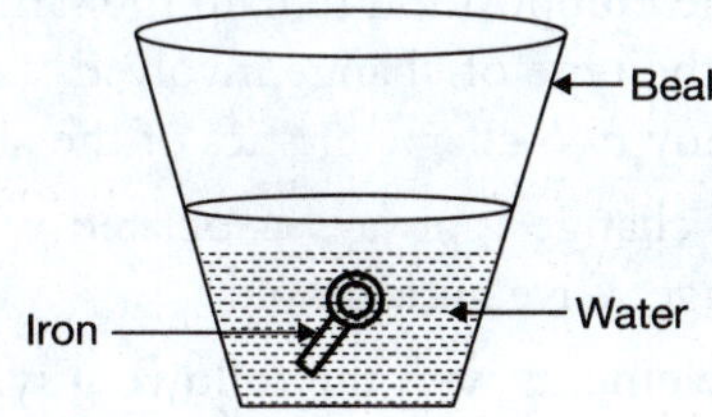

(c) Name the product formed in the following change.

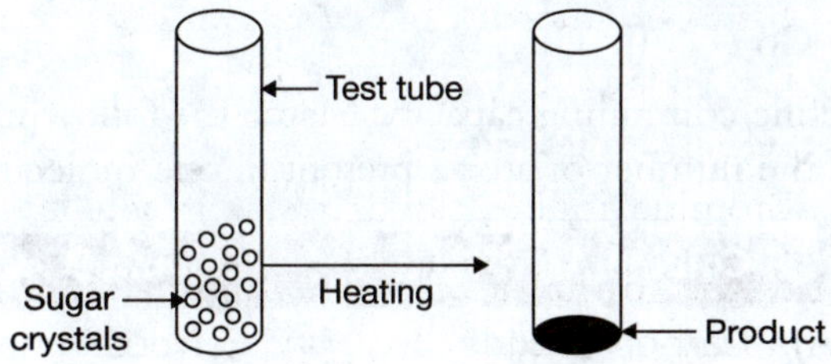

40. Explain the type of changes involved in the below chart.

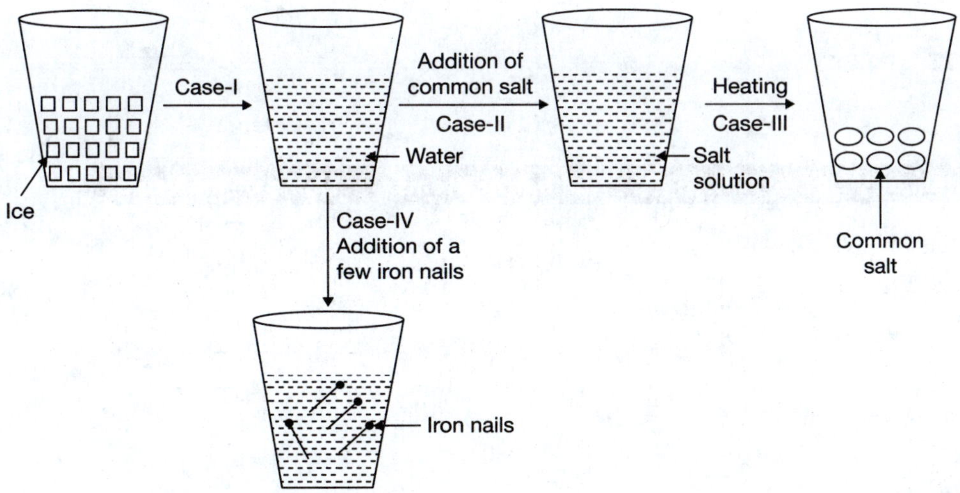

41. Study the given diagram and answer the following questions.

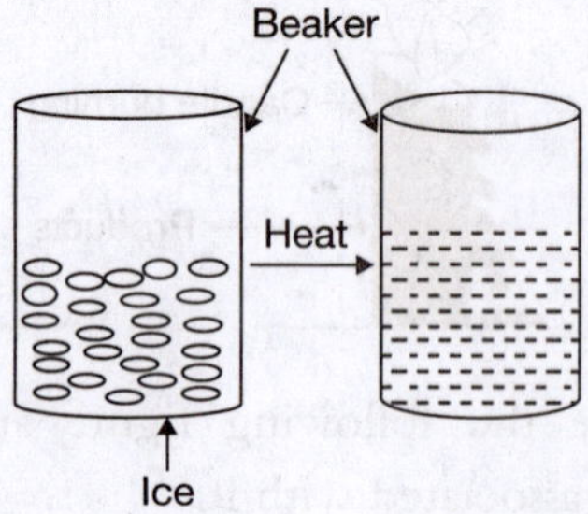

(a) Does the composition remain the same?
(b) Name the type of change involved.
(c) Write any two characteristics of the above change.

42. A desirable change is always associated with an undesirable change. Give an example.

43. Name the elements with the following symbols.
(a) C (b) N (c) Si (d) Br
(e) Cl (f) Ag (g) W (h) Hg
(i) Co (j) Cr

44. Define combining capacity. Match the following based on the number of atoms present in one molecule.

Column A		Column B	
(A)	Carbon dioxide	(a)	Ferrous sulphide
(B)	Calcium carbonate	(b)	Sodium oxide
(C)	Aluminium chloride	(c)	Copper sulphate
(D)	Hydrochloric acid	(d)	Methane
(E)	Sodium carbonate	(e)	Phosphorous acid
(F)	Sulphuric acid	(f)	Sulphur trioxide

45. Write the formulae of compounds with the following information and the names of the molecules.
(a) 2 phosphorus atoms, 5 oxygen atoms.
(b) 1 calcium atom, 2 oxygen atoms, 2 hydrogen atoms.
(c) 1 iron atom, 1 sulphur atom, 4 oxygen atoms.
(d) 1 potassium atom, 1 chlorine atom, 3 oxygen atoms.
(e) 3 sodium atoms, 1 phosphorus atom, 4 oxygen atoms.

46. Represent the following in terms of their formulae.
(a) 5 atoms of sodium
(b) 3 molecules of oxygen
(c) 4 molecules of hydrochloric acid
(d) 10 molecules of carbon monoxide
(e) 2 molecules of nitrogen dioxide

Essay Type Questions

47. Complete the following table.

Molecules	Names of elements	Number of atoms	Name of molecules
1 NaOH	–	–	–
–	–	16	Ammonia
–	Sodium, hydrogen, carbon, oxygen	12	–
3 H_2SO_4	–	–	–
–	–	5	Methane

PRACTICE QUESTIONS COMPETITION WING

Level 1: Apply Your Concepts

Direction for questions from 1 to 5.
Fill in the blanks.

1. The symbol of magnesium is _____.
2. The smallest and ultimate particle of an element is called _____.
3. Atoms of _____ (or) _____ can be regarded as molecules.
4. The number of atoms in one molecule of oxygen is _____.
5. Three atoms of chlorine are represented as _____.

Directions for questions from 6 to 9.
Select the correct alternative from the given options.

6. Which of the following observations indicates that the burning of coal is a chemical change?
   (a) Formation of ash (b) Evolution of heat
   (c) Production of smoke (d) All of the above
7. **Assertion (A):** Fixing of a metal rim on to the wooden wheel of a cart is a physical change.
   Reason (R): Metals expand on heating and contract on melting.
   Choose the correct option.
   (a) Both A and R are true, and R is the correct explanation for A.
   (b) Both A and R are true, but R is not the correct explanation for A.
   (c) A is true and R is false.
   (d) A is false and R is true.
8. **Assertion (A):** Ripening of fruits is a desirable physical change .
   Reason (R): Physical changes do not result in the formation of new substances .
   Choose the correct option.
   (a) Both A and R are true, and R is the correct explanation for A.
   (b) Both A and R are true, but R is not the correct explanation for A.
   (c) A is true and R is false.
   (d) A is false and R is true.
9. What type of change is formation of coal?

Option	Desirable Change	Reversible Change	Slow Change	Periodic Change
(a)	✓	✗	✓	✗
(b)	✗	✓	✓	✗
(c)	✓	✗	✓	✗
(d)	✓	✗	✗	✓

Level 2: Review Your Concepts

10. Molecules of some elements and compounds are given below. Identify hydrogen, hydrogen chloride, water, carbon dioxide, carbon disulphide, carbon tetrachloride.

(a) 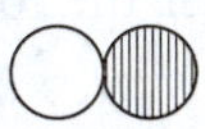
(b) 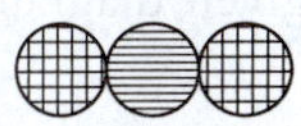
(c) 
(d) 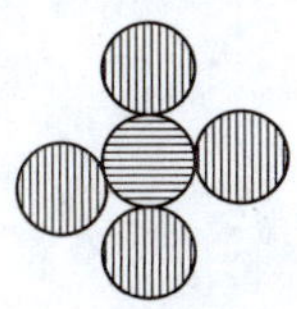
(e) 
(f) 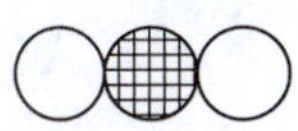

11. Complete the following table.

	Molecule	Elements	Total number of atoms in one molecule
(a)	Sodium hydroxide	–	–
(b)	Calcium carbonate	–	–
(c)	Methane	–	–
(d)	Nitrogen dioxide	–	–
(e)	Glucose	–	–
(f)	Baking soda	–	–
(g)	Silicon dioxide	–	–
(h)	Vinegar	–	–
(i)	Sugar	–	–
(j)	Washing soda	–	–

12. Arrange the following compounds in the increasing order of the number of oxygen atoms in one molecule.

Glucose, sugar, baking soda, sand, sulphuric acid

(a) Glucose < sugar < baking soda < sand < sulphuric acid

(b) Sugar < glucose < baking soda < sand < sulphuric acid

(c) Sand < baking soda < sulphuric acid < glucose < sugar

(d) Glucose < sulphuric acid < sugar < baking soda < sand

13. Identify true or false statements among the following and rewrite the correct statements.

(a) An element is made up of many kinds of atoms.

(b) $3O_2$ contains six atoms of oxygen.

(c) One molecule of calcium oxide contains three atoms.

(d) Formula of nitrogen dioxide is NO_2.

(e) In Fe_2O_3, the combining power of iron is 2 and that of oxygen is 3.

14. Correct the following statements.

(a) Symbol of copper is Co

(b) Silicon is a liquid

(c) The German name of tin is stannum

(d) Blue vitriol is $CuSO_4 . 6H_2O$

(e) Formula of magnesium sulphide is Mg_2S

15. Identify the physical and chemical changes among the following.

(a) Preparation of liquefied petroleum gas

(b) Usage of liquefied petroleum gas

(c) Formation of manure

(d) Formation of glass

(e) Breaking of glass

16. Classify the following into different changes.

(a) Making of dough from flour

(b) Digestion of food

(c) Germination of seeds

(d) Burning of paper

Level 3: Assess Your Concepts

17. Calculate the ratio of the number of atoms of the first element to the last element in the formulae of the following compounds.

(a) Common salt (b) Chalk

(c) Nitric acid (d) Ammonia

(e) Hydrogen sulphide (f) Sugar

18. Analyze the given diagrams and answer the following questions.

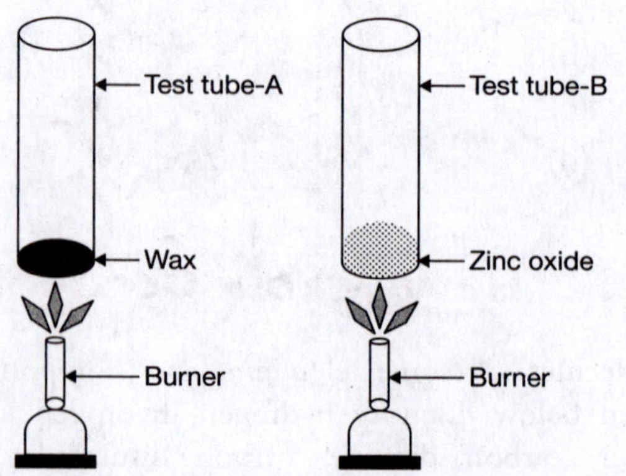

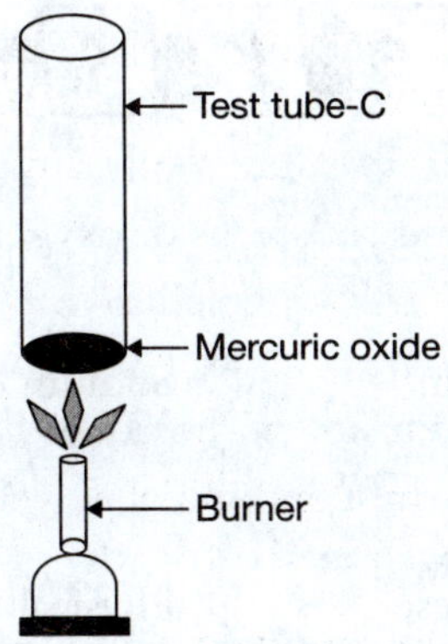

(a) Identify the test tube(s) in which new substance(s) is/are formed.

(b) Does the composition change in all the test tubes? Give reasons.

(c) Identify the colour changes associated with the relevant physical change given.

19. Write the formula of the substance involved in the following

(a) Rusting of iron when it reacts with oxygen in the atmospheric air.

(b) Name the compound formed form 3 sodium atom, 1 phosphorus atom and 4 oxygen atoms.

20. Calculate the ratio of number of atoms of the first element to last element in the following.

(a) Sodium carbonate

(b) Alcohol

(c) Nitric acid

21. State true or false and rewrite the correct statement.

(a) One molecule of sulphuric acid contains two sulphur.

(b) In Fe_2O_3 the combining power of iron is 3 and that of oxygen is 2.

(c) Preparation of liquefied petroleum gas is a chemical change.

AT

ANSWER KEYS

Crossword

Across

2. Sulphur 4. Desirable change 7. Plumbum 9. Sodium carbonate
11. Hydrargyrum 12. Periodic change 13. Eight

Down

1. Five 2. Sodium bicarbonate 3. Manganese 5. Physical change
6. Lead sulphide 10. Three

Classroom Wing

Very Short Answer Type Questions

1. Symbol 2. 3 3. Kalium 4. (b) 5. (c) 6. (b)
7. (c) 8. (d) 9. (a) 10. (b) 11. reversible
12. periodic 13. non-periodic 14. physical 15. chemical 16. (c) 17. (d)
18. (a) 19. (d) 20. (c)

Short Answer Type Questions

30. (A) → (c); (B) → (f); (C) → (a) (D) → (b); (E) → (d); (F) → (e)
31. (A) – (b) – (iii); (B) – (c) – (iv); (C) – (d) – (v); (D) – (e) – (ii); (E) – (a) – (i)
44. (A) → (b), (B) → (d), (C) → (f), (D) → (a), (E) → (c), (F) → (e)

Competition Wing

Level 1: Apply Your Concepts

1. Mg 2. Atom 3. noble gases (or) inert gases 4. two 5. 3Cl
6. (d) 7. (b) 8. (d) 9. (c) 12. (c)

Level 2: Review Your Concepts

13. (a) False; (b) True; (c) False; (d) True; (e) False

Level 3: Assess Your Concepts

17. (a) 1 : 1 (b) 1 : 3 (c) 1 : 3 (d) 1 : 3 (e) 2 : 1 (f) 12 : 11
20. (a) 2:3; (b) 2:1; (c) 1:3 21. (a) False; (b) True; (c) False

Hints and Explanations

CLASSROOM WING

Very Short Answer Type Questions

1. Symbol.
2. The formula of sulphur trioxide is SO_3. The number of oxygen atoms in a molecule is 3.
3. The Latin name of potassium is Kalium.
4. Bromine is diatomic, Phosphorous is polyatomic (atomicity is 4), Helium and copper are monoatomic elements.
   Hence, the correct option is (b).
5. Symbol of iron (Fe) is derived from its Latin name that is ferrum.
   Hence, the correct option is (c).
6. $O_3 \rightarrow 3$ atoms : $S_8 \rightarrow 8$ atoms
   $Cl_2 \rightarrow 2$ atoms : $N_2 \rightarrow 2$ atoms
   Hence, the correct option is (b).
7. $CO_2 \rightarrow 2$ oxygen atoms,
   $HNO_3 \rightarrow 3$ oxygen atoms
   $H_2SO_4 \rightarrow 4$ oxygen atoms,
   $CaO \rightarrow 1$ oxygen atom.
   Hence, the correct option is (c).
8. $6\ CaO \rightarrow 6$ oxygen atoms
   $6H_2O \rightarrow 6$ oxygen atoms
   $3NaHCO_3 \rightarrow 9$ oxygen atoms
   $4CaCO_3 \rightarrow 12$ oxygen atoms
   Hence, the correct option is (d).
9. Mg_2O is the incorrect formula.
   Hence, the correct option is (a).
10. The Latin name of silver is argentum.
    Hence, the correct option is (b).
11. A change which can be reversed is called reversible change.
12. Swinging of clock pendulum is a periodic change.
13. Rusting of iron is a non-periodic change.
14. Magnetization of iron is a physical change.
15. Burning of coal is a chemical change.
16. The curdling of milk is a chemical change.
    Hence, the correct option is (c).
17. Earthquakes are non-periodic changes.
    Hence, the correct option is (d).
18. Burning of crackers is a chemical and fast change.
    Hence, the correct option is (a).
19. Burning of candle is a chemical and irreversible change.
    Hence, the correct option is (d).
20. Physical change is a temporary change.
    Hence, the correct option is (c).

Short Answer Type Questions

21. (a) The smallest particle of matter, which may or may not have independent existence but can take part in a chemical reaction is called an atom.
    (b) The smallest unit of matter which always exists independently is called molecule.
    (c) Symbol can be defined as the shorthand notation which represents an atom of an element.
    (d) Formula is defined as the shorthand notation which represents a molecule of an element or a compound.
22. (a) O_3 (b) P_4 (c) Ne
23. (a) Iron (Ferrum) (b) Zinc
    (c) Aluminium (d) Carbon
24. (a) **Ozone** is a triatomic molecule while others are diatomic molecules.
    (b) **Co** is the symbol for cobalt which is an element while others are compounds.
    (c) **Sl** is not the symbol for any element while others are symbols for the respective elements.
    (d) **Bromine** is liquid non-metal and others are solids.
25. The formulae of different compounds for the given elements are: CaO, CaS, Na_2O, Na_2S, Fe_2O_3, Fe_2S_3.

26. (a) In A_2B combining powers A → 1, B → 2

(b) In X_2Y_3, combining powers X → 3, Y → 2

(c) In DE_2, combining powers D → 2, E → 1

(d) In G_3H_2, combining powers G → 2, H → 3

27. Al and O ⇒ Al → 3; O → 2 ⇒ Al_2O_3

Al and S ⇒ Al → 3, S → 2 ⇒ Al_2S_3

Al and N ⇒ Al → 3, N → 3 ⇒ AlN

28. Incorrect formulae: CaO_2, Mg_2S_3, FeO_2, Ca_3S_2, Zn_2O, Fe_2S.

Correct formulae: CaO, MgS, FeO or Fe_2O_3, CaS, ZnO, FeS or Fe_2S_3.

29. **Solids:** Glucose, Sodium hydroxide, baking soda, sugar

Liquids: Vinegar, nitric acid.

30. **Atomicity** is the number of atoms which make up a molecule of an element.

(A) → (c); (B) → (f); (C) → (a)

(D) → (b); (E) → (d); (F) → (e)

31. The elements are provided with symbols based on their English or Latin names.

(A) → (b) → (iii); (B) → (c) → (iv);

(C) → (d) → (v); (D) → (e) → (ii);

(E) → (a) → (i)

32. (a) B (b) S (c) Ar (d) Ca

(e) Se (f) Cu (g) Pb (h) Ba

33. (a) Burning of a match stick, glowing of an electric bulb.

(b) Formation of curd from milk, formation of manure.

(c) Sneezing, rusting of iron.

(d) Melting of ice, evaporation of water.

(e) Germination of seeds, cooking of food.

34. (a) A chemical change is defined as a change in which the molecular composition of the substance changes and new substances are formed.

(b) A change which can be reversed is called reversible change.

(c) A change which occurs again and again after fixed intervals of time is called periodic change.

(d) A physical change is defined as a change in which the molecular composition of the substance remains unchanged and no new substance is formed.

35. **Reversible changes:** Freezing of water, glowing of bulb, magnetization of iron.

Irreversible changes: Burning of candle, curdling of milk, burning of paper.

36. Differences between physical and chemical changes:

Physical change	Chemical change
No change in the molecular composition of the substance, no new substance is formed.	Change in the molecular composition of the substance, new substance (s) is (are) formed.
The change is generally temporary.	The change is generally permanent.
Net energy change may or may not be there.	Energy may be released or absorbed.
There is no change in the weight of the substance undergoing the change.	There may be an apparent change in the weight of the substance undergoing the change.

37. (a) Magnesium on burning combines with oxygen to form magnesium oxide(white ash). Hence, the weight is found to be increased.

(b) Since rusting is a chemical change, a new substance is formed. In this change, iron reacts with oxygen and moisture in the air to form iron oxide. Hence, the weight of rusted iron is more than that of the original metal.

38. (a) Physical change (b) Physical change

(c) Chemical change (d) Chemical change

(e) Chemical change (f) Physical change

39. (a) Products – CO_2 and H_2O

(b) Rusting of iron.

(c) Sugar charcoal (or) Carbon

40. **Case I:** Melting of ice ⇒ Physical change

Case II: Addition of common salt to water. ⇒ Physical change

Case III: Heating of salt solution involves evaporation. ⇒ Physical change

Case IV: Rusting of iron nails ⇒ Chemical change

41. (a) Yes, composition remains the same.

(b) Physical change

(c) (i) In physical change no new substances are formed.

(ii) Physical change is a temporary change.

42. Spraying chemicals on vegetables and fruits to kill insects is a desirable change for the farmer but it is an undesirable change for people who consume them.

43. (a) Carbon (b) Nitrogen
(c) Silicon (d) Bromine
(e) Chlorine (f) Silver
(g) Tungsten (h) Mercury
(i) Cobalt (j) Chromium

44. The number of atoms of an element in which one atom of a particular element combines is called **combining capacity** of that element.

CO_2, Na_2O ⇒ 3 atoms
$CaCO_3$, CH_4 ⇒ 5 atoms
$AlCl_3$, SO_3 ⇒ 4 atoms
HCl, FeS ⇒ 2 atoms
Na_2CO_3, $CuSO_4$ ⇒ 6 atoms
H_2SO_4, H_3PO_3 ⇒ 7 atoms
(A) → (b); (B) → (d); (C) → (f)
(D) → (a); (E) → (c); (F) → (e)

45. (a) P_2O_5 ⇒ Phosphorus pentoxide
(b) $Ca(OH)_2$ ⇒ Calcium hydroxide
(c) $FeSO_4$ ⇒ Ferrous sulphate
(d) $KClO_3$ ⇒ Potassium chlorate
(e) Na_3PO_4 ⇒ Sodium phosphate

46. (a) 5 Na (b) 3 O_2(c) 4HCl
(d) 10 CO (e) 2 NO_2

Essay Type Questions

47.

Molecule	Names of elements	Number of atoms	Names of molecules
1 NaOH	Sodium, oxygen, hydrogen	3	Sodium hydroxide
4 NH_3	Nitrogen, hydrogen	16	Ammonia
2$NaHCO_3$	Sodium, hydrogen, carbon oxygen	12	Baking soda
3 H_2SO_4	Hydrogen, sulphur, oxygen	21	Sulphuric acid
CH_4	Carbon, hydrogen	5	Methane

COMPETITION WING

Level 1: Apply Your Concepts

1. The symbol of magnesium is Mg.
2. The smallest and ultimate particle of an element is called atom.
3. Atoms of noble gases or inert gases can be regarded as molecules.
4. The number of atoms in one molecule of oxygen is two.
5. Three atoms of chlorine are represented as 3Cl.
6. All the given observations indicates that the burning of coal is a chemical change.

   Hence, the correct option is (d).
7. **Assertion (A):** Fixing of a metal rim on to the wooden wheel of a cart is a physical change-True.

   Reason (R): Metals expand on heating and contract on melting-True.

   But (R) is not the correct reason of (A).

   Correct reason for the given assertion: The process of fixing of a metal rim on to the wooden wheel of a cart does not result into the formation of a new substance. Choice(b)

   Hence, the correct option is (b).
8. **Assertion (A):** Ripening of fruits is a desirable physical change-False .

   Reason (R): Physical changes do not result in the formation of new substances-True .

   (A) is false and (R) is true.

   Hence, the correct option is (d).
9. Formation of coal is a desirable, slow, nonperiodic and irreversible change.

   Hence, the correct option is (c).

Level 2: Review Your Concepts

10. Hydrogen – (e)

    Hydrogen chloride – (a)

    Carbon tetrachloride – (d)

    Carbon dioxide – (b)

    Carbon disulphide – (c)

    Water – (f)

11.

Molecule	Elements	Formula	Total number of atoms in one molecule
(a) Sodium hydroxide	Sodium, hydrogen, oxygen	NaOH	3
(b) Calcium carbonate	Calcium, carbon, oxygen	$CaCO_3$	5
(c) Methane	Carbon, hydrogen	CH_4	5
(d) Nitrogen dioxide	Nitrogen, oxygen	NO_2	3
(e) Glucose	Carbon, hydrogen, oxygen	$C_6H_{12}O_6$	24
(f) Baking soda	Sodium, hydrogen, carbon, oxygen	$NaHCO_3$	6
(g) Silicon dioxide	Silicon, oxygen	SiO_2	3
(h) Vinegar	Carbon, hydrogen, oxygen	CH_3COOH	8
(i) Sugar	Carbon, hydrogen, oxygen	$C_{12}H_{22}O_{11}$	45
(j) Washing soda	Sodium, carbon, oxygen, hydrogen	$Na_2CO_3 . 10 H_2O$	36

12.

Compound	Formula
Sand	SiO_2
Baking soda	$NaHCO_3$
Sulphuric acid	H_2SO_4
Glucose	$C_6H_{12}O_6$
Sugar	$C_{12}H_{22}O_{11}$

Hence, the correct option is (c).

13. (a) False ⇒ An element is made up of the same kind of atoms.

(b) True

(c) False ⇒ One molecule of calcium oxide contains one oxygen atom and one calcium atom.

(d) True

(e) False ⇒ In Fe_2O_3, the combining power of iron is 3 and that of oxygen is 2.

14. (a) Symbol of copper is Cu.

(b) Silicon is a solid.

(c) The Latin name of tin is stannum.

(d) Blue vitriol is $CuSO_4 \cdot 5H_2O$.

(e) Formula of magnesium sulphide is MgS.

15. (a) Physical change

(b) Chemical change

(c) Chemical change

(d) Chemical change

(e) Physical change

16. (a) Slow change, desirable change, irreversible change, non-periodic change and physical change.

(b) Slow change, desirable change, irreversible, non-periodic and chemical change.

(c) Slow change, desirable change, irreversible, non-periodic and chemical change.

(d) Slow change, desirable change, irreversible, non-periodic and chemical change.

Level 3: Assess Your Concepts

17. (a) Common salt ⇒ NaCl

$\therefore$ Required ratio $= \frac{1}{1} = 1 : 1$

(b) Chalk ⇒ $CaCO_3$

$\therefore$ Required ratio $= \frac{1}{3} = 1 : 3$

(c) Nitric acid ⇒ HNO_3

$\therefore$ Required ratio $= \frac{1}{3} = 1 : 3$

(d) Ammonia ⇒ NH_3

$\therefore$ Required ratio $= \frac{1}{3} = 1 : 3$

(e) Hydrogen sulphide ⇒ H_2S

$\therefore$ Required ratio $= \frac{2}{1} = 2 : 1$

(f) Sugar ⇒ $C_{12}H_{22}O_{11}$

$\therefore$ Required ratio $= \frac{12}{11} = 12 : 11$

18. (a) Heating of mercuric oxide is a chemical change. Hence in test tube – C new substance is formed.

(b) Heating of wax and zinc oxide are physical changes. Hence, in test tube – A and test tube – B, the molecular composition remains the same.

(c) In test tube – B change in colour is observed. Zinc oxide is white in colour and turns to yellow on heating.

19. (a) When iron (Fe) reacts with oxygen (O_2) a thin layer of rust formed on iron known as iron oxide (Fe_2O_3).

(b) Na_3PO_4 (sodium phosphate)

20. (a) Na_2CO_3

Na = 2

O = 3

$\frac{Na}{O} = \frac{2}{3} = 2 : 3$

(b) C_2H_5OH

$C = 2$

$H = 1$

$$\frac{C}{H} = \frac{2}{1} = 2:1$$

(c) HNO_3

$H = 1$

$O = 3$

$$\frac{H}{O} = \frac{1}{3} = 1:3$$

21. (a) False: One molecule of sulphuric acid contains 1 sulphur

H_2SO_4.

(b) True

(c) False: Preparation of liquefied petroleum gas is a physical change.

CHAPTER

10

Amazing Air

Remember

Before beginning this chapter, you should be able to:

- List the uses of air
- Recall substances essential for life

Key Ideas

After completing this chapter, you should be able to:

- Describe atmosphere
- Explain the components of air
- Understand the significance of air
- Define rusting
- Understand the cause and effect of air pollution

Scientific Crypt

A Tribute to Leon Teisserenc de Bort (1855-1913)

Leon Teisserenc de Bort (1855-1913) was a visionary French meteorologist known for his astonishing discovery of the "Stratosphere" layer of the atmosphere in the entire history of meteorology. He explored the atmosphere with unmanned high-altitude gas balloons and conceived the idea of dividing the atmosphere into layers, forever changing our perception of the air that surrounds us.

Born on November 5, 1855, in Paris, France, he developed a passion for science from an early age and studied at École Polytechnique in Palaiseau, France. After serving in the French military and conducting meteorological observations in Algeria (North Africa), he dedicated his entire life to the study of meteorology.

Leon Teisserenc de Bort's legacy as a pioneer in atmospheric science continues to shape our understanding of the Earth's atmosphere. His legacy provided greater insights into the understanding of the structure and dynamics of the amazing atmosphere, driving advancements in aviation and aeronautics.

FUN TIME

CROSSWORD

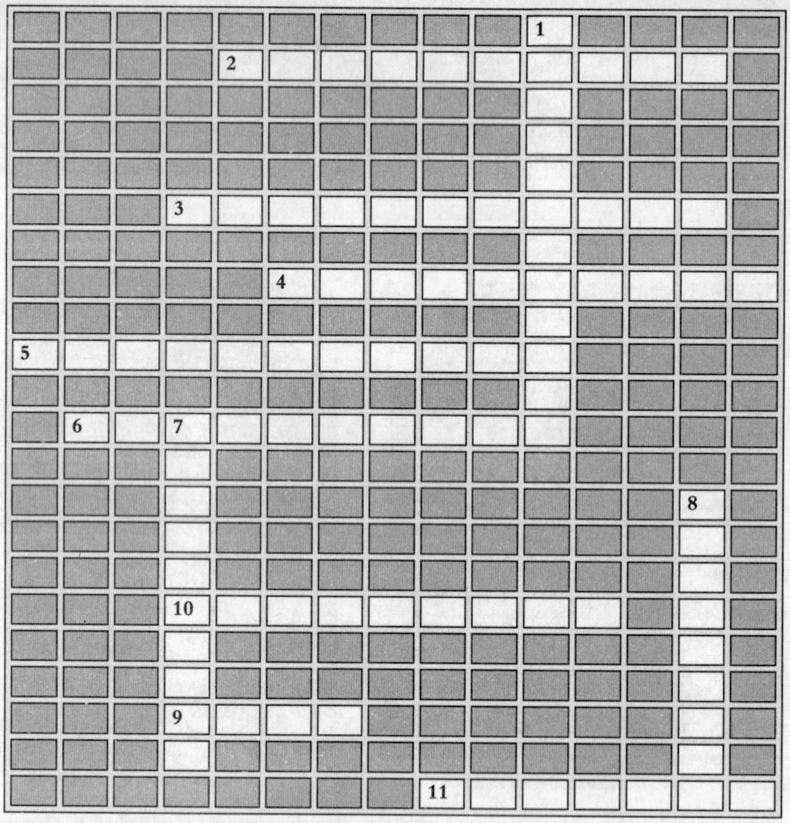

Across

2. A process in which a substance takes up oxygen with the release of energy in the form of heat and light.
3. A part of solar radiation that constitutes highly energetic and harmful radiation.
4. This extends up to 690–950 km above the earth's surface.
5. Lowest layer of atmosphere
6. The thick layer of air surrounding the earth.
9. Due to global warming earth temperature_____.
10. The air ________ is the addition of harmful substances to air due to natural phenomena or human activities.
11. The slow conversion of iron into its hydrated oxide.

Down

1. The layer of atmosphere above the troposphere which extends up to 50 km above the earth's surface.
7. The layer just above the stratosphere.
8. The phenomenon by which the solar _________ is trapped by the atmosphere to maintain moderate temperature on the earth's surface is known as greenhouse effect.

INTRODUCTION

Air is necessary for our survival and hence, is the most important source for all. We can feel the air around us but cannot see it in spite of being present all around us. In order to survive, every living organism need air (oxygen) to breathe. It protects us from harmful UV rays from the sun by being present in the form of a protective blanket around the earth which is called atmosphere. In this chapter, we will learn about air, its composition, and importance.

Air—Importance and Characteristics

Do you know what substances are essential for life?

- Air
- Shelter
- Water
- Clothes
- Food

Now, let us ask ourselves can we live without food? Maybe a few days. Can we live without water? Probably, few hours or a day or two. Now imagine that there is no air around us, how long can we survive? We won't last even a few minutes.

Air is very essential for the purpose of breathing. We can't live without breathing. That means air is the most important substance necessary for life.

Interestingly, it is not possible to see air with naked eyes, it can only be felt. All living organisms require air for breathing. Apart from breathing, air also helps in facilitating burning. Wood, charcoal, kerosene, cooking gas etc., burn in the presence of air to produce heat. Heat is a form of energy which is required for all essential activities like cooking of food, running of vehicles etc.,

Air is not present everywhere in the universe, it is only our planet which is gifted with this amazing substance 'AIR'.

Info Bytes!

Despite feeling weightless, the air in the atmosphere actually has weight and exerts pressure on everything. It's the atmospheric pressure that helps us breathe.

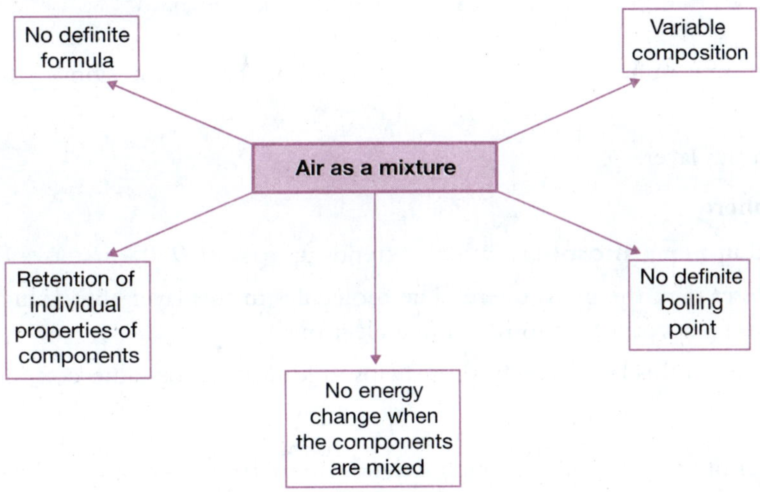

Figure 10.1 Characteristics of air

Atmosphere

The thick layer of air surrounding the earth is known as **atmosphere**. The atmosphere extends only up to 320 kilometres above the surface of earth, so air is present only up to this level.

The one and only primary source of heat energy is sun. Heat reaches the earth from sun by means of radiation.

Info Bytes!

John Mayow proved the presence of active and inactive components in air.

It is evident that around 50°C of temperature is naturally unbearable. That means only a minute amount of solar radiation reaches the earth. A part of solar radiation constitutes highly energetic and harmful radiation known as **ultraviolet radiation**. Atmosphere absorbs this radiation and prevents it from reaching the earth's surface. That means atmosphere protects us from harmful rays of the sun. Only a part of the solar radiation reaches the earth during the day, and hence, moderate temperature is maintained on the earth.

But, if the entire heat is re-radiated back from the earth, the earth would get extremely cold at night. In that case, living beings cannot survive and there would be no life on earth.

The atmosphere traps a part of the radiation and allows the rest of the radiation to be re-radiated back.

Adding to this, during night also some heat energy is retained in the earth's atmosphere. Therefore, some moderate temperatures are maintained. These moderate temperatures make the survival of life possible on the earth.

Layers of Atmosphere

Our atmosphere is divided into five layers on the basis of variations in chemical composition, density and temperature at different heights from the surface of the earth.

Troposphere

- The layer of atmosphere which begins at the earth's surface and extends up to 20 km height is called **troposphere**.
- It holds the maximum percentage of the total mass of the atmosphere.
- The density of the air and temperature gradually decrease with height.
- Most of the weather phenomena occur in this layer due to rapid variations in temperature.

Stratosphere

- The layer of atmosphere above the troposphere which extends up to 50 km above the earth's surface is called **stratosphere**.
- It holds 19 per cent of the atmospheric gases.
- Aeroplanes fly in this layer.

Mesosphere

- The layer above the stratosphere which extends to about 8590 km above the earth's surface is called **mesosphere**.
- Meteorites burn up in this layer.

Thermosphere or Ionosphere

- This layer is also called **upper atmosphere** which extends up to 690–950 km above the earth's surface.
- The density of air is lesser than the mesosphere. The molecules in this layer absorb highly energetic radiations and get ionised. Hence, this layer consists of ions and free electrons.
- Radio waves get reflected in this layer which, thus, helps in long-distance radio communications.

Exosphere

- It is the outermost layer of the atmosphere which extends up to 10,000 km above the earth's surface.
- This layer absorbs harmful ionising radiations.

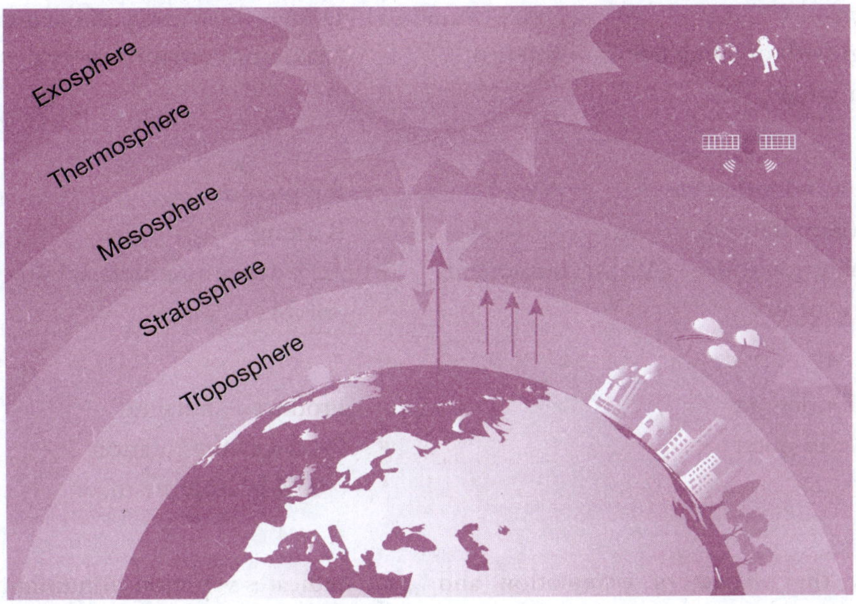

Figure 10.2 Layers of atmosphere

Composition of Air

The air in our atmosphere consists of a mixture of a number of gases. Joseph Priestley, Antoine Lavoisier, and Henry Cavendish were among the first scientists to study about the different constituents of air.

By volume, air is made up of nitrogen (78%), oxygen (21%), argon (0.93%), carbon dioxide (0.03%) and small amount of other gases along with water vapour.

Info Bytes!

Names of oxygen and nitrogen were coined by Lavoisier.

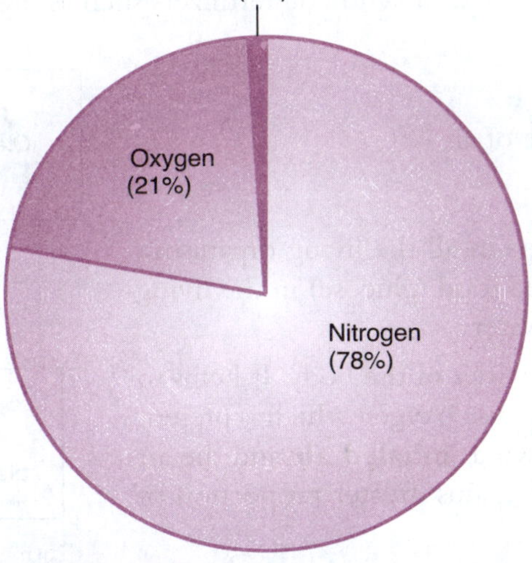

Figure 10.3 Composition of Air

Konnect

Humans breathe in more nitrogen with every breath than oxygen but our body doesn't use it the same way, it uses oxygen.

Properties of the Constituents

Nitrogen

- Odourless, colourless, and tasteless gas
- 78% by volume in air
- Does not undergo burning
- Non-supporter of combustion

- Very unreactive gas
- Essential for the growth of living beings (Proteins)
- Slightly soluble in water
- Dilutes the activity of oxygen (Inactive component)
- Maximum proportion in air

Oxygen

- Colourless, tasteless, odourless gas
- Supporter of life (Respiration)
- Supporter of combustion (Fuels) (Active component)
- 21% by the volume in air
- Respiration
- Rusting
- Added to atmospheric air by the process of photosynthesis
- Soluble in water

Carbon Dioxide

- Colourless and odourless gas
- Moderately soluble in water
- Fire extinguisher
- Product of burning
- Product of respiration
- 0.03% by volume in air

Water Vapour

- Added to air by the process of evaporation and transpiration (Water cycle)
- Variable proportions in air
- Condensation to give rain
- Indicates variation in humidity
- Rusting takes place
- Forms micelles with dust particles

Other Components

- Argon (Inert gases)
- Dust particles
- Impurities

Importance of Nitrogen

Nitrogen is the most important constituent element in chlorophyll and proteins. It is one of the major nutrients for plants.

Usually, soils are deficient in nitrogen as nitrogen containing salts are highly soluble in water. It is supplied to the soils in the form of natural fertilizers such as compost, manure etc., or synthetic fertilizers such as urea, CAN, etc.

Importance of Air

Following are the points which highlight the importance of air.

Respiration

Respiration can be defined as a chemical process occurs in all the living organisms, in which oxygen reacts with the simplest form of digested food (glucose) in the living cells to produce energy along with carbon dioxide and water.

Respiration releases energy which helps in various activities of the body. It helps to maintain the body temperature. Aquatic plants and animals use oxygen which is present in dissolved form in water. The air we breathe in is known as **inhaled air** and the air we breathe out is known as **exhaled air**. Exhaled air contains greater proportion of carbon dioxide than the inhaled air.

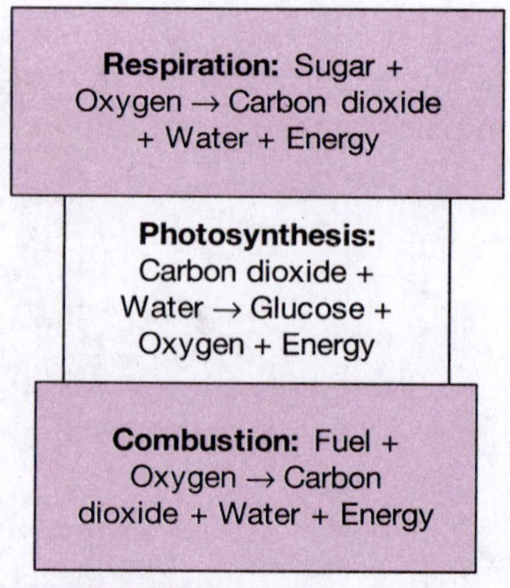

Figure 10.4 Importance of Air

Plants breathe through the minute openings on the surface of leaves called **stomata**. Respiration takes place at slower rate in plants than in animals as they have lesser activity than animals.

Though oxygen is being consumed during the process of respiration and combustion continuously, the proportion of oxygen in air remain constant. Oxygen is continuously being added to the atmospheric air by the process of photosynthesis that takes place in green plants.

Photosynthesis

Photosynthesis can be defined as the process in which the green parts of the plants, such as leaves, absorb carbon dioxide gas from the atmospheric air and convert it into glucose (starch) and oxygen in the presence of water, chlorophyll, and sunlight.

As the carbon dioxide formed during the above processes is being consumed during the process of photosynthesis, the balance of oxygen and carbon dioxide is maintained in the atmospheric air.

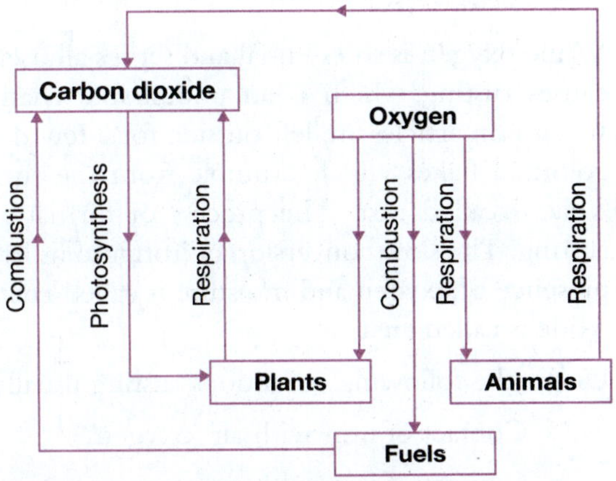

Figure 10.5 Balance of oxygen and carbon dioxide in the atmosphere

Combustion

Combustion or burning is a process in which a substance takes up oxygen with the release of energy in the form of heat and light. Carbon dioxide and water vapour are the products of combustion.

The material which undergoes combustion with the release of large amount of heat energy and light energy is known as a **fuel**. Some of the common fuels are wood, coal, charcoal, kerosene, petrol, diesel, Liquefied Petroleum Gas (LPG) and Compressed Natural Gas (CNG).

The heat produced in combustion is utilized for various domestic and industrial purposes.

Combustion and respiration both require oxygen and generate the same products, still there are significant differences between the two.

Table 10.1 Comparison between combustion and respiration

Combustion	Respiration
Fast process	Slow process
Heat and light are released	Only heat is released
Very high temperature	Body temperature
Not a natural continuous process	Natural continuous process

Uses of Air

It's important to understand the diverse uses of air. First and foremost, air is crucial for respiration, allowing humans and animals to breathe and obtain the oxygen necessary for survival. Other uses of air are summarize in Figure 10.6.

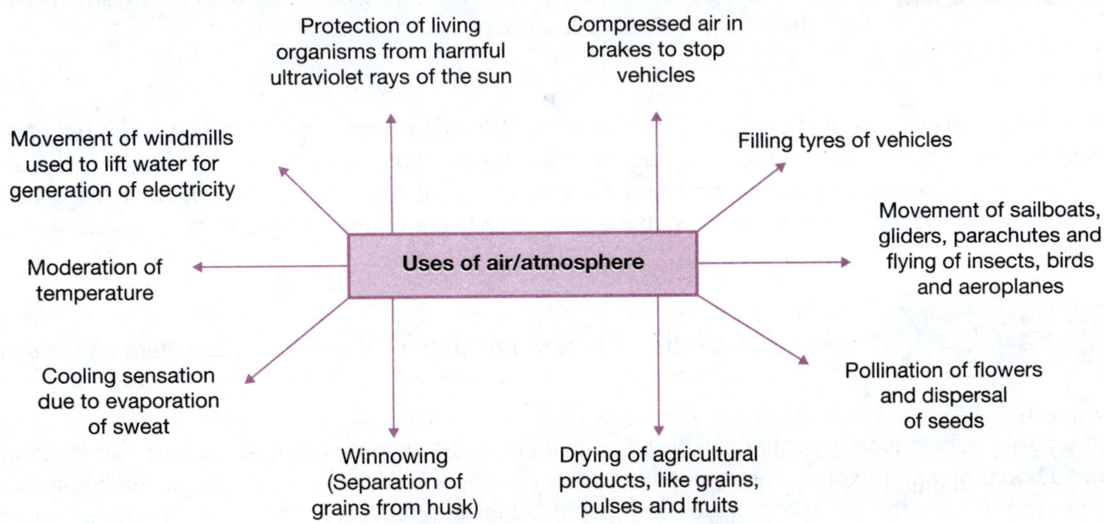

Figure 10.6 Uses of air

Rusting

While oxygen is so essential and serves all useful purposes, it also causes rusting which is an undesirable change. What happens when iron articles are left outside for a few days? We find brown coloured flakes which crumble from the surface of the article. That is called rust. The process of formation of rust is called rusting. The slow conversion of iron into its hydrated oxide in the presence of oxygen and moisture is called **rusting**. The hydrated oxide is called **rust**.

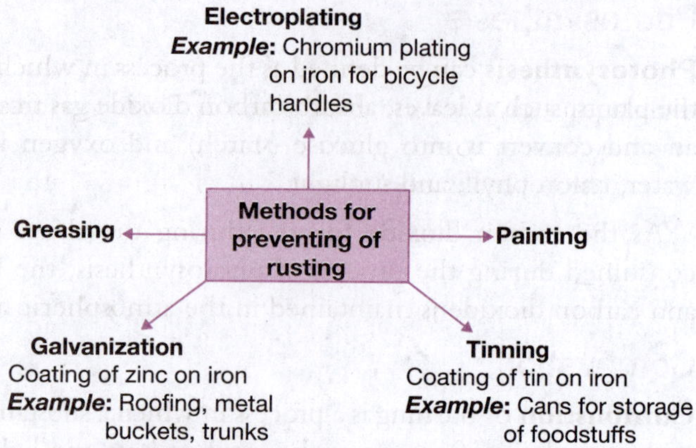

Figure 10.7 Methods to prevent rusting

Under the following conditions rusting usually takes place.

1. Contact of iron with air (oxygen)
2. Contact of iron with moisture

We can adopt various methods to prevent rusting by preventing the contact of the iron article with humid air.

Info Bytes!

The reddish-brown colour of Mars is due to iron oxide, essentially rust, present on its surface.

EXAMPLE 10.1

Mention the similarity and difference between rusting and tarnishing.

SOLUTION

Both rusting and tarnishing are examples of corrosion reactions that involve the degradation of metals due to their interaction with the environment. They both result in a change in the appearance and properties of the metal surface. However, rusting specifically refers to the oxidation of iron or iron-containing alloys when exposed to moisture and oxygen, resulting in the formation of iron(III) oxide or rust. Tarnishing, on the other hand, can occur on a variety of metals like silver, copper, and brass, and is caused by their reaction with sulfur-containing compounds in the air, leading to the formation of a dull, gray or black layer on the metal surface.

EXAMPLE 10.2

When a person wears glasses and enters a warm room after being in cold weather, the glasses often fog up. However, if the same glasses are placed in the warm room without being worn, they remain clear. Give reason.

SOLUTION

When a person is outside in cold weather, the glasses become cold. When the person then enters a warm room, the warm moist air from the room comes in contact with the cold surface of the glasses. This causes the water vapour in the air to condense on the glasses, forming tiny water droplets, which gives the appearance of fog. On the other hand, if the glasses are already at room temperature when placed in the warm room, there is no significant temperature difference to cause condensation, so they remain clear.

EXAMPLE 10.3

"Temperature affects the capacity of air to hold moisture." Comment on the statement.

SOLUTION

Warm air has the ability to hold more moisture compared to cold air. This is why, on a hot day, the air can feel more humid as it contains a larger amount of water vapour. Conversely, on cold days, the air holds less water vapour, leading to drier conditions. This is also the reason behind the formation of dew or frost in colder temperatures. When the air temperature drops, it can't retain as much moisture, causing the excess water vapour to condense into water droplets or frost. Thus, the capacity of air to hold moisture is directly influenced by its temperature.

Role of Carbon Dioxide in Atmosphere

During the day, the land gets heated up by solar radiation. This heat is re-radiated back during night. But, carbon dioxide has the capacity to trap a part of this heat. Therefore, some part of radiation is retained in the atmosphere while the rest is re-radiated. Thus, carbon dioxide in the atmosphere helps to retain heat and maintain moderate temperature on the earth's surface. This phenomenon is greenhouse effect. This is responsible to sustain life on earth.

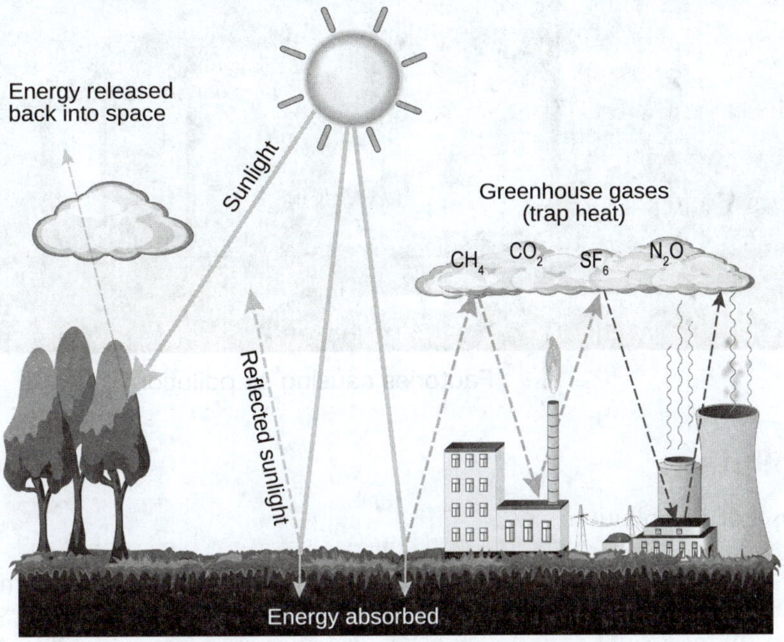

Figure 10.8 Trapping of solar radiation

The phenomenon by which the solar radiation is trapped by the atmosphere in order to maintain moderate temperature on the earth's surface is called **greenhouse effect**.

When excess of CO_2 is added to the atmosphere, the temperature of the earth increases enormously. In such specific case, CO_2 causes air pollution.

Global Warming

Global warming is the process that causes the Earth's temperature to rise and gradually increase further to the increased levels of carbon dioxide and other gases.

Global warming primarily caused by human activities. When people burn fossil fuels like coal, oil, and natural gas for energy, they release greenhouse gases into the atmosphere. These gases, including carbon dioxide and methane, trap heat and lead to a warming effect on the planet. This warming contributes to changes in climate patterns, such as more extreme weather events, rising sea levels, and disruptions to ecosystems.

Global warming can be decreased by conservation of plants, 3R's(Reduce, reuse and recycle), Reducing the dependence on fossil fuel.

Air Pollution

The addition of harmful substances to air or imbalance in the natural composition of air due to the natural phenomena or human activities is called **air pollution**.

Figure 10.9 Factories causing air pollution

Causes of Air Pollution

Following are the main causes of air pollution:

- Global warming: The causes of global warming are mentioned below:
  - Excess usage of fossil fuels
  - Deforestation
  - Thermal power plants
  - Industrialization
- The other common air pollutants are sulphur dioxide, carbon monoxide, nitrogen dioxide, ozone, chlorofluorocarbons, etc.
- SO_2 and NO_2 gases dissolve in rainwater and eventually it results in acid rain.
- Sources of harmful gases are automobile exhausts, industries and thermal power plants.
- Carbon monoxide reduces the oxygen intake by blood and it results in lesser oxygen intake and suffocation.
- Ozone is also a greenhouse gas which adds to global warming.
- Chlorofluorocarbons result in ozone depletion.

Konnect

Term 'Smog' is a combination of 'Smoke' and 'Fog'. It is formed by a number of pollutants and has serious negative effects on plants and animals.

Table 10.2 Sources and effects of air pollutants

Pollutant	Source	Effect
SO_2 and CO_2	Thermal power plants; automobile industries	Acid rains
Carbon monoxide	Automobile exhausts	Reduction in oxygen intake causes suffocation
Ozone	Industries	Greenhouse gas – global warming
Chlorofluorocarbons	Refrigeration systems	Ozone depletion

Info Bytes!

Taj Mahal at Agra is damaged due to acid rain.

It is very important, especially now as the air quality has gone down tremendously, to adopt strict measures to control and prevent air pollution. Some of these methods are given in the following diagram:

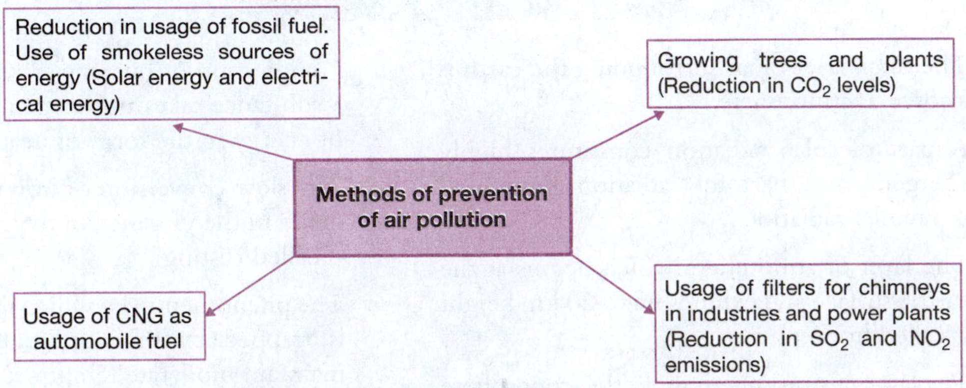

Figure 10.10 Methods to prevent air pollution

EXAMPLE 10.4

The characteristics of some gases are given below. Explain how they cause pollution.

(a) A colourless, odourless gas which turns lime water milky.

(b) A colourless, pungent gas which turns lime water milky.

SOLUTION

(a) CO_2 causes increase in temperature of earth's surface and results in global warming.

(b) SO_2 results in acid rain which makes the water bodies acidic and it makes the soils acidic and less fertile. It also gives off smoke (smog) which reduces visibility.

POINTS TO REMEMBER

- The thick layer of air surrounding the earth is known as atmosphere.
- A part of solar radiation constitutes highly energetic and harmful radiation known as ultraviolet radiation.
- The layer of atmosphere which begins at the earth's surface and extends up to 20 km height is called troposphere.
- The layer of atmosphere above the troposphere which extends up to 50 km above the earth's surface is called stratosphere.
- The layer above the stratosphere which extends to about 8590 km above the earth's surface is called mesosphere.
- Ionosphere extends up to 690–950 km above the earth's surface.
- Exosphere is the outermost layer of the atmosphere which extends up to 10,000 km above the earth's surface.
- Combustion or burning is a process in which a substance takes up oxygen with the release of energy in the form of heat and light.
- The slow conversion of iron into its hydrated oxide in the presence of oxygen and moisture is called rusting.
- The phenomenon by which the solar radiation is trapped by the atmosphere in order to maintain moderate temperature on the earth's surface is called greenhouse effect.
- Global warming is the process that causes the Earth's temperature to rise and gradually increase further to the increased levels of carbon dioxide and other gases.
- The addition of harmful substances to air or imbalance in the natural composition of air due to the natural phenomena or human activities is called air pollution.

DW

PRACTICE QUESTIONS CLASSROOM WING

Very Short Answer Type Questions

Directions for questions from 1 to 9.
Select the correct alternative from the given options.

1. Major component of CNG is ______.
   (a) Butane (b) Methane
   (c) Ethane (d) Propane
2. The products of combustion of glucose are:
   (a) Water vapour, carbon dioxide
   (b) Water vapor, hydrogen
   (c) Hydrogen, carbon monoxide
   (d) Carbon monoxide, carbon dioxide
3. Who named the active component of air as oxygen?
   (a) Cavendish (b) Mayow
   (c) Lavoisier (d) Priestley
4. Which among the following compounds is used to identify the presence of water vapour in the atmosphere?
   (a) Carbon dioxide
   (b) Phosphorus
   (c) Lime water
   (d) Anhydrous copper sulphate
5. The envelope of air that surrounds the earth is called:
   (a) Atmosphere (b) Lithosphere
   (c) Hydrosphere (c) Exosphere
6. Which of the following is false?
   (a) Air occupies space
   (b) Air has mass
   (c) Air can be compressed
   (d) Air does not dissolve in water
7. The gas assimilated by plants for the synthesis of proteins is ______.
   (a) Carbon monoxide (b) Nitrogen
   (c) Oxygen (d) Carbon dioxide
8. Gas X → Non-combustible and not a supporter of combustion
   Gas Y → Combustible as well as a supporter of combustion.
   What could be X and Y?
   (a) X → Oxygen, Y → Nitrogen
   (b) X → Carbon dioxide, Y → Oxygen
   (c) X → Oxygen, Y → Carbon dioxide
   (d) X → Carbon dioxide, Y → Argon
9. The fuel used in cement factories, steel mills and glass factories ______.
   (a) LPG (b) Wood
   (c) Coal (d) CNG

Directions for questions from 10 to 13.
Fill in the blanks.

10. The products of combustion of fossil fuels are ______ and ______.
11. The increase in the proportion of ______ in air leads to global warming.
12. $SO_3 + H_2O \rightarrow$ ______.
13. The gases which cause acid rain are ______ and ______.

Directions for questions from 14 to 15.
Select the correct alternative from the given options.

14. Identify the true statement among the following.
    (a) CO is a greenhouse gas.
    (b) Global warming decreases the fertility of soil.
    (c) Global warming causes melting of ice caps.
    (d) Acid rain causes unseasonal rains.
15. ______ is the source of SO_2.
    (a) Air conditioners
    (b) Thermal power plants
    (c) Refrigeration systems
    (d) Degradation of organic wastes

Short Answer Type Questions

16. Increased concentration of greenhouse gases causes global warming. Why?

17. Why mirror turns misty when air from lungs is blown gently on to it?

18. Coastal regions tend to have higher humidity (% of water vapour in air) compared to non-coastal regions. Why?

19. Match the following.

Column A	Column B
(A) Troposphere	(a) Aeroplanes fly in this layer
(B) Stratosphere	(b) Radio waves get reflected in this layer
(C) Ionosphere	(c) Most of the weather phenomenon occurs
(D) Mesosphere	(d) Meteorites burn up in this layer

20. Explain the importance of water vapour present in the atmosphere.

21. Why are industrial areas prone to acid rain?

22. The composition of air in terms of percentage of its various components is given.

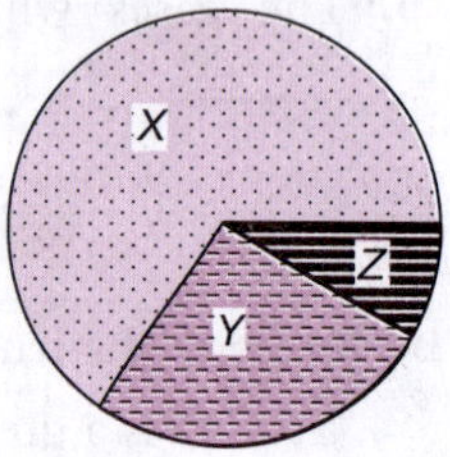

(a) Identify X and Y.

(b) Mention any two uses of X and Y.

(c) Identify the gases present in Z.

23. How is the balance of oxygen in atmospheric air maintained?

24. Both the active component and the inactive components of atmosphere play important roles. Illustrate.

25. Gas X is the heaviest component of natural air.

(a) Identify X.

(b) Mention the characteristic properties of X pertinent to combustion.

26. Though air contains only about 0.03% of carbon dioxide, it is a very important component of air. Give reasons.

27. What is the observation when air comes in contact with a cool surface?

28.

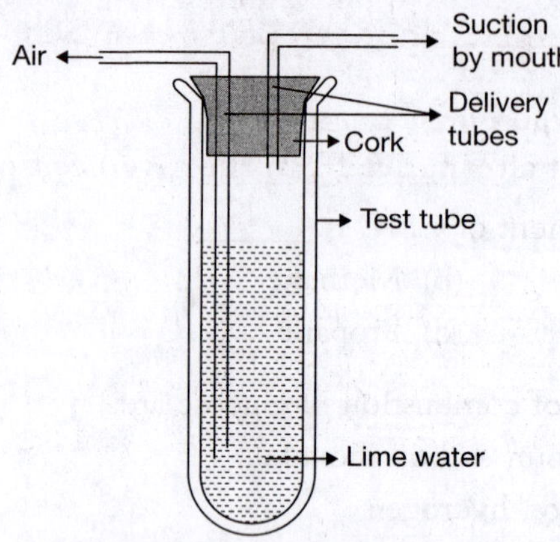

(a) Write the chemical name of the substance taken in the test tube.

(b) What is the observation? Give reasons.

(c) The air present in the test tube as shown in the diagram is sucked out. Why?

29. The dust particles come into air from a number of sources. Give some examples for such sources.

30. Calculate the volume of oxygen and nitrogen present in 250 L of air.

31. What is global warming? Mention the different ways of minimizing global warming.

32. What is air pollution?

33. Mention the effects of acid rain.

34. What are the different ways of minimizing air pollution?

35. Why are tall chimneys used in some factories?

36. Give reasons for the following.

(a) Policemen regulating traffic often wear masks.

(b) When water is heated, bubbles are observed.

37. It is not advisable to cook food on a wood fire in a closed room. Give reasons.

38. Between galvanized iron containers and tinned iron containers which are used to preserve food material? Justify your answer.

39. Explain the role of catalytic converters in automobile engines.

40. Why do earthworms come out of soil in rainy season?

41. What conclusions can be drawn based on the following diagrams?

(a)

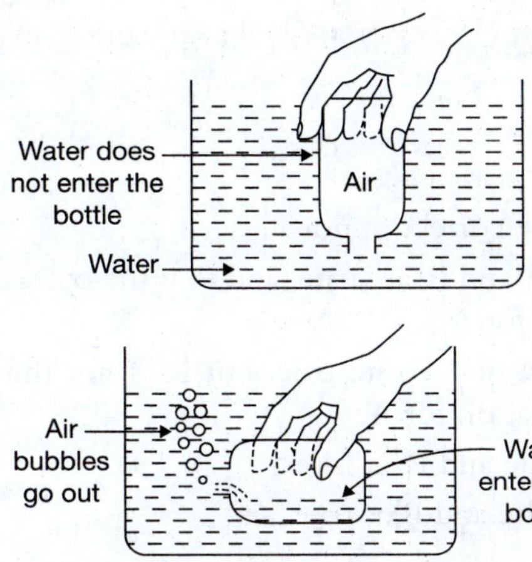

(b)

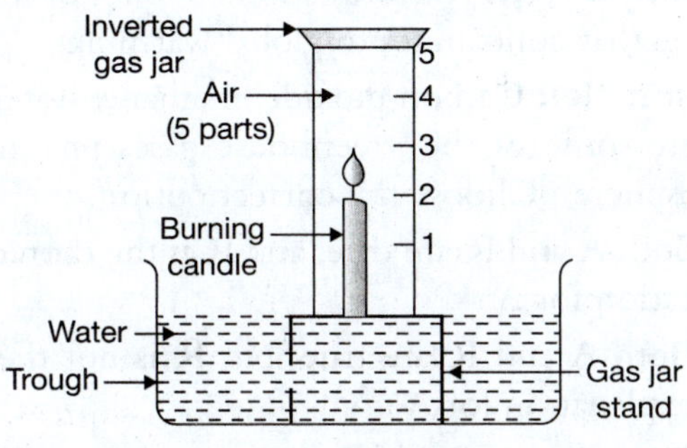

(a)

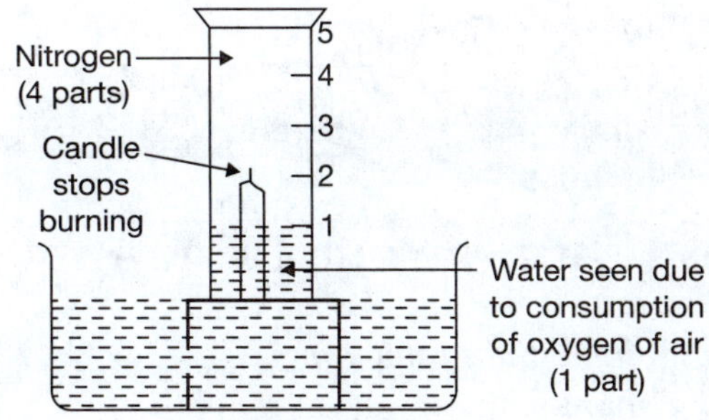

(b)

(c)

42. Can an empty bottle be filled with water, when it is inverted into a basin of water vertically?

If not, what is the correct way of filling the bottle with water? Justify your answer.

Essay Type Questions

43. (a) What are the major components of air?

(b) Among these, which is the active component and which is the inactive component?

(c) Give any four characteristics of air as a mixture.

44. Observe the given figure and answer the following questions.

(a) Will the observation be same in both the flasks?

(b) What inference can be drawn from the given experiments?

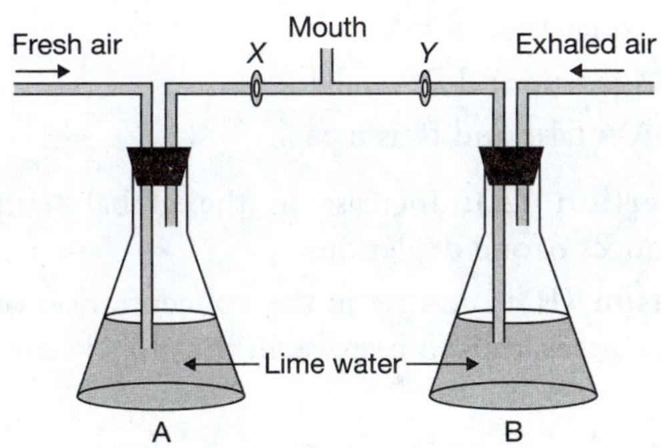

PRACTICE QUESTIONS COMPETITION WING

Level 1: Apply Your Concepts

Directions for questions from 1 to 5.
Fill in the blanks.

1. The ratio of oxygen and nitrogen in air is about ______ by volume.
2. The active component of air is ______.
3. The oxide of carbon that turns lime water milky is ______.
4. ______ and ______ are formed when fuel is reacted with oxygen.
5. ______ is necessary for combustion.

Directions for questions from 6 to 10.
Select the correct alternative from the given options.

6. **Assertion (A):** Air is a mixture of gases.
   Reason (R): In mixtures, components retain their chemical properties.
   Choose the correct option.
   (a) Both A and R are true, and R is the correct explanation for A.
   (b) Both A and R are true, but R is not the correct explanation for A.
   (c) A is true and R is false.
   (d) A is false and R is true.
7. **Assertion (A):** Increase in the global temperature enhances ozone depletion.
   Reason (R): Increase in the concentration of greenhouse gases leads to increase in the global temperature.
   Choose the correct option.
   (a) Both A and R are true, and R is the correct explanation for A.
   (b) Both A and R are true, but R is not the correct explanation for A.
   (c) A is true and R is false.
   (d) A is false and R is true.
8. **Assertion (A):** Deforestation is one of the main factors that contributes to global warming.
   Reason (R): Carbon dioxide, methane, water vapour etc are some of the greenhouse gases present in the atmosphere . Choose the correct option.
   (a) Both A and R are true, and R is the correct explanation for A.
   (b) Both A and R are true, but R is not the correct explanation for A.
   (c) A is true and R is false.
   (d) A is false and R is true.
9. ______ coating is done on the iron cans that are used for storage of food.
   (a) zinc (b) tin
   (c) chromium (d) aluminium
10. The volume of oxygen present in 750 L of air is:
   (a) 172.5 L (b) 187.5 L
   (c) 157.5 L (d) 225.5 L

Level 2: Review Your Concepts

11. Study the given figure and complete the given table.

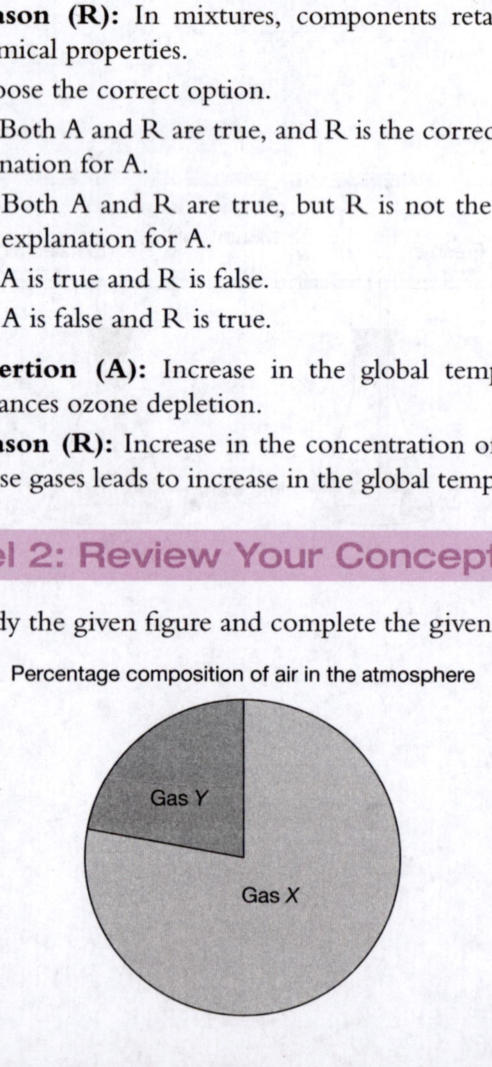

	X	Y
Name of the gas		
Percentage by volume		
Solubility in water		
Reactivity		
Supporter of combustion		

12. The mountaineers carry oxygen gas cylinders with them while climbing high mountains. Give reasons.

13. Name the component of air which extinguishes fire. Give reasons.

14. Mention the essential requirements for rusting of iron.

15. How balance of oxygen and carbon dioxide in the atmosphere is maintained?

16. How will you show that air is essential for burning?

Level 3: Assess Your Concepts

17. 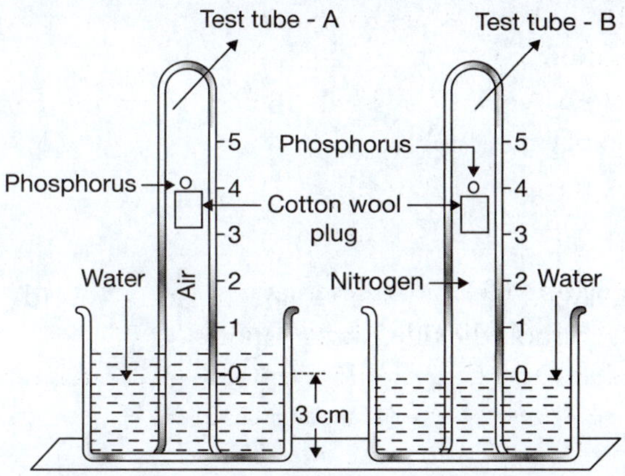

(a) Identify the mistake(s) in the above diagram and give justification.

(b) What inference can be drawn from the above diagrams?

18. Answer the following questions based on the diagram given.

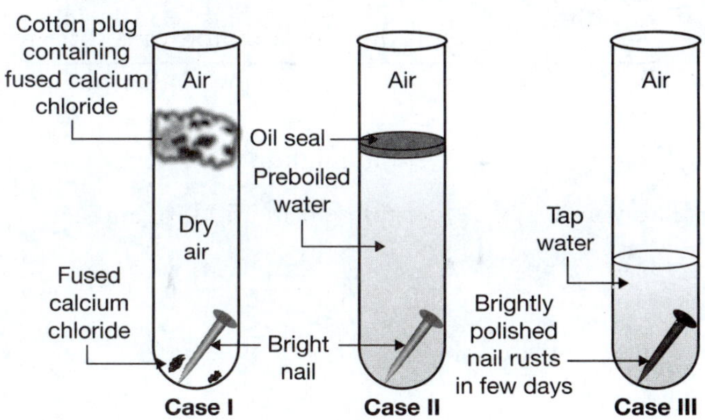

(a) Predict the observation. Justify.

(b) Draw the conclusions based on the above observations.

19. How much volume of oxygen is present in 1000 L of air?

20. (a) Given other name of $Ca(OH)_2$.

(b) What reaction is observed in the test tube?

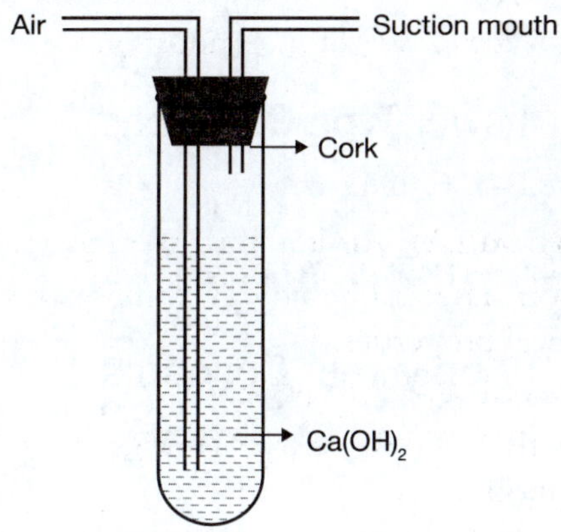

21. It is not advisable to use burning coal in winters in closed room. Why?

AT

ANSWER KEYS

Crossword

Across

2. Combustion 3. Ultraviolet 4. Ionosphere 5. Troposphere 6. Atmosphere
9. Rise 10. Pollution 11. Rusting

Down

1. Stratosphere 7. Mesosphere 8. Radiation

Classroom Wing

Very Short Answer Type Questions

1. (b) 2. (a) 3. (c) 4. (d) 5. (a) 6. (d)
7. (b) 8. (b) 9. (c) 10. carbon dioxide, water vapour
11. CO_2 12. H_2SO_4 13. SO_2, NO_2 14. (c) 15. (b)

Short Answer Type Questions

19. A-c,B-a, C-b, D-d 30. 195 L, 52.5 L

Competition Wing

Level 1: Apply Your Concepts

1. 7 : 26 2. oxygen 3. carbon dioxide 4. Carbon dioxide and water vapour
5. oxygen 6. (a) 7. (d) 8. (b) 9. (b) 10. (c)

Hints and Explanations

CLASSROOM WING

Very Short Answer Type Questions

1. Major component of CNG is methane.
   Hence, the correct option is (b).
2. The products of combustion of glucose are water vapour and carbon dioxide.
   Hence, the correct option is (a).
3. Lavoisier named the active component of air as oxygen.
   Hence, the correct option is (c).
4. Anhydrous copper sulphate is used to identify the presence of water vapour in the atmosphere.
   Hence, the correct option is (d).
5. The envelope of air that surrounds the earth is called atmosphere.
   Hence, the correct option is (a).
6. Air can dissolve in water.
   Hence, the correct option is (d).
7. The gas assimilated by plants for the synthesis of proteins is nitrogen.
   Hence, the correct option is (b).
8. X is carbon dioxide and Y is oxygen.
   Hence, the correct option is (b).
9. Coal is used in cement factories, steel mills, and glass factories.
   Hence, the correct option is (c).
10. The products of combustion of fossil fuels are carbon dioxide and water vapour.
11. The increase in the proportion of carbon dioxide in air leads to global warming.
12. $SO_3 + H_2O \rightarrow H_2SO_4$
13. The gases which cause acid rain are SO_2 and NO_2.
14. Global warming causes melting of ice caps.
    Hence, the correct option is (c).
15. Thermal power plants are the source of SO_2.
    Hence, the correct option is (b).

Short Answer Type Questions

16. Increased concentration of greenhouse gases causes global warming due to the increased greenhouse effect beyond what is necessarily required to maintain a habitable environment on Earth.
17. Exhaled air contains greater amount of water vapour than the normal air. When this air comes in contact with the surface of the mirror, it condenses to form tiny water droplets and gives the appearance of mist. As a result, the mirror surface turns misty. Hence mirror turns misty when air from lungs is blown gently on to it.
18. Coastal regions tend to have higher humidity (% of moisture or water vapour in air) compared to non-coastal regions due to their proximity to large water bodies such as seas or oceans. these water bodies serve as a source of moisture for the surrounding air through evaporation, leading to increased humidity in coastal areas.
19. Match the following.

Column A	Column B
(A) Troposphere	(c) Most of the weather phenomenon occurs
(B) Stratosphere	(a) Aeroplanes fly in this layer
(C) Ionosphere	(b) Radio waves get reflected in this layer
(D) Mesosphere	(d) Meteorites burn up in this layer

20. (i) Essential for the growth of plants and animals.
    (ii) Prevents excessive vaporization of water from body.
    (iii) Help in the formation of fog, mist, clouds.
21. Many industries release oxides of nitrogen and sulphur in to the atmosphere. These oxides dissolve in rain water which leads to acid rain. Hence, industrial areas are prone to acid rain.

22. (a) X is nitrogen and Y is oxygen.

(b) (i) Nitrogen dilutes the activity of oxygen.

(ii) Nitrogen is essential for the growth of plants.

(iii) Oxygen is essential for respiration.

(iv) Oxygen supports combustion.

(c) Z contains carbon dioxide, argon, helium, water vapour.

23. Oxygen consumed by living beings during respiration and due to burning of fuels is constantly replenished by plants through the process of photosynthesis.

24. Active component is oxygen which is essential for respiration and combustion.

Inactive component is nitrogen which dilutes the activity of oxygen and is essential for the growth of plants.

25. (a) X is carbon dioxide.

(b) Carbon dioxide is neither combustible nor supporter of combustion.

26. (i) Carbon dioxide is essential for photosynthesis. In the presence of sunlight green plants use carbon dioxide from air and water vapour from soil to make food by the process of photosynthesis.

(ii) Carbon dioxide extinguishes fire.

(iii) Carbon dioxide is a green house gas.

27. The water vapour present in air gets condensed coming in contact with the cool surface. Hence, tiny droplets of water are observed on the cool surface.

28. (a) Lime water that is the solution of calcium hydroxide is taken in the test tube.

(b) Lime water turns slightly turbid due to the carbon dioxide present in air.

(c) The air present in the test tube is sucked in order to create low pressure in the test tube. Due to low pressure, air rushes through the lime water.

29. Blowing of wind, traffic on the roads, dusting at home, earth moving operations, construction activities and agricultural particles are the sources of dust particles.

30. Volume percentage of nitrogen in air is 78%

$\Rightarrow$ 100 L of air contains 78 L of nitrogen

$\therefore$ 250 L of air contains $\frac{78 \times 250}{100} = 195$ L of nitrogen

Volume percentage of oxygen in air is 21%

$\Rightarrow$ 100 L of air contains 21 L of oxygen

$\therefore$ 250 L of air contains $\frac{250 \times 21}{100} = 52.5$ L of oxygen.

31. Enormous increase in the surface temperature of earth due to increase in the levels of carbon dioxide and other gases, such as methane, ozone in atmosphere is called global warming. Reduction in the use of fossil fuels and controlling deforestation are some measures to prevent global warming. Growing more and more plants is obviously the most essential requirement for controlling global warming.

32. The variation in the composition of atmospheric air due to the addition of harmful gases to the atmospheric air is called air pollution.

33. (i) The fertility of the soil decreases

(ii) The crops get damaged

(iii) Water bodies get polluted

(iv) Marble statues or monuments get corroded

34. (i) Reducing the growth of population

(ii) Arresting deforestation

(iii) Increasing greenery

(iv) Synthesis of eco-friendly chemicals

(v) Judicious use of natural resources

35. Tall chimneys facilitate the release of smoke at higher altitudes so that living beings on the earth's surface do not get affected much.

36. (a) Policemen wear masks in order to protect themselves from smoke and dust particles emitted by vehicles.

(b) When water is heated, the air dissolved in it comes out in the form of tiny bubbles.

37. In a closed room, wood undergoes incomplete combustion to form carbon monoxide. Inhalation of CO reduces the oxygen carrying capacity of haemoglobin in the blood. Hence, excess inhalation of CO can be fatal.

38. In galvanization process, zinc is used to coat on iron. The chemical reactivity of Zinc is much more than that of tin. Hence, food stuff cannot be stored in galvanized container. Tin coated iron containers are used to preserve food.

39. Catalytic converters help in the conversion of more harmful carbon monoxide into less harmful carbon dioxide and oxides of nitrogen that causes acid rain into N_2 which is inert in nature.

40. Earthworms live inside the soil and get oxygen required for respiration from the air trapped in the gaps between the soil particles. In rainy season, all the spaces in soil get filled by rainwater. Hence, the earthworms come out of the soil to get air for respiration.

41. (a) Air occupies space.
(b) One fifth of air contains oxygen; oxygen supports burning.
(c) Air contains water vapour.

42. Since the bottle is filled with air, water cannot occupy this space unless a passage is provided for the expansion of air. Hence, the bottle should be inverted obliquely.

Essay Type Questions

43. (a) Major components of air are nitrogen and oxygen.
(b) Nitrogen is the inactive component and oxygen is the active component.
(c) Characteristics of air as a mixture is as follows.
(i) Variable composition of air in different places on earth.
(ii) No net change in energy is involved in the mixing up of gases in air.
(iii) No definite boiling point for liquid air.
(iv) Separation of air into various components can be done by physical methods.
(v) The properties of different gases are retained in the air.
(vi) Air has no definite chemical formula.
(vii) Air does not exhibit definite chemical properties of its own.

44. (a) Lime water in both the flasks turns milky, but the extent of milkiness is more in flask B than that in A.
(b) Exhaled air contains more carbon dioxide than normal air.

COMPETITION WING

Level 1: Apply Your Concepts

1. The ratio of oxygen to nitrogen in air is 7 : 26 by volume.
2. The active component of air is oxygen.
3. The oxide of carbon that turns lime water milky is carbon dioxide.
4. Fuels react with oxygen to form carbon dioxide and water vapour.
5. The major gas necessary for combustion is oxygen.
6. **Assertion (A):** Air is a mixture of gases-True.
   Reason (R): In mixtures, components retain their chemical properties-True.
   Both (A) and (R) are true and (R) is the correct explanation of (A).
   Hence, the correct option is (a).
7. **Assertion (A):** Increase in the global temperature enhances ozone depletion-False.
   Reason (R): Increase in the concentration of greenhouse gases leads to increase in the global temperature-True.
   (A) is false and (R) is true.
   Hence, the correct option is (d).
8. **Assertion (A):** Deforestation is one of the main factors that contributes to global warming -True.
   Reason (R): Carbon dioxide, methane, water vapour etc are some of the greenhouse gases present in the atmosphere-True.
   Both (A) and (R) are true but (R) is not the correct explanation of (A).
   Hence, the correct option is (b).
9. Iron cans used for storage of foodstuffs are coated with tin.
   Hence, the correct option is (b).
10. Percentage by volume of oxygen in air = 21%
    Therefore, volume of oxygen present in 750 L of air = $750 \times 21/100 = 157.5$ L
    Hence, the correct option is (c).

Level 2: Review Your Concepts

11.

	X	Y
Name of the gas	Nitrogen	Oxygen
Percentage by volume	78%	21%
Solubility in water	Very slightly soluble	Soluble
Reactivity	Very less	Very high
Supporter of combustion	Does not support combustion	Supports combustion

12. With the increase in height, the percentage of oxygen decreases. Hence, breathing becomes difficult and to facilitate breathing mountaineers carry oxygen gas cylinders with them.
13. Carbon dioxide is used to extinguish fire. CO_2 is a non-supporter of combustion and non-combustible gas. Moreover, it is heavier than air and cuts off the contact between air and fire, and hence, it can be used to put off the fires.
14. Essential requirements for rusting are the presence of oxygen/air and water.
15. During photosynthesis plant uses carbon dioxide and releases oxygen. Plants also consume oxygen for respiration, but they produce more of it than they consume. Oxygen in air is used by living organisms present in air, water or soil during respiration. This shows the interdependence of plants and animals and thus the balance of oxygen and carbon dioxide in the atmosphere is maintained.
16. If you invert a glass tumbler over a burning candle, you will notice that the candle extinguishes after sometime. This is because the oxygen that supports burning is cut off when it is covered by the tumbler, and hence the candle stops burning.

Level 3: Assess Your Concepts

17. (a) The level of water in test tube B should be higher. Water should occupy 1/5th of the total volume of the test tube B.

(b) Since 1/5th of the total volume of air is consumed due to the burning of phosphorous, this space gets occupied by water.

18. (a) In case I, rusting does not take place.

In case II, rusting does not take place.

In case III, rusting takes place.

In case I, fused calcium chloride is taken which absorbs the moisture as a result of which the air in the test tube remains dry. Hence, rusting doesn't take place.

In case II, boiled water is taken which is devoid of oxygen. The layer of oil on the surface of water prevents entry of air into the test tube. Therefore, rusting is prevented in this.

(b) Air (oxygen) and water/moisture are essential for rusting to take place.

19. Percentage by volume of oxygen in air = 21 %

Therefore, volume of oxygen present in 1000 L of air

$$= 1000 \times \frac{21}{100}$$

= 210 L

20. (a) The other name for calcium hydroxide $Ca(OH)_2$ is lime water.

(b) In the test tube, calcium hydroxides turns slightly turbid as reaction occurs between carbon dioxides (in air) and $Ca(OH)_2$

21. As in closed room, sufficient amount of oxygen will be not present Hence, coal will have burnt incompletely and produce carbon – monoxide carbon – monoxide gas is very poisonous and will lead to suffocate the person in a closed room.

CHAPTER

11

Water—A Wonder Liquid

Remember

Before beginning this chapter, you should be able to:

- Know the importance of water
- Identify availability of water under different conditions

Key Ideas

After completing this chapter, you should be able to:

- Explain existence of water in three states—solid, liquid, and gaseous
- Understand physical properties of water
- Describe purification of water
- Understand causes, effects, and prevention of water pollution
- Describe rainwater harvesting

Scientific Crypt

A Tribute to Joseph Black (1728-1799)

Joseph Black (16 April 1728 – 6 December 1799) was a Scottish physicist and chemist, known for his discoveries like latent heat, specific heat and carbon dioxide. Born in Bordeaux, France, Black moved to Scotland at a young age and pursued his education at the University of Glasgow.

Joseph Black's most notable discovery was latent heat, unveiled through meticulous experiments with heat and gases. He proposed the concept of heat transfer during phase transition without temperature change. Despite challenges due to limited tools for precise measurements, his perseverance and scientific acumen led to ground breaking insights.

Joseph Black's discovery of latent heat stands as a testament to his brilliance and intellectual curiosity, inspiring generations of scientists and earning him recognition as a Fellow of the Royal Society and a member of the French Academy of Sciences. His legacy lives on through chemistry buildings named in his honour at the University of Edinburgh and the University of Glasgow.

FUN TIME

CROSSWORD

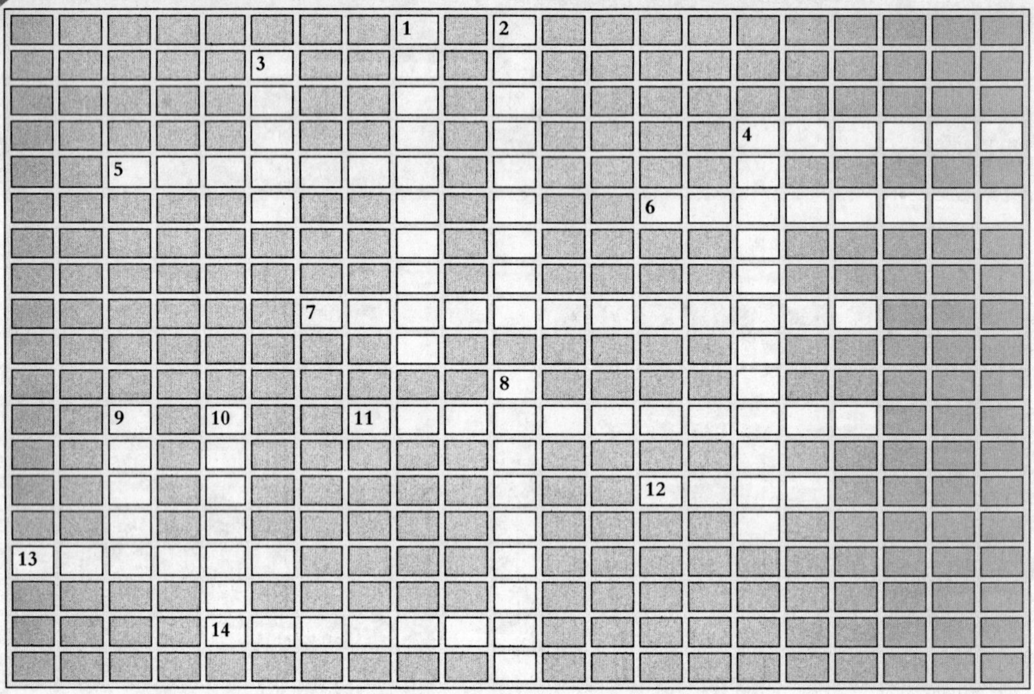

Across

4. When water takes heat from its surroundings and changes into this gaseous form.
5. Water which is fit for consumption or drinking.
6. Specific heat of this nature of a substance can be defined as the amount of heat required to raise the temperature of 1 g of substance by 1°C.
7. Preventing the wastage of water in any form and preservation of available water for future is termed this.
11. The solution which can dissolve more amount of solute in it is.
12. Water vapour in the atmosphere condenses to form these small flakes of ice.
13. Latent heat of this is the amount of heat required to change 1 g of solid to liquid without any change in temperature.
14. Substances that dissolve in water are termed this.

Down

1. The collection of rainwater directly and storage of it for later use is called rainwater _____
2. Substances that do not dissolve in water are termed as_____
3. The gaseous form of water at or above 100°C.
4. Latent heat of this is the amount of heat required to convert 1 g of water into steam without any change in temperature.
8. The solution which cannot dissolve any more solute in it is termed this.
9. Balls of ice that fall down along with rainwater during winter.
10. A solution in which the solvent is water.

INTRODUCTION

Water is the second most important resource required to survive on our planet. It covers about 71% of Earth's surface out of which 96.5% is saline (found in seas and oceans) in nature. We cannot consume saline water or use it in our domestic chores as it has high salt content. So, there is only 3% water that is available for us. Hence, it can be seen how important it is for us to save water and use it judiciously. In this chapter, we shall learn the different states in which water is available to us and various ways to conserve the water.

Different States of Water

Water in natural form is available in liquid at normal atmospheric conditions. However, the existence of water in all the three physical states in nature is possible.

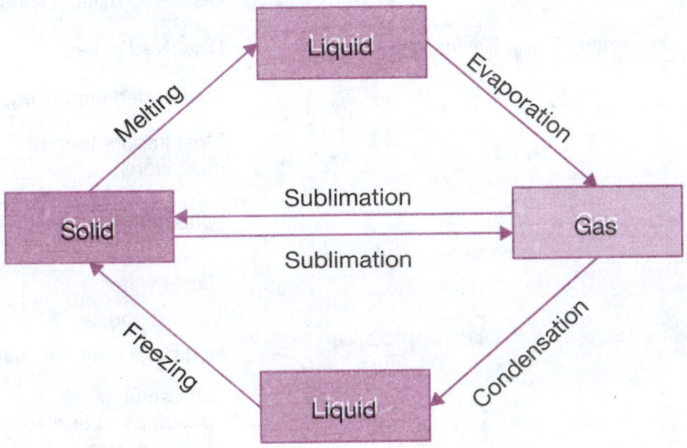

Figure 11.1 Interconversion of different states of water

Info Bytes!

The solid state of water, which we commonly know as ice, has a unique property: it's less dense than its liquid state. This is why ice floats on water.

Solid State

Characteristics of solid state of water are:

1. The solid form of water is ice.
2. The freezing point of water is 0°C.
3. When the temperature in any region falls below 0°C, water freezes to form ice (frozen water).
4. In extremely cold regions, during winter season, water vapour in the atmosphere condenses to form small flakes of ice called **snow**.
5. However, during winter, balls of ice fall down along with rainwater, known as **hails**.

Figure 11.2 Solid state of water - Ice

Liquid State

Characteristics of liquid state of water are:

1. It is the most common state available in nature.
2. Dew is also a liquid form of water.
3. Water vapour condenses to form water.

Figure 11.3 Liquid state of water

Gaseous State

Characteristics of gaseous state of water are:

1. When water takes heat from its surroundings and changes into gaseous form, it is called **water vapour**.
2. When water is subjected to heating, water goes into gaseous state at 100°C which is the boiling point of pure water under normal conditions.
3. This gaseous form of water at or above 100°C is called **steam**.

Figure 11.4 Gaseous state of water - water vapour

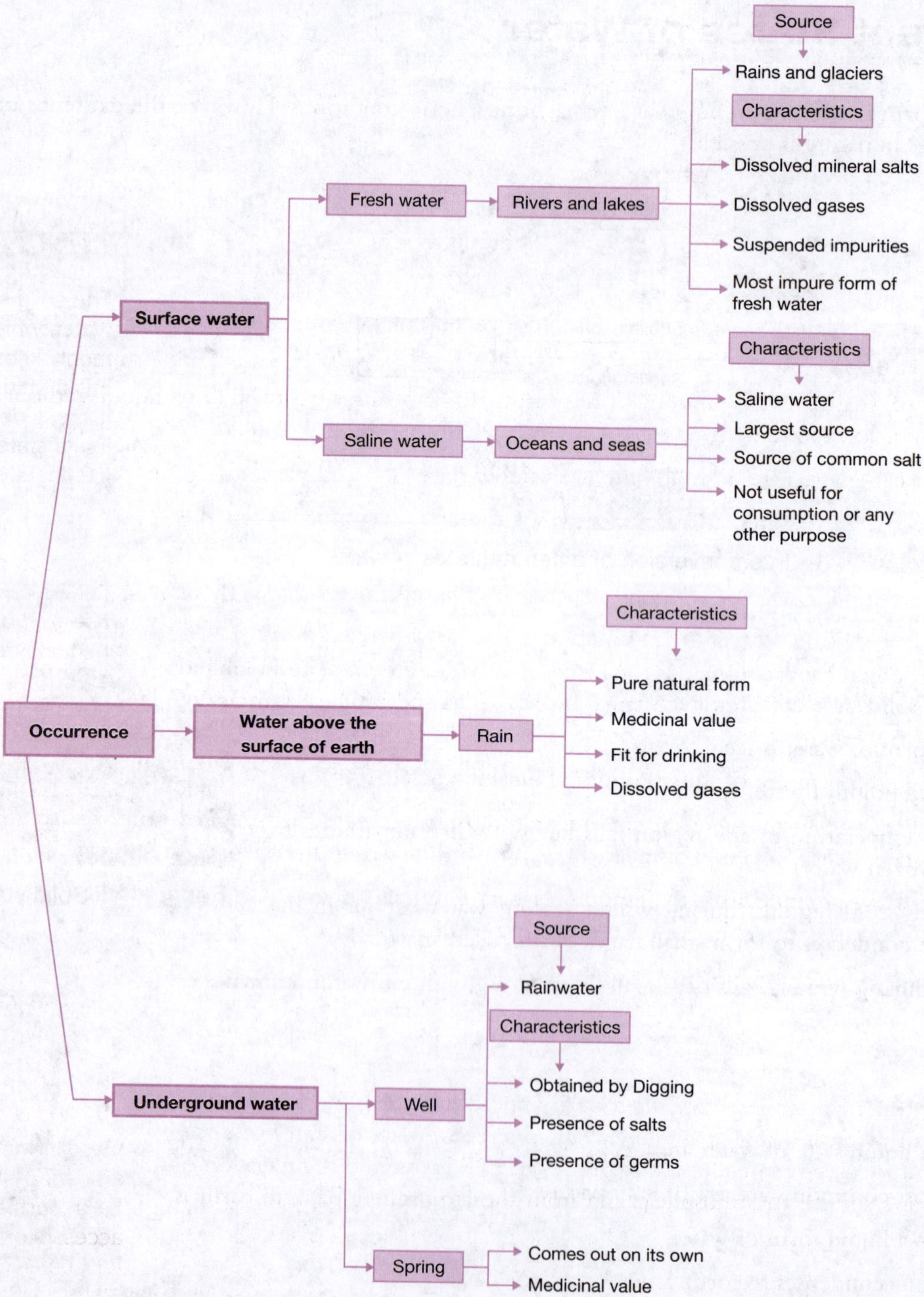

Figure 11.5 Availability of water in different areas of the Earth

Role of Heat During Interconversion of State of Matter

- When ice is subjected to heating at 0°C, there is no change in temperature. The heat is utilized in changing the state of ice from solid to liquid. It is stored in the water in the form of latent heat.

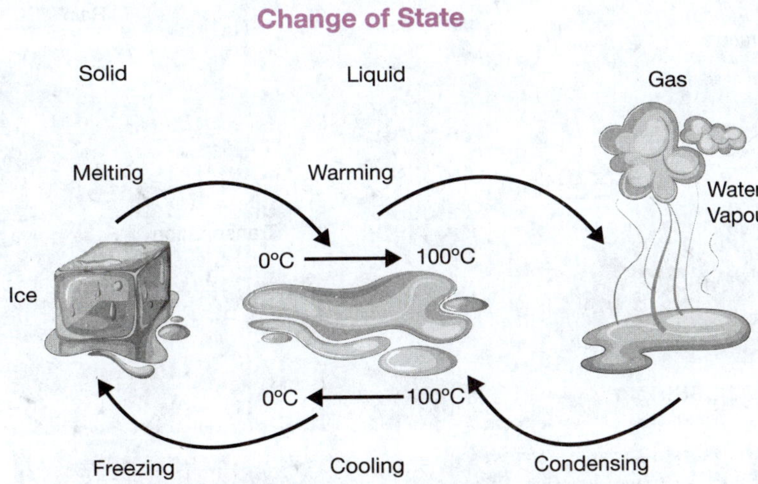

Figure 11.6 Interconversion of state of matter

Latent heat of fusion is the amount of heat required to change 1 g of solid to liquid without any change in temperature. For ice, the value is 80 cal/g.

- At 0°C, water can exist either in solid state or in liquid state.
- Once the ice melts to water and if the supply of heat is continued, then the temperature of water increases.
- The increase in the temperature of liquid depends on the specific heat capacity of the liquid.

  Specific heat capacity of a substance can be defined as the amount of heat required to raise the temperature of 1 g of substance by 1°C. The specific heat capacity of water is 1 calorie/g/°C.

> **Info Bytes!**
> Anhydrous copper sulphate turns from white to blue colour, when subjected to water.

- This increase in temperature of water continues until it reaches 100°C.
- At 100°C, there is no further increase in temperature of water. The heat supplied is utilized to convert the water into gaseous state, that is, steam. This heat energy remains hidden in the steam as latent heat.

  Latent heat of vaporization is the amount of heat required to convert 1 g of liquid into gaseous without any change in temperature. The value latent heat for water is 540 cal/g.

Water Cycle

The three states of water can be interconverted from one state to the other by changing the conditions, such as by heating or cooling. This interconversion of states of water occurs in nature and it can be represented by water cycle. The continuous circulation of water from the earth's surface to atmosphere and from the atmosphere back to earth is called **water cycle**.

> **Info Bytes!**
> Despite the vast amount of water on Earth, less than 1% is accessible fresh water for humans to use.

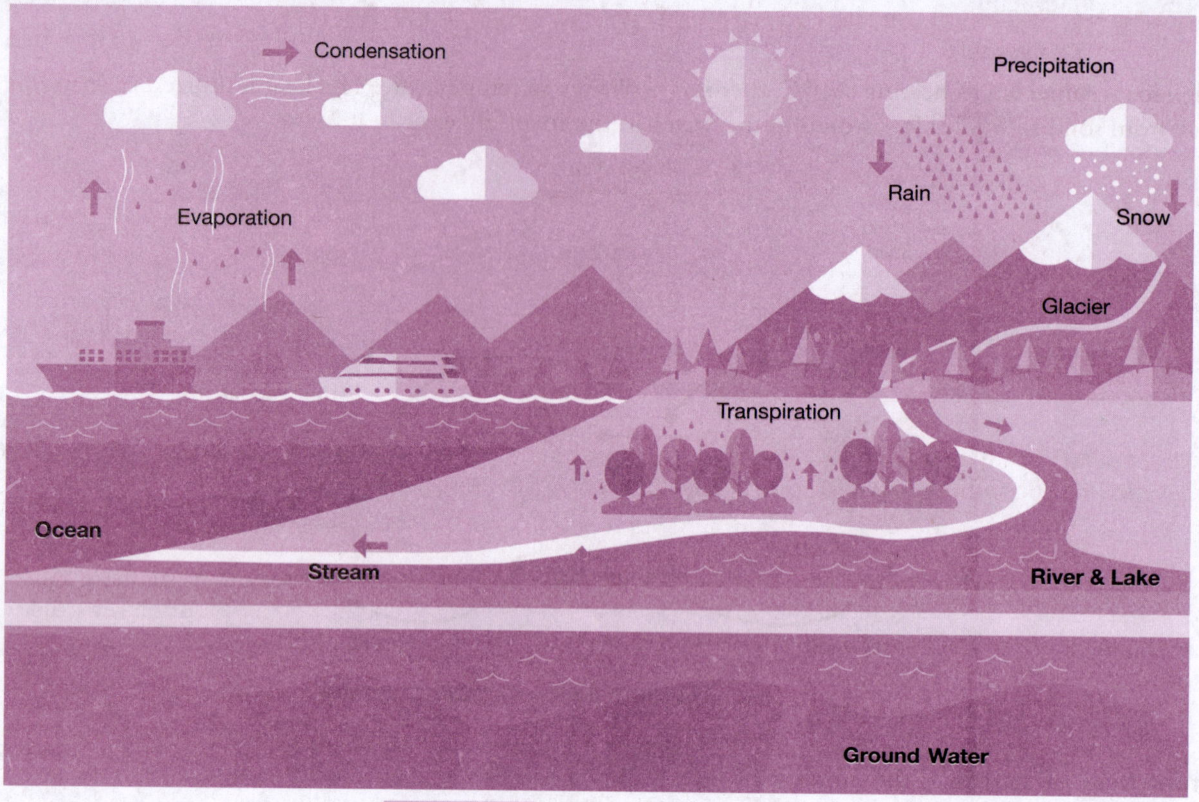

Figure 11.7 Water cycle in nature

Physical Properties

Some of the physical properties of water are tabulated below.

Table 11.1 Physical properties of water

Parameter	Property
Nature	Transparent, colourless odourless and tasteless liquid
Freezing point	0°C
Boiling point	100°C
Density	1 g/cc at 4°C. Water has maximum density of 1 g/cc at 4°C. Above and below 4°C, water possesses lower density.

Solvent Property of Water

The substances which dissolve in water are called **soluble substances**. The substances which do not dissolve in water are called **insoluble substances**. Water can dissolve a wide variety of substances in it. Hence, it is considered as a universal solvent. The substances can be solids, liquids or gases.

Gases such as oxygen and carbon dioxide are present in dissolved state in water. The universal solvent property of water is responsible for almost all the uses of water which makes it a wonder liquid. By being able to dissolve various types of substances, water has innumerable applications in our daily life. The solvent property of water is also responsible for water pollution.

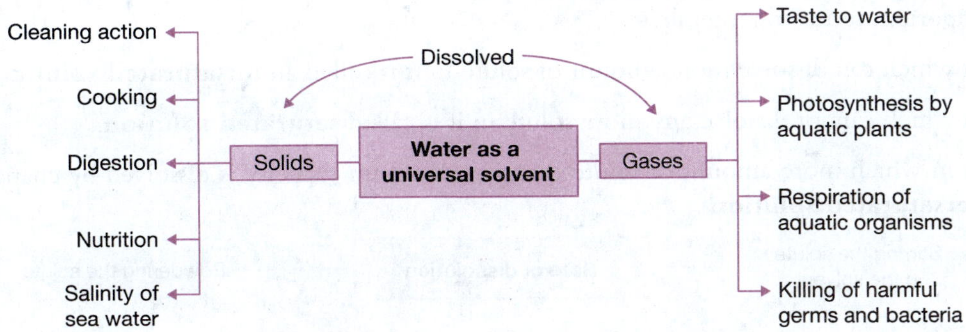

Figure 11.8 Solvent property of water

Example: For instance, take 36 g of common salt which can be dissolved in 100 g of water to form a saturated solution at 20°C. The solubility of common salt in water is 36 g at 20°C.

EXAMPLE 11.1 Five samples of natural water from various sources are taken in five beakers in equal quantities. These are labelled as E, F, G, H, and I and heated until all the water evaporates. When observed, it was found that the sample marked 'H' left the largest amount of residue. In contrast, the sample marked 'I' left the least amount of residue. 'E', 'F', and 'G' left gradually increasing amounts of residue in that order.

(a) Identify H and I. **(b)** Predict the sources of E, F, and G.

SOLUTION

(a) The natural water sample H which left the most residue upon evaporation is likely to be seawater, due to its high dissolved salt content. The sample marked 'I' that left the least amount of residue is probably distilled water, which has nearly all of its impurities removed.

(b) Given the gradual increase in residue:

- 'E' could be rainwater as it has very few dissolved salts.
- 'F' might be spring water, which typically has a moderate amount of dissolved minerals.
- 'G' can be identified as river water, as it usually contains more dissolved salts than rain or spring water but less than seawater.

Water as Universal Solvent

When some amount of sugar or salt is added to water, you observe that the solid disappears. The resultant liquid has a sweet or salty taste respectively. The liquid is a mixture of two components. The solid component (sugar or salt) is the solute and the liquid component (water) is the solvent. The uniform mixture of the above components is the solution.

A **solution** can be defined as the homogenous mixture of two or more components. A solution in which the solvent is water is called an aqueous solution.

The component which undergoes change in physical state is known as a **solute** and the other component is known as a **solvent**.

Konnect

The maximum amount of substance that can be dissolved in a fixed weight of the solvent (100 g) to make a saturated solution is called **solubility** of the substance at that temperature.

$$\text{Solvent} + \text{Solute} \Rightarrow \text{Solution}$$

To the above sugar solution, if we add little more sugar, it gets dissolved in the solution. Such a solution is called an unsaturated solution.

At some stage, the solution reaches a state when the added sugar does not dissolve in it and remains at the bottom. Such a solution is known as a saturated solution. However, when the above solution is heated, the sugar remaining at the bottom also disappears. Though the solution reached its maximum dissolving capacity, but by heating it is possible to dissolve more amount of sugar in it. That means temperature affects solubility.

Following are important terms to remember:

- The solution which can dissolve more amount of solute in it is called an **unsaturated solution**.
- The solution which cannot dissolve any more solute in it is called **saturated solution**.
- The solution in which more amount of solute than its maximum capacity is dissolved by changing the conditions is called **supersaturated solution**.

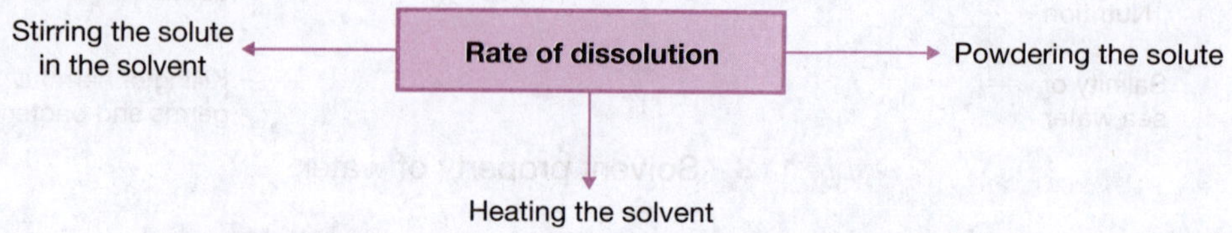

Figure 11.9 Methods of increasing rate of dissolution

Types of Water

Potable water is the water which is fit for consumption or drinking. This water should contain some dissolved minerals and salts, but it should be free from suspended impurities as well as harmful germs and bacteria.

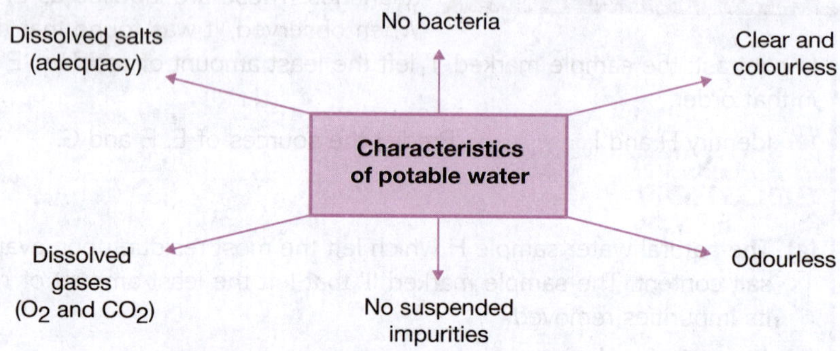

Figure 11.10 Characteristics of potable water

Natural sample of water when subjected to distillation gives the purest form of water which is devoid of even minerals and salts. This water is called **distilled water** and is suitable for laboratory use. But it is not suitable for consumption, as it does not contain essential minerals required by human body.

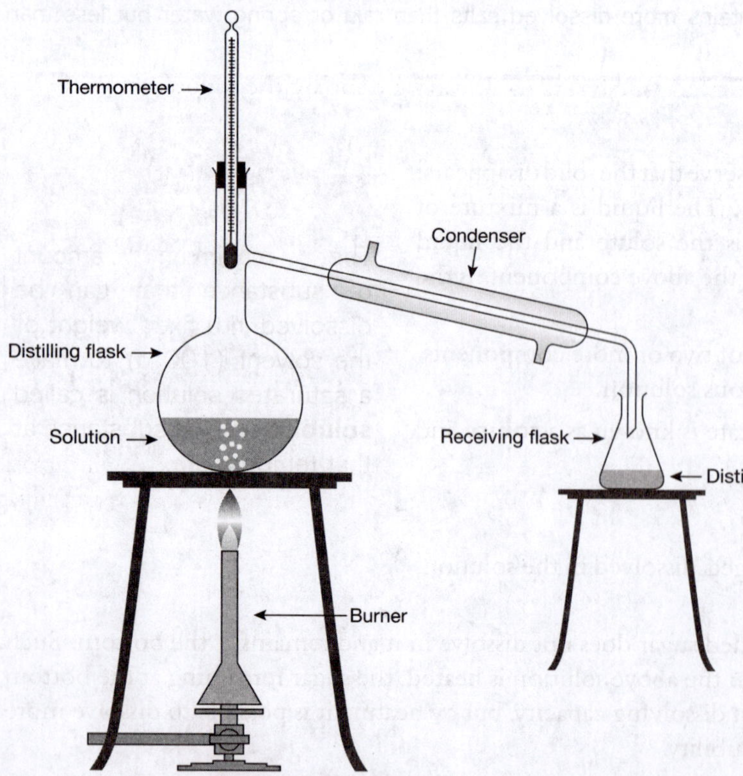

Figure 11.11 Distillation of natural water

Konnect

Distillation of water can also be carried out by continuous water instead of conventional distillation apparatus.

Purification of Water

Running river water contains the following impurities:

- Fine particles of sand and clay
- Dead organic matter (wood, straw, dead animals)
- Bacteria, germs, etc.
- Mineral salts
- Dissolved gases

Purification of water can be carried out in three steps:

1. Sedimentation 2. Filtration 3. Sterilization

Sedimentation

Following steps are followed:

1. Running river water → Basins, tanks or reservoirs (Addition of potash alum).
2. Settling of suspended solid matter at the bottom of the liquid.
3. Removal of larger suspended particles.

Figure 11.12 Sedimentation

Filtration

Following steps are followed:

1. Water passed through beds of sand and gravel.
2. Removal of fine suspended particles.
3. Clear water, devoid of all insoluble, suspended matter is obtained.

Sterilization

Removal of germs and bacteria (microorganisms) is known as **sterilization**. It can be done by the following ways:

1. **Exposure to air and sunlight:**
   - Water in reservoirs is exposed to air and sunlight over a large surface area.
   - Oxygen in air helps in burning and sunlight has the effect of burning the germs to death.

   Limitation – Sunlight cannot reach the bottom layers of water and cannot be highly effective in the removal of germs.
2. **Boiling:** Prolonged boiling can destroy bacteria as they cannot survive at such high temperature.

   Limitation – Cannot be applied on a large scale.
3. **Chemical treatment:** This is the most effective method. Chlorine and ozone are the chemicals which can kill bacteria, and thus, sterilize the water effectively. Treatment of water with chlorine is called **chlorination** whereas treatment of water with ozone is called **ozonization**.

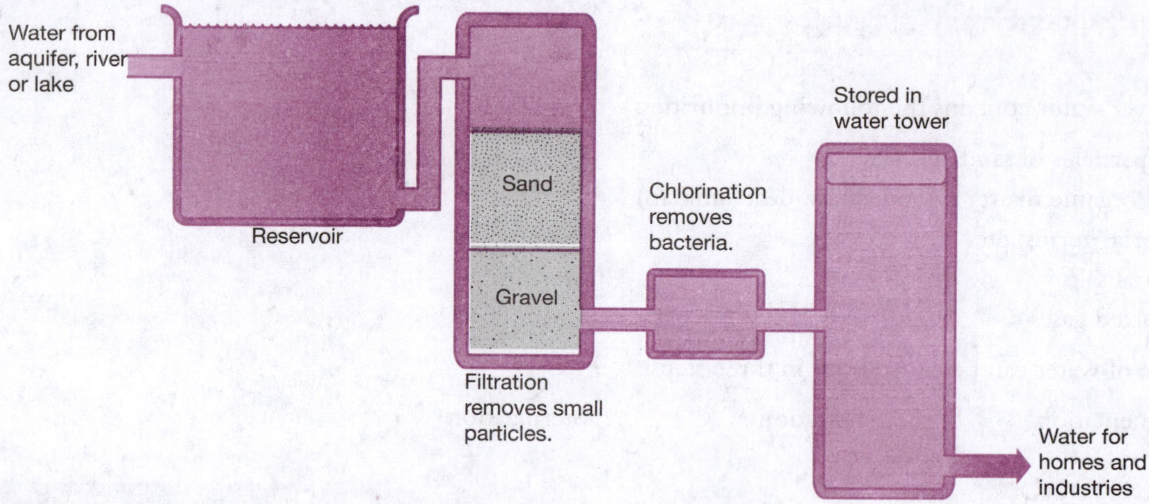

Figure 11.13 Filtration and Sterilization

Water Pollution

The harmful substances released from industries and power plants make the water impure. This process of contamination of water is called **water pollution**.

> **Konnect**
> A single oil spill can devastate marine life and take decades or even centuries to fully clean up.

Rainwater is the purest form of natural water as it contains only dissolved gases. As the rainwater reaches the rivers, lakes, ponds and well, many salts and impurities dissolve in water.

Naturally occurring water contains three types of impurities:

1. Insoluble substances
2. Soluble substances
3. Microorganisms

Water in rivers, ponds and lakes gets contaminated with unwanted and harmful substances. Polluted water changes the physical, chemical and biological characteristics which in turn affect the biosphere.

Table 11.2 Sources, effects and prevention of water pollution

Source of Pollution	Method	Effect	Prevention
Defecation in open fields by human beings and animals.	• Excreta of humans and animals in streams and rivers.	• Spread of diseases and epidemics.	• Usage of pit latrines. Conversion of excreta into useful manure. • Conversion of cow dung into biogas. Gas used for cooking and slurry useful as manure.
Pollution caused by industries.	• Addition of metallic salts of mercury, lead, cadmium, chromium and arsenic which are poisonous.	• Death of aquatic plants and animals. • Serious diseases for animals which consume water.	• Chemical treatment of water coming out of factories before discharging into rivers.
Pollution caused by agricultural operation.	• Usage of artificial/ synthetic fertilizers. • Spraying of pesticides and insecticides.	• Percolation of these chemicals through the soil and leaching away of these chemicals into water bodies.	• Usage of natural manure in place of synthetic fertilizers. • Usage of natural pesticides (neem oil). • Avoiding spraying of pesticides during rainy season. • Usage of drip irrigation.

Uses of Water

The most important uses of water include drinking and irrigation. So, water is a life supporting substance. Most part of the water in nature is saline water and is unfit for usage. The small fraction of fresh water available should be saved and used judiciously. The primary source of any kind of water is rainwater. Lack of proper rain leads to decrease in both the surface water as well as the undergroundwater. Such prolonged periods of absence of rains may result in drought. Therefore, preventing the wastage of water in any form and preservation of available water for future is called **conservation of water**.

Konnect

Aside from drinking, the average person uses 50-80 gallons of water per day for activities like bathing, cooking, and cleaning.

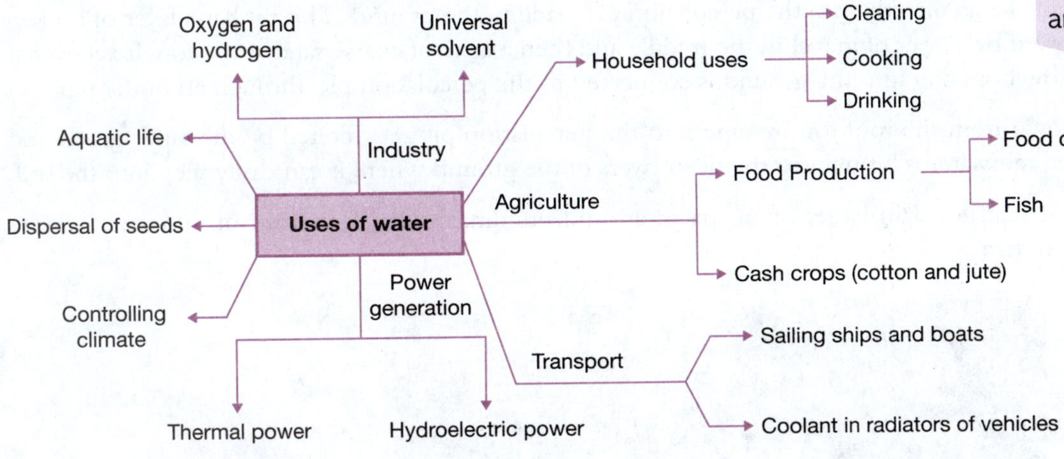

Figure 11.14 Water and its different uses in our day-to-day activities

Water Conservation

Water is very much useful for almost all the activities involved in daily life. Water also finds significance in industrial processes and agricultural needs. However, the fresh water available in nature is of very less percentage. Adding to that, many human activities leading to pollution and wastage of water further reduce the availability of water. Therefore, the efficient water management involves the judicious usage of water and also trapping and storing the rainwater. This is called **water conservation**.

Methods of Water Conservation

- Rainwater harvesting
- Recycling of wastewater
- Use of modern and efficient irrigation methods such as drip irrigation
- Creation of awareness in public for judicious use of water in daily life activities

Rainwater Harvesting

Rainwater harvesting can be described with the help of following points:

1. The collection of rainwater directly and storage of it for later use is called **rainwater harvesting**.
2. Rainwater harvesting can be done in two ways:
   (i) Collection of rainwater in tanks.
   (ii) Arrangement for efficient percolation of rainwater into the ground to recharge the groundwater.

Info Bytes!

In the state of Rajasthan in India, traditional rainwater harvesting structures called 'johads' have helped revive dry rivers and improve the groundwater level.

3. The main purpose of rainwater harvesting is to increase the availability of groundwater thereby overcoming the storage of water over long periods.
4. This can be done either by roof top rainwater harvesting or by harvesting of rainwater from open spaces and buildings.

Roof-Top Rainwater Harvesting

Let us discuss roof top rainwater harvesting with the help of following points:

1. The rainwater from the roof tops can be brought down through pipes and collected in big underground tanks made of concrete. The stored rainwater can be used in times of need after filtration.
2. This water can also be made to go directly into the percolation pit made in the ground. This pit has a layer of broken bricks at the bottom followed by a layer of gravel in the middle and then a layer of coarse sand at the top. It is covered by a concrete slab. A narrow bore dug into the ground is connected to the percolation pits through an outlet pipe.
3. The rainwater brought down from the roof top by pipe into the percolation pit gets filtered by the sand, gravel and broken bricks. The filtered rainwater is brought to the deep layers of the ground where it can easily seep into the soil.
4. If these recharge pits are constructed in large, open spaces around buildings, a large amount of rainwater can be collected in short period of time.

Figure 11.15 Roof top rainwater harvesting

Rainwater Harvesting from Open Spaces

Percolation pits with concrete slabs having holes are constructed in open spaces around buildings. The rainwater falling in the open spaces enters the percolation pits through the holes on the slabs. It gets filtered in the percolation pit that enters the recharge well through the outlet pipe and gradually seeps into the soil. The main objective of rainwater harvesting is to replenish the groundwater to avoid the water shortage problem in times of scarcity of rainfall.

EXAMPLE 11.2 In what way, are electric water purifiers superior to the ceramic water filters for the purification of water for domestic purposes?

SOLUTION

Ceramic water filters contain candles made of fine clay. Clay being porous allows the filtration of suspended impurities and some bacteria from water. But, it does not remove all the germs and disease-causing microorganisms from water as they are usually smaller than the pore size. Electric water purifiers work on the principle that ozone has the ability to kill the germs. It contains a source of UV radiation which converts oxygen to ozone which can kill the disease-causing microorganisms thereby making the water totally safe for drinking. These purifiers also have candles for filtering the suspended impurities. The water coming out of these purifiers is free from both suspended impurities and microorganisms.

EXAMPLE 11.3 How can you lower the solubility of a solute in a saturated solution?

SOLUTION

When a saturated solution is subjected to cooling, then the solubility of the substance decreases. Hence, some of the dissolved solute will precipitate out, as the solution can no longer hold the same amount of solute in the dissolved state.

POINTS TO REMEMBER

- ✔ Water in natural form is available in liquid at normal atmospheric conditions.
- ✔ In extremely cold regions, during winter season, water vapour in the atmosphere condenses to form small flakes of ice called snow.
- ✔ However, during winter, balls of ice fall down along with rainwater, known as hails.
- ✔ When water takes heat from its surroundings and changes into gaseous form, it is called water vapour.
- ✔ The gaseous form of water at or above 100°C is called steam.
- ✔ Latent heat of fusion is the amount of heat required to change 1 g of solid to liquid without any change in temperature. For ice, the value is 80 cal/g.
- ✔ Specific heat capacity of a substance can be defined as the amount of heat required to raise the temperature of 1 g of substance by 1°C. The specific heat capacity of water is 1 calorie/g °C.
- ✔ Latent heat of vaporization is the amount of heat required to convert 1 g of water into steam without any change in temperature. The value is 540 cal/g for water.
- ✔ The continuous circulation of water from the earth's surface to atmosphere and from the atmosphere back to earth is called water cycle.
- ✔ The substances which dissolve in water are called soluble substances. The substances which do not dissolve in water are called insoluble substances.
- ✔ A solution can be defined as the homogenous mixture of two or more components. A solution in which the solvent is water is called an aqueous solution.
- ✔ The solution which can dissolve more amount of solute in it is called an unsaturated solution.
- ✔ The solution which cannot dissolve any more solute in it is called saturated solution.
- ✔ The solution in which more amount of solute than its maximum capacity is dissolved by changing the conditions is called supersaturated solution.
- ✔ Potable water is the water which is fit for consumption or drinking.
- ✔ Preventing the wastage of water in any form and preservation of available water for future is called conservation of water.
- ✔ The collection of rainwater directly and storage of it for later use is called rainwater harvesting.

PRACTICE QUESTIONS CLASSROOM WING

Very Short Answer Type Questions

Directions for questions from 1 to 5.
Fill in the blanks.

1. In very cold places, water vapour condenses to produce ______.
2. The specific heat capacity of water is ______.
3. The value of latent heat of fusion of ice is ______.
4. The density of pure water at 4°C is ______.
5. The rainwater is devoid of ______ impurities.

Directions for questions from 6 to 11.
Select the correct alternative from the given options.

6. Identify the water which can neither be used for irrigation nor for drinking.
   (a) River water (b) Sea water
   (c) Rainwater (d) Well water
7. Identify the process which is not a part of water cycle.
   (a) Evaporation (b) Condensation
   (c) Transpiration (d) Sublimation
8. Which of the following water samples is totally devoid of suspended impurities?
   (a) River water
   (b) Rainwater
   (c) Spring water
   (d) Ocean water
9. ______ does not possess any taste.
   (a) River water (b) Distilled water
   (c) Rainwater (d) Well water
10. One gram of steam is condensed to water at 100°C. Which of the following complies with this process?
   (a) 540 cal of heat is absorbed
   (b) 80 cal of heat is absorbed
   (c) 540 cal of heat is released
   (d) 80 cal of heat is released
11. Units for specific heat capacity of a substance are:
   (a) cal/g/°C (b) cal g/°C
   (c) cal/g (d) cal/°C

Directions for questions from 12 to 21.
Fill in the blanks.

12. The water fit for human consumption is called ______.
13. Water acts as a ______ solvent.
14. ______ and ______ gases are present in dissolved state in natural water.
15. When vaporization and condensation of water are carried out simultaneously, the process is known as ______
16. A solution which cannot dissolve any more amount of solute in it is called ______.
17. The liquid obtained by the condensation of vapour is called ______.
18. Purification of drinking water in cities involves passing water through beds of ______ and ______.
19. The settling down of suspended matter at the bottom of a liquid is known as ______.
20. The removal of germs from water is called ______.
21. Water is a compound containing hydrogen and oxygen was proven by ______.

Directions for questions from 22 to 26.
Select the correct alternative from the given options.

22. Which of the following is considered to be a method of sterilization?
   (a) Boiling (b) Exposure to sunlight
   (c) Chlorination (d) All of these
23. Addition of which substance hastens the process of sedimentation in water?
   (a) Potash alum (b) Bleaching powder
   (c) Chlorine (d) Sand
24. Ozonization of water removes which of the following impurities?
   (a) Fine particles of sand
   (b) Large suspended particles
   (c) Microorganisms
   (d) All of the above

25. The least effective method for the removal of germs from water:
(a) Boiling (b) Exposure to air and sunlight
(c) Chlorination (d) Ozonization

26. ______ is used in car batteries.
(a) River water (b) Chlorinated water
(c) Distilled water (d) Tap water

Short Answer Type Questions

27. The same amount of sugar, when taken in its powdered form, dissolves quickly in water compared to its crystalline form. Why?

28. Define the following.
(a) Undergroundwater
(b) Latent heat of fusion of ice
(c) Latent heat of vaporization of water
(d) Specific heat capacity

29. Drip irrigation is considered an effective technique for reducing water pollution resulting from agricultural operations. Why?

30. How is hydel power generation carried out?

31. The taste of spring water differs from place to place. Justify.

32. All the rivers ultimately drain into seas. However, river water is not saline while sea water is saline. Why?

33. Well water is considered to be safer for consumption than river water. Give reason.

34. Water is considered as the universal solvent. Give reason.

35. Explain the principle involved in the usage of hot water bottles to warm beds in cold countries.

36. In cold countries hot water pipes are arranged inside the concrete floors and walls. Give reason.

37. 100 g of water and 100 g of steam are considered at 100°C. What is the extra amount of heat energy possessed by steam than water?

38. Water in swimming pools remains cool even during hot summer. Give reason.

39. Explain the role of water in controlling the climate.

40. Between chlorination and ozonization of water, which is a more effective method? Why?

41. Distilled water is not fit for consumption. Give reason.

42. Does the size of the solute particles affect the solubility of the substance? Explain.

43. How can heating affect the formation of a solution?

44. Explain how exposure of water to air and sunlight purify water? To what extent this method is effective?

45. How do fertilizers cause water pollution?

46. Distinguish between surface water (fresh water) and undergroundwater with respect to composition.

47. Define water cycle.

48. Mention the identification test for water.

49. Define the following terms.
(a) Solution (b) Solute
(c) Solvent (d) Potable water

50. Why monsoon is so important?

51. Why do we see water droplets (dew) on leaves in winter?

52. What happens if it does not rain for a long period?

53. Sea water is not fit for drinking. Why?

54. Why rain clouds look grey in colour?

Essay Type Questions

55. A river water sample is poured in four containers and subjected to four different processes as shown in the following diagram:

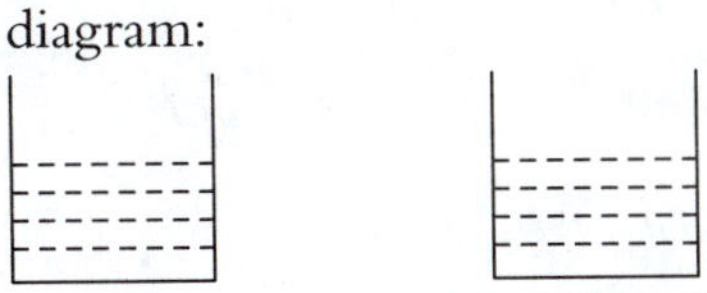

A
Addition of potash alum and filtration

B
Filtered water subjected to boiling

C
Water subjected to evaporation and distillation

D
Water subjected to filtration and passing of ozone

Answer the questions by analysing the given diagram.

(a) Which water is the most suitable for consumption?
(b) What are the disadvantages of other water samples?
(c) What happens when fish are placed in the containers A, B, C and D?

56. Some ice cubes are kept in a beaker and a thermometer is placed in it. What could be the change in temperature observed in the thermometer? Justify?

PRACTICE QUESTIONS COMPETITION WING

Level 1: Apply Your Concepts

Directions for questions from 1 to 5.
Fill in the blanks.

1. ______ or __________ is the largest source of natural water.
2. Water suitable for accurate laboratory work can be obtained by ______.
3. ______ impart freshness and sparkling appearance to water.
4. ______ water is rich in minerals which have medicinal value.
5. The gaseous form of water at 100°C is known as ______.

Directions for questions from 6 to 10:
Select the correct alternative from the given options

6. **Assertion (A):** Water vapour in air is due to evaporation of water from the Earth to the atmosphere.
   Reason (R): Evaporation can take place at any temperature below the boiling point of the liquid.
   Choose the correct option.
   (a) Both A and R are true, and R is the correct explanation for A.
   (b) Both A and R are true, but R is not the correct explanation for A.
   (c) A is true and R is false.
   (d) A is false and R is true.
7. **Assertion (A):** River water is a fresh water and hence is a potable water.
   Reason (R): Freshwater is the water that contains only minimal quantities of dissolved salts in it.
   Choose the correct option.
   (a) Both A and R are true, and R is the correct explanation for A.
   (b) Both A and R are true, but R is not the correct explanation for A.
   (c) A is true and R is false.
   (d) A is false and R is true.
8. Which among the following is not an application of dissolved gases in water?
   (a) Taste of water
   (b) Photosynthesis of aquatic plants
   (c) Salinity of sea water
   (d) Respiration of aquatic organisms
9. Which among the following is not a sterilization method of water?
   (a) Boiling
   (b) Chemical treatment
   (c) Exposure to sunlight
   (d) Sedimentation
10. Which among the following process is not involved in water cycle?
    (a) Melting (b) Evaporation
    (c) Sublimation (d) Condensation

Level 2: Review Your Concepts

11. Calculate the heat required to convert 250 g of ice into water at the same temperature (0°C).
12. 50 g of pure water is taken at 20°C. What is the amount of heat required to raise its temperature to 80°C?
13. Some amount of purple coloured potassium permanganate is added to a beaker of water and stirred. How can you separate the component from the above mixture? Is it possible to recover back both the components? Explain.
14. The solubility of a certain substance does not change with temperature. How can you make an unsaturated solution of such substance saturated?
15. The solubility of a certain substance is 40 at 25°C. What does it mean?

Level 3: Assess Your Concepts

16. Latent heat of fusion of ice is 80 cal/g. Calculate how much amount of heat is to be supplied to convert 1 kg of ice to 1 kg water.

17. Solubility of common salt in water is 36 g at 20°C. Find the amount of salt to be dissolved in 50 g of water to make it a saturated solution at the same temperature.

18. Answer the following questions:
    (a) Explain how electricity is produced from water?
    (b) Anjali was standing in her balcony on a rainy day and asked her father that why rain clouds look grey in colours. What could be the correct answer her father gave her?

19. Answer the following questions:
    (a) What is latent heat of fusion of ice and latent heat of vaporization of water?
    (b) Which of the following is more effective method for disinfecting water—Chlorination or ozonization?

AT

ANSWER KEYS

Crossword

Across

4. Vapour 5. Potable 6. Capacity 7. Conservation 11. Unsaturated
12. Snow 13. Fusion 14. Soluble

Down

1. Harvesting 2. Insoluble 3. Steam 4. Vaporization 8. Saturated
9. Hails 10. Aqueous

Classroom Wing

Very Short Answer Type Questions

1. Snow 2. 1 cal/g/°C 3. 80 cal/g 4. 1 g/cc 5. Suspended
6. (b) 7. (d) 8. (c) 9. (b) 10. (c) 11. (a)
12. Potable water 13. Universal 14. Oxygen and carbon dioxide 15. Distillation
16. Saturated solution 17. Distillate 18. Sand and gravel 19. Sedimentation
20. Sterilization 21. Henry Cavendish 22. (d) 23. (a) 24. (c)
25. (b) 26. (c)

Short Answer Type Questions

37. 54 kcal

Competition Wing

Level 1: Apply Your Concepts

1. Sea or ocean 2. Distillation 3. Dissolved gases 4. Spring 5. Steam
6. (b) 7. (d) 8. (c) 9. (d) 10. (c)

Level 2: Review Your Concepts

11. 20 kcal 12. 3000 cal

Hints and Explanations

CLASSROOM WING

Very Short Answer Type Questions

1. In very cold places, water vapour condenses to produce snow.
2. The specific heat capacity of water is 1 cal/g/°C.
3. The value of latent heat of fusion of ice is 80 cal/g.
4. The density of pure water at 4°C is 1 g/cc.
5. The rainwater is devoid of suspended impurities.
6. Sea water can neither be used for drinking nor for irrigation.

   Hence, the correct option is (b).
7. Sublimation is not a part of water cycle.

   Hence, the correct option is (d).
8. Spring water is totally devoid of suspended impurities.

   Hence, the correct option is (c).
9. Distilled water does not posses any taste.

   Hence, the correct option is (b).
10. When 1 gram of steam is condensed to water at 100°C, 540 cal of heat is released.

    Hence, the correct option is (c).
11. Units of specific heat capacity of a substance are cal/g/°C.

    Hence, the correct option is (a).
12. The water fit for human consumption is called potable water.
13. Water acts as a universal solvent.
14. Oxygen and carbon dioxide gases are present in dissolved state in natural water.
15. When vaporization and condensation of water are carried out simultaneously, the process is known as distillation.
16. A solution which cannot dissolve any more amount of solute in it is called saturated solution.
17. The liquid obtained by the condensation of vapour is called distillate.
18. Purification of drinking water in cities involves passing water through beds of sand and gravel.
19. The settling down of suspended matter at the bottom of a liquid is known as sedimentation.
20. Removal of germs from water is called sterilization.
21. Henry Cavendish proved that water is a compound containing hydrogen and oxygen.
22. Boiling, exposure to sunlight and chlorination are considered to be the methods of sterilization as they can kill bacteria and germs.

    Hence, the correct option is (d).
23. Addition of potash alum hastens the process of sterilization.

    Hence, the correct option is (a).
24. Ozonization removes only microorganisms from water as ozone has the ability to kill the germs.

    Hence, the correct option is (c).
25. Exposure to air and sunlight is the least effective method for the removal of germs from water as sunlight cannot enter into the deeper layers of water.

    Hence, the correct option is (b).
26. Distilled water is used in car batteries.

    Hence, the correct option is (c).

Short Answer Type Questions

27. Increased surface area and smaller particle size of powdered sugar allow it to come into contact with the solvent (water) more effectively, resulting in a faster dissolution process.
28. (a) Undergroundwater is defined as the water which percolates through the upper layer of the earth's surface and gets collected on the solid rocks beneath.

    (b) Latent heat of fusion is defined as the amount of heat required to convert 1 gram of ice (solid) into water at its freezing point.

    (c) Latent heat of vaporization of water is defined as the amount of heat required to convert 1 gram of water into steam at its boiling point.

(d) Specific heat capacity of a substance is defined as the amount of heat required to raise the temperature of 1 gram of the substance through 1°C without any change in state.

29. Drip irrigation delivers water directly to the plant roots in small and controlled amounts. This targeted irrigation system helps minimize water wastage and runoff, reducing the chances of agricultural pollutants, such as fertilizers and pesticides, from being washed into nearby water bodies. Hence, it is considered as an effective technique for reducing water pollution resulting from agricultural operations.

30. Water falling from a height is used to move the turbine and generate electricity.

31. Spring water is nothing but the water emerged out from underground pool. Undergroundwater is the water collected by the percolation of rainwater through the layers of porous rock and soil. As the water seeps through, it dissolves the mineral salts present in the soil and rocks. Therefore, the taste of spring water depends on the nature of soil and rocks at the particular place.

32. Rivers while draining into the seas deposit the suspended matter at the mouth forming delta. They carry the dissolved salts into the seas. As a result, the water becomes concentrated with dissolved salts. This imparts salinity to sea water.

33. Well water is obtained by digging the soil up to the undergroundwater table. This water is collected by the percolation of rainwater through the layers of soil and rocks. As the water passes through the layers of soil (gravel and sand), it gets filtered naturally. In this process, suspended impurities and germs are removed. On the other hand, the river water during its course carries large amount of suspended impurities and microorganisms along with it. Therefore, well water is pure and relatively safer for consumption than river water.

34. Water can dissolve a wide variety of substances in it. It can dissolve many gaseous substances and many solid substances. Hence, water is considered as a universal solvent.

35. Due to the high specific heat capacity of water, it can absorb large amount of heat without getting vaporized. Hot water also remains hot for a long time as it gets cooled slowly. As a result, the heat in the hot water bottles radiates heat slowly to keep the building beds warm.

36. Water has high specific heat capacity. When hot water is circulated through the water pipes inside the concrete floors or walls, it radiates heat slowly to the building thereby keeping the inside building warm.

37. 1 g of water required 540 cal of heat for getting converted into steam at 100°C. That means 1 g of steam possess 540 calories of extra heat than 1 g of water. Therefore, 100 g of steam contains 54,000 cal of (54 kcal) more heat than 100 g of water at 100°C.

38. Water in swimming pools remains cool even during hot summer. This is because water has high specific heat capacity and requires large amount of heat for raising the temperature.

39. Water has high specific heat capacity. It gets heated up and cooled down slowly. In coastal regions, the land gets heated up rapidly. While water gets heated up slowly during the day. Similarly, they get cooled down also at different rates. This differential heating followed by cooling of land and water sets up the convection currents, like sea breeze and land breeze. These sea breezes and land breezes help in moderation of temperature of the atmosphere in coastal regions. The difference between day and night temperatures is less in coastal areas due to this reason. Even the difference between the winter and summer temperature is less for the same reason.

40. Treatment of water with chlorine to kill the germs and bacteria in it is called chlorination. Passing ozone through water to kill the germs and bacteria is called ozonization. Though both chlorine and ozone can kill the germs and bacteria, ozone is more effective than chlorine for the same purpose. This is because when the relative proportions of ozone and chlorine required are compared, ozone is required in much lesser proportion when compared to chlorine. Moreover, chlorine is generally used in excess quantity, and hence imparts little odour to the water and also causes minor health problems. Therefore, ozone is more effective than chlorine.

41. Distilled water does not contain the mineral salts required for our body. It does not possess adequate amounts of dissolved gases. Hence, it has insipid or bland taste.

42. The size of the particles does not affect the amount of substance that can be dissolved in the solvent. It only affects the rate of dissolution of the solute. The smaller the size of the particles, the greater is the rate of dissolution of the solute. This is due to the fact that the surface area in contact with the solvent increases with the decrease in the size of the particles.

43. Increase in temperature results in increase in solubility as well as the rate of dissolution of a substance. As solubility of a solute generally increases with temperature, the solution becomes unsaturated on heating. The solute also dissolves at a faster rate on heating.

44. Air contains oxygen. As oxygen helps in burning, when water is exposed to air and sunlight; the germs are burnt to death. That is why water in town reservoirs is exposed to air and sunlight over a large surface area.

45. Fertilizers usually contain nitrogen salts which are highly soluble in water. These salts are leached away by rainwater and reach the water bodies. They make the water in water bodies acidic. In this way, fertilizers cause water pollution.

46. Surface water contains appreciable amounts of suspended impurities in addition to the dissolved gases and dissolved salts. Underground water contains only dissolved salts and gases, but does not contain appreciable amounts of suspended impurities.

47. The change of water from one form to another taking place repeatedly in nature can be represented as a cyclic process and is known as water cycle.

48. Water or water vapour turns white anhydrous copper sulphate to blue.

49. (a) Solution is defined as a homogeneous mixture of two or more components.

(b) The component which undergoes change in physical state during the formation of a solution is called solute.

(c) The component which does not undergo any change in physical state is called solvent.

(d) The water which is fit and safe for human consumption is known as potable water.

50. Monsoon is important because:

(i) Most of the rainfall occurs during the monsoon season.

(ii) Rains bring relief especially after hot summer days.

(iii) Sowing of many crops depends on the arrival of monsoon.

51. On a warm day, water evaporates from the warm ground into the air. During night, the warm ground continues to radiate heat into the air. As the ground begins to cool, the air will not able to hold all the moisture. Water vapour in the air will begin to condense. That's why we see water droplets on leaves in winter.

52. No rain for a long period can cause the following:

(i) The soil becomes dry.

(ii) The level of water in ponds and wells of the region goes down and some of them may even dry up.

(iii) The groundwater may also become scarce. This may lead to drought.

53. Sea water is not fit for drinking because it has many salts dissolved in it which is not good for human body.

54. As more and more water droplets gathers, clouds gets thicker, denser and less transparent. Thus, rain clouds look gray in color.

Essay Type Questions

55. (a) Water in container D is the safest one for consumption as ozone kills the disease-causing germs and bacteria. The water is devoid of both suspended impurities as well as microorganisms.

(b) (i) Water in container A is devoid of suspended impurities, but contains the germs and bacteria. Consumption of this water may lead to a number of water borne diseases.

(ii) Sample B – Filtration removes all suspended impurities. Boiling to some extent kills the germs and bacteria. But, this water is devoid of dissolved gases and has insipid taste.

(iii) Sample C – The water sample is distilled water. This is devoid of dissolved salts and dissolved gases. This is not fit for consumption.

(c) Fish die when they are kept in containers B or C because the water does not contain dissolved oxygen required for the respiration of fishes.

56. The temperature in the thermometer remains unaltered until the entire ice melts. The heat absorbed from the surroundings is utilized for the conversion of solid state to liquid state by overcoming intermolecular forces of attraction.

COMPETITION WING

Level 1: Apply Your Concepts

1. Sea or ocean is the largest source of natural water.
2. Water suitable for accurate laboratory work can be obtained by distillation.
3. Dissolved gases impart freshness and sparkling appearance to water.
4. Spring water is rich in minerals which have medicinal value.
5. The gaseous form of water at 100°C is known as steam.
6. **Assertion (A):** Water vapour in air is due to evaporation of water from the Earth to the atmosphere-True.
   Reason (R): Evaporation can take place at any temperature below the boiling point of the liquid-True.
   Both (A) and (R) are true but (R) is not the correct explanation of (A).
   Hence, the correct option is (b).
7. **Assertion (A):** River water is a fresh water and hence is a potable water-False.
   Reason (R): Freshwater is the water that contains only minimal quantities of dissolved salts in it-True.
   (A) Is false and (R) is true.
   Hence, the correct option is (d).
8. Salinity of sea water is due to dissolved salts in water.
   Hence, the correct option is (c).
9. Sedimentation is not a sterilization method. It is used to remove suspended solid matter.
   Hence, the correct option is (d).
10. Sublimation is not involved in water cycle.
    Hence, the correct option is (c).

Level 2: Review Your Concepts

11. 1 g of ice requires 80 cal of heat to get converted to water at 0°C. 250 g of ice requires 20000 cal (20 kcal) of heat to get converted to water.
12. 1 g of water requires 1 cal of heat to raise its temperature by 1°C. 50 g of water should require 50 cal of heat to raise its temperature by 1°C. The raise in temperature here is 60°C (80°C – 20°C). To raise the temperature by 60°C, 3000 cal of heat (3 kcal) is required.
13. Potassium permanganate dissolves in water forming a solution. On evaporation of this solution, water vaporizes leaving behind the crystals of potassium permanganate. By the process of distillation, it is possible to recover both potassium permanganate and water.
14. As unsaturated solution contains lesser amount of solute than its maximum capacity on subjecting the solution to evaporation, some amount of water vaporizes. Since lesser amount of water is present in the solution and the amount of solute is same, the solution at some stage may become saturated as the solubility of the substance remains same even on heating.
15. The solubility of a substance is said to be 40 at 25°C when 40 g of the substance is dissolved in 100 g of water to make a saturated solution at that temperature.

Level 3: Assess Your Concepts

16. Given latent heat of fusion of ice is 80 cal/g.
    Amount of heat to be supplied to convert 1 kg (1000 g) of ice to 1 kg water is:
    1 g of ice needs = 80 cal of heat to convert into water.
    1000 g of ice needs = 80 × 1000 = 80 kcal of heat to convert into 1 kg water.
17. Given solubility of common salt in water is 36 g at 20°C.
    Solubility of a substance is defined as the amount of the substance to be dissolved in 100 g of the solvent to make it a saturated solution at that temperature.
    100 g of water requires = 36 g of salt to be dissolved to make it a saturated solution at 20°C
    50 g of water requires = (36 × 50)/100 = 18 g of salt to be dissolved to make it a saturated solution at 20°C
18. (a) Water falling from a height is used to move the turbine and generate electricity.
    (b) As large amount of water droplets gathers and clouds get thicker and becomes less transparent. Therefore, rain clouds look grey in colour.
19. (a) Latent heat of fusion of ice is the amount of heat requires to convert 1 gram of ice into water at its freezing point.
    Latent heat of vaporization of water is the amount of heat required to raise the temperature of 1 gram of substances through 1°C without any change in state.
    (b) Both chlorine and ozone can kill germs but ozone is more effective because ozone is required in lesser amount than that of chlorine. In addition to it, a chlorine is used in excess quantity, it imparts little odour to the water.

Unit III

Biology

In this Unit

- ✶ **Chapter 12** Environment—An Eternal Gift to Mankind
- ✶ **Chapter 13** Plants—Nature's Wonderful Food Factories
- ✶ **Chapter 14** Movement—An Amazing Activity
- ✶ **Chapter 15** Health—Our Greatest Wealth

CHAPTER 12

Environment—An Eternal Gift to Mankind

Remember

Before beginning this chapter, you should be able to:

- Identify plants and animals in your surrounding
- Distinguish non-living things and living beings in our environment

Key Ideas

After completing this chapter, you should be able to:

- Understand the relationship between the habits and habitats of organisms
- Describe the adaptations of living organisms with respect to their food habits and habitats
- Get a comprehensive idea of interdependence of organisms amongst each other and with their environment

Scientific Crypt

A Tribute to Rachel Carson (1907–1964)

Rachel Carson (1907-1964) was a trailblazing environmental scientist whose influence transcended borders. Her work, despite being born in the United States, has struck a chord with students in India and around the world. Her seminal book, "Silent Spring," published in 1962, exposed the dangers of pesticides like DDT, demonstrating how they harmed not only the environment but also human health.

Rachel Carson's scientific discoveries were not only eye-opening, but they also fueled the modern environmental movement around the world.

Despite criticism and opposition from powerful interests, Carson's commitment to truth and the environment resulted in the ban of DDT and the establishment of the United States Environmental Protection Agency (EPA).

Rachel Carson's legacy is an inspiration for Indian students. Her advocacy for a healthier planet serves as a reminder to others that they, too, can help protect India's diverse ecosystems and preserve the country's natural beauty.

FUN TIME

CROSSWORD

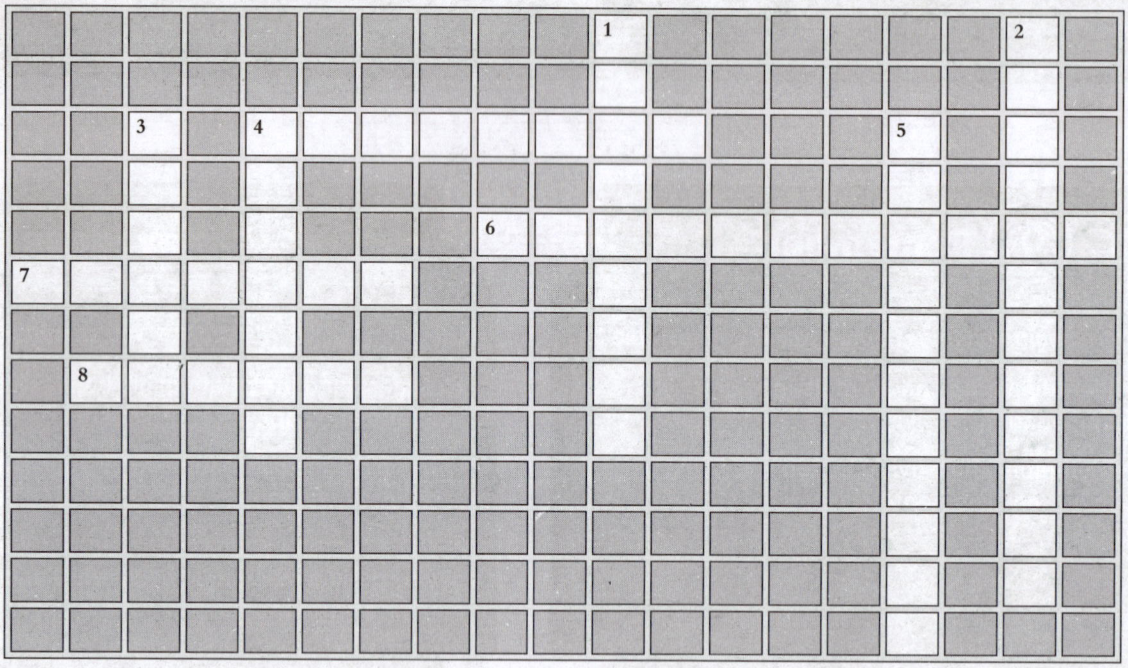

Across

4. Animals that live on trees
6. Process by which energy is released by the oxidation of food
7. The study of living organisms in relation to the environment
8. An aquatic ecosystem with a high salt content

Down

1. Type of terrestrial ecosystem where grass is the main producer
2. The biological process by which organisms can give rise to young ones
3. An example of a plant showing response to stimuli
4. Non-living components of our environment
5. A mode of nutrition of green plants

INTRODUCTION

Earth is a unique planet in our solar system that supports life. Earth is made up of minerals, rocks, soil, water and has numerous plants and animal species. Plants and animals need food, oxygen and other materials for their survival.

All living components are dependent on the non-living components for their survival. Both living and non-living things together constitute **environment**. Thus, environment can be defined as a collection of all the living and non-living elements and their effects that influence all lifeforms. Environment comprises two components namely, biotic and abiotic components.

1. The biotic component includes all the living elements. *Examples* include plants, animals and microorganisms.
2. The abiotic component includes all the non-living elements. *Examples* include soil, water, etc.

Living beings are characterized by some specific features, and these features are not found in non-living things.

Characteristic Features of Living Beings

Following are the specific features of living beings.

Structural Organization

Living organisms are made up of cells. A **cell** is the basic structural and functional unit of life in all living organisms. Based on the number of cells, organisms are classified into two types.

Organisms

- Unicellular → Made up of only single cell.
  Examples: *Amoeba*, *Paramecium*, bacteria, etc.
- Multicellular → Made up of large number of cells.
  Examples: Human beings, dogs, a rose plant, etc.

Figure 12.1 Classification of organisms based on the number of cells

> **Info Bytes!**
> A mature tree produces enough oxygen for 18 people to breathe!

Multicellular organisms possess a specific structural organization. In these organisms, the cells group together to form different tissues. These tissues constructively combine to form organs. Organs form organ systems. Different organ systems combine to form an organism.

Cells → Tissues → Organs → Organ systems → Organism

Figure 12.2 Levels of cellular organization

Growth

The permanent and irreversible increase in the size of a plant body or an animal body is known as growth. After birth, growth is seen in all living organisms. The increasing number of tissues results in the growth of an organism.

Examples: The growth of a small seedling into a big tree and the growth of a human baby into an adult.

Plants grow throughout their lives but in animals growth occurs only up to a certain period.

Fixed Lifespan

All living organisms grow from young ones to adults and they live only for a certain period of time. They live, sustain, prosper, wither away and die after a specific time. The period from birth to natural death of an organism is called 'lifespan'. The lifespan is different for different organisms. Generally, plants have a greater lifespan than animals. The lifespan of animals are highly variable ranging from a few seconds to a few years.

Table 12.1 Lifespan of some organisms

Organism	Lifespan
Cat	12–18 years
Horse	25–30 years
Dog	10–20 years
Monkey	20–25 years
Human	70–80 years

Info Bytes!

Mayflies have the shortest lifespan on Earth, 24 hours or even less!

Response to Stimuli

All living organisms respond to the changes in the surrounding environment. These changes in our surroundings that make us respond to them, are called stimuli. For example, if we abruptly step on a sharp object like a thorn, while walking barefoot, we immediately pull our leg away without a conscious effort.

This is known as response to stimuli. Similarly, plants also respond to the changes in the environment. One of the best example is 'touch-me-not' plant, also called, *mimosa pudica,* whose leaves close or fold when someone touches them.

Reproduction

As living organisms have a fixed lifespan, it is essential for living organisms to procreate their own kinds in order to continue the species generation after generation. All living organisms produce their young ones during their Lifetime. Reproduction, either asexual or sexual, is the biological process by which living organisms reproduce an offspring similar to themselves. Reproduction in plants mainly takes place with the help of seeds. Seeds when sowed in the soil develop into plants under suitable conditions. This process is known as germination. In certain plants, the roots, stems and leaves of the plant are also capable of developing into new identical plants. In some animals, reproduction takes place by laying eggs followed by hatching. Some animals carry out the process of reproduction by giving birth to young ones. The young ones of all diverse animals are given different names.

Table 12.2 Animals and their young ones

Animals	Young ones
Dog	Puppy
Cat	Kitten
Rabbit	Kitten/Kit
Sheep	Lamb
Lion/tiger	Cub
Cattle	Calf

The life cycle of a typical animal can be represented from birth to death in the following way:

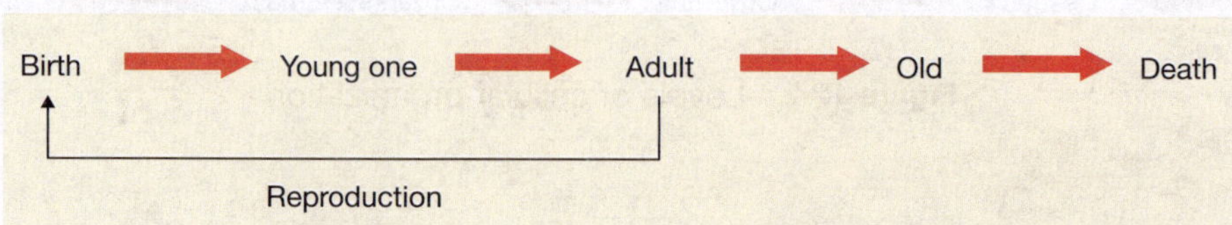

Figure 12.3 Life cycle of a typical animal

Consumption of Food

The living organisms need food for growth and survival. The consumption of food by living organisms is known as nutrition.

Nutrition is of two types:

1. Autotrophic nutrition
2. Heterotrophic nutrition

Autotrophic Nutrition

Autotrophic nutrition is the mode of nutrition in which the organisms make their own food and do not depend on other organisms for food. The word 'autotroph' originates from two words, where 'auto' means self and 'troph' means food. Many plants make their own food by the process of photosynthesis. Hence, they are called autotrophs. The process of food preparation by green plants in the presence of sunlight by absorbing carbon dioxide and water vapour present in the surrounding environment is known as **photosynthesis**.

The process of photosynthesis can be represented in the equation form as follows:

$$\text{Carbon dioxide} + \text{Water} \xrightarrow[\text{Chlorophyll}]{\text{Sunlight}} \text{Glucose} + \text{Oxygen}$$

$$6CO_2 \quad + 6H_2O \quad \rightarrow \quad C_6H_{12}O_6 \; + 6O_2$$

Heterotrophic Nutrition

Heterotrophic nutrition is the mode of nutrition in which the organisms depend on other organisms for food. Animals do not make their own food and are called heterotrophs. The word 'heterotroph' originates from two words, where 'hetero' means other and 'troph' means food.

All the animals are heterotrophs and they are further classified based on the type of food they consume.

- Herbivores
- Carnivores
- Omnivores
- Scavengers
- Decomposers

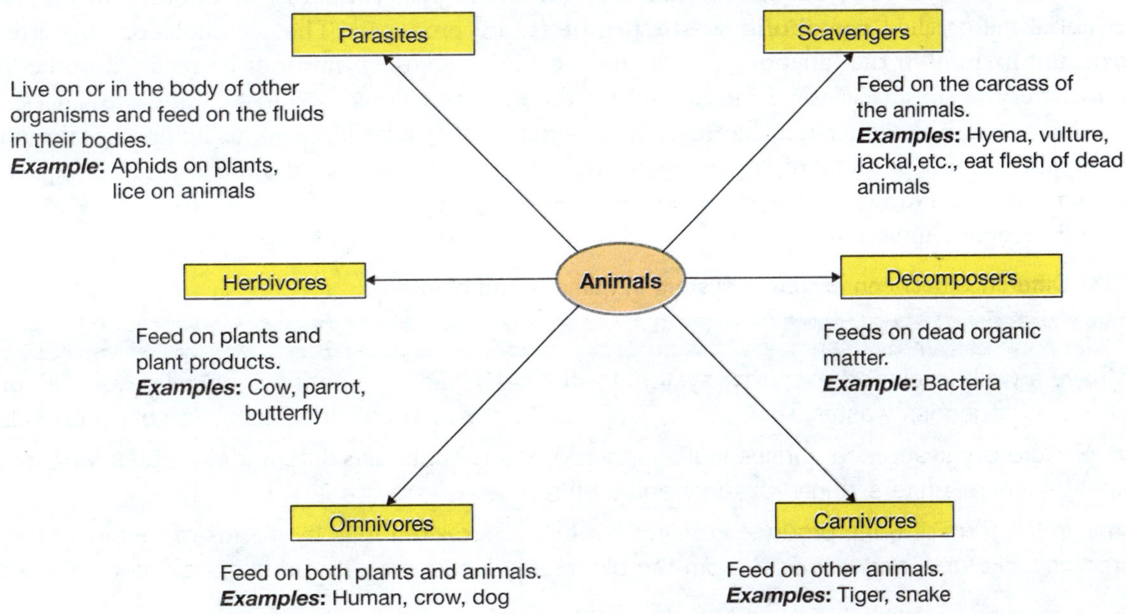

Figure 12.4 Classification of animals based on their food habits

Respiration

Food is essential for living beings not only for growth, but also for the fulfillment of energy requirement to carry out various activities. The consumed food is converted to energy in the presence of oxygen. The burning of any substance with oxygen is known as **oxidation**. The process in which energy is released by oxidation of food is known as **respiration**.

The process of respiration can be represented by the following equation.

$$\text{Food} + \text{Oxygen} \xrightarrow[\text{Cell}]{\text{Living}} \text{Carbon dioxide} + \text{Water} + \text{Energy}$$

The process of respiration takes place in two phases, breathing and internal respiration. The process of inhaling oxygen and exhaling carbon dioxide is known as breathing. The process of breathing in oxygen is known as inhalation. The oxidation of food substances with oxygen is known as internal respiration. During this process, carbon dioxide is released. The process of breathing out carbon dioxide is known as exhalation. Different animals possess different organs for breathing and internal respiration.

Konnect

Most reptiles such as snakes, are carnivores; however, the common iguana, a large arboreal lizard, also known as the green iguana, is considered one of the few herbivorous lizards.

Table 12.3 Some organisms and their respiratory organs

Organisms	Organs for Respiration
Human beings	Lungs (Nose for breathing)
Fish	Gills
Frog	Skin, lungs
Earthworm	Skin

Plants respire with the help of **stomata**. Oxygen is released by the plants during the process of photosynthesis. The oxygen which is essential for respiration is reabsorbed by plants. The excess oxygen is released into the atmosphere to maintain the percentage level of oxygen in the atmosphere. This oxygen is utilized by the animals for the purpose of respiration.

Figure 12.5 Stomata

Excretion

The cells of all living organisms carry out various activities in order to perform bodily functions. During these activities, some waste materials, also called **metabolic waste products**, are produced. The accumulation of waste materials is potentially toxic and harmful to the functioning of living organisms. So, they must not be retained in the bodies of the living organisms. Every organism has some mechanism for the disposal (throwing out) of waste substances. The process of disposing all waste materials generated due to cellular activities that take place in all living organisms is known as **excretion**. Generally, animals produce **nitrogenous wastes** and excrete them in the form of urine. Apart from urine, animals also excrete sweat as a waste. In plants, the excretory products are stored in flowers, fruits, bark and yellow leaves which are shed off at regular intervals.

Table 12.4 Difference between excretory system in humans and plants

Excretory system in humans	Excretory system in plants
1. Humans have a well-developed excretory system for the elimination of nitrogenous wastes.	1. Plants do not have a well-developed excretory system for the elimination of nitrogenous wastes.
2. The human excretory system comprises kidneys, blood vessels that join them, ureters, urinary bladder and urethra.	2. Plants use different strategies for excretion.
3. Excretion is in the form of urine produced to filter out the waste products, like urea and uric acid, from the blood.	3. Excretion is by means of tannin, gums, essential oils, etc., stored in special cells.

EXAMPLE 12.1 Is a seed living or non-living?

SOLUTION

A seed is a living entity as it possesses the potential to germinate and grow into a mature plant when provided with the right conditions. While it may remain dormant and not show the typical signs of life, such as growth or respiration, for extended periods, it still contains life within. This dormant state allows it to survive in unfavourable conditions until it encounters the right environment for germination. Therefore, a seed is considered a living entity.

EXAMPLE 12.2 The wheels of a car move forward, but it is not a living thing. How do you explain this?

SOLUTION

The wheels of a car move forward but this movement is not spontaneous as it takes place under the effect of an external force. In the case of a car, that external force is provided by the engine and transmission. Similarly, any non-living thing can move when acted upon by an external force. Movement in living organisms, on the other hand, takes place at the expense of their internal energy, making it spontaneous. The movement of animals or humans can be for various purposes such as seeking food, exploring their surroundings, or escaping from danger. In some cases, movement may also occur as a response to stimuli.

EXAMPLE 12.3 Distinguish between omnivores and insectivores.

SOLUTION

The term 'omni' means all, so the animals that feed on both plants and animals are referred to as omnivores. These animals have a varied diet and possess teeth suitable for both grinding plant materials and tearing flesh. For example, bears, humans, and pigs. The term 'insectivore' indicates animals that primarily feed on insects. These animals often have sharp, pointed teeth or specialized mouthparts to catch and consume insects. For example, anteaters, frogs, and many species of birds.

Adaptation

The changes in the behaviour or structure of organisms, allow them to survive in a particular habitat. Many organisms adapt to their habitat by the following means, i.e., modifications, migration and hibernation.

The process in which unique features are acquired by the organisms which enable them to live comfortably in a particular habitat is called **adaptation**.

Habitat

We have already discussed that the environment is made up of biotic and abiotic components. The community in which living organisms, like plants, animals and microorganisms live is called biotic community. The surrounding of an environment comprising air, water, soil, etc., is called abiotic community. All living organisms require non-living environment or abiotic community for their survival. The environment in which a particular organism lives comfortably is known as habitat.

Living organisms sustain in two types of habitats.

1. Terrestrial (Land habitat)
2. Aquatic (Water habitat)

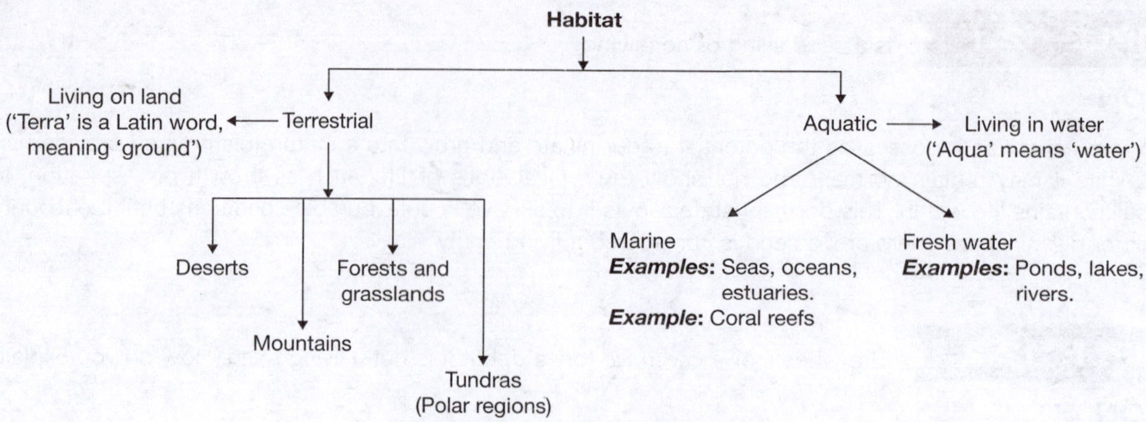

Figure 12.6 Types of habitats

Terrestrial (Land Habitat)

The word 'terrestrial' originated from a Latin word '*terra*' which means 'ground'. The plants and trees living in terrestrial habitats are called mesophytes. They possess the characteristic features of typical plants.

Depending on the climatic conditions, the terrestrial habitats are further classified into various types.

- Deserts
- Forests and grasslands
- Mountains
- Tundras

Forests and grasslands form the most important type of terrestrial habitats. They possess maximum density of flora and fauna. The forests are generally associated with warm and wet climate as they get plenty of rain throughout the year. The grasslands are usually present in the lower altitudes of mountains. They possess windy climate with moderate rainfall. They are inhabited by a variety of plants and animals due to the availability of plenty of water, shelter and food in these regions. The characteristic structural features of the animals living in these habitats depend on their mode of nutrition. The structural features of the animals are closely linked to their feeding habits.

Info Bytes!

Amazon forest is home to around 2.5 million species of insects!

Aquatic (Water Habitat)

The word 'aquatic' originated from a Latin word '*aqua*' which means 'water'.

Depending on the nature of water, the aquatic habitats are classified into two types:

1. Fresh water
2. Marine

Info Bytes!

The Mariana Trench is the deepest habitat on Earth, and organisms living there endure immense pressures.

Each habitat is associated with its distinct and characteristic climatic conditions. These biotic factors interact with each other as they depend on each other for their nutrition and other needs. All organisms depend on plants for oxygen. The organisms living in each particular habitat possess certain structural features. These features help them to adjust to the existing climatic conditions of that habitat.

The organisms living in aquatic habitat possess certain structural features which are totally different from that of the terrestrial organisms. The plants living in water are called hydrophytes. They possess stomata on the upper surface of leaves while the mesophytes possess stomata on the lower surface of leaves. Hydrophytes can be floating on water or submerged in water and their features also depend on this adaptability. The animals which live in water are called aquatic animals; most of these animal species cannot survive on land. However, there is a class of animals which live on both land and in water, these are called amphibians.

Adaptations of Animals Based on Feeding Habits

Animals are adapted differently on the basis of their feeding habits. Plant eaters are called herbivores and flesh eaters are called carnivores.

Adaptations in Herbivores

The forests serve as a home to many herbivorous animals due to the availability of variety of plants and trees.

Herbivores →

Wide and blunt teeth	Grazing and grinding ***Examples:*** Cow, sheep
Ability of chewing the cud	Bring back the swallowed grass to mouth for rechewing ***Examples:*** Cattle, goats
A pair of sharp incisors in jaws	Gnaw the food items like nuts ***Examples:*** Squirrels, rabbits
Straw-like mouth parts	Suck nectar from flowers ***Examples:*** Humming birds, butterflies

Figure 12.7 Feeding habits of herbivores

Arboreal means living in trees. Many herbivorous animals spend majority of their life on trees. Such animals are called arboreal animals.

Examples: Monkeys, orangutans, etc.

Features of Arboreal Animals

In addition to some common features of herbivores, the arboreal animals also possess some features which make them suitable to live on trees.

Some of the features are:

- Strong and muscular legs assist arboreal mammals to run, jump and climb trees.
- Long limbs help them to swing flexibly from one branch to another.
- Long tail to grasp branches of the trees.

Info Bytes!

Giraffes have a long tongue (up to 45 cm) to help them pull down leaves from tall trees.

Adaptations in Carnivores

Forests are the main habitats for carnivorous animals. Carnivores possess some structural features which enable them to hunt other animals and eat their flesh.

Carnivores →

Sharp and pointed teeth Sharp claws Powerful jaws	Tearing of flesh ***Examples***: Lion, tiger.
Long and sticky tongue	Catching insects ***Examples***: Chameleon, frogs.
Curved and pointed beak	Tear flesh of the prey ***Example***: Eagles, hawks
Several small and sharp teeth	Bite off flesh ***Example***: Sharks

Figure 12.8 Feeding habits of carnivores

Carnivorous animals are also called **predator animals** as they hunt other animals for food. The herbivores which become food for these animals are called **preying animals**. Preying animals and predator animals possess contrasting structural features. Predator animals have specific features which enable them to find their prey easily. Preying animals have certain features which enable them to escape from predators and protect themselves. Predator animals have their eyes located in front of the face. They also possess strong legs to run swiftly and hunt the preying animals.

Examples: Lion, bear, etc.

Preying animals have their eyes located on the sides of head for a wide range of vision and they possess long ears. These features help them to sense the animals which are around for hunting.

Examples: Deer, rabbit, etc.

Some of these animals also show camouflage. **Camouflage** is the ability of an animal to change its bodily features, such as variation in colour or spots on the bodies. This feature enables the animal to be out of vision of its preying or predator animals.

Examples: Brown colour of animals in the grasslands, spots present on the skin of jaguars.

Adaptations in Omnivores

Gradually, as civilization progressed, forests have been cleared out, so few animals were domesticated as a result of deforestation. However, these animals are adapted to this new environment and they feed on both plants and animals as well. These domesticated animals have certain features which enable them to acquire both modes of nutrition. These animals possess specific features from both herbivores and carnivores. It is due to the fact that they consume both plants and flesh of animals.

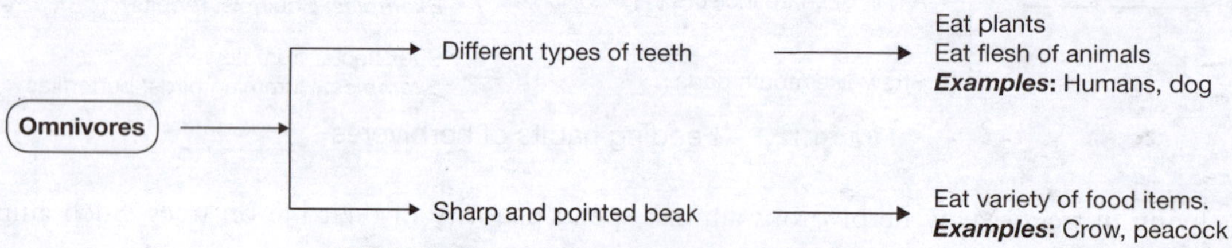

Figure 12.9 Feeding habits of omnivores

Adaptations in Plants and Animals Based on Habitats

Based on the surrounding environmental conditions, living organisms adapt accordingly to adjust to those conditions.

> **Info Bytes!**
> The Welwitschia plant, found in the Namib Desert, can live for over 1,000 years with just two leaves.

Adaptations in Grasslands Environment

Grasslands usually have a tropical climate with plenty of rainfall. The various adaptations found in plants and animals present in grasslands are given in the following flow diagram.

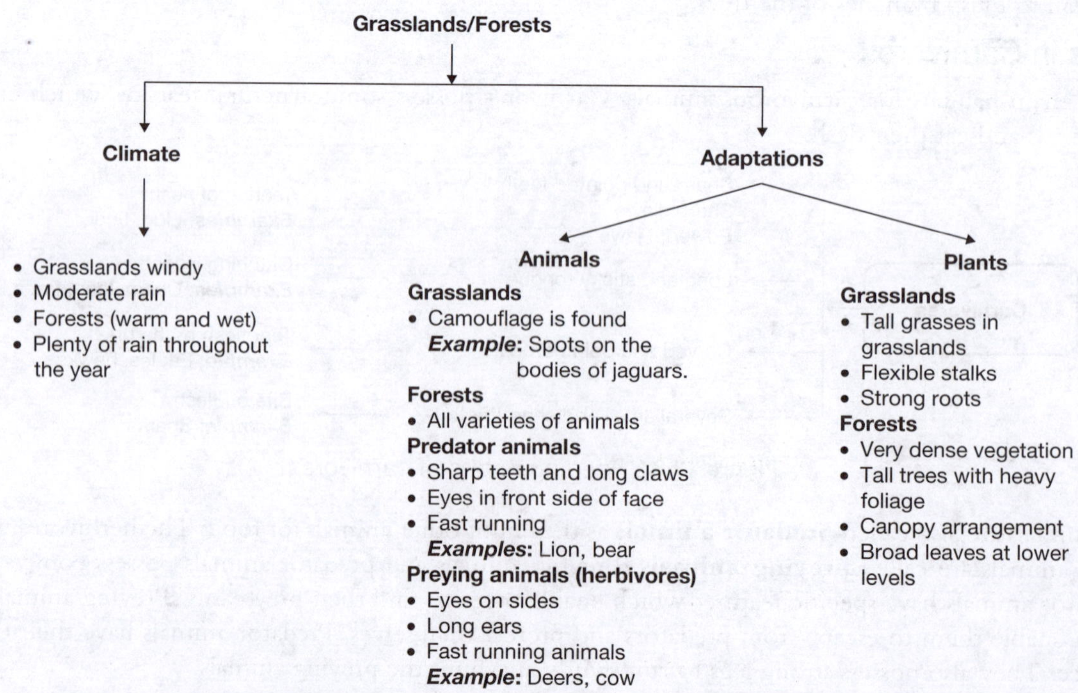

Figure 12.10 Adaptations present in grasslands

Adaptations in Mountains

Mountains are associated with varying climatic conditions, here the climate depends upon the altitude. Generally, at high altitudes, the climate is cold and windy, and it may be associated with snowfall in some areas.

Next to forests, mountains have large population of plants and animals. Plants and animals living in these regions develop certain structural features to make them suitable for this kind of climate.

Mountains

Climate

- Rocky terrain
- Cold and windy
- Climate varies with altitude
- Snowfall

Adaptations

Plants

- Leaves reduced to needle-like structures
- Thick waxy coating on the surface of parts
- Cone-shaped trees with sloping branches

***Examples*:** Pine, cedar

Animals

- Very strong hooves
- Thick fur/long hair on body
- Hibernation (winter sleep)
- Breeding in summer

***Examples*:** Yaks, bears, mountain goats, snow leopards

Figure 12.11 Adaptations present in mountain region

Adaptations in Desert Region

Deserts are mainly associated with very hot and dry climate with very little rainfall. So, the plants and animals in these regions are adapted to these conditions, and hence, they have some distinct features. The plants living in desert regions are known as xerophytes and they possess certain unique features. The animals living in desert regions also possess specific features to tolerate the extreme climatic conditions in deserts.

> ***Info Bytes!***
>
> Desert covers around one fifth of the Earth's surface and they are present on every continent.

Deserts

Climate

- Very hot during summer
- Very cold during winter
- Sandy soil dry due to scanty rainfall.

Examples: Thar, Sahara, Gobi, etc.,

Adaptations

Plants (Xerophytes)

- Long roots
- Fleshy stems to store food and water
- Leaves reduced to spines
- Stem with chlorophyll
- Less number of stomata.

Examples: Cactus, *Acacia*

Animals

- Ability to drink and store large amount of water
- Development of hump with stored fat
- Ability to tolerate heat
- Feet with leathery soles
- Long and thick eye lashes
- Ability to close the nostrils
- Summer sleep (long period)

Examples: Camel, coyote

- Some are nocturnal and live in burrows

Examples: Desert rats and snakes

Figure 12.12 Adaptations present in desert region

Opuntia Cactus Camel Fennac fox

Figure 12.13 Some plants and animals of desert

Adaptations in Tundra Region

The tundra region is also known as polar regions. It is associated with very cold and dry climate. The subsoil remains frozen for most part of the year. There is scarce or less density of vegetation as the frozen soil and the climatic conditions are not suitable for the growth of plants. In tundra region, very few kind of animal species adapt to survive. They possess some structural features which make them tolerate very extreme climatic conditions.

> **Info Bytes!**
> Antarctica is the largest desert on Earth!

Tundras

Climate

Very cold and dry frozen subsoil

Adaptations

Plants

- Scanty vegetation
- Short plants in groups
- Ability to carry out photosynthesis at low temperature and low sunlight
- Photosynthesis at low temperature and low sunlight
- Cone-shaped trees

Examples: Arctic Moss, Arctic Willow, Caribou Moss, Bearberry (*Arctostaphylos*)

Animals

- Feathers
- Thick layer of fat (blubber)
- Staying together in groups

Examples: Muskox, Arctic wolf, and brown bear

Figure 12.14 Adaptations present in tundra region

Adaptations in Aquatic Region

Adaptations seen in plants and animals of aquatic habitat are given below in a flow diagram.

Aquatic habitat

Adaptations

Plants (Hydrophytes)

- Special roots
- Hollow stems with air sacs
- Stomata on upper surface
- Floating plants
- Flat, large floating leaves

Examples: Lotus, water lily

- Submerged plants

Example: *Vallisneria*

Animals

- Streamlined bodies
- Gills for breathing
- Fins and tail for swimming
- Air bladders
- Ocean animals

Examples: Dolphins and whales possess flippers, blow hole and webbed feet of frogs.

Figure 12.15 Adaptations present in the aquatic habitat

Ecosystem

Plants require soil for their growth. They also require carbon dioxide and water vapour from the atmospheric air for preparation of food. Herbivorous animals depend on plants for their nutrition. Carnivorous animals depend on other animals for their food. Plants also release oxygen into the atmosphere by the process of photosynthesis. The released oxygen is taken up by the animals during respiration. Thus, it is evident that plants and animals are dependent on the abiotic community for their survival. The biotic community and the abiotic community in the environment are in constant interaction with each other. Therefore, living organisms should be studied in relation to their environment. The study of living organisms in relation to their environment is known as **ecology**. The constant interaction between abiotic components and the biotic components in a habitat forms a system known as **ecosystem**. Sun is the primary source of energy in any ecosystem. Stability of an ecosystem depends on its number of producers and decomposers.

Components of an Ecosystem

The biotic components of ecosystem are:

- Producers
- Consumers
- Decomposers

> **Info Bytes!**
> Decomposer performs a worthy service as Earth's cleanup squad! Without them, dead insects, dead leaves, and dead animals would pile up everywhere!

All green plants trap solar energy and prepare food by utilizing the resources in atmosphere. They provide food for all the living organisms on earth. Hence, these plants are called producers. They constitute the first level of any ecosystem. These plants and plant products are consumed as food by the herbivorous animals. The energy stored in the plants is transferred to the herbivorous animals when consumed. These animals further fall prey to the next level of animals, i.e., carnivores. The energy stored in the body of herbivores is transferred to the carnivores. The herbivores and the carnivores are together called consumers. The herbivores are called primary consumers. The carnivores are called secondary consumers. This level is followed by tertiary consumers. They form the second, third and fourth levels of the ecosystem. In any ecosystem, there are certain carnivorous animals which cannot be eaten by any other organisms. These are considered as top carnivores.

Example: Lion is a top carnivore. But when the animals of any level die, some animals feed on the carcass of the animals, these animals are called scavengers.

Example: Vulture is a scavanger. When the plants and animals die, the microorganisms present in the soil decompose the dead matter. These microorganisms are called decomposers.

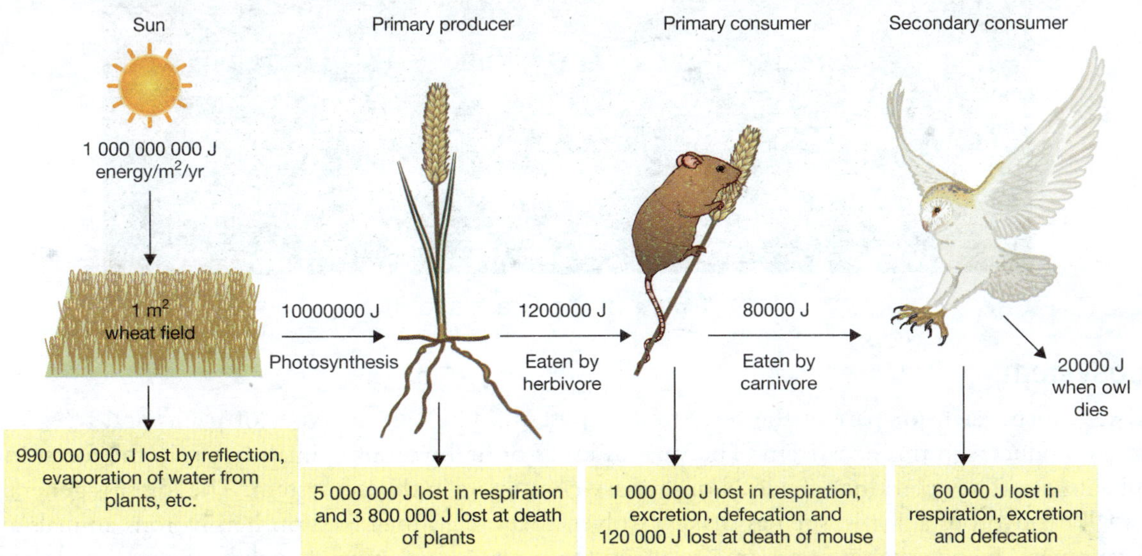

Figure 12.16 A typical food chain showing energy circulation

In this way, the energy is transferred from one level to the other level of organisms in an ecosystem. The nutrients required for the growth of plants are added to the soil by the decomposition of the dead matter of living organisms.

Types of Ecosystems

Depending on the type of habitat inhabited by different organisms, there are various kinds of ecosystems.

- Grass ecosystem
- Forest ecosystem
- Pond ecosystem
- Sea ecosystem or marine ecosystem

> **Info Bytes!**
> Coral reefs, although they cover just 0.1% of the ocean's surface, support about 25% of all marine species.

The abiotic components of any ecosystem remain the same but the biotic components vary from one type of ecosystem to the other.

Grassland Ecosystem

Grassland ecosystem is a type of terrestrial ecosystem. Grass is the main producer in this ecosystem. Grasslands may also be inhabited by some herbs and shrubs, so they collectively constitute to form producers. Grazing animals, such as rabbits, sheep and insects, like grasshoppers, termites, etc., depend on the producers for their food. These herbivorous animals act as primary consumers in this type of ecosystem. Animals like frogs and lizards which generally inhabit grasslands feed on the insects. These carnivores act as secondary consumers in this ecosystem. Animals such as snakes feed on the above carnivores and act as tertiary consumers. These can also be consumed by animals, such as hawks which form the top carnivores.

Figure 12.17 Grassland

Forest Ecosystem

Forest ecosystem forms a major part of the terrestrial ecosystem. The various types of plants and trees which inhabit the forest act as producers in this ecosystem. The various kinds of herbivorous animals living in the forest include deers, beetles, elephants, etc. They constitute the level of primary consumers in this ecosystem. The forest is generally inhabited by various small carnivorous animals, such as snakes, wolves, foxes, etc., they feed on herbivorous animals and form the secondary consumers. Forests shelter as a home to many top carnivorous animals, such as tigers, lions, bears, etc., they form the tertiary consumers in forest ecosystem.

Figure 12.18 Forest

Pond Ecosystem

Ponds are generally shallow water systems with still water. Various types of aquatic plants grow along the edges in the mud. Algae and aquatic plants act as producers in this ecosystem. Insects and small fish feed on these plants, these herbivores act as primary consumers. Animals, such as frogs and large fish feed on the above animals and act as secondary consumers. Birds, such as eagles and kingfishers feed on the frogs and snakes living in the pond, so they act as tertiary consumers. All the ecosystems possess microorganisms, such as fungi and bacteria. The organisms in any ecosystem sustain and die. These dead organisms are decomposed by these microorganisms and are converted to soil nutrients, so they are called decomposers. These nutrients are taken up by the plants for the preparation of food and growth. The cycle of this interaction between various biotic and abiotic components of ecosystem continues.

Figure 12.19 Pond

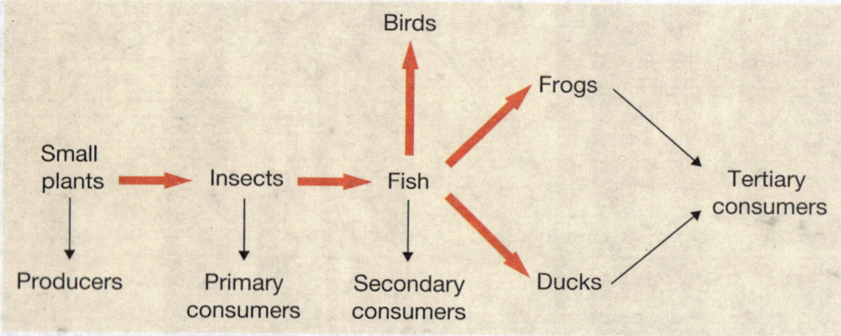

Figure 12.20 Pond ecosystem – schematic diagram

Sea or Marine Ecosystem

Sea or marine ecosystem is an aquatic ecosystem with high salt content. The sea ecosystem is similar to a pond ecosystem. The sea is a larger ecosystem when compared to pond, and hence has a larger variety of plants and animals which are independent of each other.

Figure 12.21 Underwater marine life

Food Chain and Food Web

In each ecosystem, there are different kinds of organisms at each level. Hence, an animal can get different alternative organisms for its nutrition. Similarly, different organisms may consume same type of organisms. Hence, the food chains are not simple and do not run in a single direction.

An ecosystem consists of a sequence of organisms linked together by means of food. The link between various organisms for the purpose of food is known as food chain. In general, a food chain with different levels or components can be represented in the following way.

Producers → Herbivores → Small carnivores or omnivores → Big carnivores

Example: Grass ecosystem can have a number of food chains.

Grass → Deer → Lion

Grass → Rabbit → Tiger

Grass → Insect → Frog → Snake → Eagle or Hawk

Grass → Grasshopper → Crow → Fox

Flower (Producer) → Caterpillar (Primary Consumer) → Frog (Secondary Consumer) → Snake (Tertiary Consumer) → Owl (Top Consumer)

Algae → Fish → Seal → Shark

Grass → Grasshopper → Frog → Snake → Hawk

Figure 12.22 Flowchart showing different types of food chains in a grass ecosystem

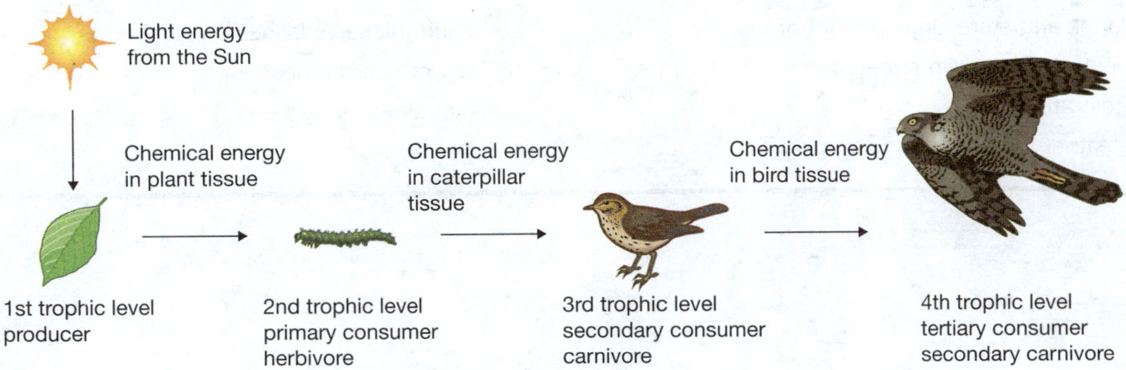

Figure 12.23 A typical grass-type food chain

The animals generally do not survive on a single type of organism. Every organism consumes more than one type of animal. Every animal is eaten by more than one type of animals.

Therefore, different food chains are interconnected to each other.

The interwoven pattern of several interconnected food chains is known as a food web.

Info Bytes!

A food chain is a linear sequence of organisms whereas food webs consist of many interconnected food chains.

Figure 12.24 Food web

Info Bytes!

Phytoplankton, microscopic plants in oceans, are often the starting point for aquatic food chains.

EXAMPLE 12.4 Justify that if there is no existence of plants, no animals can survive on earth.

SOLUTION

Sun is the ultimate source of energy and no animal can use the solar energy directly. Green plants are the only organisms which are capable of trapping the solar energy as they contain a green pigment called chlorophyll. Thus, the solar energy is converted into chemical energy and then stored in the food prepared by the plants. This energy gets transferred to other organisms through the food chain. Thus, if plants are non-existent, then animals have to starve for food. Plants release oxygen by the process of photosynthesis and this oxygen is essential for the respiration in animals.

EXAMPLE 12.5 Mention the features of camel which make it adapted to desert habitat.

SOLUTION

Characteristic features developed in camel due to adaptation are as follows:

- Ability to drink and store large amount of water
- Development of hump with stored fat
- Ability to tolerate heat
- Feet with leathery soles
- Long and thick eye lashes
- Ability to close the nostrils
- Summer sleep (long period)

POINTS TO REMEMBER

- Environment can be defined as a collection of all the living and non-living elements and their effects that influence all life forms.
- A cell is the basic structural and functional unit of life in all living organisms.

  Following are the specific features of living beings:
  - ✓ Living organisms are made up of cells. A cell is the basic structural and functional unit of life in all living organisms.
  - ✓ Living beings grow. The permanent and irreversible increase in the size of a plant body or an animal body is known as growth.
  - ✓ The period from birth to natural death of an organism is called 'lifespan'. The lifespan is different for different organisms.
  - ✓ Living things respond to stimuli with respect to changes in our surroundings.
  - ✓ Reproduction, either asexual or sexual, is the biological process by which living organisms reproduce an offspring similar to themselves.
  - ✓ The consumption of food by living organisms is known as nutrition. Nutrition is of two types: Autotrophic nutrition and Heterotrophic nutrition
  - ✓ The process in which energy is released by oxidation of food in living organisms is known as respiration.
  - ✓ The process of disposing all waste materials generated due to cellular activities that take place in all living organisms is known as excretion.
- The process in which unique features are acquired by the organisms which enable them to live comfortably in a particular habitat is called adaptation.
- The environment in which a particular organism lives comfortably is known as habitat.
- Living organisms sustain in two types of habitats - Terrestrial (Land habitat) and Aquatic (Water habitat).
- Animals are adapted differently based on their feeding habits. Plant eaters are called herbivores and flesh eaters are called carnivores.
- Based on the surrounding environmental conditions, living organisms adapt accordingly to adjust to those conditions such as grassland, mountains, desert region, Tundra region, aquatic region.
- The study of living organisms in relation to their environment is known as ecology.
- The constant interaction between abiotic components and the biotic components in a habitat forms a system known as ecosystem.
- The biotic components of ecosystem are: Producers, Consumers and Decomposers.
- Depending on the type of habitat inhabited by different organisms, there are various kinds of ecosystems namely grass ecosystem, forest ecosystem, pond ecosystem and sea ecosystem or marine ecosystem
- The link between various organisms for the purpose of food is known as food chain.
- The interwoven pattern of several interconnected food chains is known as a food web.

PRACTICE QUESTIONS CLASSROOM WING

Very Short Answer Type Questions

Direction for questions from 1 to 7.
Fill in the blanks.

1. ______ is the process in which energy is released in living organisms.
2. Reproduction is the process in which ______ are produced.
3. The process by which seeds develop into new plants is called ______.
4. Animals that live inside the body of a host and feed on its body fluids are called ______.
5. Animals that produce nitrogenous wastes usually excrete them from their bodies in the form of ______ and ______.
6. The environment in which a living organism lives comfortably is called ______.
7. The herbivores that become food for carnivores are also called ______.

Direction for question from 8 to 13.
Select the correct alternative from the given options.

8. Identify the multicellular organism among the following.
   (a) Hydra
   (b) *Amoeba*
   (c) *Paramecium*
   (d) Yeast
9. Excretion in plants takes place through
   (a) the urinary bladder.
   (b) excretion in the form of uric acid.
   (c) storage in special cells.
   (d) None of the above
10. Which of the following is not a feature associated with carnivores?
    (a) Sharp and pointed teeth
    (b) A curved and pointed beak
    (c) A long and sticky tongue
    (d) Straw-like mouth parts
11. Which of the following is a characteristic feature of omnivores?
    (a) Different types of teeth
    (b) Thick and long fur on the body
    (c) Breeding during summers
    (d) Ability to drink and store large amounts of water
12. Which of the following are the biotic components of the ecosystem?
    (a) Producers and Consumers
    (b) Only consumers
    (c) Only producers
    (d) Producers, consumers, and decomposers
13. Respiration can be defined as
    (a) a process by which energy is released by the oxidation of food.
    (b) a process by which energy is consumed by the oxidation of food.
    (c) a process by which energy is released by the reduction of food.
    (d) a process by which energy is consumed by the reduction of food.

Direction for question from 14 to 22.
Fill in the blanks.

14. ______ are known as decomposers.
15. The place where the biotic community lives is called ______.
16. The ability of an animal to have a concealed appearance so that it is not seen by its predator is called ______.
17. Thick and waxy coating on plant parts reduces the ______.
18. A frog has ______ feet.
19. ______ colour of predating animals is an adaptation in dry grasslands.
20. Chewing the cud is the characteristic feature of ______.
21. ______ beak is useful in eating variety of food items.
22. Butterflies have ______ like mouth parts.

Direction for question from 23 to 31.
Select the correct alternative from the given options.

23. Which of the following organisms is indirectly dependent on plants?
(a) Rabbit (b) Butterfly
(c) Cow (d) Bear

24. Which of the following pairs shows prey-predator relationship?
(a) Rabbit-Carrot (b) Butterfly-Flower
(c) Owl-snake (d) Hen-chick

25. Which among the following is an artificial ecosystem?
(a) Garden (b) Forest
(c) Pond (d) Lake

26. The series of organisms taking part at various biotic levels is called
(a) Food chain (b) Food web
(c) Ecosystem (d) Biome

27. Canopy type of arrangement of trees is found in which type of habitat?
(a) Desert (b) Tundra
(c) Rainforests (d) Grasslands

28. The presence of leaves reduced to needle-like structures is the characteristic feature of which habitat?
(a) Mountains (b) Deserts
(c) Tundras (d) Rainforests

29. What is the characteristic feature of preying animals in grasslands?
(a) Eyes in front side
(b) Eyes on the sides of head
(c) Sharp teeth
(d) Long claws

30. Identify the adaptation of plants in desert habitat.
(a) Waxy coating on leaves
(b) Cone shaped trees
(c) Sloping branches
(d) Thick and fleshy stems

31. Which animal has long ears?
(a) Polar bear (b) Kangaroo
(c) Camel (d) Deer

Direction for question from 32 to 34.
Pick the odd one out.

32. Wood, car, clock, chair.

33. Stomata, lungs, gills, spiracles.

34. Grasshopper, insect, butterfly, mosquito.

35. Match Column I with Column II.

Column I	Column II
Animal	**Young one**
(A) Deer	(a) Tadpole
(B) Goat	(b) Joey
(C) Frog	(c) Fawn
(D) Horse	(d) Calf
(E) Kangaroo	(e) Kid
(F) Giraffe	(f) Colt

Direction for question from 36 to 38.
Find the co-related terms.

36. Food chain : Producer :: Herbivore : ______

37. Vulture : ______ :: Cheetah : Tertiary consumer

38. Primary consumer : Rabbit :: ______ : Grass

39. Match Column I with Column II.

Column I	Column II
Organism	**Teeth**
(A) Horse	(a) Several small and sharp teeth
(B) Squirrel	(b) All variety of teeth
(C) Shark	(c) Wide and blunt teeth
(D) Cat	(d) A pair of sharp incisors

Short Answer Type Questions

Direction for question from 40 to 48.
Answer the following questions.

40. How does growth in plants differ from animals?

41. Justify whether if seed is living or non-living.

42. How do you categorize leather and bone as a living or non-living thing? Give appropriate reason in support of your answer.

43. Compare both plants and animals regarding their response to stimuli.

44. Distinguish between autotrophic and heterotrophic mode of nutrition.

45. Why do animals show locomotion?

46. Humans come under omnivores. Give reason.

47. Explain the method of nutrition in tapeworm.

48. What is the role of scavengers in cleaning environment?

Direction for question from 49 to 52.
Give scientific reasons.

49. Give reason why plants are called autotrophs.

50. Give reason why unicellular organisms are also known as microorganisms.

51. Give reason why leeches are considered as parasites.

52. State the reason why rabbit is considered as a herbivore and tiger as a carnivore.

Direction for question from 53 to 58.
Answer the following.

53. How do plants in a pond get carbon dioxide for photosynthesis? Explain.

54. Name the ecological adaptations shown by desert plants (xerophytes).

55.

Answer the following questions based on the above figure.

(a) Identify the animal and its habitat.

(b) Mention the characteristic features for adaptation in the habitat.

(c) Mention any other animal which lives in the same habitat.

(d) The trees in these habitats are usually cone shaped. Give reason.

56.

A B

Answer the following questions based on the above figure.

(a) Identify the plant B and predict the habitat.

(b) What does the activity shown in the above diagram (refer Figure A) indicate?

(c) List out the adaptations of the plant B for the habitat.

57. Define the terms habitat and adaptation.

58. Define the following terms.

(a) Ecosystem

(b) Food chain

(c) Food web

(d) Ecology

Direction for question from 59 to 60.
Give scientific reasons.

59. Both the deer and the lion depend on plants for food. Give reason.

60. Both cat and tiger are carnivores. What is the difference between the modes of feeding?

Essay Type Questions

61. Explain aquarium as an ecosystem.

62. Mention the features of fish for adaptation to aquatic ecosystem.

PRACTICE QUESTIONS COMPETITION WING

Level 1: Apply Your Concepts

Direction for question from 1 to 5.
Fill in the blanks.

1. Plants synthesize food by the process of _______.
2. A chick _______ from the egg.
3. All living things are made up of _______.
4. The movement of animals from one place to another is known as _______.
5. Plants manufacture food in the form of _______.

Direction for question from 6 to 12.
State whether true or false. Rewrite the false statements.

6. Plants grown in shade tend to bend away from sunlight.
7. Plants stop growing after a certain period of time.
8. Animals show quick response to stimulus.
9. Plants require oxygen for photosynthesis.
10. Plants show uniform growth.
11. Human is a herbivore.
12. Why do certain animals have a winter sleep?

Level 2: Review Your Concepts

13. 

Answer the following questions based on the given figure.

(a) What does the above diagram indicate?
(b) Mention the terms associated with the change.
(c) Define the terms mentioned in (b)
(d) Explain the phenomenon in brief.

14. Construct a food chain with five trophic levels
15. Outline the steps to construct an artificial aquatic ecosystem in your house.
16. What are top carnivores and how are they different from other carnivores in the ecosystem?
17. Cuscuta plant is a parasite. Justify this statement.
18. Compare the mode of reproduction in hen and cow.

Level 3: Assess Your Concepts

19. Tiger feeds on other animals. Does it mean that plants are not needed for the survival of tigers?
20. From the below given figure identify X and Y in the given food chain.

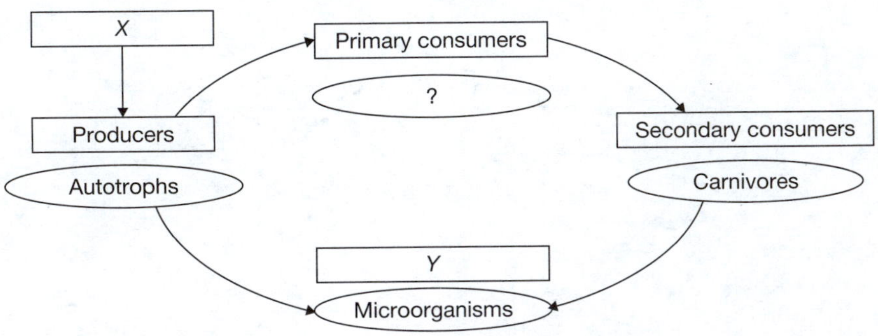

21. Answer the following questions:
    (a) Discuss any two adaptation of cactus.
    (b) Leeches we considered as parasite comment.

22. Answer the following.
    (a) Explain the phenomenon seen in 'touch me not plant'.
    (b) Discuss any two adaptation of animals in tundra region.

23. Can you imagine the world without bacteria?

AT

ANSWER KEYS

Crossword

Across

4. Arboreal 6. Respiration 7. Ecology 8. Marine

Down

1. Grassland 2. Reproduction 3. *Mimosa* 4. Abiotic 5. Autotrophic

Classroom Wing

Very Short Answer Type Questions

1. Respiration 2. Offspring 3. Germination 4. Parasites 5. Urine and sweat
6. Habitat 7. Preying animals/prey 8. (a) 9. (c) 10. (d)
11. (a) 12. (d) 13. (a) 14. Microorganisms
15. Habitat 16. Camouflage 17. Transpiration 18. Webbed
19. Light brown 20. Cattle (grazing animals) 21. Sharp and pointed
22. Straw 23. (d) 24. (c) 25. (a) 26. (a)
27. (c) 28. (a) 29. (b) 30. (d) 31. (d)
32. Wood 33. Stomata 34. Mosquito
35. (A) → (c), (B) → (e), (C) → (a), (D) → (f), (E) → (b), (F) → (d) 36. Ecosystem
37. Scavenger 38. Producer 39. (A) → (c), (B) → (d), (C) → (a), (D) → (b)

Competition Wing

Level 1: Apply Your Concepts

1. Photosynthesis 2. Hatches 3. Cells 4. Locomotion 5. Starch 6. False
7. False 8. True 9. False 10. False 11. False
12. Animals undergo hibernation to escape from extreme cold climatic conditions.

Hints and Explanations

CLASSROOM WING

Very Short Answer Type Questions

8. Hydra is the multicellular organism.

Hence, the correct option is (a).

14. Microorganisms are known as decomposers.

15. The place where the biotic community lives is called its habitat.

16. The ability of an animal to have a concealed appearance so that it is not seen by its predator is called camouflage.

17. Thick and waxy coating on plant parts reduces the transpiration.

18. A frog has webbed feet.

19. Light brown colour of predating animals is an adaptation in dry grasslands.

20. Chewing the cud is the characteristic feature of cattle (grazing animals).

21. Sharp and pointed beak is useful in eating variety of food items.

22. Butterflies have straw-like mouth parts.

23. Bear is a carnivore and depends on other animals for food. But it indirectly depends on plants as the animals which serve as food for it may be herbivorous as they eat only grass.

Hence, the correct option is (d).

24. Prey–predator relationship is seen in owl–snake

Hence, the correct option is (c).

25. Garden is an example of artificial ecosystem.

Hence, the correct option is (a).

26. The series of organisms taking part at various biotic levels is called food chain.

Hence, the correct option is (a).

27. Canopy type of arrangement of trees is found in rainforests.

Hence, the correct option is (c).

28. The presence of leaves reduced to needle-like structures is the characteristic feature of mountain habitat.

Hence, the correct option is (a).

29. Eyes on the sides of head is the characteristic feature of preying animals in grasslands.

Hence, the correct option is (b).

30. Thick and fleshy stems is the adaptation of plants in desert habitat.

Hence, the correct option is (d).

31. Deer has long ears.

Hence, the correct option is (d).

32. Wood is part of living thing and since it is cut off from the tree it is a dead matter.

33. Stomata help in the respiration of plants.

34. Mosquito feeds on blood, and hence, it is not a herbivore.

35. Match Column I with Column II.

Column I	Column II
Animal	**Young one**
(A) Deer	(c) Fawn
(B) Goat	(e) Kid
(C) Frog	(a) Tadpole
(D) Horse	(f) Colt
(E) Kangaroo	(b) Joey
(F) Giraffe	(d) Calf

36. Producer is a part of food chain while herbivore is part of ecosystem.

37. Vulture is a scavenger.

38. Grass is a producer in the ecosystem.

39. The correct match is:

Column I	Column II
Organism	**Teeth**
(A) Horse	(c) Wide and blunt teeth
(B) Squirrel	(d) A pair of sharp incisors
(C) Shark	(a) Several small and sharp teeth
(D) Cat	(b) All variety of teeth

Short Answer Type Questions

40. The growth in plants is continuous till they die. In animals, the growth continues only up to a certain age. In plants, growth is non-uniform and is mostly confined to root tips and shoot tips apart from lateral growth. But in animals, the growth is more or less uniform.

41. Seed is also a living entity as it is made up of living cells. Therefore, it is able to give rise to a baby plant after germination.

42. Biologically, the things can be classified into three categories. They are living, non-living and dead. Leather and bone are parts of living organisms. But once they are taken out, they lose life. Hence, they are considered to be dead things.

43. Both plants and animals respond to external stimuli. Animals show quick response to stimuli while plants show slow response to stimuli. Plants show response only to certain stimuli, generally light and touch. Animals show response to many stimuli, such as light, heat, pressure, smell, etc.

44. Auto means self and trophic means food. The mode of nutrition in which the organisms are capable of making their own food is called autotrophic mode of nutrition. Hetero means different; the organisms which cannot make their own food and depend on other organisms for food are said to show heterotrophic mode of nutrition.

45. Animals show movement for the following purposes.
   (a) Search for food
   (b) Search for shelter
   (c) Protection from enemies

46. Human beings consume both plant products and animal products as food. Humans eat various plants parts as vegetables, fruits, seeds and leaves. At the same time, they consume animal products, such as milk, eggs, meat, etc. The word 'Omni' means all. Since humans eat both plants and animals, they are said to be omnivores.

47. Tapeworm is a parasite which lives in the intestine of human. It feeds on the food consumed and digested by the humans. The mode of nutrition is said to be parasitic.

48. Animals which feed on dead animals are known as scavengers.
   Dead bodies of various organisms in the environment pollute the surroundings.
   Scavengers feed on these dead bodies thereby helping in keeping the surroundings clean.

49. Green plants prepare their own food from carbon dioxide and water in the presence of sunlight. Since they are capable of making their own food, they are known as autotrophs.

50. Unicellular organisms are small and tiny and cannot be seen with naked eyes. As they can be seen through a microscope, they are also called microorganisms.

51. Leeches depend upon the host tissue for their food. They are blood sucking parasites.

52. Rabbit is considered as herbivore because it eats only plants.
   Tiger is considered as carnivore because it feeds only on flesh.

53. Carbon dioxide gas is present in the dissolved form in the pond water. The plants living in pond utilize this carbon dioxide for photosynthesis.

54. **Adaptations in desert plants (Xerophytes)**
   - Long roots
   - Fleshy stems to store food and water
   - Leaves reduced to spines
   - Stem with chlorophyll
   - Less number of stomata

   Example: Cactus, *Acacia*

55. (a) The given animal is penguin and its habitat is in polar regions.
   (b) Features for adaptation are:
      (i) Presence of feathers and thick layer of fat under the skin called blubber to protect it from cold.

(ii) Generally penguins stay in groups to remain warm.

(c) Polar bear and yak are other animals which live in this habitat.

(d) The trees of this habitat are usually cone-shaped because it prevents snow gets deposited on their leaves.

56. (a) The plant in pot B is cactus. It lives in desert habitat.

(b) The activity indicates that in cactus, the transpiration is reduced to a large extent when compared to normal plant.

(c) Adaptations:

(i) Long roots to go deep into the water table.

(ii) Leaves reduced to spines to reduce loss of water by transpiration.

(iii) Thick and fleshy stem which is green in colour to facilitate photosynthesis.

(iv) Waxy coating on stem to prevent transpiration.

57. The environment in which a particular organism lives comfortably is called habitat. The features and habits that the organisms acquire which enable them to live comfortably in a particular habitat is called adaptation.

58. (a) **Ecosystem:** A system formed by the interaction of biotic components with the abiotic components is called ecosystem.

(b) **Food chain:** A series of organisms linked to each other through food is known as food chain.

(c) **Food web:** The interwoven pattern of several interconnected food chains is called food web.

(d) **Ecology:** The study of living organism in relation to their environment is called ecology.

59. Deer is a herbivore. It directly depends on the plants for food.

Lion is a carnivore. It does not directly depend on plants for food.

Lions can survive only when it can find herbivores, such as deer for food.

Therefore, lion indirectly depends on plants for food.

60. The cat is a first stage carnivore as it feeds on herbivores and small animals. Tiger is a second stage carnivore as it feeds on first carnivores. Tiger cannot be eaten by any other animal, and hence, it is considered as the top carnivore.

Essay Type Questions

61. The electric bulb in an aquarium provides light energy for the plants to produce food. The carbon dioxide required for photosynthesis is provided by fishes during respiration. The oxygen released by the plants is utilized by the fishes for respiration. The excretory matter of fishes provides nutrition for the plants. Sand provides habitat for plants. The bacteria present in the sand act as decomposers to break down the dead remains if any. Thus, an aquarium is like a mini pond ecosystem.

62. Adaptations of fish:

(i) Streamlined body for swimming.

(ii) Skin covered with water proof scales to prevent decay.

(iii) Presence of gills to facilitate breathing in water.

(iv) Presence of fins for swimming.

COMPETITION WING

Level 1: Apply Your Concepts

6. False: Plants grown in shade tend to bend towards the sunlight.
7. False: Animals stop growing after a certain period of time.
8. True
9. False: Plants require carbon dioxide for photosynthesis.
10. False: Plants do not show uniform growth.
11. False: Human is an omnivore.
12. Animals undergo hibernation to escape from extreme cold climatic conditions.

Level 2: Review Your Concepts

13. (a) The given diagram indicates the drooping of leaves of 'Touch me not plant' or sensitive plant when touched.
    (b) Touch is the stimulus. The drooping of leaves is the response of the plant.
    (c) Nastic movement occurs in response to a stimulus. It is independent of its direction.
    (d) On touching the leaves of the given plant, they droop down. After few minutes, the wilted leaves recover and stand erect.
14. Flower (Producer) 1 → Caterpiller (Consumer) 2 → Frog (Consumer) 3 → Snake (Consumer) 4 → Owl (Consumer) 5
15. Take a clear glass trough, add some rocks, pebbles, a layer of soil and some aquatic plants. Add water, attach a filter to replenish the oxygen in the water. Now introduce fishes and an artificial ecosystem is ready.
16. In any ecosystem, there are certain carnivorous animals that cannot be eaten by any other carnivore. Thus, they are called top carnivores. For example, a lion and an owl are both carnivores but unlike a lion, an owl can be consumed by other animals such as snakes; thus, top carnivores are different from other carnivores.
17. A Cuscuta plant usually grows on a host plant. It remains attached to the plant and obtains nutrition from that plant, always at the cost of the growth of the host plant. Thus, the Cuscuta is considered a parasite, albeit an ectoparasite which grows outside the body of the host plant.
18. Hen lays eggs. These eggs when hatched produce young ones that is chicken. Cows give birth to young ones directly.

Level 3: Assess Your Concepts

19. Tiger is a carnivore, and hence, it does not directly depend on plants for food. However, tiger feeds on other herbivores, such as deer. The herbivores in turn depend on plants for their food. That means, the tiger, though is a carnivore, indirectly depends on plants for its food. That means, herbivore animals survive only if plants are there in the ecosystem.
20. X is identified as sunlight.
    Y is identified as decomposers.

21 (a) • Cactus have thick and fleshy stem that facilitate photosynthesis.
   • Waxy coating on stem to prevent transpiration.
   (b) Leeches are blood- sucking parasite and only depends on host tissue, that is why they are considered as parasite.

22 (a) When we touch the leaves of 'Touch me not plant' they droop down and within few minutes, they witted leave recover and stand erect.
   (b) • Animal have thick layer of fat.
   • Animal stays together in group.

23. No. Bacteria are an essential part of the environment as they act as decomposers for the dead plants and animals. As all living beings have a fixed lifespan, the plants and animals die after a certain age. If bacteria are not there in the ecosystem, the dead organisms would be piled up in the environment and the habitats will not be liveable places. Moreover, the dead matter undergoes decay thereby adding minerals to the soil. Thus, the soil becomes suitable for growth of plants. If bacteria are not there, the soil will become unsuitable for the growth of plants. As the survival of all living organisms depends on plants, the world cannot exist without bacteria.

CHAPTER 13

Plants—Nature's Wonderful Food Factories

Remember

Before beginning this chapter, you should be able to:

- Understand the importance of plants in environment
- Identify the parts of a plant

Key Ideas

After completing this chapter, you should be able to:

- Understand the basic structure of plants
- Describe the various parts of plants and their functions
- Understand how plants reproduce and new plants grow

Scientific Crypt

A Tribute to Theophrastus (371–287 BCE)

Theophrastus (b. 371-287 BCE) is known as the "Father of Botany." His life spanned a period when scientific understanding of the natural world was still in its infancy. His work, particularly his seminal text "Enquiry into Plants," was, however, nothing short of revolutionary. Theophrastus meticulously documented his observations of various plants in this comprehensive treatise, classifying them based on their characteristics and growth habits. His keen eye for detail led him to recognise the critical role of leaves in photosynthesis, a fundamental concept that is still central to botany today.

Theophrastus' dedication to scientific inquiry paved the way for the development of botany. His work laid the groundwork for future botanists, paving the way for modern understanding of plant biology. While awards and accolades were not part of Theophrastus' world in ancient Greece, his enduring legacy speaks volumes. His contributions continue to enrich education and inspire aspiring botanists all over the world.

FUN TIME

CROSSWORD

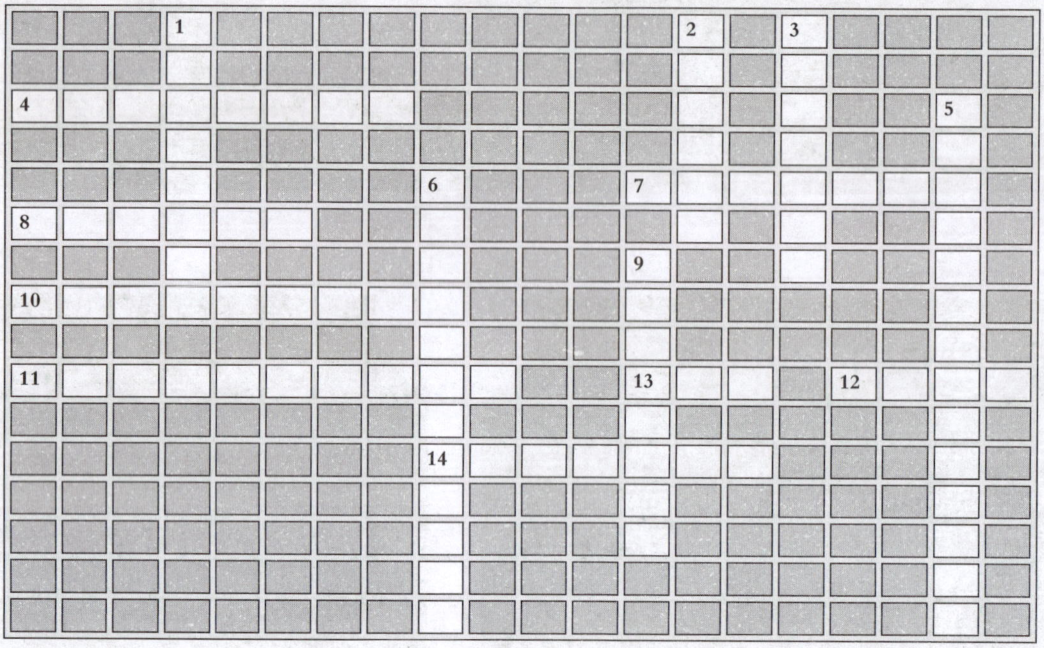

Across

4. Modified stems that coil around a hard object
7. Function of spiny leaves in prickly poppy
8. Fusion of male and female gamete results in its formation
10. Arrangement of leaves where successive leaves are present in opposite sides and only one leaf is present at each node
11. Veins and veinlets in the lamina of the leaf are divided to form a network
12. Aerial roots that grow from the branches
13. _____ contain seed and has thick walls
14. _____ of plant can be rough, hairy, or velvety etc.

Down

1. Adventitious modified roots which store food in turmeric
2. Sub aerial stem modification seen in water hyacinth which arises from the axil of leaf and has thick internodes
3. Type of germination in which hypocotyl grows rapidly and cotyledon is pulled above the ground
5. Breathing roots found in mangroves
6. Cluster of roots having same thickness and size and arises from the base of the stem
9. Leaf which consists of small segments of leaflets

INTRODUCTION

Plants are the oldest group of living organisms on earth. They first appeared around 470 million years ago. Plants form the first level of any ecosystem in the environment. Hence, they are considered the most important organisms for the survival of life on earth. Plants play a prominent role in the ecosystem, adding to this, the various parts of the plants provide useful products, such as food materials, medicines, fuel, etc. This makes the study of plants an essential part of Science. The study of plants is known as Botany. Theophrastus (who was a student of Aristotle) is known as the Father of Botany.

On the basis of presence or absence of flowers, plants are classified into two types:

1. Flowering plants – which bear flowers.

   Examples: Rose plant, jasmine plant, etc.

2. Non-flowering plants—which do not bear flowers.

   Examples: Moss, pines, etc.

All the flowering plants possess well-defined root system and shoot system.

> **Info Bytes!**
> The cellular structure of plants has evolved over 500 million years, giving rise to a myriad of species, each tailored to its environment.

Structure of a Plant

Though found in different habitats, all plants have a basic structure. A typical plant consists of an underground root system and above the ground shoot system.

Plant

Root system
The underground part of the plant

- **Characteristics**
  - Not green in colour.
  - Grows downward into the soil.
  - Does not bear leaves, flowers, fruits, etc.
  - Primary root with side branches.
  - Bears fine hair-like particles called root hair.
- **Functions**
  - Fixes the plant in the soil.
  - Absorbs water and minerals for the plant.
  - Binds the soil particles together.

Shoot system
The part of the plant which grows above the soil

- **Characteristics**
  - Usually green in colour in case of young plants.
  - Bears leaves, flowers and fruits.
- **Functions**
  - Preparation of food.
  - Transportation of water and food.
  - Reproduction.

Figure 13.1 Division of plant structure into root and shoot systems

Root System

The root system constitutes the underground part of the plant. Roots grow downwards into the soil and do not bear leaves, flowers, etc. Roots develop from the radicle of the seed. Roots help in the fixation of a plant in the soil. The main function of the root system is to absorb water and minerals from the soil. Roots bind the soil particles together. The tip of each branch of the root has a cap-like structure known as root cap. It protects the tip of a growing root. The thin hair-like structures present on the surface of the roots are called root hair. Root hair help in the absorption of water and minerals from the soil.

Based on the structure and origin, root system is classified into two types. They are:

1. Tap root system
2. Fibrous root system

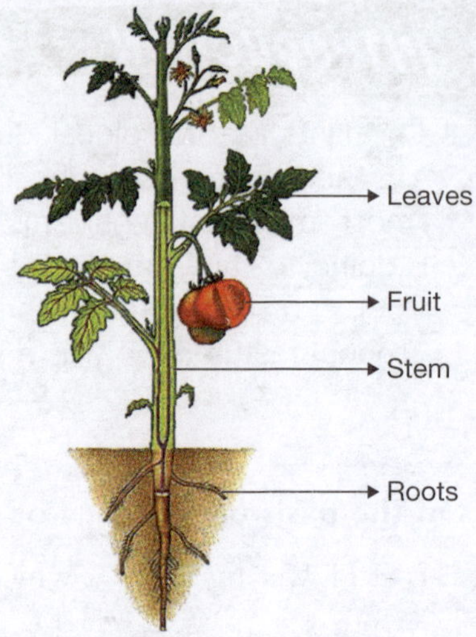

Figure 13.2 A typical plant showing all parts

Root system

Tap root system (True root system)

- Thick main root—Primary root
- Side branches—Secondary roots with root hair.
- Origin—Radicle of the germinating seed.

Tap roots make plants hard to pull out of the ground.
Examples: Pea, grams.

Fibrous root system (Adventitious root system)

- Cluster of roots of same thickness and size.
- Arise from the base of the stem.
- Origin—Stem or leaves

Plants having fibrous roots are easily pulled out from the ground.
Examples: Maize, wheat.

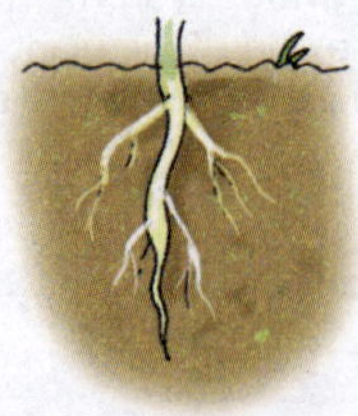

Tap root

Fibrous root

Figure 13.3 The two types of root system

Root Modifications

Apart from the main function, i.e., to absorb water and minerals from the soil, the root system in certain plants undergoes changes in the structure to perform different kind of functions, these are known as root modifications.

The different kinds of functions supported by modified roots are:

- Storage of food
- Giving additional support to the plants
- Performing some special functions

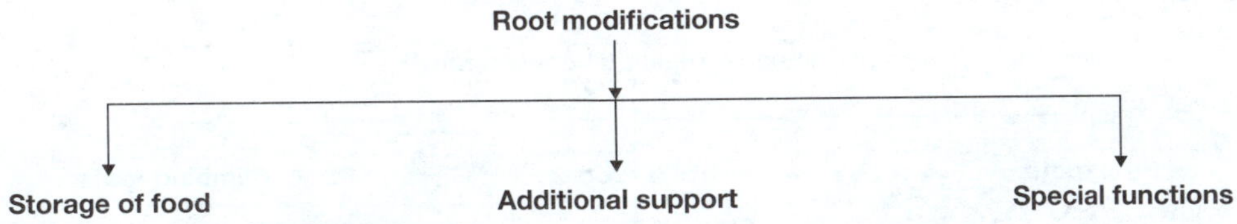

Figure 13.4 Different types of root modifications

Storage of Food

Roots in certain plants become swollen and fleshy due to the accumulation of stored food. Both primary and adventitious roots undergo these modifications. During the process of food storage, they attain different shapes in different plants.

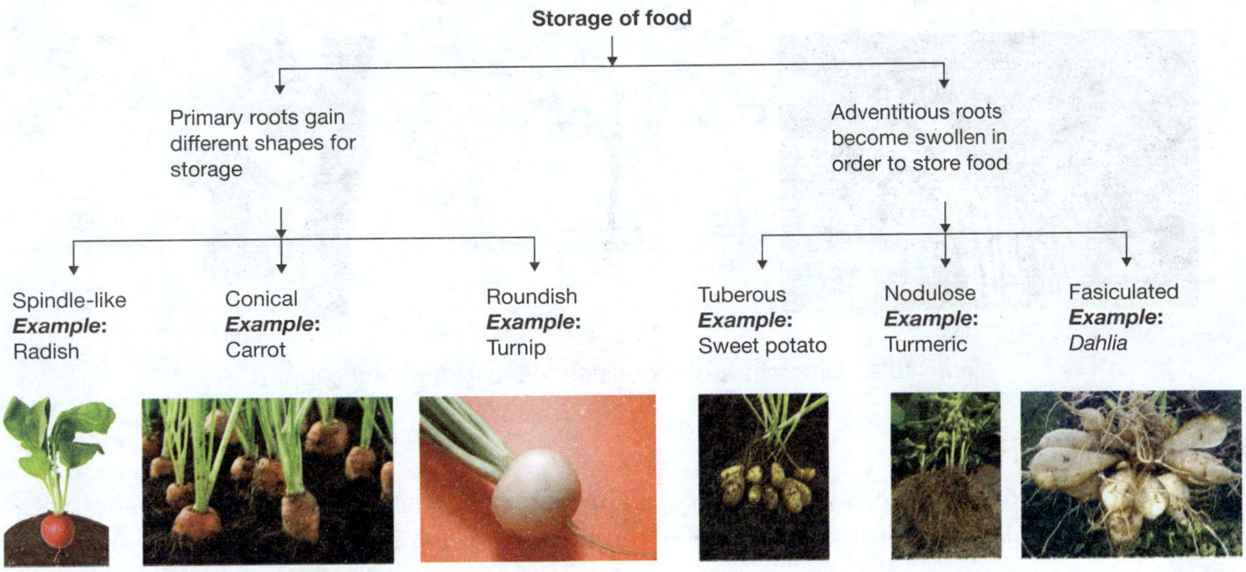

Figure 13.5 Different root modifications for storage of food

Additional Support

Generally, roots provide support to the plants. But in case of certain plants, this support is not sufficient. In such cases, some roots get modified into various forms and provide additional support to the plant.

There are three different forms of roots which provide additional support. They are:

- Prop roots
- Stilt roots
- Climbing roots

Prop roots are aerial roots which grow from the branches. They grow downwards and penetrate into the soil to give support to the plant. These roots are developed on big trees which need additional support to withstand their own weight.

Examples: Banyan tree, figs, etc.

Stilt roots grow from lower nodes. They grow obliquely downwards into the soil. These roots develop in plants with weak stems.

Examples: Sugarcane, maize, etc.

Climbing roots are cluster of aerial roots which develop from nodes or internodes. They cling or twine around the availability of support and help the plant climb upwards. Climbing roots are often seen in creepers.

Examples: Money plant, betel plant, etc.

Types of Roots
(which provides additional support)

Prop roots
- Aerial roots growing vertically downward from the horizontal branches.
- They penetrate into the soil and give support.

Examples: Banyan tree, figs.

Stilt roots
- Adventitious roots grow from lower nodes.
- Grow obliquely downwards into soil.
- Present in plants with weak stem.

Examples: Sugarcane, maize

Climbing roots
- Cluster of aerial roots develop from nodes or internodes.
- Cling or twine around the support and helps the plant climb upwards.

Examples: Money plant, betel plant.

Figure 13.6 Different root modifications for additional support

Special Functions of Roots

Roots in some plants are modified to perform some special functions. This type of modification depends on the habitat in which the plants live or the mode of absorption of nutrients from soil or from the atmosphere.

The following are the different root modifications based on the special functions:

- Nodular roots
- Parasitic roots
- Epiphytic roots
- Breathing roots

Nodular roots bear small swellings called nodules on the roots. The bacteria, *Rhizobium*, present in these nodules convert the atmospheric nitrogen into ammonia which help increase the fertility of soil. Hence, these roots are also called nitrogen-fixing roots. It is an efficient way to supplement the soil and improve the nitrogen content of soil.

Examples: Gram, peas, soybean, etc.

Parasitic roots are adventitious roots called haustoria (singular: haustorium) which protrude into the host plant for the absorption of nutrients. They are present in parasitic plants which do not prepare their own food but depend on other plants for their food.

Examples: *Cuscuta, Cassytha, etc.*

Breathing roots are the roots which rise above the soil like cones which bear minute pores called pneumatophores. Such roots absorb atmospheric air for respiration. These modifications are seen in plants which grow in marshy places.

Examples: White mangrove, *Avicennia.*

Epiphytic roots are hanging aerial roots. They absorb moisture from the air through the spongy tissue present on their tips. These roots grow aerially on the host plant.

Examples: Orchids, mosses.

Special functions

Nodular roots

- Bear small swellings called nodules on the roots.
- Nitrogen-fixing roots.
  Examples: Grams, peas.

Parasitic roots

- Adventitious roots called haustoria protrude into the host plant for absorption of nutrients.
- Found in parasitic plants.
  Examples: *Cuscuta, Cassytha.*

Epiphytic roots

- Hanging aerial roots.
- Grow aerially on the host plant.
  Examples: Orchids, mosses.

Breathing roots

- Roots come above the soil like cones.
- Minute pores called pneumatophores are present on the roots.
- Roots absorb atmospheric air for respiration.
- Found in plants which grow in marshy places.
  Examples: White mangrove, *Avicennia*.

Figure 13.7 Different root modifications for special functions

Figure 13.8 Different roots performing special functions

EXAMPLE 13.1

Give reason why soil erosion can be prevented by growing grass in garden.

SOLUTION

Roots have a strong erosion-reducing effect. Roots help in holding the soil particles together. Blowing away or washing away of the soil particles is prevented by growing grass in garden. Hence, soil erosion can be prevented.

Shoot System

The shoot system is the portion of the plant which grows above the soil, i.e., it is the aerial part of the plant. Shoot develops from the plumule of the seed. The stem, leaves, flowers, buds, branches and fruits are parts of the shoot system.

Shoot system

- Stem
- Leaves
- Flowers
- Fruits

Figure 13.9 Parts of a shoot system

Stem

Stem is the main and the strongest part of the shoot system. The stem is protected by the bark in older plants. The structure of stem is such that it supports all parts of the shoot system. The stem grows towards the source of the light. The stem conducts water and minerals from the soil to the leaves. Plants can be categorized into three types based on the structure of stem.

Plants

Herbs

- Non-woody plants
- Green and tender stems
- Few branches
- Usually short

Examples: Tulsi, lettuce.

Shrubs

- Taller than a herb
- Branching of stem at the base
- Stems thick and not hard

Examples: Rose, lemon.

Trees

- Woody plants
- Many branches on a single stem
- Taller than shrubs
- Height and width depends on age

Examples: Mango, neem.

Figure 13.10 Types of plant based on stem structure

In all categories of plants, the stem possesses almost the same features or characteristics in structure and performs the same functions. Given below is a flowchart with important structural features and functions of stem.

Stem

Structural features

- The strongest part of a plant which bears nodes, internodes and vegetative buds.
- Nodes—Area on the stem where leaves and branches originate.
- Internode—The part of stem between two nodes.
- Apical bud—The undeveloped shoot present at the tip of the stem.
- Axillary bud—The bud present at the axil of leaf.

Functions

- Acts as a link between roots and leaves.
- Facilitates exposure of leaves to sunlight.
- Manufacture food in young plants.
- Transport of water and minerals from roots to leaves.
- Transport of food from leaves to other parts of the plant.

Figure 13.11 Structural features and functions of stem

Info Bytes!

Both the bark and leaf of cinnamon plant are used as edible spices!

Modifications of Stem for Various Function

The stem of a plant performs different functions in addition to support and transport of water and minerals. Three different types of modifications of stem are discussed below.

Functions of Stem

- Underground stem modifications for storage of food
- Subaerial stem modifications for giving additional support
- Aerial stem modifications to serve other functions

Figure 13.12 Stem modifications for different functions

Underground Stem Modifications

In certain plants, stems grow under the soil-like roots. These are useful for the storage of food and are called underground stem modifications.

Types of Underground Stems

Tuber
- Lower branches of stem grow below the ground and swell at the tips forming **tubers**.
- Number of buds are present which are called eyes.
- Eye can produce a new shoot.

Example: Potato

Rhizome
- These are irregular in shape.
- Creep horizontally below the soil.
- Scaly leaves, buds, nodes, internodes.

Examples: Ginger, banana, fern.

Bulb
- Condensed disc-shaped stem with a terminal bud.
- Overlapped by scaly leaves.
- Thick and fleshy inner leaves store food.

Examples: Onion, garlic.

Corm
- Round condensed stem flattened from top to bottom.
- Covered with thin scaly leaves.

Examples: *Gladiolus*, *Amorphophallus*.

Examples of various types of underground stem modifications for storage of food are potato, ginger, onion, etc.

Dark, round, outgrowths as eyes

Figure 13.13 Types of underground stem modifications

Info Bytes!

The cactus has modified its stems to store water and its leaves into spikes to reduce water loss and protect against herbivores.

Subaerial Stem Modification

The stems present partly above the ground and partly below the ground are called subaerial stems. These are generally found in weak stemmed plants and they provide additional support to plants. The different types of subaerial modification are:

1. Runner
2. Stolon
3. Offset

Subaerial stem modifications

Runner
- Stem is soft, thin with slender branch.
- Creeps on the ground.

Examples: Doob grass, wood sorrels.

Stolon
- Stems grow upwards above the ground upto some extent and then bends toward the ground.

Examples: Mint, wild strawberry.

Offset
- Stem arises from the axil of leaf.
- Bears thick internodes.
- These are also called runners.

Examples: Water lettuce, water hyacinth.

Figure 13.14 Types of subaerial stem modifications

Aerial Stem Modifications

The stems which remain above the ground to perform different functions are called aerial stems and such modifications are called aerial stem modifications. These modifications take place to such an extent that they are difficult to be recognized as stems.

The four kinds of aerial stem modification are:

1. **Thorns:** Axillary buds are modified into thorns. They protect the plants from grazing animals.
2. **Tendrils:** The stem is modified into thin thread-like leafless branches called tendrils. They coil around a hard object and help the plant in climbing up.
3. **Twiners:** The aerial stem are thin thread-like structures called twiners which intertwine around their own stems. They help the plant to climb up easily.
4. **Phylloclades:** The aerial stems are modified into thick flat and green leaf-like structure called phylloclades. They perform the function of photosynthesis.

Types of Aerial stem modifications

Thorns (Protection)
- Buds modified into hard, pointed small structures called thorns.
- Protection from grazing animals.

Examples: Rose, lemon, *Duranta*.

Tendrils (Support)
- Thin thread-like leafless branches called tendrils.
- Coil around a hard object.
- Helps the plant in climbing up.

Example: Grapevine

Twiner (Climbing)
- Stems intertwine around their own stems.
- Helps the plant to climb up easily.

Example: Morning glory

Phylloclades (Photosynthesis)
- Thick, flat and green stem with nodes and internodes.
- Helps in preparation and storage of food.
- Xerophytic plants

Examples: *Cactus, Ruscus*

Figure 13.15 Types of aerial stem modifications

Leaf

Leaves are the most vital part of any plant as they prepare food by the process of photosynthesis. In most of the plants, the leaves are green in colour due to the presence of the substance called chlorophyll. The leaves of different plant varieties are in different shapes, sizes and textures. Generally, the plant can be recognized based on their characteristic appearance.

Typically, the leaf is a thin, flattened organ that arises at the node of the stem. The leaf may be attached to the stem by means of a petiole. In some plants, the leaves are directly attached to the stem.

Leaf

Structural features

- Flat, green, broad part of the shoot located on the node of the stem.
- Bud in the axil of leaf.
- No continuous growth.
- Growth of leaf stops after some age for the plant.
- Leaf base is called petiole.
- The basal part of a leaf is called stalk.
- Stalk attaches leaf to stem at node.
- The green, flat, broader part of leaf is called leaf blade or lamina.
- Midrib is the extension of petiole into leaf.
- Veins, veinlets arise from midrib.

Functions

- **Photosynthesis**—Process of food preparation with the help of carbon dioxide and water, which also releases oxygen into the air.
- **Transpiration**—Loss of excess water absorbed by the roots takes place through minute pores called stomata by the process of transpiration. Water is lost in the form of vapours.

Figure 13.16 Structural features and functions of a leaf

Types of Leaves

The leaves can be broadly categorized as simple leaves and compound leaves on the basis of their structure.

Types of leaves

Simple leaf

- Lamina as a single piece.
- Margin incisions do not reach up to the midrib or petiole.

Examples: Mango, peepal, banyan, prickly poppy.

Compound leaf

- Margin incisions reaching the midrib or petiole.
- Leaf as a group of small segments called leaflets.

Examples: Rose, cotton.

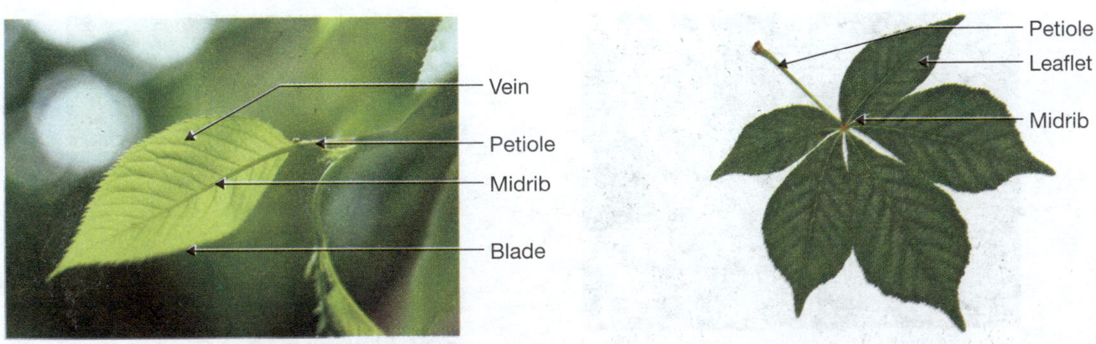

Figure 13.17 Types of leaves on the basis of structure

Arrangement of Leaves

There are three different ways in which the leaves can be arranged on the axis or stem.

Arrangement of leaves

- **Alternate**
  - One leaf from each node.
  - Successive leaves in opposite directions.

  Examples: Mint, peepal, china rose.
- **Opposite**
  - Two leaves from each node.
  - Two leaves in opposite directions.

  Examples: Lemon, mango.
- **Whorled**
  - More than two leaves from each node.

  Examples: *Nerium oleander, Japanese clethra.*

Figure 13.18 Types of leaves on the basis of arrangement

Venation

The pattern of arrangement of veins on the leaf blade or lamina is called venation.

There are two types of venation in plants—reticulate and parallel.

Venation of leaves

- **Reticulate**: Veins and veinlets in the lamina divide repeatedly and form a network on the lamina. ***Examples***: Neem, rose.
- **Parallel**: Veins run parallel to each other from the base to the tip of the lamina. ***Examples***: Banana, grass, wheat.

Figure 13.19 Types of leaves on the basis of pattern of arrangement of veins

Leaf Modifications

Like in the case of roots and stems, leaves in certain plants undergo changes in the structure to perform additional functions. These are known as leaf modifications. The different kinds of functions supported by leaf modifications are:

1. Storage of food
2. Giving additional support to the plants
3. Defence
4. Protection
5. Reproduction
6. Performing some special functions

> **Info Bytes!**
> Cabbage has 92% water content

Opuntia

Cactus

- Entire leaf or part of the leaf modified into spines.
- Protection from grazing animals.
- Reduction of loss of water.
  Example: Prickly poppy.

- In weak stemmed plants, leaves or leaflets get modified into tendrils.
- Makes the plant stand erect around support.
- Exposes leaves to sunlight.
  Examples: Sweet pea, masur, glory lily.

Leaf modifications → **Defence**, **Support**, **Reproduction**, **Protection**, **Storage of food**

Reproduction
- Buds developed on the leaves grow into new plants.
  Examples: *Bryophyllum*, *Begonia*.

Protection
- Thin and dry scaly leaves.
- Protection to buds.
  Examples: Ginger, onion.

Storage of food
- Fleshy and thick leaves.
  Examples: Onion, garlic.

Bryophyllum

Ginger

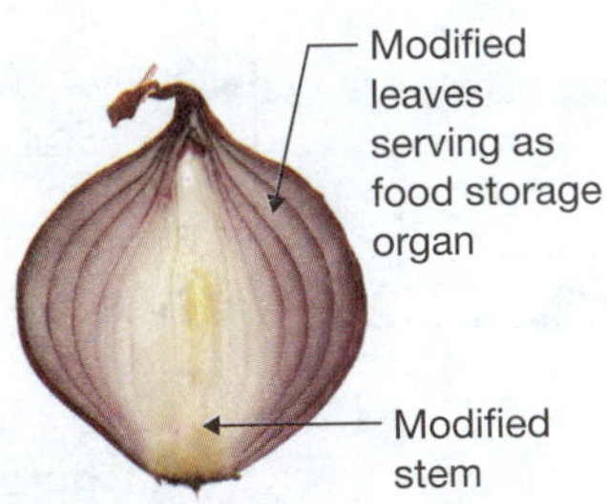

Onion

Figure 13.20 Types of leaf modifications for different functions

Apart from the various functions of leaf modifications discussed, following are the special functions of leaf modifications.

- Most of the plants are autotrophs and do not depend on other organisms for nutrition. However, there are plants which grow in soils where nitrogen is not sufficient for the plants to prepare their food.
- Plants which grow in nitrogen-deficient soils derive their nutrition either partially or totally from the insects, they trap them when approached. These plants are called insectivorous plants or carnivorous plants.

  Examples: Pitcher plant, bladderwort, Venus flytrap.

- In insectivorous plants, the leaf gets modified into a structure which helps the plant in trapping the insects when it comes nearby.

Info Bytes!

We get tears when we cut onions because they secrete sulfuric gas which irritate the nerves around the eyes.

Pitcher plant → Leaf lamina converted into pitcher; Apex of leaf modified into lid; Petiole becomes leaf-like

Pitcher plant

Venus flytrap → Leaves with long-pointed hair; Midrib like a hinge

Venus flytrap

Bladderwort → Highly segmented leaves; Some segments of leaves modified into small bladder-like structure; Bladder with entry point in one direction

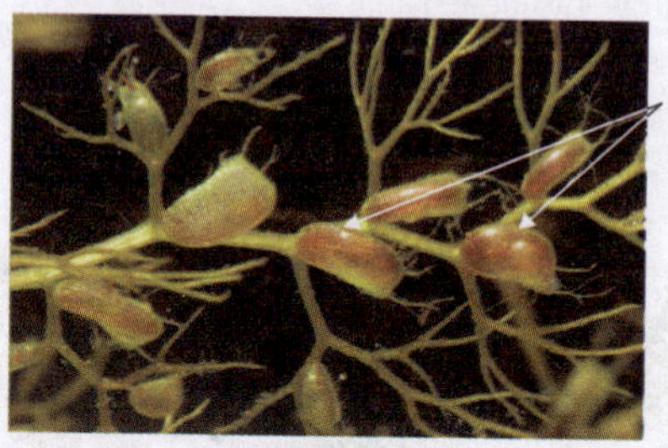

Bladderwort

Figure 13.21 Leaf modifications for special functions

EXAMPLE 13.2 What is the difference between a stem and a branch?

SOLUTION

A stem is the main structural part of the plant which gives rise to branches, leaves, flowers, and roots. It originates from the seedling and provides support to the plant. A branch, on the other hand, is an offshoot of the stem. It bears leaves, flowers, and sometimes fruits but doesn't give rise to roots. Each branch has its point of origin on the stem or another branch, but not all stems will give rise to branches.

EXAMPLE 13.3 Garlic is a condensed plant bearing root, stem, and leaves. Justify.

SOLUTION

The outer layer of a garlic clove is white to pale yellow and consists of dry scaly leaves which shield the inner fleshy leaves. The flat base in garlic from which individual cloves arise is a stem that has fine thread-like structures on its underside, which are termed as roots. Hence, garlic is a complete condensed plant.

Flower and Reproduction in Plants

All flowering plants bear flowers. The flower is the most prominent and beautiful part of the plant, so that plant can attract pollinators. Flowers are of many different shapes, sizes, colours with different fragrances.

- Flower is the reproductive part of the plant.
- Flowers may be attached to the shoot by means of a stalk or directly attached to the shoot.
- The stalk of the flower is called **pedicel**.
- The flowers that bear a stalk are called **pedicellate flowers**.
- The flowers which do not bear stalk are called **sessile flowers**.
- The flattened portion above the pedicel is called **thalamus**.

Info Bytes!

- *Rafflesia arnoldii* is the largest flower in the world!
- Watermeal (*Wolffia globosa*) is the smallest flower in the world!

Parts of a Flower

The parts of a flower are arranged on the thalamus as rings and are known as whorls. The parts of a flower are classified into two types on the basis of their respective roles in the process of reproduction. They are:

1. Non-essential parts
2. Essential parts

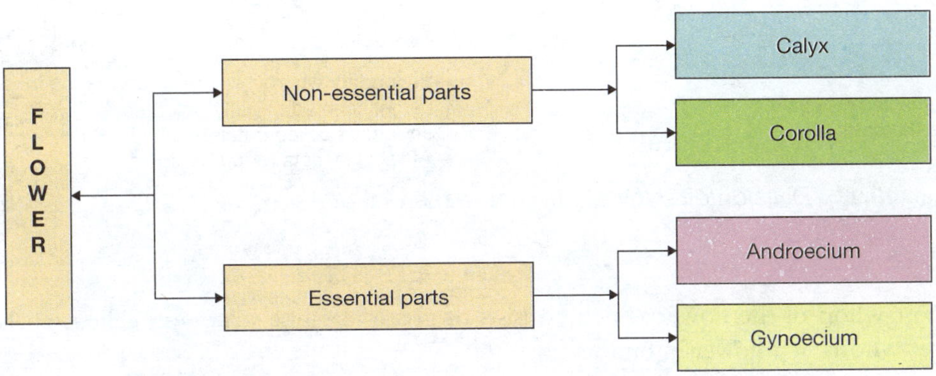

Non-essential Parts

The non-essential parts of a plant are those which are not directly involved in the process of reproduction. They play only supportive role. They are arranged in the first two whorls.

There are two non-essential parts of the flower. They are:

1. Calyx
2. Corolla

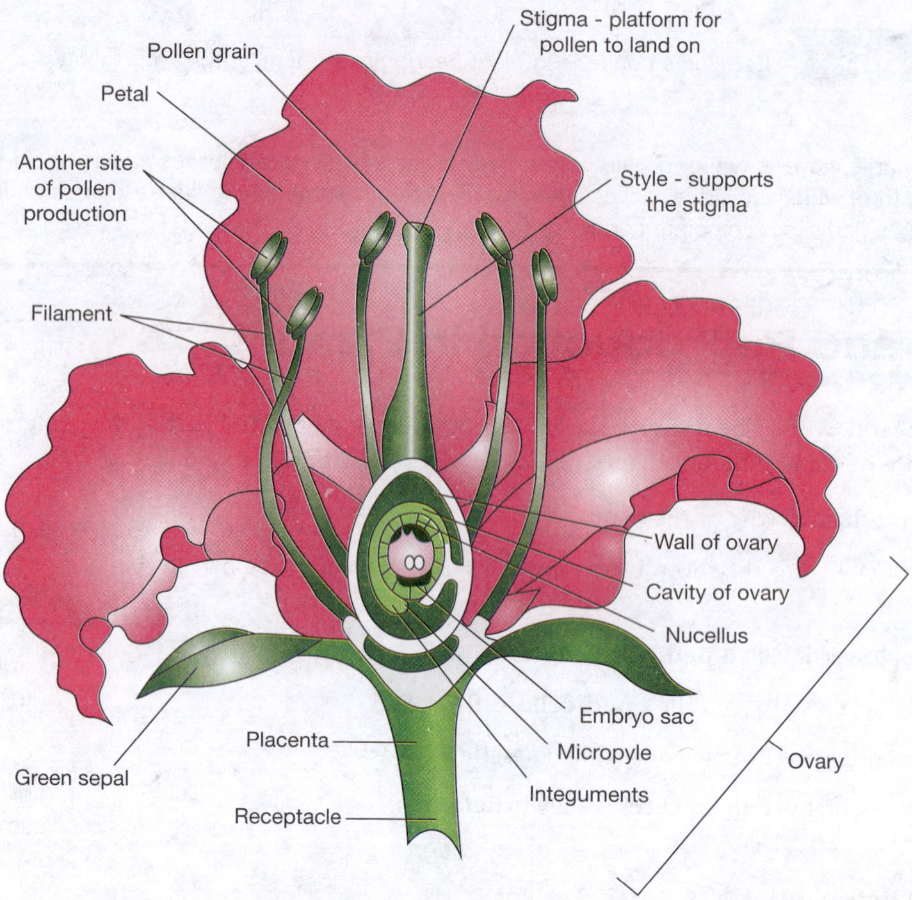

Figure 13.22 Parts of a Flower

Parts of a Flower—Non-essential

Calyx
- Outermost whorl
- Green leaf-like structures called sepals.
- Encloses and protects the parts of flower in bud stage.

Corolla
- Secondary whorl
- Large, scented brightly-coloured structures called petals.
- Attracts insects for pollination.

Figure 13.23 Division of a flower into non-essential parts

Info Bytes!

The petals of tulip plant are edible!

Calyx

Calyx is the outermost whorl of the flower which consists of green leaf-like structures called sepals. The calyx encloses and protects the inner whorls of a flower in bud stage.

Corolla

Corolla is the second whorl of the flower. It consists of brightly-coloured and scented structures called petals. The corolla serves the function of attracting the insects for pollination.

Essential Parts

The essential parts of a flower are those which are directly involved in the process of reproduction. They are arranged in the inner two whorls of the flower.

There are two essential parts of a flower, they are:

1. Androecium
2. Gynoecium

Info Bytes!

Sunflower is not a single flower!

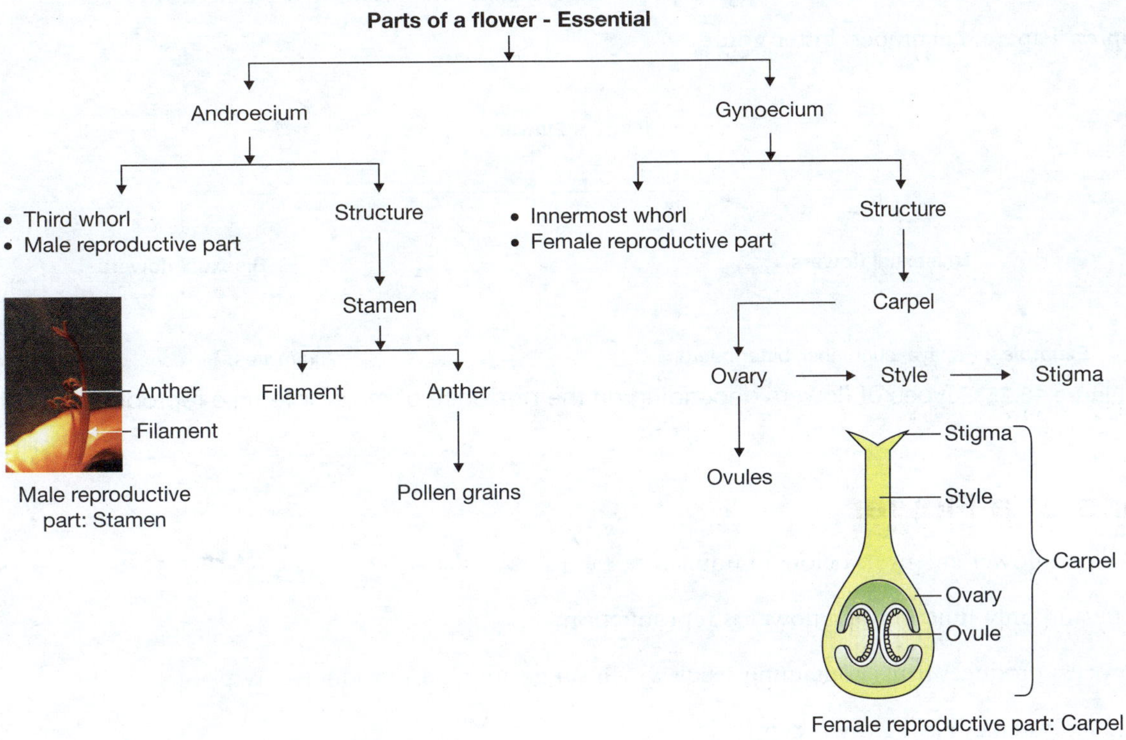

Figure 13.24 Division of a flower into essential parts

Androecium

Androecium is the third whorl of the flower and acts as the male reproductive part. Androecium is made up of long, thin and narrow stalk called filament and a small bilobed structure called anther. Anther consists of pollen grains which acts as male gametes during the process of sexual reproduction.

Gynoecium

Gynoecium is the innermost whorl of the flower which acts as the female reproductive part. Gynoecium is also known as pistil which consists of carpel. The carpel bears ovary, style and stigma. **Ovary** is the swollen part at the base of the carpel. Ovary bears ovules which consist of female gametes. They take part in sexual reproduction. **Style** is a long narrow, tubular structure which acts as a passage for the entry of male gamete into the ovary. **Stigma** is the disc-like part present at the top of style which helps in pollination.

Types of Flowers

- The flowers are classified into the following two types depending on the presence of both male and female reproductive parts in the same flower or in separate flowers.
  1. Bisexual flowers or complete flowers
  2. Unisexual flowers or incomplete flowers
- In bisexual flowers, both male and female reproductive organs are present in the same flower.

  Examples: *Hibiscus*, gulmohar.

> **Info Bytes!**
>
> *Selenicereus grandiflorus* bloom only once a year.

- In unisexual flowers, the male and female reproductive organs are present in separate flowers.

  Examples: Papaya, cucumber, bitter gourd.

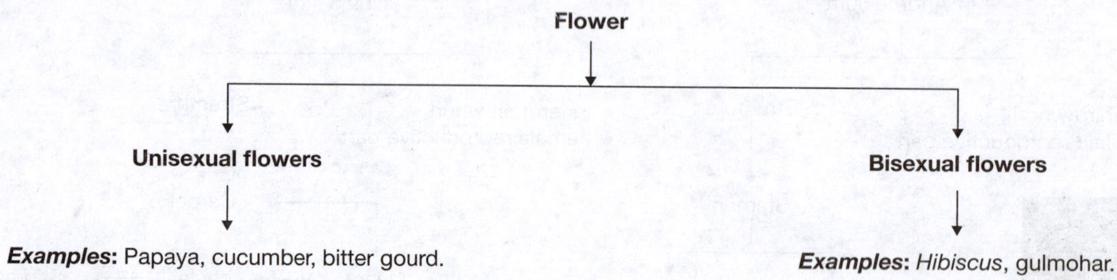

Figure 13.25 Types of flowers depending on the presence of male or female reproductive parts

Functions of a Flower

The functions of a flower are given below in points.

- The one and only function of a flower is reproduction.
- This process produces fruits containing seeds which on germination produce new plants.
- Reproduction takes place in two steps.
  - Stage I: Pollination
  - Stage II: Fertilization
- The pollen grains contain male gametes while the ovary contains ovules which contain the female gametes.
- The fusion of male and female gametes takes place only when the pollen grains from the anther reach the stigma of the carpel.

Pollination

The transfer of pollen grains from the anther to the stigma is known as pollination. The type of pollination depends upon the type of flowers apart from other factors. In unisexual flowers, only cross-pollination is possible. In bisexual flowers, both self-pollination and cross-pollination are possible depending on other factors. Cross-pollination requires some agents for the transfer of pollen grains. Cross-pollination results in genetic diversity.

Types of pollination

- **Self-pollination**: Transfer of pollen grains from the anther to the stigma of the same flower or another flower of same plant
- **Cross-pollination**: Transfer of pollen grains from the anther of one flower to the stigma of another flower of another plant

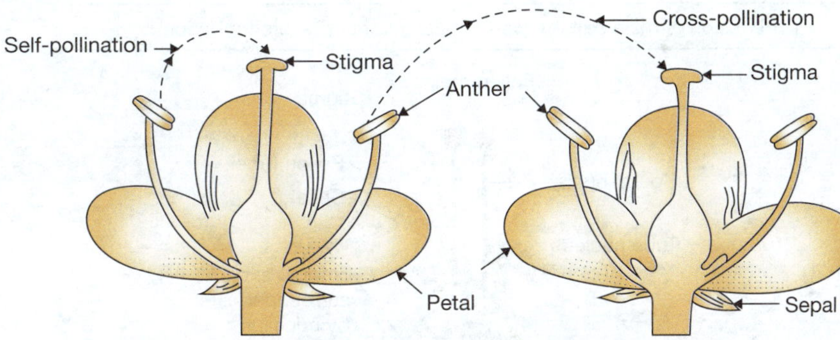

Self-pollination and cross-pollination

Figure 13.26 Flower showing both self and cross-pollination

Different agents of cross-pollination are given below in the form of a flowchart.

Agents of cross-pollination

Insects	***Examples:*** *Dahlia*, marigold.
Animals	***Examples:*** *Helianthus*, orchids.
Wind	***Examples:*** Sugarcane, grass.
Water	***Examples:*** Water lily, *Vallisneria*.

Figure 13.27 Different agents of cross-pollination

> **Info Bytes!**
> There are 2,00,000 animal species which act as pollinators!

> **Info Bytes!**
> Some plants can reproduce without even needing a partner. This asexual reproduction method is called 'apomixis.'

Fertilization

The fusion of male gamete with female gamete to form a zygote is known as fertilization. In plants, fertilization is a process of sexual reproduction.

The process of fertilization takes place in four steps:

Germination of pollen grains on the stigma

↓

Growth of pollen tube downwards into the style

↓

Passage of male gametes into the ovary through pollen tube

↓

The fusion of male gamete with female gamete (Zygote formation)

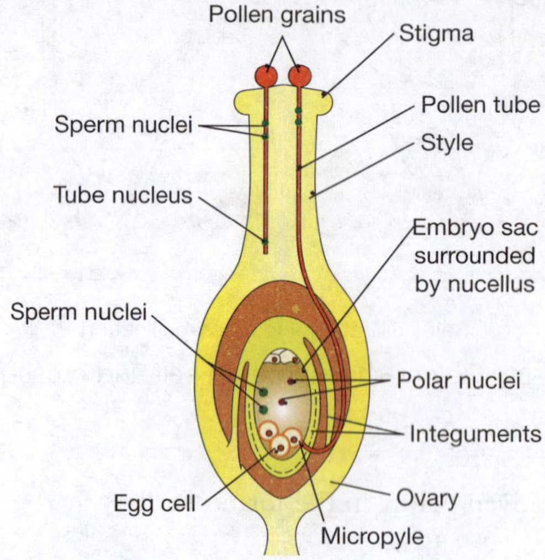

Figure 13.28 Fertilization taking place in the ovary of a flower

Changes Taking Place After Fertilization

The following changes take place after fertilization.

1. Sepals, petals and stamens fall off.
2. Increase in the size of ovary to become fruit. The ripening ovary forms the fruit, which contains one or more seeds. The fruits can be fleshy (papaya) or dry (pea) depending on the wall of the ovary. These fruits tend to grow as long as the plant grows and eventually falls off, dispersing seeds at various places.
3. Development of ovules into seeds. The seeds contain an embryo which develops into a baby plant in future. The seeds also contain one or two cotyledons which contain food for developing embryo. Depending on the number of cotyledons in a seed, the plants are classified into two categories.
   (i) **Monocotyledons** which contain seeds with one cotyledon.
   (ii) **Dicotyledons** which contain seeds with two cotyledons.

Seeds

- Monocotyledonous seeds → ***Examples*:** Paddy, wheat, maize.
- Dicotyledonous seeds → ***Examples*:** Pea, groundnut.

Figure 13.29 Types of seeds on the basis of number of cotyledons

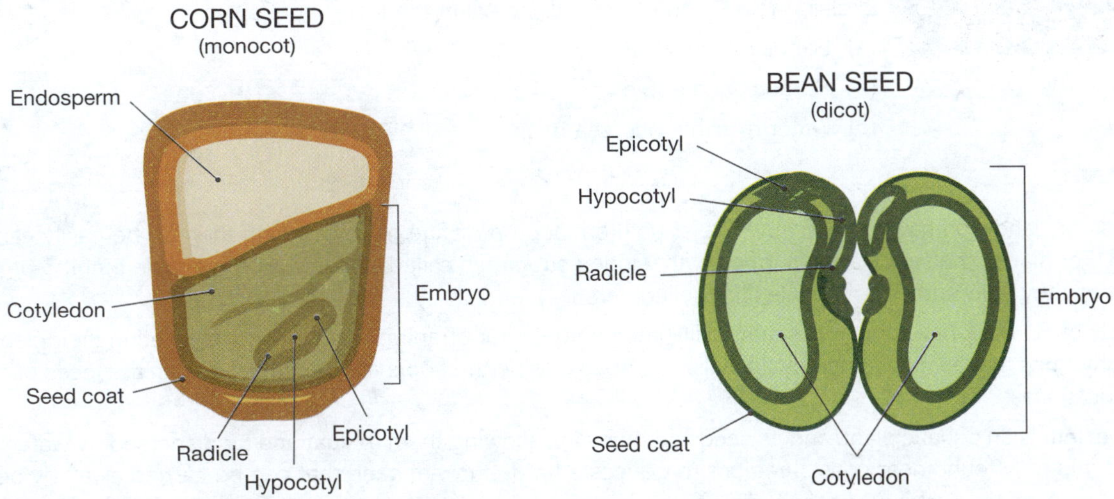

Figure 13.30 Structure of (a) Monocot seed (b) Dicot seed

The seed becomes active in the presence of water, air, suitable temperature and soil and it grows into a young plant, this process is called germination. The germinating seed develops into two parts.

1. **Radicle** which grows into root system.
2. **Plumule** which grows into shoot system.

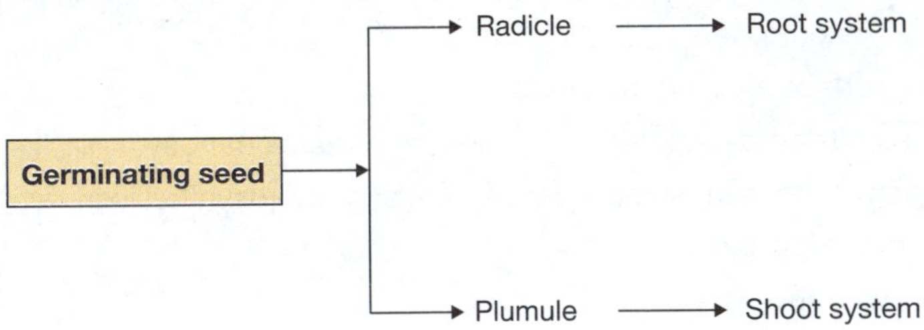

Figure 13.31 Parts of a germinating seed

Seed germination is of two types:

1. Epigeal–in which the hypocotyl elongates rapidly and pulls the cotyledon out of the ground.
2. Hypogeal–in which the epicotyl elongates and cotyledons remain under the ground.

Figure 13.32 Epigeal germination

Figure 13.33 Hypogeal germination

The transport of seeds away from the parent plant for the sake of germination is called seed dispersal. The different agents of dispersal are birds, water, wind, animals, etc.

EXAMPLE 13.4

Explain the method of seed dispersal in the following plants.

(a) Dandelion and maple

(b) Burdock and apple

(c) Water hyacinth and sea bean

SOLUTION

(a) The seeds of dandelion have a parachute-like structure made up of fine hairs, allowing them to be easily carried away by the wind. For maple, the seeds are equipped with winged structures called samaras, which enable them to be dispersed by the wind as they spin to the ground like little helicopters.

(b) The seeds of Burdock have tiny hooks that easily latch onto the fur of animals or clothing, facilitating their dispersal. Apples have fleshy fruits that are consumed by animals. The seeds inside the apple are then dispersed in the feces of these animals to new locations.

(c) Water hyacinth is an aquatic plant, and its seeds are buoyant, allowing them to float and be dispersed by water currents. The sea bean, typically found near coastal regions, produces a hard, buoyant seed that can be carried away by ocean currents for long distances before being deposited on a new shoreline.

EXAMPLE 13.5

Write down the characteristics of leaves which make them suitable for conserving water in desert plants and for maximizing photosynthesis in rainforest plants.

SOLUTION

The characteristics of leaves which make them suitable for conserving water in desert plants are:

(a) Thick, waxy cuticle to reduce water loss

(b) Small or no leaves to reduce surface area for transpiration

(c) Stomata often located in deep pits or closed during the hottest parts of the day

The characteristics of leaves which make them suitable for maximizing photosynthesis in rainforest plants are:

(a) Large surface area to capture maximum sunlight

(b) Thin, flexible leaves allowing for light penetration

(c) High density of stomata for efficient gas exchange.

POINTS TO REMEMBER

- On the basis of presence or absence of flowers, plants are classified into flowering and non-flowering plants.
- A typical plant consists of an underground root system and above the ground shoot system.
- Based on the structure and origin, root system is classified into two types—Tap root system and Fibrous root system
- The different kinds of functions supported by modified roots are storage of food, additional support and performing some special functions.
- Different roots which provide additional support. They are Prop roots, Stilt roots and Climbing roots.
- Roots in some plants are modified to perform some special functions. This include Nodular roots, Parasitic roots, Epiphytic roots and Breathing roots.
- The stem, leaves, flowers, buds, branches and fruits are parts of the shoot system.
- Plants can be categorized into three types based on the structure of stem – Herbs, Shrubs and Trees.
- Three different types of modifications of stem are:
  - ✓ Underground stem modifications for storage of food
  - ✓ Subaerial stem modifications for giving additional support
  - ✓ Aerial stem modifications to serve other functions
- Tuber, rhizome, bulb and corm are underground stem modifications.
- Runner, stolon, and offset are subaerial stem modification.
- The four kinds of aerial stem modifications are thorns, tendrils, twiners, phylloclades.
- Leaf is a thin, flattened organ that arises at the node of the stem.
- leaves can be broadly categorized as simple leaves and compound leaves on the basis of their structure.
- There are three different ways in which the leaves can be arranged on the axis or stem – alternate, opposite, and whorled.
- The pattern of arrangement of veins on the leaf blade or lamina is called venation. There are two types of venation in plants—reticulate and parallel.
- leaves in certain plants undergo changes in the structure to perform additional functions. These are known as leaf modifications.
- Flower is the reproductive part of the plant.
- The parts of a flower are classified into two types—essential and non-essential.
- Calyx and corolla are the non-essential parts.
- Androecium and gynoecium are the essential parts.
- Bisexual and unisexual flowers are the different types of flowers.
- The transfer of pollen grains from the anther to the stigma is known as pollination.
- The fusion of male gamete with female gamete to form a zygote is known as fertilization.
- The germinating seed develops into two parts. Radicle which grows into root system and Plumule which grows into shoot system.
- Seed germination is of two types epigeal and hypogeal.

PRACTICE QUESTIONS CLASSROOM WING

Very Short Answer Type Questions

Direction for question from 1 to 3.
Fill in the blanks.

1. Aerial roots arising from branches which give support to the plant are ______.
2. Sweet potato is an example of_____.
3. Seeds bearing two cotyledons possess ______ root system.

Direction for question from 4 to 11.
Select the correct alternative from the given options.

4. The conditions required by seeds to germinate include:
   (a) air and water
   (b) water only
   (c) suitable temperature, soil and water
   (d) air, water, suitable temperature, and water
5. The main function of corolla is
   (a) to make a flower appear beautiful.
   (b) to make a flower more aesthetic and presentable.
   (c) to attract insects for pollination.
   (d) to attract wind for pollination.
6. Calyx and corolla are
   (a) non-essential whorls.
   (b) accessory whorls.
   (c) essential whorls.
   (d) Both (a) and (b)
7. Sessile flowers are
   (a) pedicellate flowers.
   (b) complete flowers.
   (c) non stalk bearing flowers.
   (d) incomplete flowers.
8. Leaves containing buds that grow into new plants
   (i) helps in reproduction.
   (ii) are found in Bryophyllum and Begonia.
   (iii) protect the buds.
   (iv) are found in ginger and onion.
   (a) Only (i) (b) Only (i) and (ii)
   (c) (i), (ii) and (iii) (d) Only (iii) and (iv)
9. Identify the aerial root system which provides additional support to the plant.
   (a) Tap root system
   (b) Fibrous root system
   (c) Prop root system
   (d) Tuberous root system
10. From which part of the germinating seeds does the root develop?
    (a) Radicle (b) Plumule
    (c) Cotyledons (d) Endosperm
11. Identify the group of plants which develop respiratory roots.
    (a) Cactus (b) Water hyacinth
    (c) *Avicennia* (d) Orchids

Direction for question from 12 to 22.
Fill in the blanks.

12. The protective outer brown covering of stem and branches is called _______.
13. _______ buds lead to increase in the height of the plant.
14. The part that connects roots with leaves and flowers is ______.
15. In weak stemmed plants, thread-like structures twine around support and are called _______.
16. _______ plants trap insects.
17. _______ is the broad expanded part of the leaf which helps in photosynthesis.
18. In _______ leaves, the lamina is cut into small leaflets.
19. If single node bears more than two leaves, such an arrangement is known as _______.
20. *Opuntia* is an example of ______ plant.
21. The place on the plant stem where leaves arise is known as ________.
22. Plants having green tender stems with very few branches are grouped as________.

Direction for question from 23 to 32.
Select the correct alternative from the given options.

23. Identify the buds of a potato commonly called eyes.
(a) Terminal buds (b) Axillary buds
(c) Scaly buds (d) Floral buds

24. Which part of the cactus plant is modified into spine?
(a) Stem (b) Roots
(c) Leaves (d) Branches

25. Identify the function(s) of stem.
(a) Conduction (b) Photosynthesis
(c) Respiration (d) Both (a) and (b)

26. The part which connects the lamina of leaf with stem is
(a) Veins (b) Petiole
(c) Midrib (d) Leaf base

27. Name the venation in which veins form a network.
(a) Reticulate (b) Parallel
(c) Simple (d) Compound

28. Identify the main organs of respiration in plants.
(a) Root (b) Stem
(c) Leaves (d) Branches

29. In which of the following plants, underground stem modification is observed?
(a) Ginger (b) Onion
(c) Carrot (d) Beetroot

30. Identify the process by which roots pull water from the soil.
(a) Respiration (b) Transpiration
(c) Photosynthesis (d) Transportation

31. The plants that grow in nitrogen deficient soil is
(a) *Opuntia* (b) *Vallisneria*
(c) Neem (d) Venus flytrap

32. In which plant opposite arrangement of leaves at nodes is seen?
(a) Mango (b) Sunflower
(c) Guava (d) Mustard

Direction for question from 33 to 40.
Fill in the blanks.

33. The circular arrangements of parts in a flower is known as ________.

34. ________ is the basal swollen part of a flower in which the floral parts are arranged.

35. The flower is protected in bud condition by ______.

36. The microscopic body that contains male reproductive cell in plants is ______.

37. _______ flowers contain both stamens and pistil.

38. After fertilization _______ is formed from ripened ovary.

39. The fruit is the modified _______ of the flower.

40. Pollen is received by ______ after pollination.

Direction for question from 41 to 46.
Select the correct alternative from the given options.

41. Which of the following parts is present in a carpel?
(a) Pollen grain (b) Thalamus
(c) Ovary (d) Anthers

42. Identify the third whorl of the flower.
(a) Calyx (b) Stamens
(c) Corolla (d) Carpels

43. Name the type of flower consisting of all the four whorls.
(a) Vegetative flower (b) Incomplete flower
(c) Complete flower (d) Ornamental flower

44. Identify the product formed after the fusion of two gametes.
(a) Embryo (b) Zygote
(c) Egg (d) Pollen

45. In which of the following flowers large amount of pollen is produced?
(a) Animal pollinated (b) Water pollinated
(c) Insect pollinated (d) Wind pollinated

46. Name the part that connects the stigma to the ovary.
(a) Thalamus (b) Style
(c) Pedicel (d) Filament

47. Match Column I with Column II.

Column I	Column II
(A) Sweet potato	(a) Fibrous root system
(B) *Rhizophora*	(b) Tap root system
(C) Grape vine	(c) Storage root
(D) *Bougainvillea*	(d) Classified under shrub
(E) Balsam	(e) Mangrove plant
(F) Cereals	(f) Climber

Direction for question from 48 to 52.
Pick the odd one out.

48. Secondary roots, tap roots, lateral roots, root clusters.

49. Carrot, turnip, radish, potato.

50. Anchoring, absorption, photosynthesis, conduction.

51. Dahlia, banyan, sugarcane, money plant.

52. Stem, root, leaf, flower.

Direction for question from 53 to 55.
Find the co-related terms.

53. Spread horizontally : _______ :: Stand upright : Climber

54. Prop root : Sugarcane :: _______ : Pepper

55. _______ : Root :: Reproductive part : Fruit

Direction for question from 56 to 57.
State whether true or false.

56. After seed germination, radicle gives rise to root system.

57. Roots help in upward conduction.

58. Match Column I with Column II.

Column I	Column II
(A) Petiole	(a) Transpiration
(B) Lamina	(b) Absorption
(C) Stomata	(c) Protection
(D) Bark	(d) Photosynthesis
(E) Roots	(e) Connection

Direction for question from 59 to 62.
Pick the odd one out.

59. Nodes, internodes, bark, petiole.

60. Hibiscus leaf, neem leaf, mango leaf, lotus leaf.

61. Turmeric, ginger, corn, onion.

62. *Nepenthes, Utricularia, Drosera,* gulmohar.

Direction for question from 63 to 66.
Find the co-related terms.

63. _______ : Hibiscus :: Whorled : *Nerium*

64. _______ : Potato :: Rhizome : Ginger

65. Spines : *Opuntia* :: _______ : Sweet pea

66. Grasses : Parallel venation :: Bean : _______

Direction for question from 67 to 74.
State whether true or false.

67. Leaves of plants are called food factories.

68. Plants with parallel venation bear tap root.

69. Loss of water in the form of droplets is called transpiration.

70. Leaflets are present in simple leaves.

71. Arrangement of leaves on the stem with one leaf arising from each node is known as alternate arrangement.

72. Photosynthesis takes place in the absence of sunlight.

73. The outermost dry layer of onion is scaly leaf.

74. Nodes are present in root system.

Direction for question from 75 to 78.
Pick the odd one out.

75. Ovary, anther, filament, pollen grains.

76. Sepals, petals, anthers, flower.

77. Papaya flower, guava flower, apple flower, orange flower.

78. Paddy, wheat, maize, bean.

Direction for question from 79 to 82.
Find the co-related terms.

79. Anther : _______ :: Pistil : Ovary

80. Tomato : Fleshy Fruit :: _______ : Dry fruits

81. Ovary : Fruits :: _______ : Seeds

82. _______ : Root system :: Plumule : Shoot system

Direction for question from 83 to 87.
State whether true or false.

83. Flowers that do not bear stalk are called sessile flowers.

84. Axillary buds help in the sexual reproduction of the plant.

85. In plants after fertilization, the ovary develops into fruits and ovules develop into seeds.

86. Wind pollinated flowers produce nectar and are brightly-coloured.

87. Ovules are found in stigma.

Direction for question 88.
Select the correct alternative from the given options.

88. What is the fate of the following organs of a flower after fertilization?

(a) Sepals (b) Petals
(c) Stamens (d) Ovary
(e) Ovule

Short Answer Type Questions

89. Give the difference between creepers and climbers.

90. Apart from conduction, roots help in breathing. Discuss.

91. Roots are modified to perform additional functions. Explain with examples.

92.

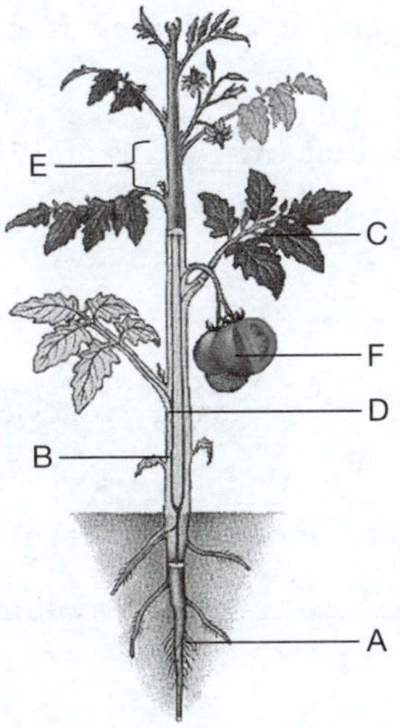

(a) Identify the parts A, B, C, D, E and F.

(b) What are the major functions of A?

(c) List out the vegetative parts from the given figure.

(d) What is the function of C?

Direction for question from 93 to 95.
Answer the following questions.

93. Distinguish between rhizome and stem tuber.

94. Name the process by which exchange of gases and elimination of water take place in plants.

95. Give reason why the stem is green and fleshy in cactus.

Direction for question from 96 to 97.
Give scientific reasons.

96. Leaves of plants are called food factories.

97. Underground modifications help in storage of food.

Direction for question from 98 to 102.
Answer the following questions.

98. Why are phylloclades usually found in desert regions?

99. How can we produce a new potato plant using only a potato?

100. Give the functions of fruit.

101. Mention the methods of seeds dispersal.

102. Flower is the reproductive part of a plant.

Direction for question from 103 to 107.
Answer the following questions.

103. Distinguish between parasitic roots and epiphytic roots and give examples.

104. Draw a comparison between the tendrils in cucumber and garden pea.

105. Give reason why bean plants are essential in crop rotation system.

106. Distinguish between root system and shoot system.

107. Distinguish between alternate and opposite leaf arrangements.

Essay Type Questions

108. Give examples for the following.

(i) Plant that does not bear leaf.

(ii) Plant that has variegated leaf.

(iii) Plant in which leaf is modified into pitcher.

(iv) Xerophytic plant with spiny leaves.

(v) Weak stemmed plant bearing tendrils.

109. Define the following terms.

(a) Venation (b) Germination

(c) Pollination (d) Fertilization

PRACTICE QUESTIONS COMPETITION WING

Level 1: Apply Your Concepts

Directions for questions from 1 to 5.
Fill in the blanks.

1. Individual members of calyx are called ______.
2. The essential whorls of a flower are ______ and ______.
3. In ______ plants, leaves are modified to trap insects.
4. When two leaves arise from each node in opposite directions, the arrangement of leaves is called ______.
5. Stems intertwining around their own stems and helping the plant to climb up are called ______.

Level 2: Review Your Concepts

6. Answer the following:
   (a) What is the difference epigeal and hypogeal germination
   (b) Discuss the agents of cross pollination with example.
7. Give reason why transpiration is a vital processes in plants.
8. Why leaves of certain plants are modified to eat insects?
9. What are the characteristics of the flowers pollinated by wind?

Level 3: Assess Your Concepts

10.

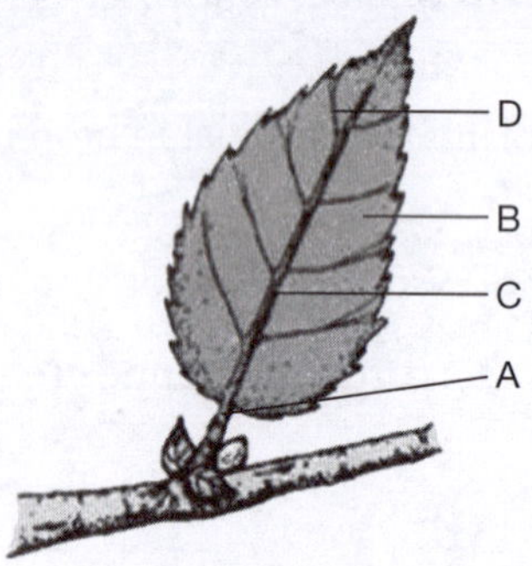

   (i) Identify the parts of a leaf A, B, C, D.
   (ii) Give the functions of A and B.
   (iii) Identify whether the leaf is simple or compound. Justify.
   (iv) Where are stomata present and what is its function?
11. Insect pollinated flowers are brightly-coloured. Give reason.
12. Explain why dry seeds do not germinate.
13. Self-pollination is not possible in papaya. Give reason.
14. Botanical Garden in Kolkata has a 200 year old banyan tree. How can you identify the tree from its physical appearance?
15. Answer the following:
   (a) Write a note on any two types of aerial stem modification.
   (b) Discuss about parasitic and breathing roots.
16. Discuss the modification seen in an onion.
17. Give reasons why aerial roots of banyan tree are not considered as true roots.

AT

ANSWER KEYS

Crossword

Across

4. Tendrils **7.** Defence **8.** Zygote **10.** Alternate **11.** Reticulate
12. Prop **13.** Pod **14.** Texture

Down

1. Nodulose **2.** Offset **3.** Epigeal **5.** Pneumatophores
6. Adventitious **9.** Compound

Classroom Wing

Very Short Answer Type Questions

1. Prop roots **2.** Storage root **3.** Tap **4.** (d) **5.** (c)
6. (d) **7.** (c) **8.** (b) **9.** (b) **10.** (a)
11. (c) **12.** Bark **13.** Terminal or apical **14.** Stem **15.** Tendrils
16. Carnivorous **17.** Lamina **18.** Compound **19.** Whorled **20.** Xerophytic
21. Node **22.** Herbs **23.** (b) **24.** (c) **25.** (d)
26. (b) **27.** (a) **28.** (c) **29.** (a) **30.** (b)
31. (d) **32.** (c) **33.** Whorl **34.** Thalamus **35.** Calyx
36. Pollen grain **37.** Bisexual **38.** Fruit **39.** Ovary **40.** Stigma
41. (c) **42.** (b) **43.** (c) **44.** (b) **45.** (d)
46. (b)

47. The correct match is:
(A) → (c); (B) → (e); (C) → (f); (D) → (d); (E) → (b); (F) → (a).

48. Root clusters **49.** Potato **50.** Photosynthesis **51.** Money plant **52.** Flower
53. Creeper **54.** Climbing root **55.** Vegetative part **56.** True **57.** True

58. The correct match is:
(A) → (e); (B) → (d); (C) → (a); (D) → (c); (E) → (b)

59. Petiole **60.** Neem leaf **61.** Onion **62.** Gulmohar **63.** Alternate
64. Tuber **65.** Tendrils **66.** Reticulate venation **67.** True **68.** False
69. False **70.** False **71.** True **72.** False **73.** True
74. False **75.** Ovary **76.** Flower **77.** Papaya flower **78.** Bean
79. Pollen grains **80.** Nuts **81.** Ovules **82.** Radicle **83.** True
84. False **85.** True **86.** False **87.** False

Competition Wing

Level 1: Apply Your Concepts

1. Sepals **2.** Androecium and gynoecium **3.** Insectivorous **4.** Opposite **5.** Twiners

Hints and Explanations

CLASSROOM WING

Very Short Answer Type Questions

47. The correct match is:

(A) → (c); (B) → (e); (C) → (f); (D) → (d); (E) → (b); (F) → (a).

A. Sweet potato	(c) Storage root
B. Rhizophora	(e) Mangrove plant
C. Grapevine	(f) Climber
D. Bougainvillea	(d) Classified under shrub
E. Balsam	(b) Tap root system
F. Cereals	(a) Fibrous root system

48. Root clusters: They are seen in monocotyledons, all others are parts seen in dicot root.

49. Potato: All are underground root modification. Potato is stem modification.

50. Photosynthesis: All are functions of root system except photosynthesis.

51. Money plant: All others show root modification.

52. Flower: All others are vegetative parts, flowers are reproductive parts.

53. Spread horizontally : Creeper :: Stand upright : Climber

54. Prop root : Sugarcane :: Climbing root : Pepper

55. Vegetative part : Root :: Reproductive part : Fruit

56. True

57. True

58. The correct match is:

(A) → (e); (B) → (d); (C) → (a); (D) → (c); (E) → (b)

59. Petiole: This is a part of leaf, and all others are stem parts.

60. Neem leaf: It is a compound leaf and all others are simple.

61. Onion: It is leaf modification and others are stem modifications.

62. Gulmohar: All other are carnivorous plants.

63. Alternate : Hibiscus :: Whorled : *Nerium*

64. Tuber : Potato :: Rhizome : Ginger

65. Spines : *Opuntia* :: Tendrils : Sweet pea

66. Grasses : Parallel venation :: Bean : Reticulate venation

67. True

68. False: Plants with parallel venation bear fibrous roots.

69. False: Loss of water in the form of water vapour is transpiration.

70. False: Leaflets are present in compound leaves.

71. True

72. False: Photosynthesis takes place in the presence of sunlight.

73. True

74. False: Nodes are absent in root system.

75. Ovary: It is the female part of a flower, all others are male parts.

76. Flower: Others are parts present in flower.

77. Papaya flower: It is a unisexual flower, others are bisexual.

78. Bean: It is a dicotyledonous seed and all others are monocotyledons.

79. Anther : Pollen grains :: Pistil : Ovary

80. Tomato : Fleshy fruits :: Nuts : Dry fruits

81. Ovary : Fruits :: Ovules : Seeds

82. Radicle : Root system :: Plumule : Shoot system

83. True

84. False: Vegetative buds help in the growth of the plants.

85. True

86. False: Insect pollinated flowers produce nectar and are brightly-coloured.

87. False: Ovules are found in ovary.

88. The sepals, petals and stamens fall off after the fertilization. The ovary is converted to fruit. The ovules are converted into seeds.

Short Answer Type Questions

89. Both creepers and climbers are weak stemmed plants which cannot grow without support.

Creepers	Climbers
• Spreads horizontally along the soil.	• Grows erect when support is given.
• Fibrous roots develop at every nodal point for support. Examples: Pumpkin, watermelon, etc.	• Highly coiled tendrils give extra support to grow erect. Examples: Grapevine, cucumber, etc.

90. Plants that grow in saline marshy habitat are known as mangroves. The lateral roots of such plants produce vertically upwards aerial projections. These projections are known as breathing roots or pneumatophores. Pneumatophores help in respiration, hence, they are known as respiratory roots.
Examples: *Rhizophora, Avicennia.*

91. Apart from the normal functions of roots as conduction, anchoring and absorption, roots also perform additional functions by modifications (undergoing certain changes).
   (a) Storage roots (tuberous roots): These are swollen roots which help in storage.
   Examples: Carrot, beetroot, radish.
   (b) Prop roots or supporting roots: These are aerial roots developing from branches or stem region and provide support to the plant.
   Examples: Banyan, maize, sugarcane.
   (c) Respiratory roots or breathing roots or pneumatophores: These are aerial roots seen in marshy plants and they help in respiration or breathing.
   Examples: *Avicennia* and *Rhizophora.*

92. (a) Parts of identification.
   A-root; B-stem; C-leaf; D-Node; E-Internode and F-flowers.
   (b) 'A' is root system which is present underground and it helps in anchorage, absorption and conduction.
   (c) The vegetative parts in the given figure are root, stem and leaves.
   (d) Functions of 'C' that, leaves are involved in preparation of food (starch) in the presence of light (photosynthesis).

93. Underground main stem that creeps horizontally below the surface of soil is called rhizome. This is fleshy and helps in storage.
Example: Ginger tubes.

Underground part of root or structure derived from tip of underground branches is tuber. This helps in storage of starch.
Examples: Potato, beetroot.

94. The process by which elimination of water and exchange of gases takes place in plants is transpiration. This process takes place through tiny pores present on the leaves called stomata.

95. Cactus is a xerophytic plant. The stem of the plant is modified into flat, green, fleshy structure, which helps in storage of water and also performs photosynthesis. The leaves are modified to spines and it helps in reducing transpiration.

96. Leaves of plants contain green pigment called chlorophyll. This pigment traps solar energy. The water absorbed by the plant along with inorganic substances present in the leaf helps in the formation of starch. Starch is the stored food material in leaves. The food is formed and stored in leaves, so these leaves are known as food factories.

97. Underground modifications are seen in root, stem and leaves. Underground roots are swollen and they store food in them. They are called tuberous roots.
Example: Carrot

Underground stem helps in storage and it also helps the plant to survive during unfavourable conditions.
Example: Potato

Underground leaves are bulb-like structures bearing fleshy leaves which store food.
Example: Onions

Hence, all the underground modifications help in storage.

98. Phylloclades are modified stems that are thick, flat and green. They help in photosynthesis and also in storage of food. In desert conditions where water is scant, in order to decrease the water lost via stomata, leaves are modified into spines. So, here the stems take up the

function of photosynthesis. This is why phylloclades are found in desert regions.

99. Potatoes are tubers (underground stem modifications) that store a lot of food. A number of buds called eyes are present on the surface of potatoes. When potatoes along with eyes are sown under the soil and watered, new shoots are formed from these eyes which develop into new potato plants.

100. Fruits protect seeds from unfavourable climatic conditions and also from animals. They also help in dispersal of seeds by means of various methods and helps in continuation of its own species. They help in reproducing their own identical species.

101. The different ways of seed dispersal are given below:

(a) Dispersal by Wind: Seeds of plants that are dispersed by wind are light-weight and have some hair-like structures and help seeds to be dispersed by wind to long distances.
Example: Dandelion, cotton, etc.

(b) Dispersal by Water: Seeds dispersed by water are found in those fruits which are light and ability to float. It is commonly found in aquatic plants or plants which are found near water bodies. The fruit bearing seeds bursts liberating seeds and develops into a new plant.
Example: Coconut, water lily.

(c) Dispersal by Animals: Some fruits bear spine-like structure or thorns which get stuck to the fur of animals and gets dispersed. Seeds of juicy fruits are eaten by some birds and animals along with fruits. These seeds get dispersed with bird or animal droppings.
Examples: Beggar tick, *Xanthium*.

(d) Dispersal by Bursting: Few fruits burst open when they get mature and disperse their own seeds. The force of bursting is enough to spread the seeds to long distances.
Examples: Ladyfinger, castor, etc.

102. Flower helps in sexual reproduction. Male part in the flower produces male gametes and pollen grains. Female part in the flower is pistil which produces female gametophyte. Fusion of male and female gamete (fertilization) takes place in ovary producing zygote which develops into new individual plants. Hence, flower is considered the reproductive part.

103.

Epiphytic roots	Parasitic roots
• Roots that grow on other plant for support.	• Roots that grow on other plant for absorbing nutrients.
• They do not cause damage on which it grows. Examples: Mosses, Orchids.	• They cause damage to the plant on which it grows. Examples: *Rafflesia*, *Cuscuta*

104. In cucumber, the stem is modified into tendril while in sweet pea the leaf is modified into tendril.

105. Bean plants possess root nodules with nitrogen fixing bacteria. These bacteria are capable of converting the atmospheric nitrogen into soluble nitrate salts. Since nitrogen is an important nutrient mineral for the plants, the soil becomes enriched with nitrogen, and so, these plants are important in crop rotation system.

106.

Root system	Shoot system
Not green in colour.	Usually green in colour in young plants.
Grows downward into the soil.	Grows upwards above the soil.
Absorption of water and minerals is the main function.	Support to plant is the main function. In young plants, it also carries out photosynthesis.
Does not bear leaves, flowers and fruits.	Bears leaves, flowers and fruits.

107.

Alternate	Opposite
One leaf arises from each node.	Two leaves arise from each node.
The leaves at successive nodes are in opposite direction. Examples: Mint, peepal	The leaves at successive nodes are parallel. Examples: Jasmine, guava

Essay Type Questions

108. (i) The flowering plant that does not bear leaf is cuscuta.

(ii) Leaves having patches of green, yellow, white and red (different colours is a variegated leaf). ***Example:*** Money plant.

(iii) Plant in which leaf is modified to pitcher is nepenthes (pitcher plant).

(iv) Xerophytic plant with spiny leaves is cactus or *Opuntia*.

(v) Weak stemmed plant bearing tendrils is grape-vine or cucumber.

109. (a) The arrangement pattern of veins in the lamina of leaf is called venation.

(b) The process in which the embryo in the seed becomes active in the presence of water, air and suitable temperature and soil grows into a young plant is called germination.

(c) The transfer of pollen grains from the anther to the stigma is called pollination.

(d) The fusion of male gamete with female gamete to form a zygote is called fertilization.

COMPETITION WING

Level 2: Review Your Concepts

6. (a)

Epigeal	Hypogeal
In it, the hypocotyl elongated rapidly and pulls the cotyledon out of ground.	In it, epicotyl elongates and cotyledons remains under the ground.

(b) Insect: Dahlia, marigold

Animal: Helianthus, orchids

Wind: Sugarcane, grass

Water: Water, lily, Vallisneria

7. When a plant is watered, only 5 per cent of the water is absorbed by the plant. Excess of water is released in the form of water vapour on the leaves and the process is called transpiration. The transpiration process helps in movement of nutrient. It causes cooling effect to the plant, when the pores close and open, the exchange of gases take place. Hence, transpiration is considered a vital process.

8. Plants that grow in nitrogen-deficient soil require extra nitrogen for its growth and development. The leaves of such plants are modified into bladder-like structures called pitcher which helps in trapping insects. The insects trapped are digested by plants to compensate the lack of nitrogen. These plants are also called carnivorous plants.

9. Characteristics of wind pollinated flower are: Flowers are very small in size; it cannot be seen by insects. These flowers do not possess nectar or fragrance (scent). They contain dry pollen which can fly easily by blowing of wind. Pollen is produced in large quantities.

Level 3: Assess Your Concepts

10. (i) The identified parts are: (A) Petiole (B) Lamina (C) Midrib (D) Veins.

(ii) Functions of (A) is connection and (B) is photosynthesis.

(iii) The leaf is a simple leaf.

(iv) Stomata are present below the surface of leaf which helps in transpiration.

11. Brightly-coloured flowers attract insects. Insect visit flowers for nectar. When they rest on the flower, pollen gets stuck to their body. Thus, pollen gets transferred from one flower to other helping pollination.

12. Dry seeds are known as dormant seeds. They remain alive without germinating for months or years. When the seed is soaked in water, enzymes get activated by absorbing water, and thus, it helps in germination and development of embryo.

13. Papaya is a unisexual plant and male and female flowers are separate. Hence, self-pollination is not possible.

14. The banyan tree possesses the characteristic prop roots which arise from the branches and grow downwards like ropes. This is a distinguishing feature of the banyan tree. Being the oldest tree, it has the crown circumference of more than 400 metres.

15. (a) (i) Thorns: Buds modified into hard pointed small structures called thorns.

(ii) Phylloclade's: Thick, flat and green stem with nodes and internode

They help in preparation and storage of food.

(b) Parasitic root: These are adventitious root known as historian that protrudes into the host plant for the absorption of nutrition's.

Breathing roots: These roots rise above the soil like cone that bear minute pores called pneumatophores.

16. Onion shows both stem and leaf modification. Its stem is modified into a condensed disc shape structure. It has a terminal bud overlapped by numerous scaly leaves.

The leaves are modified into outer dry and scaly leaves which are protective in functions.

17. Aerial roots of banyan tree grow downwards from the main stem and branches. These roots are called prop roots. They act as pillars giving support to huge horizontal branches of banyan tree. The supporting roots or prop roots are one of the root modifications.

CHAPTER

14

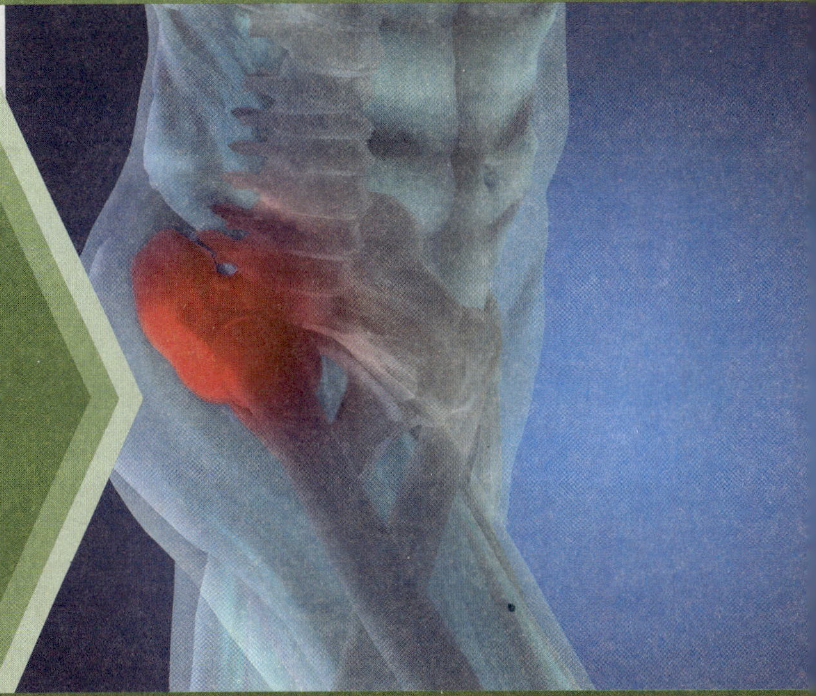

Movement—An Amazing Activity

Remember

Before beginning this chapter, you should be able to:

- Recall the importance of movement in the activity of living organisms
- Discuss some of your daily activities

Key Ideas

After completing this chapter, you should be able to:

- Describe skeletal system, and movement and locomotion in humans
- Describe structure of skeletal system and muscular system
- Understand the coordinated functioning of different systems during a movement

Scientific Crypt

A Tribute to Jean-Baptiste de Lamarck (1744–1829)

A pioneering French biologist, Jean-Baptiste de Lamarck (1744–1829), left an indelible mark on the study of life on Earth. He was a pivotal figure in biology in the 18th century, introducing revolutionary ideas about evolution and movement within the animal kingdom.

Lamarck is renowned for proposing an early theory of evolution, arguing that organisms evolve over time in response to their surroundings. He proposed that species could evolve through a process known as "acquisition of acquired traits." Although Darwin's ideas largely superseded this theory, it laid the groundwork for future evolutionary thought.

His contributions to the study of invertebrates such as mollusks and worms were also significant. Lamarck's work on taxonomy and classification helped to structure the chaotic world of living organisms.

While Lamarck's theories were not universally accepted during his lifetime, his pioneering spirit and dedication to understanding the natural world paved the way for modern evolutionary theory. His work continues to inspire scientists, cementing his place in biology history.

FUN TIME

CROSSWORD

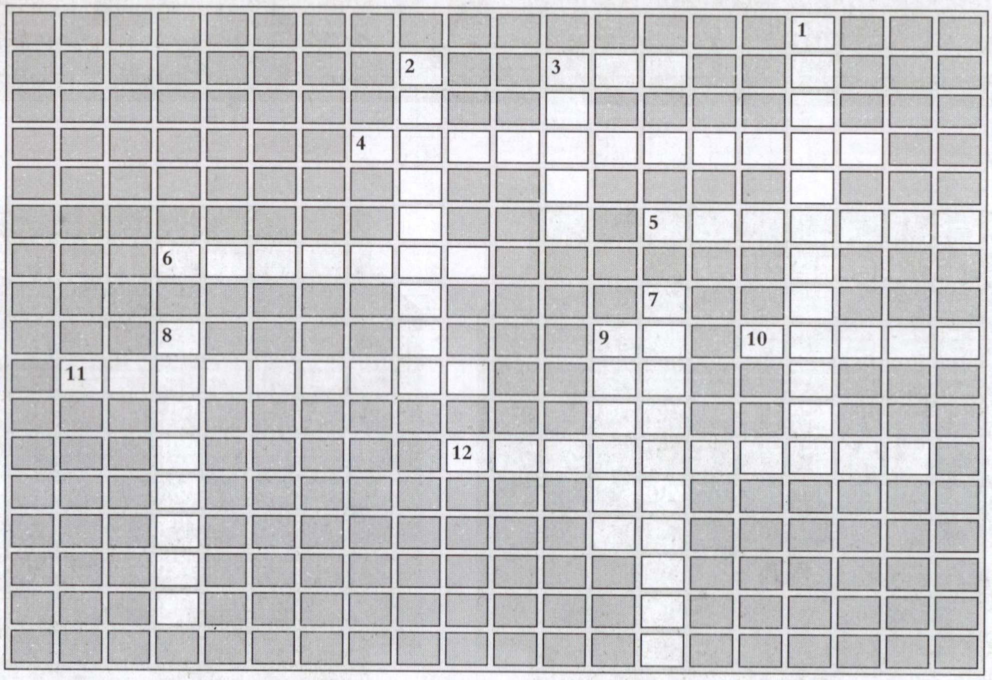

Across

3. Example of ball and socket joint
4. A group of organs that work together to perform an activity
5. Bones are attached to muscles with the help of __________.
6. 8 bones present in the wrist
10. Substance secreted by the foot of a snail to make the track slippery
11. Bones of the toes and fingers
12. Soft pulpy substance inside long bones (two words)

Down

1. The skeletal structure which is located on the lateral portion of the body and supports and connects limb bones
2. Soft protective structure present at the end of bones at joints
3. Joint present in the elbow
7. Main characteristic that distinguishes animals from plants based on their ability to move
8. Another name for vertebral column
9. Muscles which contract when lower arm is moved in the upward direction

INTRODUCTION

Living organisms are endowed with the gift of movement. They can move their body parts or the body as a whole on their own without any external force. This ability of movement distinguishes living things from non-living things as non-living things may show movement only when an external force acts on them. Living organisms include both plants and animals; they both have the ability to show movement. The basic difference between their movements is that plants do not show movement from one place to another as they are fixed at a particular place in the soil. Animals carry out various activities which involve the movement of body parts without changing their position and such movements are called body movements. The activity carried out by the body parts without the displacement of an organism from one place to another is called movement.

Examples: Chewing, writing, etc. Animals carry out many activities which involve the displacement of an organism from its original position. The activity carried out by any organism which involves the displacement of an organism from its original position is called locomotion.

Examples: Walking, running, climbing, etc. Animals show locomotion for the following purposes:

- In search of food
- Protection from enemies
- Reproduction

Organs for Locomotion

Different animals exhibit different modes of locomotion. Different animals possess different specialized features for the ability of locomotion. These structures or organs which carry out locomotion in diverse animals are known as **locomotory organelles**. Based on the complexity of structure, animals can be categorized as unicellular and multicellular organisms, however, both of them show locomotion. But the mode of locomotion differs widely in different organisms. Different modes of locomotion require different locomotory organelles. In unicellular organisms, single cell performs all the bodily activities. These organisms possess primitive organelles for locomotion.

Some of these locomotory organelles are given below.

Table 14.1 Different animals and their locomotory organelles

Animal	Locomotory organelle
Amoeba	Pseudopodia
Euglena	Flagella
Paramecium	Cilia
Hydra	Tentacles
Earthworm	Setae

Multicellular organisms possess well-defined structural organization and have more complex systems for movement and locomotion. All the multicellular organisms have a body organization as they have cells specialized to carry out specific tasks. The mode of locomotion and the systems for locomotion in various animals depend on their habitat and the level of body organization.

Examples: Birds have wings for flying and fish have fins for swimming.

Human beings are the most advanced organisms in the entire animal kingdom. So, the human body possesses the most complex and well-structured body organization. Hence, human beings possess specific systems for movement and locomotion.

Organization in Human Body to Carry Life Activities

The human body is made up of specialized systems for carrying out various bodily activities. Being the most advanced level of body organization, the human body is made up of innumerable number of cells.

1. A group of similar cells which are specialized to perform a particular function is called tissue.

   Example: Blood comprises RBCs, WBCs and platelets.

2. A group of different tissues works together to perform a specific function, this is called organ.

   Example: Lungs for respiration

3. A group of organs which work together to perform an activity in the body is called organ system.

   Example: Mouth, stomach, small intestine, large intestine, all these organs constitute to form the digestive system.

Figure 14.1 Levels of cellular organization

The various types of organ systems present in human body are:

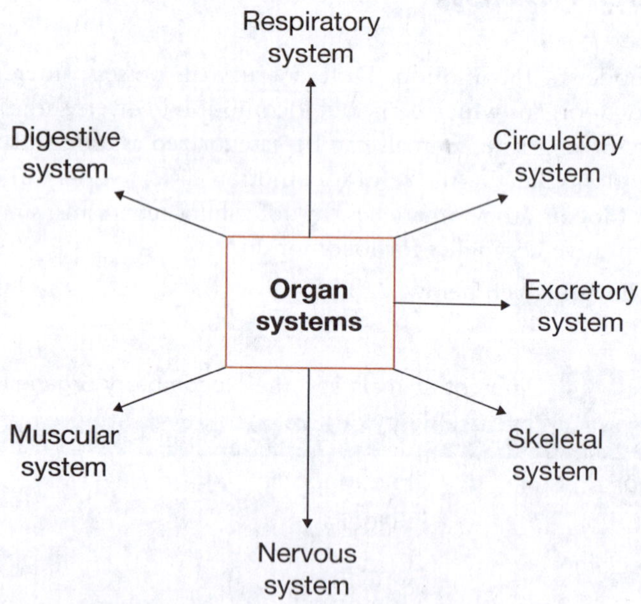

Figure 14.2 Human body—major organ systems

Body Movements and Locomotion in Human Beings

Locomotion is the main characteristic feature of animals which chiefly distinguishes animals and plants. In human beings, various body movements and the activity of locomotion are controlled by skeletal system and muscular system. The skeletal system is made up of bones and the muscular system is made up of muscles. The coordinated functioning of these two systems results in the locomotion of humans. These two systems are assisted by the other systems such as the nervous system. All the bodily functions are carried out by various systems in coordination with each other.

Skeletal System

The system which supports the overall body by providing a definite shape and helps in the movement is known as skeletal system. **Skeleton** is the framework of bones in the body. Let us now learn some points about bones.

1. The adult human skeleton consists of 206 bones. In infants, there are around 300 bones at the time of birth. But many of these bones get fused together to form 206 bones during the growth of baby into an adult.
2. Bones form the framework of a body and are made up of strong and non-fixable living tissues.
3. They are very hard on the outer side and soft on the inner side.
4. The soft pulpy substance inside the bone is called **bone marrow**. The blood cells originate in the bone marrow.
5. The bones are connected to each other by means of structures called joints.
6. The soft structure present at the end of bones at joints is known as **cartilage**.
7. The cartilage is a tough elastic tissue softer than bone found at the ends of bones at the joints.

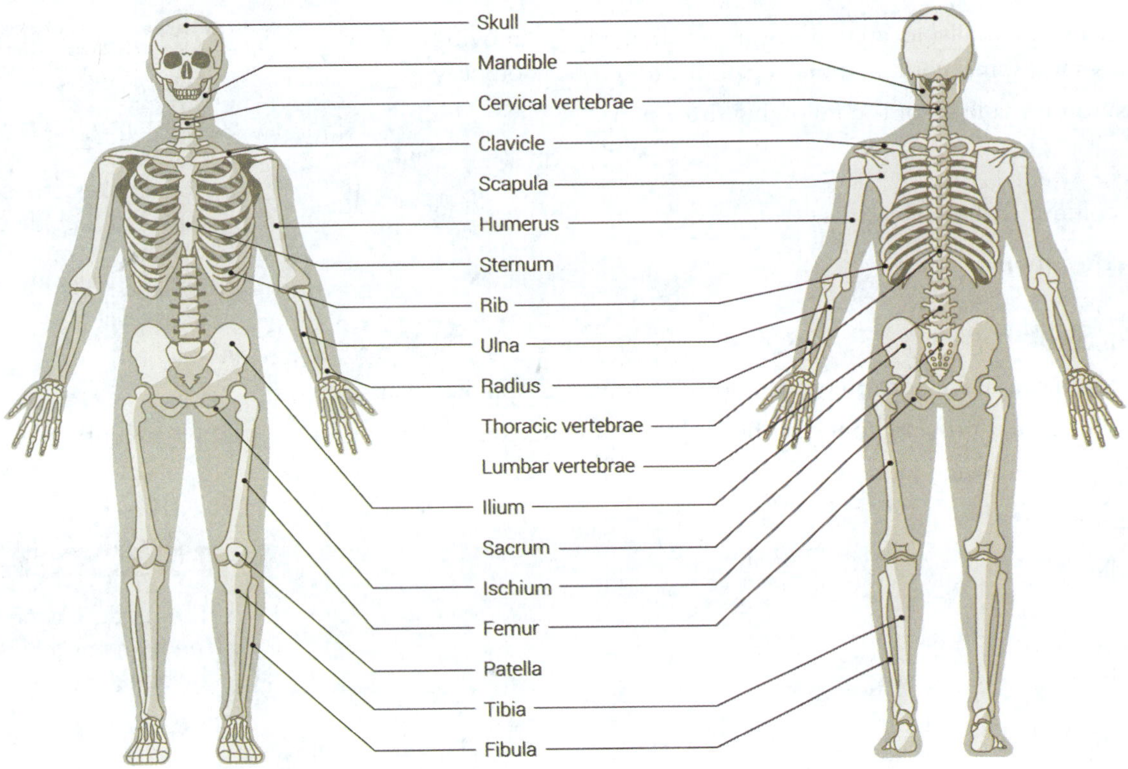

Figure 14.3 Human skeleton—showing bones in our body

Functions of Skeletal System

The skeletal system performs the following functions:

(i) **Movement of body organs:** Joints in our skeleton system facilitate body movements.

(ii) **Protection to vital organs:** The bony framework protects internal organs from injury by covering or surrounding them. For example, ribcage protects the lungs and heart.

(iii) **Shape and support to body:** It forms hard framework inside our body. Without the skeletal system, our body would be a limp mass of organs, muscle, and skin.

(iv) **Mineral reserve:** Acts as a reservoir for a number of minerals important to the functioning of the body, especially calcium, and phosphorus.

Info Bytes!

Bones are stronger than steel!

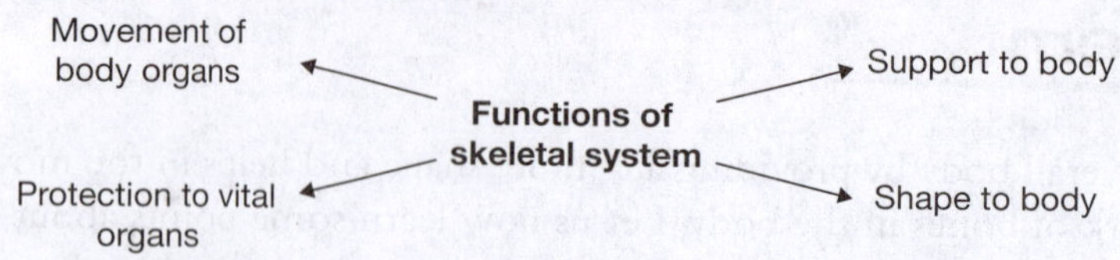

Figure 14.4 Functions performed by the skeletal system

Parts of a Human Skeleton

Based on the position and the location of bones in the body, the skeletal system is divided into two parts. They are:

1. Axial skeleton
2. Appendicular skeleton

Axial Skeleton

Axial skeleton is the centrally located portion of the body. It provides support and protection to the brain, spinal cord, and the organs in the ventral body cavity.

The axial skeleton is made up of the following three parts:

1. Skull
2. Vertebral column (Backbone)
3. Sternum (Breastbone)

Info Bytes!

Our bones are constantly being replaced. The entire human skeleton is replaced roughly every 10 years through a process called bone remodelling.

Appendicular Skeleton

The bones located on the lateral portion of the body constitute the appendicular skeleton.

The skeleton which supports and connects the limb bones with axial skeleton is known as appendicular skeleton.

It is made up of the following four parts;

1. Pectoral girdle
2. Pelvic girdle
3. Forelimbs
4. Hindlimbs

Info Bytes!

The hardest bone in the human body is the jawbone!

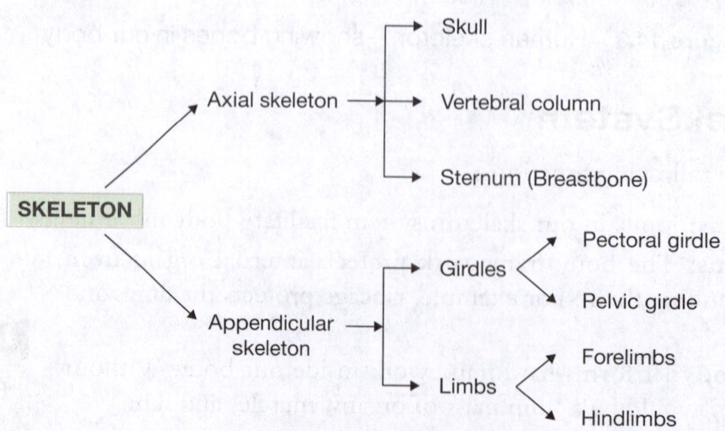

Figure 14.5 Division of human skeleton into axial and appendicular skeleton

Parts of Axial Skeleton

The axial skeleton is made up of the skull, the sternum, and the vertebral column. Let us now discuss them one by one.

Skull

- Skull is a bony framework of head. It provides helmet-like protection to our brain.
- It is made up of cranium and facial bones.
- **Cranium** is a hard bony plate made up of 8 flat bones fused together.
- All the bones in the cranium are **immovable**.
- Cranium encloses and protects the brain.
- The bones present in the facial part are called facial bones.
- Altogether, there are 14 facial bones; including the lower jaw bone and upper jaw bone.
- Lower jaw bone is the **only movable bone** in the skull region.
- The skull possesses some cavities or sockets which enclose the eyes and ears.

Konnect

Teeth are the strongest substance in your body being made up of enamel and dentin.

Vertebral Column

- Vertebral column is also called **backbone** as it provides support to the body.
- It runs from the base of the skull to the lower back.
- The vertebral column is made up of 33 small irregularly shaped bones joined together.
- These small bones which make up the vertebral column are called **vertebrae**.
- The vertebrae are arranged in the shape of 'S'. This makes the vertebral column strong and flexible.
- Each vertebra has a hole in the centre. These holes in all the vertebrae are placed one below the other to form a canal.
- The spinal cord runs through this canal. The vertebral column is also called spine as it encloses and protects the spinal cord.
- The **spinal cord** is a long thin, tubular structure which arises from the brain. It is made up of nervous tissue.
- It helps in the body movement.

Sternum

- Sternum is also known as **breastbone**.
- The sternum is made up of hard immovable bone present in the chest cavity.
- It serves as a place of attachment for the bones of ribcage.
- The 12 pairs of thin curved bones present on the lateral side of the chest region are called **ribs** or **rib bones**.
- The first 7 pairs of ribs are joined to the vertebral column on the back side and to the sternum on the front side, these are called **true ribs**.

- The next 3 pair of ribs do not join the sternum directly but are connected to the 7th rib by cartilage, these are false ribs. The last 2 pair of ribs are smaller in size than the others and do not reach to the front of the body. These are **floating ribs**.
- These 12 pairs of ribs along with the sternum and the part of vertebral column attached by rib bones constitute the ribcage.
- This ribcage gives protection to the heart and lungs. Ribcage also assists in respiration as ribs provide surface for the attachment of muscles concerned with respiratory mechanism.

Info Bytes!

About one person out of every 200 is born with an extra rib!

Axial skeleton

Skull

Structural features
- Bony framework of the head is cranium. It has 8 flat bones.
- There are 14 facial bones.
- All are immovable bones except lower jaw.

Functions
- Cranium encloses and protects the brain.
- Provides space for fixation of eyes and ears.

Vertebral column (Backbone)

Structural features
- Starts from the base of the skull to the lower back.
- The strong and flexible 33 irregularly shaped bones are called vertebrae.
- Vertebrae are arranged in the shape of S.
- There is a hole in the middle of each vertebra.
- Spinal cord runs through these holes. Hence, it is also called spine.

Functions
- Provides protection to spinal cord.
- Provides support to body. Helps in body movement.
- Provides flexibility and bending.

Sternum (Breastbone)

Structural features
- Hard, immovable bone and present in the chest region.
- The 12 pairs of thin and curved bones are called ribs.
- The 7 pair of ribs called true ribs.
- The last 2 pairs are called floating ribs.

Functions
- They work with the diaphragm to bring about the process of respiration.
- Ribcage protects the heart and the lungs.

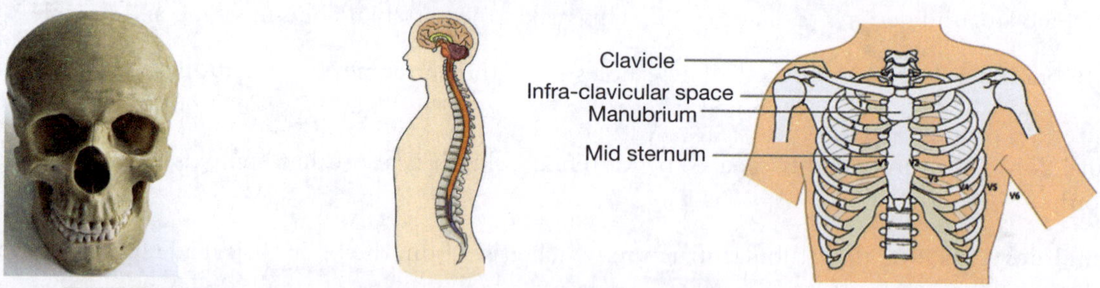

Figure 14.6 Features and functions of different parts of the axial skeleton

Parts of Appendicular Skeleton

The appendicular skeleton consists of the girdles and the limbs.

Girdles

The bones that provide support and space for the articulation (movement) of limb bones are known as girdles.

Based on the location of body, they are divided into two parts:

1. **Pectoral girdle** is located in the upper portion of the body.
2. **Pelvic girdle** is located in the lower portion of the body.

Pectoral Girdle

Pectoral girdle supports the chest region or the region below the neck on the lateral sides. It links the forelimbs with the vertebral column. It is made up of two bones, the collar bone and the shoulder bone. This girdle forms the ball and socket joints on both sides. It helps in the movement of arms and shoulders.

Pelvic Girdle

Pelvic girdle supports the hip region. It links hindlimbs with the vertebral column. It is formed by the fusion of three bones, which include one thigh bone, two shank bones and connects the hind limbs. It forms the ball and socket joints on both sides. This girdle helps in the movement of hips.

Girdles

Pectoral girdle

- Supports the chest region.
- Links forelimbs (arms) with the vertebral column.
- Made up of two bones which includes collar bone and shoulder bone.
- It is attached to forelimb and forms the ball and socket joint.
- Helps in the movement of shoulders.

Pelvic girdle

- Supports the hip region.
- Links hindlimbs (legs) with the vertebral column.
- It is formed by the fusion of 3 bones and hindlimb.
- It is attached to form the ball and socket joint.
- Helps in the movement of hips.

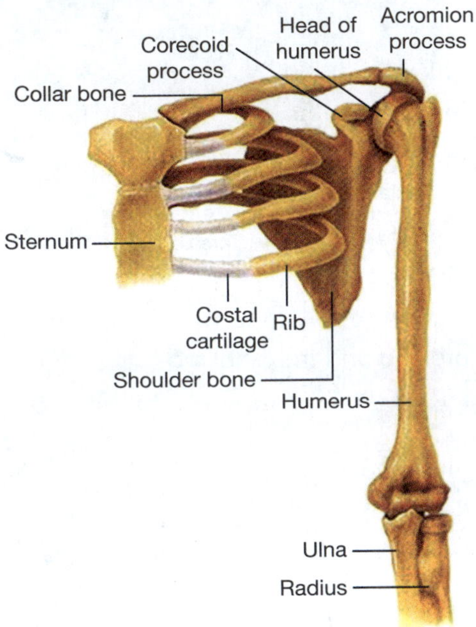

Figure 14.7 Bones present in the pectoral girdle

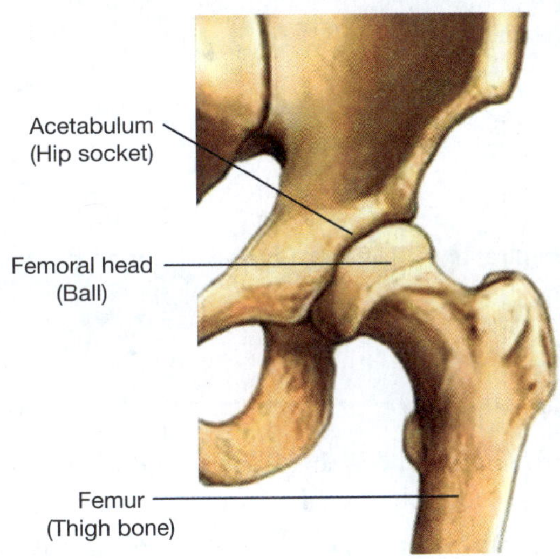

Figure 14.8 Bones present in the pelvic girdle

Limbs

The bones present in the hands and legs which are connected to the respective girdles help in the body movements to perform various activities. Each arm is made up of three long bones, which are **humerus**, **radius** and **ulna**. Each hand has 8 bones in the wrist **(carpals)** and 19 bones in the hands **(5 metacarpals)** and fingers **(14 phalanges).** Each leg is made up of three bones, which are **femur (thigh bone)**, **tibia and fibula (two shank bones).** Femur is the largest bone in the human body. Each foot has 7 bones in the ankle **(tarsals)** and 19 bones in the foot **(5 metatarsals)** and toes **(14 phalanges)**.

Info Bytes!

Hands and feet contain half of the total number of bones in the human body!

Limbs

- **Forelimbs**
  - Humerus (Upper arm)
  - Radius and ulna (Forearm)
  - Carpals (Wrist)
  - Metacarpals (Palm)
  - Phalanges (Fingers)
- **Hindlimbs**
  - Femur (Thigh bone)
  - Tibia and fibula (Shank)
  - Tarsals (Ankle)
  - Metatarsals (Sole)
  - Phalanges (Toes)

> **Info Bytes!**
> Stapes in the middle ear is the smallest bone in the human body.

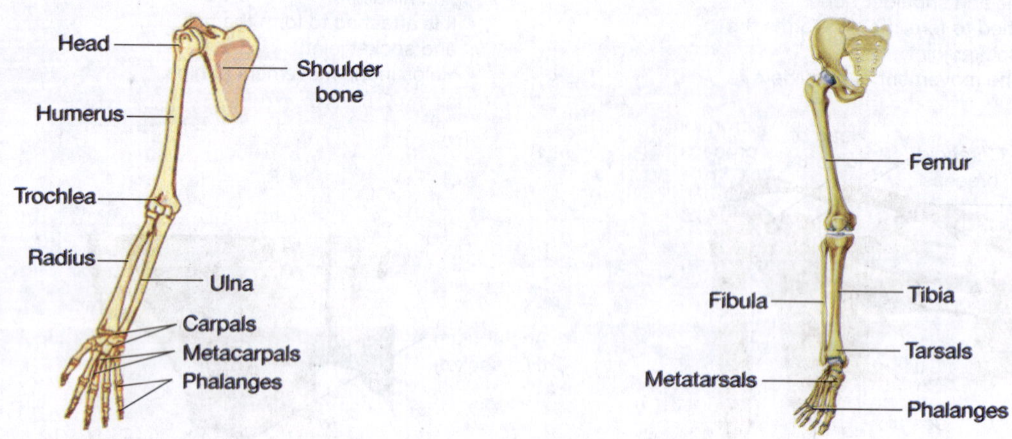

Figure 14.9 Different types of bones present in the forelimb and the hindlimb

Joints

Various bones in the human body are not free and every two bones are attached to one another. The place where two bones are attached to each other is called joint.

The joints can be of three types depending upon their ability to move.

Joints

- **Immovable joints**
  - Bones interlocked with cartilage
  - Bones of the skull
- **Freely movable joints**
  - Ball and socket joint
  - Hinge joint
  - Pivot joint
  - Gliding joint
- **Slightly movable joints**
  - Fibrous cartilage between bones
  - Joints between vertebrae

Figure 14.10 Types of joints

Freely Movable Joints

Depending on the extent and direction of movement facilitated by the freely movable joints, they are classified into four types.

Ball and Socket Joint

- This joint is formed by two bones where a ball-shaped end of one bone fits into the hollow cup shaped socket of the other bone.
- This joint allows maximum movement in all the directions. 360 degree rotation is possible with this joint.

  Examples: Hip, knee, etc.

Info Bytes!

Synovial fluid present in the joints acts as a lubricant, reducing friction and allowing smooth movement.

Hinge Joint

- This joint is formed by two bones and is similar to the hinge of a door.
- This joint allows movement only in one direction.
- It is the strongest joint.

  Examples: Upper and lower arms connected at elbow, thigh and leg connected at knee.

Gliding Joint

- It is also known as plane joint.
- A gliding joint is formed between the bones where they meet at the flat surface.
- This joint facilitates limited movement in all the directions, i.e., left and right, up and down and diagonally.

  Examples: Hand and wrist, ankle and leg, and vertebrae in spine.

Pivot Joint

- This joint is formed in such a way that one bone rotates around the other.
- It allows rotatory movement on a single axis.
- Pivot joint is formed between the head and neck. It allows forward and backward movement and the left and right movement of head.

Role Played by Joints in Skeletal System

Joints are an essential part of the skeletal system. They play the following roles:

- A joint holds the bones together.
- Joints provide space for the attachment of muscles with tendons.
- They help in the movement of body parts.
- They bear the weight of the body.

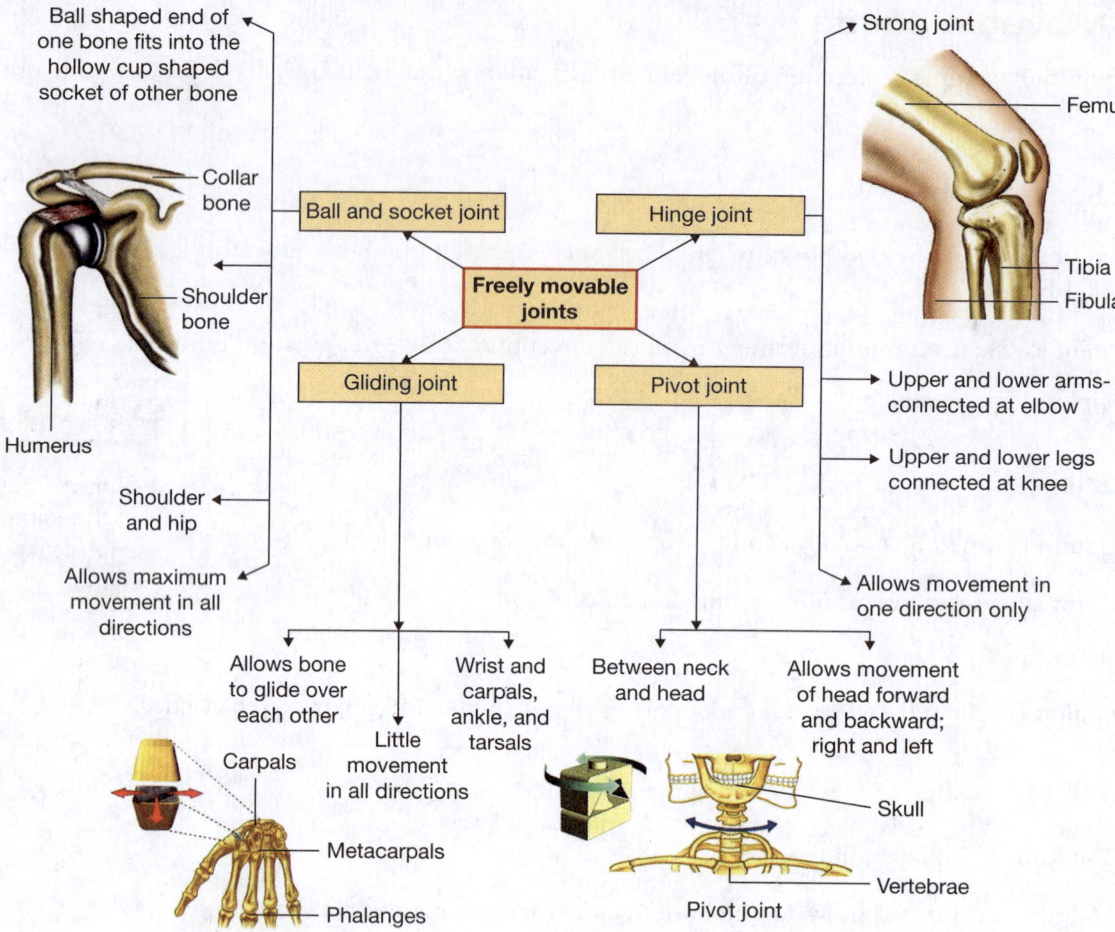

Figure 14.11 Types of freely movable joints and their examples

Muscular System

Bones cannot move on their own, they require the support of muscles for movement. Different types of muscles present in various organs of the body constitute the **muscular system**. The bones are attached to each other in a joint by means of ligaments. **Ligaments** are the bands of tough elastic tissue that hold the bones to a joint.

The muscles are attached to the bones by means of **tendons**. These muscles help the bones to move. Tendons are tough elastic tissues.

These muscles undergo successive contraction and relaxation for facilitating movement.

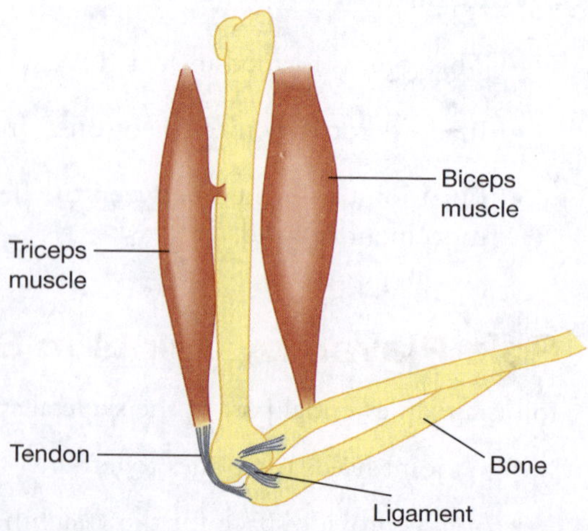

Figure 14.12 Human arm showing tendons and ligaments

Mechanism of Functioning of Muscles

The muscles attached to a bone undergo contraction and it pulls the bone. The muscles can only cause pulling effect and they cannot show pushing action. So, another muscle pulls the bone back in the opposite direction. Thus, two muscles work together to cause the movement of a bone.

Example: Movement of lower arm, the muscles involved are biceps and triceps.

Biceps: Movement of lower arm in the upward direction.

Triceps: Movement of lower arm in the downward direction.

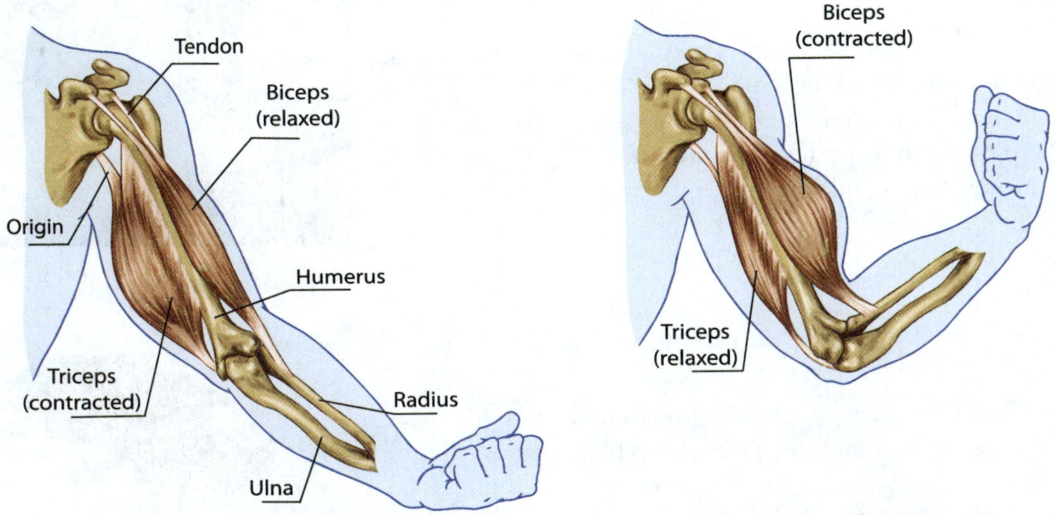

Figure 14.13 Biceps and triceps muscles showing movement of arm

> **Info Bytes!**
> The muscles of our heart are the most hard-working muscles in our body. They work continuously pumping almost 5 litres of blood per minute which amounts to 2000 gallons daily.

Role of Other Systems in Movement and Locomotion

The skeletal system and muscular system do not work independently. The other organ systems are also required for carrying out various activities that includes body movements and locomotion. Basically, energy is required to carry out various activities in the body. The energy is provided by the food consumed. The **digestive system** comprises mouth, food pipe, stomach, small intestine, large intestine and digestive glands. This system converts the complex food material into simpler substances. The digested food is absorbed into the blood. The **respiratory system** provides oxygen for the release of energy from these simpler food substances. The oxygen combines with the food absorbed into the blood. Energy is released in this process. The oxygen is transported to various organs of the body through blood by means of blood vessels. The blood vessels along with the heart forms the **circulatory system**. All the bodily activities are controlled by brain. The nerves carry messages from the brain to various organs. The brain and the nerves constitute the **nervous system**. The functioning of skeletal system and muscular system requires the transmission of messages by nervous system. The energy required for the activity is supplied by the functioning of other systems. In such way, all the body movements and its related activities take place with the coordination of other organ systems in the body.

Locomotion in Other Organisms

The organisms other than human beings do not have a well-organized skeletal and muscular system. However, they have much simpler systems and mechanisms for locomotion.

> **Info Bytes!**
> The leg bones of a bat are so thin that they can't walk!

Locomotion in Earthworm

Earthworm is an invertebrate animal. It lacks bones. The body of an earthworm is segmented. The under surface of the body is pale in colour when compared to the upper surface and it bears minute bristles, called setae. These bristles are connected with muscles at their base to get a grip on the ground. The muscles present in the body of the earthworm can contract and relax.

Locomotion in earthworm takes place in two stages.

1. **First Stage:** The earthworm extends the anterior part of the body where the setae protrude out and gets fixed to the soil forming a grip. The posterior part of the body is pulled in the forward direction due to the contraction of muscles and absorption of setae.
2. **Second Stage:** The posterior part of the body gets fixed to the ground and the anterior part of the body extends.

The muscles in the body wall help in the extension and contraction of body helping the organism to move forward.

Locomotion in Snail

The body of a snail is covered by a hard endoskeleton. The snail undergoes creeping movement with the help of a strong muscular foot which comes out of the shell. This foot is made up of muscles which undergo alternate contraction and relaxation. This creates a slow movement where the body is pushed forward. The foot also possesses special glands which secrete strong mucus and forms a slippery track on the way it moves.

Figure 14.14 Locomotion in snail

Locomotion in Cockroach

Cockroaches have a hard exoskeleton. They can walk, run, climb and fly short distances. They undergo two types of locomotion. A cockroach has three pairs of jointed legs attached to the breast region which helps it to walk on the ground. The two pairs of wings attached to the breast muscles help the cockroach to fly.

Figure 14.15 Locomotion in cockroach

Locomotion in Fish

The body of the fish is spindle-shaped and streamlined; this makes it easy to swim in water. It possesses swim bladders which help in providing upthrust (upward force) to float on water. The skeleton of the body in fish is covered with strong muscles. During swimming, the anterior part of the body bends on one side by the contraction of anterior muscles. The remaining part of the body along with tail bends in the opposite direction thereby forming a loop. Later the posterior part of the body along with the tail turns to the opposite side, thus making a jerk and pushing the body forward. A series of such jerks and movement of fins help in the forward movement of the body.

Figure 14.16 Locomotion in fish

Locomotion in Snake

The body of the snake is supported by a long backbone having numerous vertebrae. The body of a snake contains muscles which are connected to ribs, vertebrae and skin. During locomotion, the snake contracts its muscles thrusting its body from one side to the other forming loops. Each loop pushes the body against the ground which leads the body to move forward. The body of the snake is covered by scales on the surface which helps in providing grip on the uneven surface.

Figure 14.17 Locomotion in snake

Locomotion in Birds

Birds are unique animals which have the ability to fly. In birds, the forelimbs are modified into wings. The beat of the wings against the air results in the forward movement of the body. The breast muscles are strong and well-developed. They help in the movement of the wings, and hence, these are called flight muscles. The body is covered with feathers and the bones are hollow. These unique traits make the body light and suitable for flight. Apart from this, birds also possess legs for the purpose of walking when they are not in flight.

Figure 14.18 A flying bird showing locomotion

EXAMPLE 14.1 The act of walking in humans involves more than just the motion of legs; it's a result of the coordinated effort of multiple systems beyond just the skeletal and muscular systems. Discuss.

SOLUTION

Walking, a fundamental human activity, is a symphony of coordinated events. It begins with the intent to move, generated in the brain. This intent, part of the nervous system, sends signals to muscles, instigating movement. The circulatory system supplies oxygen and nutrients to these active muscles, ensuring they have the energy to contract. The respiratory system supports this by ensuring a continuous supply of oxygen and removal of carbon dioxide. Furthermore, the vestibular system in the inner ear works in tandem with vision, providing balance and spatial orientation. The integumentary system, through the skin on our feet, provides tactile feedback to adapt to different terrains. Thus, walking is a harmonized function of multiple systems in the body.

EXAMPLE 14.2 What is the similarity in the body shape of fish and birds? Justify the purpose.

SOLUTION

Both fish and birds possess streamlined body shape. Streamlined body shape means rounded in the front and narrow at the back. This shape facilitates the easy movement of fish through water and birds through air. This is because it reduces the resistance of water or air.

EXAMPLE 14.3 What is the similarity in the body shape of dolphins and aeroplanes? Justify the purpose.

SOLUTION

Both dolphins and aeroplanes possess streamlined body shapes. Streamlined body shape means rounded in the front and narrow at the back. This shape facilitates the easy movement of dolphins through water and aeroplanes through the air. This is because it reduces the resistance of water or air.

POINTS TO REMEMBER

- ✔ The structures or organs which carry out locomotion in diverse animals are known as locomotory organelles.
- ✔ A group of similar cells which are specialized to perform a particular function is called tissue.
- ✔ A group of different tissues works together to perform a specific function, this is called organ.
- ✔ A group of organs which work together to perform an activity in the body is called organ system.
- ✔ Skeleton is the framework of bones in the body.
- ✔ The adult human skeleton consists of 206 bones.
- ✔ Functions of skeletal system includes movement of body organs, protection to vital organs, support and shape to the body.
- ✔ Based on the position and the location of bones in the body, the skeletal system is divided into axial skeleton and appendicular skeleton.
- ✔ The axial skeleton is made up of the skull, the sternum, and the vertebral column.
- ✔ The appendicular skeleton consists of the girdles and the limbs.
- ✔ The place where two bones are attached to each other is called joint.
- ✔ The joints can be of three types depending upon their ability to move-Immovable joints, freely movable joints and slightly movable joints.
- ✔ Depending on the extent and direction of movement facilitated by the freely movable joints, freely movable joints can be classified into ball and socket joint, hinge joint, gliding joint and pivot joint.
- ✔ Different types of muscles present in various organs of the body constitute the muscular system.
- ✔ Ligaments are the bands of tough elastic tissue that hold the bones to a joint. They connect bone to bone.
- ✔ The muscles are attached to the bones by means of tendons.
- ✔ The organisms other than human beings do not have a well-organized skeletal and muscular system. However, they have much simpler systems and mechanisms for locomotion. For example, locomotion in earthworm, snail, cockroach, fish and birds.

PRACTICE QUESTIONS CLASSROOM WING

Very Short Answer Type Questions

Direction for questions from 1 to 10.
Fill in the blanks.

1. The ball and socket joint provides _____ degrees of rotation.
2. The vertebrae in the vertebral column are arranged in an ______-shape.
3. The total number of facial bones including the jaw bones is _____.
4. The last two pairs of ribs that do not reach the front of the body are called ________.
5. The appendicular skeleton is made up of _____ and _______.
6. In cockroach a pair of ______ helps in perceiving the sensation.
7. Earthworm moves by the contraction and relaxation of ______.
8. The tip of the nose is made up of _______.
9. The girdle that supports shoulder region is ______.
10. The joint that allows movement in only one direction is ______.

Direction for questions from 11 to 20.
Select the correct alternative from the given options.

11. Identify the joint that allows movement in all the directions.
    (a) Pivot joint
    (b) Hinge joint
    (c) Ball and socket joint
    (d) Gliding joint
12. Name the bands of tough elastic tissue that hold the bones together.
    (a) Tendon (b) Ligament
    (c) Cartilage (d) Bone
13. Which of these are parts of hindlimbs?
    (i) Femur (ii) Humerus
    (iii) Tarsals (iv) Wrist
    (a) i and ii (b) i and iii
    (c) ii and iii (d) i and iv
14. Identify the only movable bone in the skull.
    (a) Lower jaw (b) Upper jaw
    (c) Cheek bone (d) Nasal bone
15. Which animal has backbone and ribs interconnected with each other?
    (a) Fish (b) Snail
    (c) Cockroach (d) Snake
16. The adult human body consists of _____ bones.
    (a) 209 (b) 206
    (c) 207 (d) 210
17. Identify the gliding joint from the following examples.
    (a) Skull and vertebrae (b) Elbow joint
    (c) Wrist and carpals (d) Knee joint
18. The 8th, 9th and 10th pairs of ribs are called s false ribs because
    (a) they are not made of a bony structure.
    (b) they are part of the vertebrae.
    (c) they are not ribs but part of the sternum.
    (d) they are not connected to the sternum directly but via the 7th vertebra.
19. The function of the cranium is
    (a) to protect the brain.
    (b) to retain memory and reasoning.
    (c) to protect the spinal cord.
    (d) to protect vital organs like the lungs and the heart.
20. The pectoral girdle is located
    (a) near the abdomen.
    (b) in the upper portion of the body.
    (c) in the lower portion of the body.
    (d) near the hind limbs.

Direction for questions from 21 to 27.
State whether true or false.

21. Lifting of hand is caused by the contraction of muscles.
22. In birds, breastbones are modified to hold flight muscles and help in the movement.
23. The girdle that supports hip region is called pectoral girdle.

24. Clavicle is also known as breastbone.

25. Endoskeleton is seen in earthworm.

26. The pectoral girdle links the arms with vertebral column.

27. Knee joint is the ball and socket joint.

Short Answer Type Questions

Direction for questions from 28 to 33.
Answer the following.

28. Distinguish between skeleton and joint.

29. Write a note on the functions of pelvic girdle.

30. Give the importance of vertebral column in human beings.

31. Setae of earthworm helps in locomotion. Discuss.

32. Mention the type of skeleton present in earthworm.

33. Answer the given questions on the basis of the figure given.

(i) Identify the above figure and label the parts A and B.

(ii) How many small bones are present in this part?

(iii) Identify the organ which passes through the hollow tube.

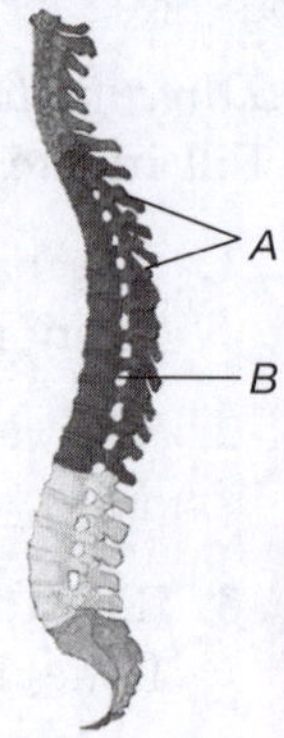

Direction for questions from 34 to 37.
Give scientific reasons.

34. Fish has a streamlined body.

35. Teeth are not considered as bones.

36. Bones of skull are immovable.

37. Spinal cord is the most vital part in human body.

Essay Type Questions

Direction for questions 38 to 39.
Answer the following.

38. **(a)** Why does your chest move up and down when you breathe?

(b) Explain the role of muscles in body movements.

39. **(a)** Name the bones that form pectoral girdle in human beings.

(b) Identify the joints present in the following.

(i) Knee (ii) Ankle

(iii) Between skull and spine (iv) Shoulder

(v) Elbow

PRACTICE QUESTIONS COMPETITION WING

Level 1: Apply Your Concepts

Direction for questions from 1 to 5.
Fill in the blanks.

1. ______ is the ability of an organism to move from one place to another.
2. The number of bones present in adult human being are ______.
3. _______ system gives protection to inner delicate organs.
4. ________ helps in the generation of blood cells.
5. The place where two bones meet is called ______.

Direction for questions 6 to 10.
Find the co-related terms.

6. _______ : Earthworm :: Foot : Snail
7. Wrist : Gliding joint :: Elbow : _______
8. 12 pairs : Ribs :: 33 : _______
9. Skeleton : Supports :: _______ : Connects
10. Humerus : Upper arm :: _______ : Thigh

Direction for questions 11 to 15.
Pick the odd one out.

11. Feathers, fins, shell, foot.
12. Femur, humerus, tibia, fibula.
13. Elbow, knee, neck, skull.
14. Skull, vertebral column, sternum, limbs.
15. Biceps, triceps, diaphragm, knee cap.

Level 2: Review Your Concepts

16. Why are last two pairs of ribs known as floating ribs?
17. Why do snakes move in zigzag manner?
18. What is the role of biceps and triceps in lifting weight?
19. Physical exercises help in keeping our bones healthy. Give reason.
20. (a) Discuss the difference between pectoral and pelvic girdle.
    (b) Name the hardest bone in the bone in the human body.
21. (a) Name the parts of axial and appendicular skeleton.
    (b) Name the locomotor organelle of amoeba, Euglena, paramecium, hydra and earth worm.

Level 3: Assess Your Concepts

22.

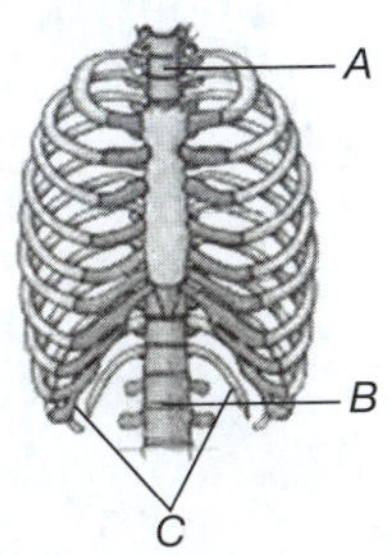

(i) Identify the given figure and label the parts A, B and C.
(ii) What is the number of bones in it?
(iii) What is the significance of C?
(iv) The given figure indicates which organ and what organs does it protect?

23. Answer the following
    (a) Why bats can't walk even though they have leg bones.
    (b) How many muscle people used while they smile and while they frown?
24. The number of bones in an adult is less than that in an infant. Give reason.
25. When a fracture occurs, bones heal naturally without any treatment. Explain.

ANSWER KEYS

Crossword

Across

3. Hip
4. Organ system
5. Tendons
6. Carpals
10. Mucus
11. Phalanges
12. Bone marrow

Down

1. Appendicular
2. Cartilage
3. Hinge
7. Locomotion
8. Backbone
9. Biceps

Classroom Wing

Very Short Answer Type Questions

1. 360
2. S
3. 14
4. floating ribs
5. girdles and limbs
6. Antennae
7. Muscles
8. Cartilage
9. Pectoral girdle
10. Hinge joint
11. (c)
12. (b)
13. (b)
14. (a)
15. (d)
16. (b)
17. (c)
18. (d)
19. (a)
20. (b)
21. True
22. True
23. False
24. False
25. False
26. True
27 False

Competition Wing

Level 1: Apply Your Concepts

1. Locomotion
2. 206
3. Skeletal
4. Bone marrow
5. Joint
6. Setae
7. Hinge joint
8. Vertebrae
9. Joints
10. Femur
11. Foot
12. Humerus
13. Skull
14. Limbs
15. Knee cap

Hints and Explanations

CLASSROOM WING

Very Short Answer Type Questions

11. The joint that allows movement in all the directions is ball and socket joint.

Hence, the correct option is (c).

12. The bands of tough elastic tissue that holds the bones together and helps in forming joints is ligament.

Hence, the correct option is (b).

13. Hindlimb is made up of bones called femur, tibia and fibula, tarsals, metatarsals and phalanges.

Hence, the correct option is (b).

14. All are immovable bones in the skull except lower jaw.

Hence, the correct option is (a).

15. Snakes are animals that have backbone and ribs interconnected with each other.

Hence, the correct option is (d).

21. True

22. True

23. False: The girdle that supports hip region is pelvic girdle.

24. False: Sternum is also called breastbone.

25. False: Endoskeleton is absent in earthworm.

26. True

27. False: Knee joint is hinge joint.

Short Answer Type Questions

28. The rigid supporting framework of an organism which supports the soft tissue is known as skeleton. The place or a point where two bones connect each other is called joint. The joint is the place of articulation which helps the body parts to provide movement.

29. Pelvic girdle is at the lower part of the trunk. It connects the lower limbs to the trunk region. It supports the weight of the body. It protects the inner delicate organs, like urinary bladder, reproductive glands and organs. Pelvic girdle enables us to walk upright.

30. Vertebral column is also called backbone. It is strong and flexible; it is made up of 33 small bones called vertebrae. It encloses and protects the spinal cord and holds the head and body upright. The joints present in between vertebrae enable us to bend or twist by providing flexibility. The fibrous cartilage present in between vertebrae acts as shock absorber. In human beings, it bears the body weight while walking and standing.

31. Skeletal system is absent in earthworm. Movement takes place by the contraction and relaxation of muscles. The body is divided into many segments and each segment bears a number of very small fine bristle-like projections called setae. In the contracted area of the body, setae project outward and fix to the soil to provide grip and pull the remaining part of the body. Thus, by constant fixing and releasing of setae and by contraction, and relaxation of muscles, movement occurs in earthworm.

32. Earthworm does not possess exoskeleton or endoskeleton. It has bristles in body segments called setae. Muscles along with setae help in locomotion.

33. (i) The given figure is identified as vertebral column.
(A) Vertebrae (B) Spine

(ii) There are 33 small bones present in the vertebral column.

(iii) The organ that passes through the hollow tube is spinal cord.

34. The body of fish is long and pointed at both the ends. This is called streamlined shape. This shape helps the animal to move faster through water, it reduces water resistance while moving. It helps the body to cut through the water more efficiently.

35. Teeth are considered as a part of skeletal system but are not considered as bones due to the following reasons.

Teeth	Bones
1. Teeth are made up of a strong substance called enamel.	• Bones are made up of calcium and phosphorous.
2. Teeth do not have regenerative capacity and cannot form new cells.	• Bones have regenerative capacity and are capable of making new bone cells.
3. Teeth neither have healing power nor can form new blood cells.	• Bones have healing power and can form new blood cells.

36. Bones of skull are made up of fibroid joints or fixed joints. These joints have no cavity and are connected to connective tissue. Skull bones are connected by immovable fibroid joints called sutures, hence, they are immovable.

37. Spinal cord is also called spine and is located in the backbone or vertebral column. It is a nervous tissue which gives out spinal nerves. These nerves help in giving responses by reflex action. It is protected by vertebral column.

Essay Type Questions

38. **(a)** The muscular layer separating thoracic and abdominal cavity is known as diaphragm. The diaphragm and ribcage help in respiration in human beings. During inhalation (breathing in), the diaphragm contracts and increases the space in chest cavity helping the lungs to expand. The muscles connected to the ribs contract raising the chest cavity. Hence, rising of the chest cavity occurs during inhalation and the air from outside enters the lungs. When diaphragm and muscles connected to ribs relax, the air is pushed out and lowering of the chest cavity occurs. Thus, chest moves up and down while breathing.

(b) Bones cannot move by themselves. They are attached to muscles. Muscles at their end have white fibres called tendons which connect them to bones. Tendons attached to bones pull the bones and make them move near the joints. Thus, tendons of muscles help in pulling the bone near the joints and help in movement. When the arm is raised, biceps decrease and become shorter and pull the arm and it helps in lifting weight.

39. **(a)** The bones that support the chest region and help in the articulation of forelimbs form pectoral girdle (shoulder girdle). It consists of a pair of collar bones. A large flat shoulder blade connected by humerus of upper arm forms the ball and socket joint.

(b) (i) Knee – Hinge joint

(ii) Ankle – Gliding joint

(iii) Between skull and spine – Pivot joint

(iv) Shoulder – Ball and socket joint

(v) Elbow – Hinge joint

COMPETITION WING

Level 1: Apply Your Concepts

6. Setae : Earthworm :: Foot : Snail
7. Wrist : Gliding joint :: Elbow : Hinge joint
8. 12 pairs : Ribs :: 33 : Vertebrae
9. Skeleton : Supports :: Joints : Connects
10. Humerus : Upper arm :: Femur : Thigh
11. Foot: It is a part of the body, others are exoskeleton.
12. Humerus: It is the bone present in hand, all others are present in leg.
13. Skull: Skull is made up of immovable joints, all others are movable.
14. Limbs: They are parts of appendicular skeleton; others are parts of axial skeleton.
15. Knee cap: It is a bone, all others are muscles.

Level 2: Review Your Concepts

16. The eleventh and twelfth pairs of ribs are known as floating ribs. They are not attached to the sternum or cartilage of sternum. They are attached only to the vertebral column and are called floating ribs.
17. Snakes have no legs but they show fast movement in a zigzag manner. The movement is carried out by alternating contraction and relaxation of a set of muscles present on the sides of the body creating series of curves. The wave-like motion pushes the body forward by pressing against the ground.
18. Biceps and triceps are the muscles of upper arm. Biceps are located in front of the upper arm, when they contract, the distance between forearm and upper arm decreases. Triceps are located at the back of the upper arm. When they contract, the elbow is extended, increasing the distance between upper arm and fore arm.
19. Physical exercises, like jogging, brisk walking, cycling and aerobics help in keeping our bones healthy. Weight bearing physical activity helps in the formation of new bone tissue and makes the bone stronger. Exercises, like swimming and cycling help in building strong muscles. Weight training exercises also increase the bone density.
20. (a)

Pectoral girdle	Pelvic girdle
1. Supports the chest region 2. It is attached to forelimbs and forms the ball and socket joint. 3. It helps in movement of shoulders	1. Supports the hip region 2. It is attached to hip form the ball and socket joints 3. It help in the movement of hips

(b) The hardest bone in the human body is the jawbone.

21. (a) Axial skeleton: Shull, vertebral column and sternum.

Appendicular skeleton: Pectoral girdle, forelimbs, hind limbs and pelvic girdle

(b) *Amoeba:* Pseudopodia

Euglena: Flagella

Paramecium: Cilia

Hydra: Tentacles

Earthworm: Setal

Level 3: Assess Your Concepts

22. (i) The given figure is identified as ribcage. A - Breastbone (sternum), B - Backbone (spine), C - Floating ribs.

(ii) These are 12 pairs in number.

(iii) Floating ribs are the pair of ribs attached only to the spine and they are not attached to the breastbone.

(iv) Ribcage protects the heart and lungs.

23. (a) The leg bone of bats is so thin that they can't walk.

(b) A person used 17 muscles while smiling and 43 muscles while they frown.

24. In infants, the number of bones is more than adults. Infants have 300 bones. As the babies grow, many small bones fuse together to form a single bone. Hence, the number of bones gets reduced changing to 206 by the time one reaches adulthood.

25. Bone is a living tissue and is a storehouse of calcium and phosphorous. When a fracture occurs, new cells are produced in large number and help in joining of the tissue. This help in healing. Calcium and phosphorous taken from the diet also help in healing process. Dressing is done if the wound is open to protect it from infection. Bandage will give support and helps in keeping the fractured bones in position without moving so that they join together.

CHAPTER

15

Health—Our Greatest Wealth

Remember

Before beginning this chapter, you should be able to:

- Understand the relation between health and food
- Identify the types of food we eat in our daily lives

Key Ideas

After completing this chapter, you should be able to:

- Describe food and nutrition
- Understand the importance of different types of nutrients
- Explain the different types of diseases
- Take preventive measures for control of various diseases
- Understand the importance of vaccination

Scientific Crypt

A Tribute to Alexander Fleming (1881–1955)

Alexander Fleming (1881-1955) was a Scottish biologist and pharmacologist whose pioneering work transformed medicine. In 1928, he made the world's first antibiotic, penicillin, by accident. Fleming's accidental discovery of mould inhibiting bacterial growth in a petri dish resulted in the development of antibiotics, which saved countless lives.

Fleming received numerous honours for his contributions, including the Nobel Prize in Physiology or Medicine in 1945, which he shared with Howard Florey and Ernst Boris Chain for their work on penicillin. This discovery paved the way for the development of antibiotics, which are now used to treat infections and save lives all over the world.

Fleming's legacy is highlighted in the chapter "Health—Our Greatest Wealth" as a reminder of the profound impact that scientific discoveries can have on our well-being, emphasising the importance of ongoing research and innovation in the field of medicine.

FUN TIME

CROSSWORD

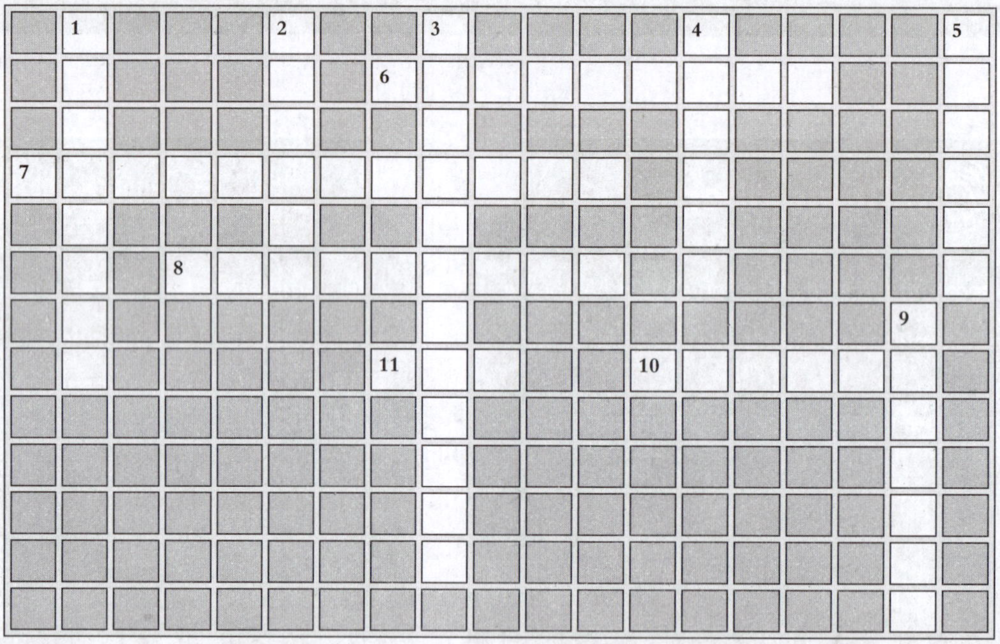

Across

6. Example of complex carbohydrate
7. Deficiency of adequate quantities of nutrients in the diet leads to
8. Deficiency of Vitamin E in males leads to
10. Spongy, bleeding gums and weakening of teeth
11. The space between two teeth

Down

1. Deficiency of protein and carbohydrate
2. Enlargement of thyroid gland
3. Pain in teeth, sensitivity to hot and cold food
4. Carbohydrate turns blue black in the presence of this solution
5. When protein is tested with the help of copper sulphate and caustic soda solution, what is the change in colour if it is a positive test?
9. A set of practices that help in the maintenance of good health and prevention of diseases

INTRODUCTION

The World Health Organization defines health as a state of complete physical, mental, and social well-being; not merely the absence of disease or infirmity. Health is the most crucial facet of our lives. Good health is imperative for positive state of mind. Healthy living is a lifelong effect. Good health keeps us productive and provides intense energy for doing our day-to-day activities.

Characteristics of Good Health

Following are the important points which define good health of a person:

- No physical ailments
- Free from mental stress
- Self-confidence and active nature

Good health can be acquired by consuming healthy, nutritious, and balanced food, sleeping well and managing stress.

Food and Nutrition

Human body is a living machine which works continuously. Energy is required for continuous work and growth of an organism. Regular exercise and healthy food help in the production of energy. Food is necessary to perform various activities in the body. The process of acquiring food by a living organism is known as **nutrition**.

Classification of Nutrition Based on the Process of Acquiring Food

On the basis of the process of acquiring food, nutrition can be of two types:

- Nutrition
  - Autotrophic → Green plants are autotrophic in nature since they can prepare their own food.
  - Heterotrophic → Animals are heterotrophic in nature since they depend on plants or animals for their food.

Figure 15.1 Classification of nutrition on the basis of the process of acquiring food

Food can also be divided on the basis of source from which it is obtained. It is generally of two types:

- Sources of food
  - Plants → In the form of fruits, vegetables, nuts, cereals, etc.
  - Animals → In the form of milk, egg, fish, honey and meat

Figure 15.2 Types of food on the basis of source

> **Info Bytes!**
>
> The food item which is neither a plant source nor an animal source is salt. It is obtained from sea water!

Table 15.1 Edible parts of plants with examples

Edible parts of plants	Examples
Root	Carrot, beetroot, radish
Stem	Ginger, turmeric, potato
Seeds	Cereals and pulses, spinach
Flower	Cauliflower, Broccoli, etc.
Fruit	Mango, apple, etc.
Seeds	Cereals and pulses

Info Bytes!

According to the Global Wellness Institute, the global health and wellness industry is worth over $4.5 trillion, showcasing the world's collective investment and interest in maintaining good health.

Nutrients

The chemical substances required for body growth and production of energy are called **nutrients**. Food is made of different types of nutrients. Nutrients help us to grow and protect us from various infections and diseases.

Classification of Nutrients Based on Their Functions

Nutrients can be divided into three categories based on their characteristics and functions.

1. Energy-giving nutrient is the nutrient which provides energy for different activities and biological processes. The energy-giving nutrients are **carbohydrates** and **fats**.
2. The body-building nutrient is the nutrient which helps in the growth of an organism and repair of injured tissues. The body-building nutrients are **proteins**.
3. Protective nutrient is the nutrient which protects an organism from diseases and it also helps in normal growth and functioning of the body. The protective nutrients are **vitamins** and **minerals**.

The following table represents the characteristics and functions of different nutrients.

Table 15.2 Characteristics and functions of different nutrients

Type	Nutrient	Characteristics	Functions
Energy-giving	Carbohydrates	• Main source of energy • Break down during the process of digestion into simple sugars. • Easily digestible	Provide energy for daily activities
	Fats	• Reserved sources of energy • Solids at room temperature • Difficult to be digested • Cholesterol is the fat present in human blood.	Provide more energy than carbohydrates
Body-building	Proteins	• Break down during the process of digestion into amino acids. • Silk fibres, hair and nails are made up of proteins.	• Growth • Repair of injured tissues
Protective	Vitamins	• Organic substances • Synthesized in plants • Vitamin B12 and vitamin D can be synthesized in human beings.	• Protection from diseases • Normal growth and functioning of body.
	Minerals	• Inorganic substances (elements) • Absorbed by the plants through soil and water.	

Classification of Carbohydrates

Based on the structural features of simple and complex carbohydrates, carbohydrates are classified into two types.

Carbohydrates

Simple carbohydrates
- Known as simple sugars
- Sweet in taste
- Can be absorbed easily
- Provide instant energy

Examples: Glucose and fructose.

Complex carbohydrates
- Known as complex sugars
- Bland in taste
- Absorbed slowly
- Provide energy slowly

Examples: Reserve food material in plants, like cellulose and starch.

Figure 15.3 Classification of carbohydrates based on absorption in the body

Info Bytes!

Honey is the only food that does not get spoiled.

Classification of Nutrients Based on Their Requirements in Our Body

Nutrients can be broadly classified into two categories based on the requirements in our body. They are **macronutrients** and **micronutrients**.

Macronutrients are the nutrients which are required in our body in large quantities. Carbohydrate, protein and fats are macronutrients. Micronutrients are the nutrients which are required in minute quantities in our body. Vitamins and minerals are micronutrients.

Macronutrients

The sources of macronutrients are given below.

Table 15.3 Macronutrients and their sources

Macronutrients	Sources	
	Plants	Animals
Fats	Vegetable oils, nuts	Butter, ghee, milk, eggs
Proteins	Cashew, almond, groundnuts	Milk and milk products, meat, fish
Carbohydrates	All cereals, potato, sweet potato	Milk

Identification of the Macronutrients Present in a Food Material

Some identity and confirmatory tests are done for the detection of carbohydrates, proteins and fats to detect their presence in various food items.

Table 15.4 Identity tests to detect the presence of carbohydrates, proteins and fats

Nutrients	Carbohydrate	Protein	Fats
Activity performed	• A small quantity of food item or a raw ingredient is taken. • 2 to 3 drops of dilute iodine solution are added to it.	• A small quantity of food item is taken in a test tube in the form of a paste or powder. • 10 drops of water are added to it and the content is shaken well. • 2 drops of copper sulphate and 10 drops of caustic soda solution are added to the content of the test tube. • The content is again shaken well.	• A small quantity of a food item is wrapped in a piece of paper and crushed in such a way that the paper does not tear. • The paper is then observed against the light.
Observation	Food item turns blue-black.	The content in the test tube turns violet.	An oily patch is observed.
Conclusion	The nutrient present is **carbohydrate.**	The nutrient present is **protein**.	The nutrient present is **fats**.

Micronutrients

Vitamins and minerals are the micronutrients required by our body.

Vitamins

Vitamins are classified on the basis of substance in which they dissolve.

> **Info Bytes!**
> Egg is the only food which contains all vitamins except vitamin C!

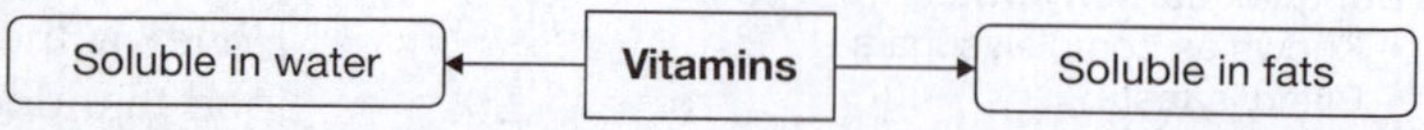

Figure 15.4 Classification of vitamins based on their solubility

Table 15.5 Vitamins with their important sources and functions along with diseases caused due to deficiency and symptoms

Solubility	Vitamins	Source	Function	Diseases Caused Due to Deficiency	Symptoms
Soluble in fats	**A**	Green leafy vegetables, carrots, cod liver oil, butter and eggs.	Healthy eyesight and skin, formation of skeletal system.	Night blindness, rupture of cornea.	Poor visibility during night.
	D	Milk, egg yolk, fish oil, butter.	Proper growth of bones and teeth.	Rickets	Bending of bones and girdles.
	E	Green leafy vegetables, soybean oil, liver.	Normal functioning of reproductive system.	Sterility in males and abortion in females.	Difficulty in producing offspring.
	K	Green leafy vegetables, soybean oil, liver.	Normal clotting of blood.	Delay in clotting of blood.	Excessive bleeding from the wound.
Soluble in water	**C**	Amla, citrus fruits, guava, green leafy vegetables, tomato.	Healthy teeth and gums, provides resistance to infection, helps in absorption and storage of iron.	Scurvy	Spongy, bleeding gums, loosening of teeth and slow healing of wounds.
	B — **B1**	Milk, cereals, nuts, yeast, whole grains. Unpolished rice (fibre rich).	Functioning of digestive system, heart, nervous and muscular system.	Beriberi	Weakness, pain in calf muscles, loss of appetite, loss of weight.
	B — **B2**	Milk, whole grains, meat, beans and leafy vegetables.	Healthy skin.	Skin disorders	Eye irritation, inflammation of tongue, cracks in corners of the mouth.
	B — **B12**	Milk, cheese, liver, fish, meat and eggs.	Formation of red blood cells, proper growth of the body.	Pernicious anaemia	Pale skin, lack of RBC, less stamina and appetite, frequent headaches.

Minerals

Minerals are naturally occurring inorganic substances that are formed due to various phenomena that happen naturally on Earth. Various minerals required by our body are given below.

Table 15.6 Minerals with their important sources and functions along with deficiency effects

Mineral	Sources	Functions	Deficiency Effects	
			Name of Disease	Symptoms
Iron	Green leafy vegetables, legumes, jaggery, liver, egg yolk, groundnut, apple, cereals.	Formation of haemoglobin in red blood cells.	Anaemia	Weakness, fatigue, loss of weight, pale skin, loss of appetite.
Iodine	Green leafy vegetables, sea food, iodized salt.	Formation of thyroxine hormone.	Goitre	Enlargement of thyroid gland, retarded growth, mental disability.
Calcium	Green vegetables, cheese, milk, eggs, whole grains, cereals.	Formation of bone and teeth, clotting of blood.	Bone and tooth decay, osteoporosis.	Weak bones, excessive bleeding from wounds, stunted growth, tooth decay, weakness.
Phosphorus	Green vegetables, nuts, cheese, milk, bajra, ragi.	Formation of bones and teeth.	Rickets	Weak bones, poor physique, mental retardation.
Sodium/ Potassium	Green leafy vegetables, sea food, iodized salt.	Contraction of muscles, transmission of nerve impulses.	Juvenile paralysis	Body weakness, muscle weakness, tiredness.
Fluorine	Tea, dry fruits, grapes, beans.	Formation of teeth, formation of bones.	Dental caries	Pain in teeth, sensitivity to hot and cold food.

Another important part of our food is dietary fibre or roughage.

Roughage

We are often advised to include a lot of raw food, such as salad, in our diet and to eat fruits along with the peel. **Plant** food material contains a lot of fibre in the form of cellulose. This dietary fibre does not have any nutritional value for us. However, it is very essential for our body. The dietary fibre or roughage, as it is commonly called, adds bulk to the undigested food material.

Info Bytes!

Oil extracted from rice husk is rich in vitamin B!

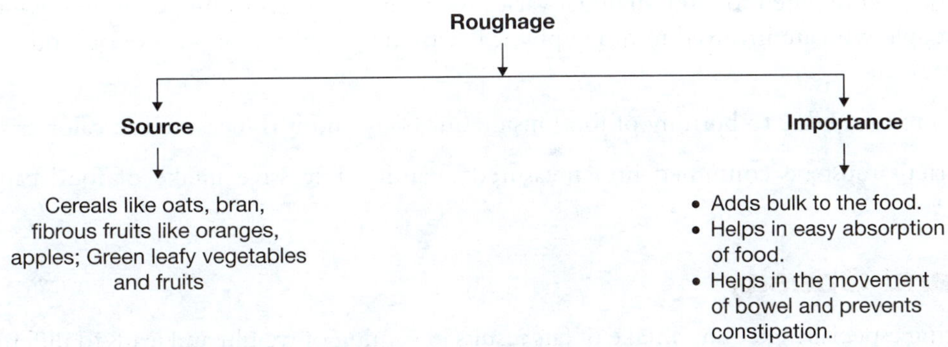

Figure 15.5 Sources and importance of roughage

Water

Apart from the essential nutrients and roughage, **water** plays an important role in the sustenance of life. Water makes up almost 70% of our body weight and it is very vital for our survival. Water acts as a medium for the digestion of all nutrients in the body. It also regulates our body temperature, transports nutrients throughout our body and also aids in excretion. We should consume 2.5–3 litres of water per day, however, this amount varies with age.

Balanced Diet

The diet which contains all the nutrients in required proportions with roughage and sufficient quantity of water is known as **balanced diet**. Balanced diet is needed to supply all nutrients to the body.

- The regular intake of balanced diet keeps us healthy.
- Inadequate consumption of the above-mentioned nutrients leads to a condition known as malnutrition.

Malnutrition

Malnutrition is the condition in which a person does not get adequate proportions of all the nutrients regularly.

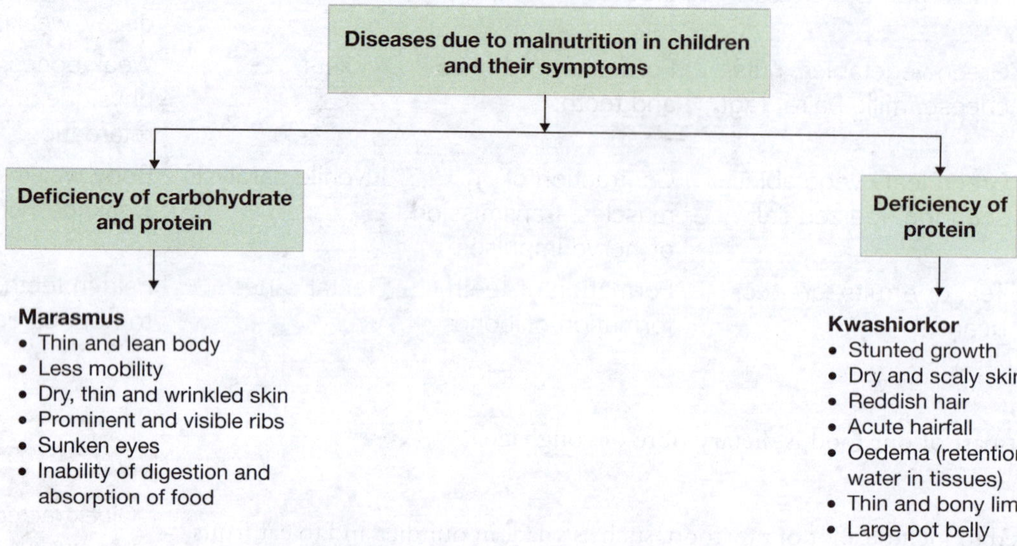

Figure 15.6 Diseases caused by malnutrition

1. Prolonged malnutrition leads to some deficiency diseases in people, particularly in children.
2. The quantity of food required for an individual varies with various stages of life. Children, young people, pregnant women and people who are involved in heavy physical activities require more intake of food since they need more energy.
3. The energy is produced due to burning of food inside our body and it is measured in calories.
4. But each nutrient must be consumed in a measured quantity. Excessive intake of food causes different health problems.

Overeating and Obesity

Unnecessary overeating especially excessive intake of fats results in gaining of weight and leads to different health problems, this condition is known as obesity. Obesity leads to different diseases, like **hypertension** and **heart problems**.

Maintenance of Good Health

Maintenance of good health not only requires balanced diet but also the inculcation of healthy habits. Sanitation and clean water are some of the basic necessities for the maintenance of our health. Let us learn some of these healthy habits.

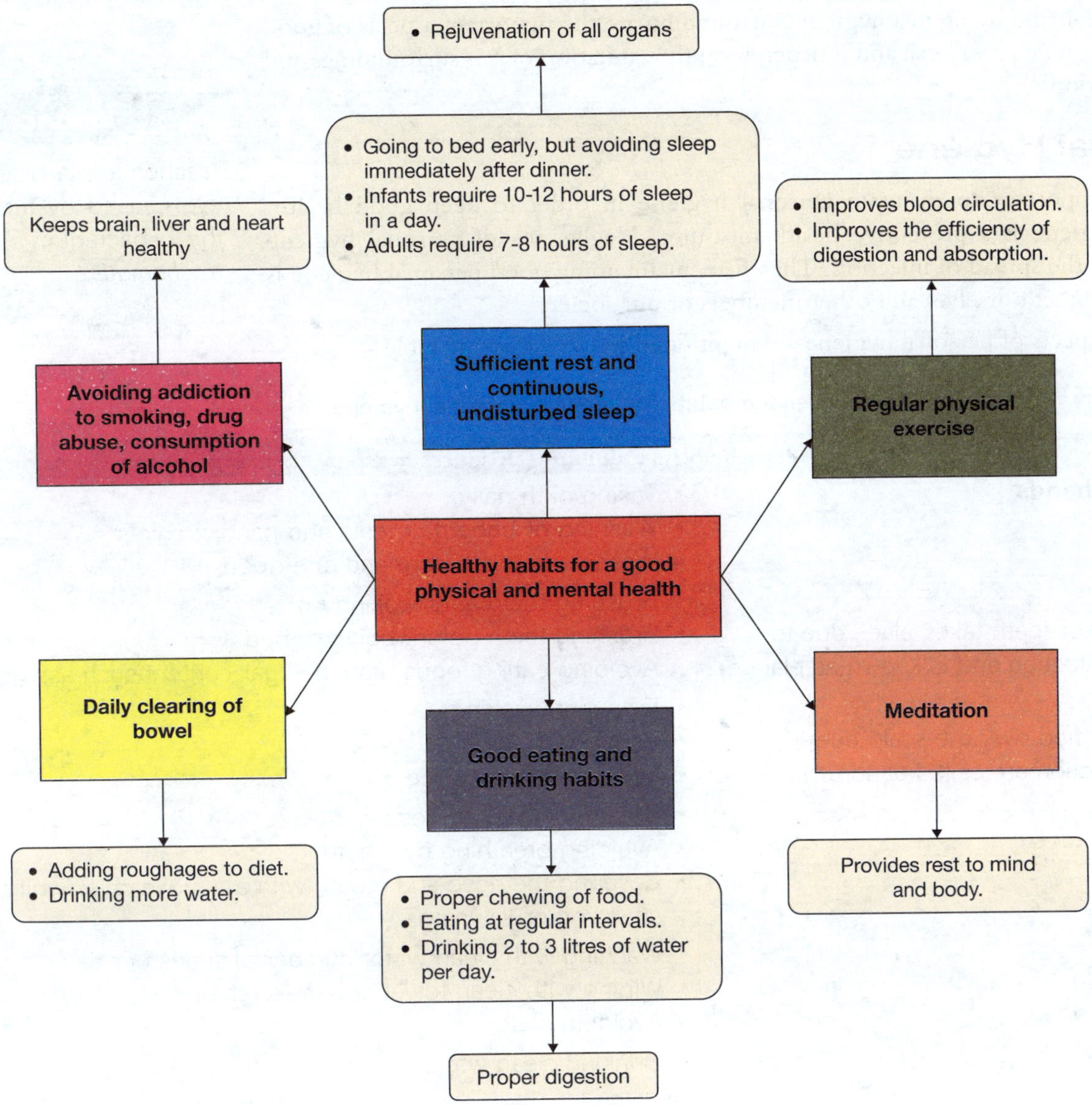

Figure 15.7 List of some healthy habits and their benefits

EXAMPLE 15.1

Carbohydrates are essential in the diet of athletes. Discuss

SOLUTION

Carbohydrates are macronutrients which are essential in the diet of athletes because:

(i) They provide a primary source of energy during physical activity.

(ii) Assist in refilling muscle glycogen stores after intense exercise.

(iii) Support optimal brain function and mental focus during competitions.

(iv) Help in recovery post-training or competition.

Hygiene

Hygiene is one of the most important requirements for good health. It is the science that deals with preservation of health. A set of practices and conditions which help in the maintenance of health and disease prevention is called hygiene. Keeping ourselves clean and living in a hygienic surrounding are the important aspects of good hygiene. Hygiene is personal and it depends on the sanitation of our surroundings and neighbourhood.

Konnect

Trachoma is a disease of the eye caused by infection with the bacterium *Chlamydia trachomatis*.

Personal Hygiene

It is very important to maintain personal hygiene in order to keep good health. Personal hygiene is a preventive health measures. Negligence of personal hygiene can result in the spread of infection. Therefore, maintaining good personal hygiene is crucial to protect ourselves and other members of our society.

Various aspects of personal hygiene are mentioned in the following table.

Table 15.7 Aspects and recommended habits for keeping personal hygiene

Aspect	Recommended Habits
Skin and hands	• Taking bath daily • Washing of undergarments and handkerchiefs • Washing hands before and after food
Mouth (Yellowing of teeth takes place due to bacterial infection and is known as plaque).	• Brushing teeth after waking up • Brushing teeth before going to bed • Avoiding eating foods high in sugar content such as chocolates
Hair (Flakes formed over the scalp due to fungal infection are called dandruff).	• Frequent washing • Regular combing • Keeping it free of lice
Breathing	• Breathing through nose • Avoiding breathing by mouth • Covering the nose and mouth with a handkerchief while sneezing or yawning
Eyes	• Washing with clean water number of times per day • Wiping with clean towel or handkerchief • Avoiding dust
Water	• Drinking clean water
House	• Living in a clean and well-ventilated house

Community Hygiene

Community hygiene is the proper maintenance of the surroundings and neighbourhood. The general community hygiene care is provided by the **municipalities** and **panchayats.**

Community hygiene involves the following measures:

- Supply of safe drinking water.
- Maintenance of open areas for fresh air.
- Maintenance of greenery and afforestation.
- Managing population by family planning.
- Spreading awareness regarding the ill effects of addiction to drug and alcohol.
- Proper disposal and management of wastes.

Proper disposal and management of wastes is necessary for maintaining community hygiene.

- Timely collection of garbage.
- Construction and maintenance of sewage pipes and drains.
- Developing parks and gardens on the dumping grounds.
- Management of wastes involves the processing of wastes generated from different sources.
- Processing of wastes can be done in two different ways, such as **composting** and **vermicomposting**.
- The vegetable and fruit peels and the excreta of animals are dumped into pits and covered by soil.
- The microorganisms present in the soil convert them into manure, this process is called composting.

Communicable Diseases

The lack of personal hygiene or community hygiene leads to the growth of microorganisms which cause diseases. Diseases which get transmitted through direct contact with an infected individual or indirectly through a vector or air or contaminated water are called communicable diseases.

Info Bytes!

Vectors are living organisms that carry and transmit infectious diseases.

The transmission of communicable diseases takes place in two different ways.

1. **Direct transmission** is the method of transfer of infectious diseases, by means of touching, biting, etc., or by droplets discharged from nose and mouth.
2. **Indirect transmission** is the method of transmission of infectious diseases that involves a vector or a medium, like air or water.

Classification of Communicable Diseases Based on the Mode of Transmission

Communicable diseases are classified into various types as shown below:

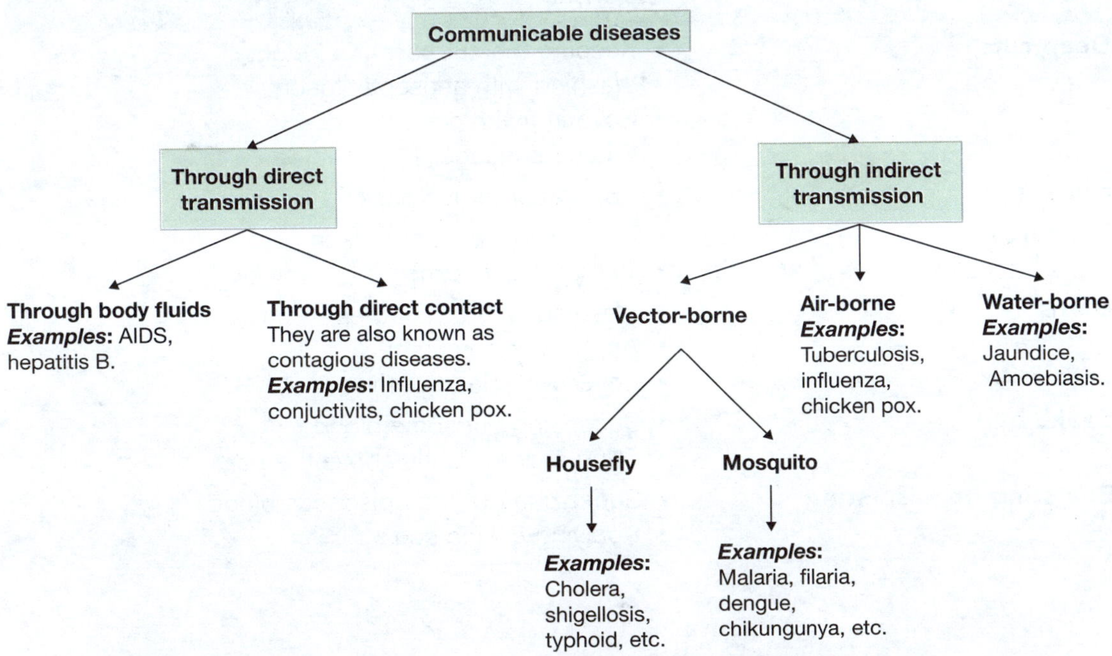

Figure 15.8 Types of communicable diseases on the basis of their transmission

Measures for the Prevention of Communicable Diseases

Following measures are useful for preventing communicable diseases:

1. Immunization of children helps protect them from life-threatening diseases. Immunization is a process of developing resistance against certain diseases, like polio, chicken pox, tuberculosis through vaccination.
2. Avoiding open eateries prevents cross-contamination.
3. Avoiding contamination through the belongings of an infected person.
4. Making the surroundings free from garbage and stagnant water.
5. Drinking safe water is vital to our health, communities, and ecosystem.

Info Bytes!

AIDS is acronym for Acquired Immune Deficiency Syndrome. It is caused by a virus called Human Immunodeficiency Virus (HIV) AIDS is not transmitted by touch!

Non-communicable Diseases

Non-communicable diseases are those diseases which do not spread from an infected person to a healthy person. They can occur due to various reasons like unhealthy lifestyle, genetics, poor nutrition, environment (poor quality of air and water), etc. Tetanus, a non-communicable disease is caused due to environmental pollution. Although the diseases previously mentioned can be avoided by implementing certain measures, certain **unexpected accidents** may also affect our well-being. People should be aware of the first aid care needed in those situations.

Konnect

The first vaccination was carried out by British doctor Edward Jenner against Small pox in 1796.

Accident and Related First Aid

First aid is the immediate care provided when a person is injured or ill until professional medical treatment is available. First aid helps in early treatment of such individuals, prevent serious injuries and in many cases save their lives. Following table lists out first-aid measures to be taken in different types of accident.

Table 15.8 First aid related to type of accident

Type of Accident	First Aid
Deep cuts	• Keeping the cut part at a height • Washing with antiseptic lotion • Covering with cotton wool • Putting bandage
Bruises	• Application of ice packs
Fractures	• Loosening cloths at broken part • Tying a sling (arm)
Burns	• Washing with cold water • Applying burn cream • Cover with clean cloth
Snake bite	• Squeezing out some blood • Tying a cloth tightly above the part
Bee sting or wasp sting	• Squeezing out the poisonous blood • Applying baking soda

EXAMPLE 15.2 Waste management systems contribute to a sustainable urban environment. Discuss.

SOLUTION

Modern cities implement effective waste management systems to handle the increasing amounts of garbage produced daily. These systems not only focus on the collection and disposal of waste but also emphasize recycling and resource recovery. Proper waste management prevents the spread of diseases, reduces environmental pollution, and conserves resources. By recycling and reusing materials, cities can ensure a cleaner and more sustainable urban environment.

EXAMPLE 15.3 As a community member, what actions can be undertaken to promote better health standards in the locality?

SOLUTION

The actions to foster improved health standards in the locality are:

(i) Organizing health awareness camps and workshops.

(ii) Ensuring clean water supply and sanitation facilities.

(iii) Setting up community-based fitness and wellness programs.

(iv) Collaborating with local health professionals for regular medical check-ups and vaccinations.

POINTS TO REMEMBER

- ✔ The process of acquiring food by a living organism is known as nutrition.
- ✔ On the basis of the process of acquiring food, nutrition can be of two types—autotrophic and heterotrophic.
- ✔ Food can also be divided on the basis of source from which it is obtained—plants and animals.
- ✔ The chemical substances required for body growth and production of energy are called nutrients.
- ✔ Nutrients can be divided into three categories based on their characteristics and functions. These are Energy-giving nutrient, body-building nutrient and Protective nutrient.
- ✔ Based on the structural complexity, carbohydrates are classified into two types—simple cabohydrates and complex carbohydrates.
- ✔ Nutrients can be broadly classified into two categories based on the requirements in our body. They are macronutrients and micronutrients.
- ✔ Carbohydrate, protein and fats are macronutrients.
- ✔ Vitamins and minerals are micronutrients.
- ✔ Roughage is the fibrous undigested part of our food which is essential for digestion process.
- ✔ Water makes up almost 70% of our body weight and it is very vital for our survival.
- ✔ The diet which contains all the nutrients in required proportions with roughage and sufficient quantity of water is known as balanced diet.
- ✔ Malnutrition is the condition in which a person does not get adequate proportions of all the nutrients regularly.
- ✔ Unnecessary overeating especially excessive intake of fats results in gaining of weight and leads to obesity.
- ✔ A set of practices and conditions which help in the maintenance of health and disease prevention is called hygiene.
- ✔ Community hygiene is the proper maintenance of the surroundings and neighbourhood.
- ✔ Diseases which get transmitted through direct contact with an infected individual or indirectly through a vector or air or contaminated water are called communicable diseases.
- ✔ Non-communicable diseases are those diseases which do not spread from an infected person to a healthy person.
- ✔ First aid is the immediate care provided when a person is injured or ill until professional medical treatment is available.

PRACTICE QUESTIONS CLASSROOM WING

Very Short Answer Type Questions

Direction for questions from 1 to 8.
Fill in the blanks.

1. ______ ______ is achieved by consuming a nutritious and balanced diet, sleeping well, and managing stress.
2. ______ are body building nutrients.
3. ______ carbohydrates are bland in taste and provide energy slowly.
4. ______ and ______ are local bodies that are responsible for maintaining general community hygiene.
5. Communicable diseases that occur through indirect transmission are ______, ______ or ______
6. High blood pressure is the symptom of ______.
7. The mineral that causes yellowing of teeth is ______.
8. Chemical substances required for the growth of body and energy production are called ______.

Direction for questions from 9 to 16.
Select the correct alternatives from the given options.

9. Potassium helps with
   (a) nerve damage.
   (b) juvenile paralysis.
   (c) formation of bones.
   (d) transmission of nerve impulses.
10. Beriberi is caused due to deficiency of
   (a) Vitamin B2 which is water soluble.
   (b) Vitamin B2 which is fat soluble.
   (c) Vitamin B1 which is water soluble.
   (d) Vitamin B1 which is fat soluble.
11. Vitamins that can be synthesized in our body are
   (a) Vitamins C and D.
   (b) B complex vitamins.
   (c) Vitamins B and C.
   (d) Vitamins D and B12.
12. Micronutrients are
   (a) required in minute quantities.
   (b) vitamins and minerals.
   (c) Both (a) and (b)
   (d) None of the above
13. Which mineral is required for the formation of thyroxine hormone?
   (a) Iodine (b) Iron
   (c) Calcium (d) Fluorine
14. Identify the reagent used to test starch.
   (a) Salt (b) Fluorine
   (c) Iodine (d) Caustic soda
15. Roughage consists of carbohydrates in the form of ______.
   (a) Sugars (b) Starch
   (c) Dietary fibres (d) Glucose
16. Identify the vitamin that helps in the clotting of blood.
   (a) D (b) A
   (c) E (d) K

Direction for questions from 17 to 29.
Fill in the blanks.

17. The practice of maintaining good health and the prevention of spreading diseases is known as ______.
18. The common diseases of eye which spread through contamination of hands are ______.
19. Yellowing of teeth due to a sticky film of saliva, food and bacteria is known as ______.
20. The science that deals with preservation of health is ______.
21. The technique used to convert agriculture and vegetable wastes to manure is ______.
22. The disease which spreads from one person to another by means of water, food or contact is known as ______.

23. The ability in human body to fight infections is developed by __________.

24. The living organisms that help in transmission of disease from one person to other are known as ______.

25. If earthworms are released into composting pits, then it is called __________.

26. Injuries formed due to rupture of blood capillaries under the skin are called ______.

27. Droplet infection is controlled by using __________ while sneezing and coughing.

28. The immediate care given to a person before taking the victim to the doctor is called ________.

29. Dengue fever is a/an __________ borne disease.

Direction for questions from 30 to 34.
Select the correct alternative from the given options.

30. Identify a disease which is transmitted by houseflies.
    (a) Malaria (b) Cholera
    (c) Plague (d) Leprosy

31. The disease AIDS comes under which category?
    (a) Communicable (b) Non-communicable
    (c) Deficiency (d) Contagious

32. Which of the following diseases is transmitted by a carrier?
    (a) Malaria (b) Hepatitis B
    (c) Chicken pox (d) Influenza

33. Oral plaque consists of which microorganisms?
    (a) Fungus (b) Virus
    (c) Microbes (d) Bacteria

34. What is the duration of undisturbed sleep required by an adult?
    (a) 12–14 hours (b) 7–8 hours
    (c) 10 hours (d) 2–3 hours

Direction for questions from 35 to 36.
Pick the odd one out.

35. Cellulose, glucose, starch, ghee.

36. Milk, meat, nuts, rice.

Direction for questions from 37 to 41.
Find the co-related terms.

37. Chapatti : Carbohydrate :: Soybean : __________

38. Iron : __________ :: Calcium : Clotting of blood

39. __________ : Tissue repair :: Fats : Insulators

40. Cholesterol : Fats :: Silk : __________

41. Carrots : Roots :: Cabbage : ________

Direction for questions from 42 to 44.
State whether true or false.

42. No mammal can digest cellulose.

43. Fats work like body's energy banks.

44. Vitamin D is synthesized in the skin when the body is exposed to sunlight.

Short Answer Type Questions

45. Why is community hygiene important?

46. What is the importance of micronutrients?

47. How is food tested for the presence of fat?

48. Give reason why doctors insist on adding green leafy vegetables to the diet.

49. When do you say that a person is healthy?

50. In which way is food necessary to maintain good health?

Direction for question 51.
Give scientific reasons.

51. Vitamins and minerals are considered protective foods.

Direction for questions from 52 to 58.
Answer the following questions.

52. Personal hygiene helps in keeping us healthy. Discuss.

53. Discuss about the following healthy habits.
    (i) Physical exercise (ii) Avoiding intoxication

54. Mention the diseases spread by direct transmission.

55. Rubbing of eyes with hands should be avoided. Give reasons.

56. List out the five deficiency disorders caused by improper consumption of vitamins.

57. 

(i) Identify the type of macronutrients present in the above figure.

(ii) Give two plant sources for the above nutrient.

(iii) Why should this nutrient be included in daily diet?

(iv) Mention the disease caused in children due to deficiency of this nutrient.

58. Discuss why poverty is considered to be one of the factors for malnutrition.

Direction for questions from 59 to 63.
Give scientific reasons.

59. Exercise helps in building health.

60. Avoid sharing personal articles, like handkerchiefs, towels, combs, etc.

61. Water pollution makes water unfit for drinking.

62. Obesity leads to heart problems.

63. Improper diet leads to malnutrition.

Direction for questions from 64.
Answer the following question.

64. Mention the different methods of hair care.

Essay Type Questions

65. Define nutrients and give their classification.

66. 

(i) Identify the nutrients A, B, C, D, E.

(ii) Give the functions of A, B, C, D, E.

(iii) Identify the substance missing in balanced diet.

(iv) 'Health is wealth'. Discuss.

67. Give one word for the following.

(a) Deficiency of iron.

(b) Deficiency of proteins in children.

(c) Disorder resulting due to overeating.

(d) Surviving on dead animals.

(e) Deficiency of iodine.

(f) Dietary fibres.

(g) Lives inside the body of the host.

(h) Chemicals substances that provide energy for day to day activities.

(i) Process of preparation of food by green plants.

(j) Seeds obtained from grasses.

68. Define nutrients and give their classification.

PRACTICE QUESTIONS COMPETITION WING

Level 1: Apply Your Concepts

Direction for questions from 1 to 5.
Fill in the blanks.

1. ________ are obtained from grasses, such as wheat, rice and maize.
2. Different items that make up food are known as ________.
3. ________ food is the food that is safe and fit to eat.
4. Animal like vultures consume dead animals, hence, they are called ________.
5. Nutrients which help in body building are ______.

Direction for questions from 6 and 7.
Match Column I with Column II.

6.

Column I	Column II
(1) Hygiene	(a) Air pollution
(2) Conjunctivitis	(b) Improper brushing
(3) Automobiles	(c) Waterborne
(4) Plaque	(d) Practice and conditions to maintain health and prevent diseases
(5) Jaundice	(e) Eye infection

7.

Column I	Column II
Vitamin	**Deficiency disorder**
(1) Vitamin C	(a) Softness of bones
(2) Vitamin K	(b) Nervous disorders
(3) Vitamin A	(c) Bleeding in gums and internal organs
(4) Vitamin D	(d) Spontaneous bleeding
(5) Vitamin B	(e) Night blindness

Direction for questions from 8 to 11.
Pick the odd one out.

8. Rickets, goitre, xeropthalmia, AIDS.
9. Chlorination, sedimentation, boiling, dumping.
10. Contamination, vaccination, immunization, healthy diet.
11. Kwashiorkar, night blindness, scurvy, rickets.

Direction for questions from 12 to 19.
Find the co-related terms.

12. Direct contact : AIDS :: ________ : Tuberculosis
13. Goiter : Non-communicable :: Conjunctivitis : ______
14. Composting : Vegetable peels :: Vermicomposting : ________
15. Brushing : Oral hygiene :: Afforestation: ________
16. Oral hygiene : ________ :: Sewage disposal : Community hygiene
17. ________ : Housefly :: Malaria : Mosquito.
18. Marasmus : Malnutrition :: ________ : Excess diet
19. Dental caries : ________ :: Anaemia : Iron

Direction for questions from 20 to 27.
State whether true or false.

20. Oral hygiene is mainly concerned with the care of eye.
21. Formation of white flakes over the scalp and hair is dandruff.
22. Ice packs are applied on the region of deep cuts.
23. Human body develops the ability to fight infection by immunization.
24. Thermometer is a medicine in first aid kit.
25. Iodine is present in sea foods.
26. Bleeding in gums and internal organs is the symptom of anaemia.
27. Deficiency of carbohydrates in diet causes kwashiorkor.

Level 2: Review Your Concepts

28. Write a note on Marasmus and kwashiorkor:

29. Cellulose acts as roughage in our diet. Give reasons.

30. (a) Write a note on protective foods

(b) Why it is recommended to add green leafy vegetable to the diet?

31. Give reasons why overpopulation causes disturbances in community hygiene.

Level 3: Assess Your Concepts

32. What happens if a protein-free diet is consumed for a prolonged period?

33. Walking barefoot must be avoided. Give reasons.

34. Compost helps in increasing the fertility of soil. Give reasons.

35. A child is provided with chapattis and rice alone. Mention the nutrients which are deficient in his body and identify the symptoms expected in the child.

36. Why are we advised to eat unpolished rice (brown rice) rather than polished rice?

37. (a) Write the name of disease caused by the deficiency of following minerals:
   (i) Calcium
   (ii) Sodium
   (iii) Iron
   (iv) Fluorine
   (v) Iodine

(b) Given example of the following:
   (i) Vector-borne communicable disease
   (ii) Air-borne communicable disease
   (iii) Water-Borne communicable disease

38. A person can die in a few days without consumption of water. Explain.

AT

ANSWER KEYS

Crossword

Across

6. Cellulose 7. Malnutrition 8. Sterility 10. Scurvy 11. Gap

Down

1. Marasmus 2. Goitre 3. Dental caries 4. Iodine 5. Violet
9. Hygiene

Classroom Wing

Very Short Answer Type Questions

1. Good health 2. Proteins 3. Complex 4. Municipalities and panchayats
5. Vector-borne, water-borne and air-borne 6. Obesity 7. Fluorine
8. Nutrients 9. (d) 10. (c) 11. (d) 12. (c) 13. (a)
14. (c) 15. (c) 16. (d) 17. Hygiene 18. Conjunctivitis
19. Plaque 20. Hygiene 21. Composting 22. Communicable disease
23. Immunization 24. Vectors 25. Vermicomposting 26. Bruises
27. Handkerchief 28. First aid 29. Vector 30. (b) 31. (a) 32. (a)
33. (d) 34. (b) 35. Ghee 36. Rice 37. Protein
38. Formation of haemoglobin 39. Proteins 40. Protein 41. Leaf
42. False 43. True 44. True

Competition Wing

Level 1: Apply Your Concepts

1. Cereals 2. Ingredients 3. Edible 4. Scavengers 5. Proteins
6. (1) → (d); (2) → (e); (3) → (a); (4) → (b); (5) → (c)
7. (1) → (c); (2) → (d); (3) → (e); (4) → (a); (5) → (b)
8. AIDS 9. Dumping 10. Contamination 11. Kwashiorkor 12. Droplet infection
13. Communicable 14. Earthworms 15. Community hygiene 16. Personal hygiene
17. Cholera 18. Obesity 19. Fluorine 20. False 21. True 22. False 23. True
24. False 25. True 26. False 27. False

Hints and Explanations

CLASSROOM WING

Very Short Answer Type Questions

14. The reagent used to test starch is iodine.

Hence, the correct option is (c).

15. Roughages are fibrous non-digestible carbohydrates which form dietary fibres.

Hence, the correct option is (c).

16. The vitamin that helps in clotting of blood is vitamin K.

Hence, the correct option is (d).

30. Cholera is the only disease transmitted by housefly.

Hence, the correct option is (b).

31. AIDS is a communicable disease which infects a person through direct contact.

Hence, the correct option is (a).

32. Mosquitoes act as carriers in the transmission of malaria. Other diseases are spread by direct transmission.

Hence, the correct option is (a).

33. Oral plaque is caused by bacteria.

Hence, the correct option is (d).

34. The duration of undisturbed sleep required by an adult is 7–8 hours.

Hence, the correct option is (b).

35. Ghee: It is a fat and all others are carbohydrates.

36. Rice: It is a carbohydrate and all others are proteins.

37. Chapatti : Carbohydrate :: Soybean : Protein

38. Iron : Formation of haemoglobin :: Calcium : Clotting of blood

39. Proteins : Tissue repair :: Fats : Insulators

40. Cholesterol : Fats :: Silk : Protein

41. Carrot : Root :: Cabbage : Leaf

42. False: Herbivores and mammals can digest cellulose.

43. True

44. True

Short Answer Type Questions

45. Community hygiene is important because it takes care of sanitation and hygiene of public places, prevents breeding of vectors and prevents the spread of communicable diseases.

46. Vitamins and minerals are micronutrients. While they are required in minute quantities in the body, they help to protect the body and also carry out various important functions.

47. A small quantity of a food item is wrapped in a piece of paper and crushed in such a way that the paper does not get torn. The paper is then observed against the light. The oily patch reveals the presence of fats.

48. Green leafy vegetables are added to diet as they contain minerals and vitamins. Minerals like calcium are present due to which formation of bones and teeth takes place. Calcium also helps in muscle movement by muscle contraction and blood clotting after injury. Vitamins like 'A' and 'D' are present. They also contain cellulose which is not digestible by human beings. This acts as dietary fibre or roughage and it helps in easy absorption of nutrients, easy movement of bowel and prevents constipation.

49. A person is said to be healthy, if the following characters are seen.

(i) Free from diseases.
(ii) Relaxed and no anxiety.
(iii) Having self-confidence.
(iv) Has the calibre to work efficiently.
(v) Without any physical ailments (handicapped).
(vi) Looks cheerful and energetic.

50. Food is required to perform various activities for survival. It is required for growth; it maintains immunity, i.e., protects our body from infections and diseases. It helps in the repair of injured parts by adding new cells.

51. Vitamins and minerals are known as micronutrients. They are needed in very minute quantities which help in controlling metabolism. Improper functioning of the body and deficiency disorders occurs due to the deficiency of vitamins. They protect the body against diseases, hence, vitamins and minerals are known as protective foods.

52. Personal hygiene involves the practices you perform in maintaining cleanliness of your body. This helps in keeping our body healthy without infections caused by micro-organisms preventing illness. The components of personal hygiene are:

(i) Hand washing—To prevent infection from microorganisms.

(ii) Taking bath regularly, changing undergarments regularly, avoid wearing tight clothes.

(iii) Avoid walking barefoot to prevent from injuries and bacterial infections.

(iv) Oral hygiene—Avoid plague building components, eat fibre rich diet. Brushing teeth before and after eating.

(v) Eye care—Avoid rubbing eyes, maintain distance while reading, protect eyes from bright sunlight, take vitamin A-rich diet.

(vi) Hair care—Do not share towels and combs. Scalp should be massaged regularly to enhance blood circulation. Balanced diet is necessary. Wash hair twice or thrice a week to protect it from parasites and dandruff.

53. The following are the healthy habits to be followed by an individual.

1. Physical exercise (physical activity)
   a. Burn excess calories.
   b. Strengthen bones and muscles.
   c. Maintenance of glucose level in blood.
   d. Controls cholesterol and blood pressure.
2. Avoiding intoxication: Tobacco, alcohol and drugs are to be avoided as they cause disturbances in physical and mental health. This, in turn shows adverse effect on the healthy community.

54. The diseases spread by direct transmission are:

- Skin diseases
- Eye infections
- Tuberculosis
- Influenza
- Tetanus
- Common cold
- AIDS
- Cholera and typhoid.

55. Rubbing of eyes with hands should be avoided. Unwashed hands contain dust and microorganisms which cause infections. Eye infections are transmitted by contact.

56.

Vitamin	Deficiency Disorder
1. Vitamin A	1. Night blindness, poor vision
2. Vitamin C	2. Scurvy
3. Vitamin D	3. Rickets
4. Vitamin B	4. Beriberi
5. Vitamin K	5. Delay in clotting of blood

57. (i) The macronutrients present in the given figure are proteins.

(ii) The two sources of the plants, such as soybeans and pulses are shown in the above figure.

(iii) This nutrient is included in daily diet for the purpose of body building.

(iv) Deficiency of this nutrient in children leads to a disease called kwashiorkor.

58. Poverty is one of the main factors for malnutrition. Many children do not get proper balanced diet due to insufficient earnings of the parents. Such children are fed with unbalanced diet. Children fed only with rice have protein deficiency in them. Nutritional requirements cannot be fulfilled due to non-availability of food. This condition leads to malnutrition.

59. Healthy habits to maintain good health are as follows:

(i) Avoid unnecessary stress and tensions.

(ii) Sleep for 7 to 8 hours.

(iii) Regular exercises, like jogging, brisk walking, swimming, cycling, etc., improves blood circulation. They also helps in keeping the heart, lungs and muscles healthy. Thus, exercise helps in building up health.

60. Handkerchiefs, towels and combs are personal articles and should not be shared by others since infectious diseases get transmitted by using them. Contaminated articles may infect the healthy person by contact. Therefore, sharing personal articles should be avoided.

61. Industrial effluents, disposal of sewage, pesticides and fertilizers used by farmers and oil spills cause water pollution. Polluted water contains unwanted poisonous chemicals and microorganisms. Polluted water causes serious diseases, like jaundice, amoebiasis and cholera. Hence, it is unfit for drinking.

62. Obesity is caused by excessive intake of fats due to which the total mass of the body increases. Excess fat gets deposited on the walls of the arteries as cholesterol.

This increases the probability of heart problems. The flow of blood slows down and this condition leads to heart attack.

63. (i) The diet which contains all the nutrients in required proportions is known as balanced diet.

(ii) Requirements of energy differ from one person to other.

(iii) Improper intake of nutrients in diet leads to malnutrition which causes deficiency disorders in children and adults.

64. Different methods of hair care are:

1. Scalp should be washed once in 2 to 3 days.
2. Massaging of scalp with oil to enhance blood circulation.
3. Combs and towels should not be shared by others.
4. Colouring agents or dyes should be avoided.

Essay Type Questions

65. The chemical substances required for body growth and the production of energy are called nutrients.

Classification of nutrients based on their requirements in our body.

- Nutrients can be broadly classified into two categories based on their amount required by the body.
- They are macronutrients and micronutrients.
- Macronutrients are the nutrients which are required in our body in large quantities.
- Carbohydrate, protein and fats are macronutrients.
- Micronutrients are the nutrients which are required in minute quantities in our body.
- Vitamins and minerals are micronutrients.

Classification of nutrients based on their functions:

- Nutrients can be divided into three categories based on their characteristics and functions.
- Energy-giving nutrient is the nutrient which provides energy for different activities and biological processes. It includes carbohydrate and fats.
- Body-building nutrient is the nutrient which helps in the growth of an organism and repairing of injured tissues. It includes protein.
- Protective nutrient is the nutrient which protects an organism from diseases and also helps in normal growth and functioning of the body. It includes vitamins and minerals.

66. Nutrients

(i) A - Carbohydrates; B - Proteins; C - Fats; D - Minerals; E - Vitamins.

(ii) A - Carbohydrates help in giving energy.
B - Proteins help in body building.
C - Fats act as source of energy and insulators.
D - Vitamins
E - Minerals
(D and E:) Protective food required for proper growth and development.

(iii) The substance missing in balanced diet is water which acts as a solvent for various metabolic processes.

(iv) In a healthy state, a person is found physically, mentally and socially fit. The defence mechanism in the body also works efficiently and it helps in fighting against various agents which disturb health. Physical, mental, social and emotional fitness is the greatest achievement in an individual. Hence, we consider 'Health is Wealth'.

67. The correct answers are:

(a) Anaemia (b) Kwashiorkor
(c) Obesity (d) Scavengers
(e) Goitre (f) Roughages
(g) Parasites (h) Carbohydrates
(i) Photosynthesis (j) Cereals

COMPETITION WING

Level 1: Apply Your Concepts

6. The correct match is:
(1) → (d); (2) → (e); (3) → (a); (4) → (b); (5) → (c)

7. The correct match is:
(1) → (c); (2) → (d); (3) → (e); (4) → (a); (5) → (b)

8. **AIDS:** It is a communicable disease, others are non-communicable diseases.

9. **Dumping:** It is the process for maintaining sanitation. All others are methods to purify water.

10. **Contamination:** It helps in transmission of diseases. Others help in the protection of diseases.

11. **Kwashiorkor:** It is a nutritional disorder, others are vitamin deficiencies.

12. Direct contact : AIDS :: Droplet infection : Tuberculosis

13. Goiter : Non-communicable :: Conjunctivitis : Communicable

14. Composting : Vegetable peels :: Vermicomposting : Earthworms

15. Brushing : Oral hygiene :: Afforestation: Community hygiene

16. Oral hygiene : Personal hygiene :: Sewage disposal : Community hygiene

17. Cholera : Housefly :: Malaria : Mosquito.

18. Marasmus : Malnutrition :: Obesity : Excess diet

19. Dental caries : Flourine :: Anaemia : Iron

20. False: Oral hygiene is concerned with the care of teeth.

21. True

22. False: Ice packs are applied on bruises.

23. True

24. False: Thermometer is a tool in first aid kit.

25. True

26. False: Bleeding in gums and internal organs is the symptom of scurvy.

27. False: Deficiency of protein causes kwashiorkor in children.

Level 2: Review Your Concepts

28. Marasmus: It is caused due to the deficiency of carbohydrates and proteins. It is characterised by thin and lean body, prominent and visible ribs, sunken eyes.
Kwashiorkor: It is caused due to deficiency of protein. It is characterised with stunted growth, acute hair falls, oedema. This and bony limbs along with reddish hair.

29. A complex carbohydrate present in the cell wall of plants is cellulose. In human beings, the enzyme cellulase is absent which helps in digesting cellulose. Hence, it acts as roughage. This roughage adds fibre to the diet and helps in easy movement of the bowel and prevents constipation.

30. (a) Vitamins and mineral are known as protective food. They are needed in very minute quantities which help in controlling metabolism. They protect the body against diseases and hence are called as protective food.
(b) Green leafy vegetables contain minerals and vitamins. They contain calcium that helps in formation such as vitamin A and vitamin D.
It contains fibres which therefore, helps in easy movement of bowed and prevents constipation.

31. Overpopulation leads to disturbances in community hygiene.
(i) Resources become limited and will not be adequate for the people.
(ii) Leads to poverty.
(iii) Poverty leads to lack of systematic livelihood in people. The lack of basic infrastructure, such as toilets and drainage facilities may lead to infections.
(iv) Industrialization is necessary to meet the demands which results in pollution.
(v) To provide shelter for the growing population, the forests are destroyed.

Level 3: Assess Your Concepts

32. Proteins are macronutrients which are required for body building.

The deficiency disorders of protein-free diet are:

a. Body metabolism decreases

b. Weight loss occurs

c. Poor muscle building

d. Occurrence of joint and muscle pain

33. Feet should be well protected and cleaned regularly. If not, injuries may occur causing wounds. Tetanus bacteria present in the soil may make entry through injuries while walking barefoot.

34. Waste materials, like vegetable peels, agricultural waste, dung of animals and dried leaves are dumped in a pit. They are allowed to get decayed and decomposed to form compost after a few months. Compost is used as manure to increase the fertility of soil.

35. A child, provided with rice and chapattis alone gets only carbohydrates in diet. The other nutrients required for the body are proteins, vitamins and minerals. The child is affected by a disease called kwashiorkor. Symptoms of this disease are swollen belly, improper muscle development and lack of mental growth.

36. It is advised to eat unpolished rice because it is fibre-rich and it helps in digestion forming bulk rich food. If rice is polished, vitamin B is lost which leads to disease, beriberi.

37. (a) Calcium: Osteoporosis

Sodium: Juvenile paralysis

Iron: Anaemia

Fluorine: Dental caries

Iodine: Goitre

(b) (i) Vector-borne communicable Disease: Cholera, malaria, dengue

(ii) Air-borne: Tuberculosis, influenza, chicken pox.

(iii) Water borne: Jaundice, cholera

38. Water is known as universal solvent, and it keeps our body cool. Several chemical reactions take place in our body in the presence of water. Human beings should drink about 1.5 to 2 litres of water every day. People may die due to lack of water, as the chemical reactions involved in metabolism do not occur in the cells.

Photo Credits

CHAPTER 1

Page 1.5—Suppakij1017. Shutterstockv / popovaphoto. 123rf.com / DesignPrax. Shutterstock; **Page 1.6**—Jan Gottwald. Shutterstock / Wilm Ihlenfeld. Shutterstock / M. Unal Ozmen. Shutterstock; **Page 1.15**—angelo gilardelli. Shutterstock / 123rf.com / DesignPrax. Shutterstock; **Page 1.19**—123rf.com / tale. Shutterstock / Karramba Production. Shutterstock / maxstockphoto. Shutterstock / Andrew Scherbackov. Shutterstock / 123rf.com; **Page 1.21**—123rf.com; **Page 1.22**—Hurst Photo. Shutterstock / Suppakij1017. Shutterstock / Arvind Singh Negi / Red Reef Design Studio. Pearson India Education Services Pvt. Ltd; **Page 1.24**—VectorMine. Shutterstock; **Page 1.25**—123rf.com / Galayko Sergey. Shutterstock; **Page 1.26**—mallinka. 123rf.com / mallinka. 123rf.com; **Page 1.27**—Ratan Mani Banerjee. Pearson India Education Services Pvt. Ltd; **Page 1.27**—curiosity. Shutterstock; **Page 1.28**—Lightspring. Shutterstock / Mohd Suhail. Pearson India Education Services Pvt. Ltd / Mohd Suhail. Pearson India Education Services Pvt. Ltd / Pradip Kumar Bhowal. Pearson India Education Services Pvt. Ltd

CHAPTER 2

Page 2.3—Petr Jilek. Shutterstock / sonyae. 123rf.com / Amit John. Pearson India Education Services Pvt. Ltd / olivier26. 123rf.com; **Page 2.3**— Matthew Howard. 123rf.com; **Page 2.4**—Arvydas Kniuksta. Shutterstock / Oxford Designers & Illustrators Ltd. Pearson Education Ltd.; **Page 2.5**—victoras / Shutterstock Sliding / JoeSAPhotos / Shutterstock; **Page 2.7**—Better Stock. Shutterstock; **Page 2.8**—Amit John. Pearson India Education Services Pvt. Ltd; **Page 2.8**—victoras / Shutterstock; JoeSAPhotos / Shutterstock; **Page 2.9**—Amit John. Pearson India Education Services Pvt. Ltd

CHAPTER 3

Page 3.1—Oxford Designers & Illustrators Ltd. Pearson Education Ltd; **Page 3.3**—PDQ Digital Media Solutions Ltd. Pearson Education Ltd; **Page 3.3**—Elnur Amikishiyev. 123rf.com; **Page 3.3**—Arvind Singh Negi / Red Reef Design Studio. Pearson India Education Services Pvt. Ltd / Mammoth Designz Studio. Pearson India Education Services Pvt. Ltd / ulubird. 123rf.com / Vuk Vukmirovic. Shutterstock / Dragon Images. Shutterstock; **Page 3.5**—Mohd Suhail. Pearson India Education Services Pvt. Ltd / Mohd Suhail. Pearson India Education Services Pvt. Ltd; **Page 3.7**—Arvind Singh Negi / Red Reef Design Studio. Pearson India Education Services Pvt. Ltd / Ultrashock. Shutterstock / Maximus256. Shutterstock / djdarkflower. Shutterstock / Andreja Donko. Shutterstock; **Page 3.7**—Mohammed Ali. Pearson India Education Services Pvt. Ltd / digieye / Shutterstock; **Page 3.8**—markusgann. 123rf.com / joingate. Shutterstock; **Page 3.8**— Vecton / Shutterstock

CHAPTER 4

Page 4.3—Veja. Shutterstock; **Page 4.3**—Studio 8. Pearson Education Ltd; **Page 4.4**—doethion. 123rf.com; **Page 4.5**— Nilabho Dhar Chowdhry. Pearson India Education Services Pvt. Ltd / Vladvm. Shutterstock / Mohd Suhail. Pearson India Education Services Pvt. Ltd / digitalreflections. Shutterstock / Ratan Mani Banerjee. Pearson India Education Services Pvt. Ltd / urfin. Shutterstock; **Page 4.6**—Mohd Suhail. Pearson India Education Services Pvt. Ltd; **Page 4.6**— Brian C. Weed / Shutterstock; **Page 4.8**—pilens. 123rf.com; **Page 4.8**—pilens. 123rf.com; **Page 4.8**—SHUTTR_US_Dec_13

CHAPTER 5

Page 5.3—liseykina. Shutterstock / Somchai Som. Shutterstock; **Page 5.3**—Danish Zaidi. Pearson India Education Services Pvt. Ltd / Sergey Furtaev. Shutterstock / Anita Patterson Peppers. Shutterstock / chudtsankov. 123rf.com / chudtsankov. 123rf.com / Danish Zaidi. Pearson India Education Services Pvt. Ltd / violetkaipa. Shutterstock / chudtsankov. 123rf.com / violetkaipa. Shutterstock / Sergey urtaev. Shutterstock / irin-k. Shutterstock; **Page 5.3**—SHUTTR_US_Feb_14; **Page 5.3**—SHUTTR_US_May_13; **Pages 5.5 and 5.6**—123rf.com / 123rf.com; **Page 5.8**—Ruslan Kuzmenkov. Shutterstock / tankist276. Shutterstock / James Clarke. Shutterstock / Reha Mark. Shutterstock / design56. 123rf.com / Aumm graphixphoto. Shutterstock; **Page 5.11**—123RF_UK_Aug_17

CHAPTER 6

Page 6.3—Maxx-Studio. Shutterstock / rasslava. 123rf.com / John Foxx Collection. Imagestate / 123rf.com / 123rf.com / MrGarry. Shutterstock; **Page 6.3**—HK Legacy; **Page 6.3**—imagedb.com. Shutterstock; **Page 6.4**—yevgeniy11. Shutterstock / ytea. 123rf.com / 123rf.com / maxim ibragimov. Shutterstock / Marynchenko Oleksandr. Shutterstock / Oxford Designers & Illustrators Ltd. Pearson Education Ltd; **Page 6.4**—design56. Shutterstock; **Page 6.5**—SHUTTR_SA_Apr_19; **Page 6.6**—Designua. Shutterstock / 123rf.com / Oxford Designers & Illustrators Ltd. Pearson Education Ltd; **Page 6.8**—Robert Spriggs. Shutterstock / Dainis Derics. Shutterstock / Oleg Bezrukov. Shutterstock / Gareth Boden. Pearson Education Ltd / ra3rn. Shutterstock; **Page 6.8**—Pearson Education Ltd; **Page 6.8**—SHUTTR_US_Aug_13; **Page 6.8**—Coleman Yuen. Pearson Education Asia Ltd; **Pages 6.9**—Studio 8. Pearson Education Ltd; **Page 6.10**—123rf.com / MrGarry. Shutterstock / ppart. Shutterstock / Sashkin. Shutterstock

CHAPTER 7

Page 7.3—goldminer. 123rf.com / MilanB. Shutterstock / MilanB. Shutterstock / 123rf.com; **Page 7.5**—takasu. Shutterstock / Snowbelle. Shutterstock; **Page 7.7**—123rf.com / HL Studios. Pearson Education Ltd / Henu Mehtani. Pearson India Education Services Pvt. Ltd / Pearson Education, Inc. / Pearson Education, Inc.; **Page 7.7**—mato. Shutterstock;

CHAPTER 8

Page 8.6—Mammoth Designz Studio. Pearson India Education Services Pvt. Ltd; **Page 8.7**—Mohd Suhail. Pearson India Education Services Pvt. Ltd / sermax55.123rf.com; **Page 8.8**—Mohd Suhail. Pearson India Education Services Pvt. Ltd; **Page 8.8**—Designua. Shutterstock; **Page 8.14**—takasu. Shutterstock / Henu Mehtani. Pearson India Education Services Pvt. Ltd / Shivani Anshuk. Pearson India Education Services Pvt. Ltd / Shivani Anshuk. Pearson India Education Services Pvt. Ltd / Mohd Suhail. Pearson India Education Services Pvt. Ltd; **Page 8.16**—Henu Mehtani. Pearson India Education Services Pvt. Ltd / phloxii.Shutterstock; **Page 8.16**—Rainer Lesniewski. Shutterstock; **Page 8.16**—Iakov Filimonov. Shutterstock

CHAPTER 9

Page 9.3—Oxford Designers & Illustrators Ltd. Pearson Education Ltd.; **Page 9.3**—Oxford Designers & Illustrators Ltd. Pearson Education Ltd; **Page 9.8**—alexoakenman.123rf.com; **Page 9.9**—Artisticco. Shutterstock / teamarbeit.123rf.com / Amit John. Pearson India Education Services Pvt. Ltd / bioraven. Shutterstock / Mohd Suhail. Pearson India Education Services Pvt. Ltd / Ratan Mani Banerjee. Pearson India Education Services Pvt. Ltd / 82808. Shutterstock / AboliC. Shutterstock / sevenke. Shutterstock; **Page 9.10**—Young Swee Ming / Shutterstock; **Page 9.11**—PDQ Digital Media Solution LTD. Pearson Education Ltd; **Page 9.11**—ruzanna. Shutterstock; **Page 9.13**—Ratan Mani Banerjee. Pearson India Education Services Pvt. Ltd / Mammoth Designz Studio. Pearson India Education Services Pvt. Ltd; **Page 9.13**—Jostein Hauge. 123rf.com

CHAPTER 10

Page 10.5—Crystal-K. Shutterstock; **Page 10.5**—HL Studios. Pearson Education Ltd; **Page 10.9**—artiomp. Shutterstock / Arvind Singh Negi / Red Reef Design Studio. Pearson India Educat; **Page 10.9**—Designua. Shutterstock; **Page 10.10**—tomas1111. 123rf.com

CHAPTER 11

Page 11.3—Happy cake Happy cafe / Shutterstock; **Page 11.3**—Amble Design / Shutterstock; **Page 11.4**—New Africa / Shutterstock; **Page 11.5**—Illustration of education chart of biology for change of state for water diagram; **Page 11.6**—"—Artisticco. Shutterstock"; **Page 11.6**—123rf.com; **Page 11.8**—Rainer Lesniewski. Shutterstock; **Page 11.9**—Kekyalyaynen / Shutterstock; **Page 11.10**—Oxford Designers & Illustrators Ltd / Pearson Education Ltd; **Page 11.12**—Mohd Suhail. Pearson India Education Services Pvt. Ltd; **Page 11.12**—Anna Nikonorova / Shutterstock

CHAPTER 12

Page 12.14—You Touch Pix of EuToch. Shutterstock / Bernadette Heath. Shutterstock / OlegD. Shutterstock / hagit berkovich. Shutterstock; **Page 12.15**—Oxford Designers & Illustrators Ltd. Pearson Education Ltd; **Page 12.16**—Jason Patrick Ross. Shutterstock / EpicStockMedia. Shutterstock; **Pages 12.17**—Chiyacat. Shutterstock / Jan Wlodarczyk / Alamy stock photo; **Page 12.19**—Oxford Designers & Illustrators Ltd. Pearson Education Ltd; **Page 12.19**—snapgalleria. Shutterstock; **Page 12.24**—123rf.com; **Page 12.24**—George Tsartsianidis. 123rf.com;

CHAPTER 13

Page 13.4—Renu Sharma. Pearson India Education Services Pvt. Ltd / Renu Sharma. Pearson India Education Services Pvt. Ltd; **Page 13.5**—Abramova Elena. Shutterstock / Lukas Gojda. Shutterstock / Sozaijiten / Madlen. Shutterstock / Kelly Marken. Shutterstock; **Page 13.6**—Wasu Watcharadachaphong. Shutterstock / David Dohnal. Shutterstock; **Page 13.7**—Kelly Marken. Shutterstock / 123rf.com / 1925492. Shutterstock / 123rf.com; **Page 13.9**—123rf.com / Swapan Photography. Shutterstock; **Page 13.10**—PeterVrabel. Shutterstock / Volodymyr Nikitenko. Shutterstock / Jan Csernoch / Alamy Stock Photo; **Pages 13.10 and 13.11**—123rf.com / Simon Laprida. Shutterstock / Steve Lovegrove. Shutterstock / You Touch Pix of EuToch. Shutterstock; **Pages 13.11 and 13.12**—Sozaijiten / Balashova Ekaterina. Shutterstock; **Pages 13.12 and 13.13**—You Touch Pix of EuToch. Shutterstock / Bernadette Heath. Shutterstock; **Page 13.13**—123rf.com / deriufra. 123rf.com / cloki. Shutterstock; **Page 13.14**—leungchopan. Shutterstock / a9photo.Shutterstock / blickwinkel / Alamy Stock Photo; **Page 13.17**—John Foxx Collection. Imagestate; **Page 13.21**—Bogdan Wankowicz. Shutterstock / Bogdan Wankowicz. Shutterstock; **Page 13.21**—Fancy Tapis. Shutterstock; **Page 13.21**—Fancy Tapis. Shutterstock

CHAPTER 14

Page 14.5—elenabsl. Shutterstock; **Page 14.8**—Croisy. Shutterstock / Mohd Suhail. Pearson India Education Services Pvt. Ltd / hfsimaging. 123rf.com; **Page 14.13**—Oxford Designers & Illustrators Ltd. Pearson Education Ltd / stihii. Shutterstock; **Page 14.14**—hayaship.123rf.com / AndrewBurgess. Shutterstock; **Page 14.14**—pilens. 123rf.com / 123rf.com / Menno Schaefer. Shutterstock;

CHAPTER 15

Page 15.17—ifong. Shutterstock / Africa Studio. Shutterstock;